# Test Bank

## for

## Campbell • Reece

## *BIOLOGY*, Seventh Edition

### William Barstow, Editor
*University of Georgia*

### Contributors

Jean DeSaix, *University of North Carolina, Chapel Hill*
Michael Dini, *Texas Tech University*
Conrad Firling, *University of Minnesota, Duluth*
Peter Follette, *Science Writer*
Mark Hens, *University of North Carolina, Greensboro*
Janice Moore, *University of Colorado*
Thomas Owens, *Cornell University*
Marshall Sundberg, *Emporia State University*
Robert Yost, *Indiana University/Purdue University, Indianapolis*
Edward Zalisko, *Blackburn College*

PEARSON

Benjamin
Cummings

San Francisco   Boston   New York  Cape Town   Hong Kong   London   Madrid   Mexico City
Montreal   Munich   Paris   Singapore   Sydney   Tokyo   Toronto

Editorial Director: Frank Ruggirello
Editor in Chief: Beth Wilbur
Project Editor: Amy Austin
Biology Marketing Manager: Jeff Hester
Managing Editor, Production: Erin Gregg
Production Supervisor: Vivian McDougal
Copy Editor: Jan McDearmon
Cover Designers: Yvo Riezebos and Stacy Wong
Manufacturing Buyer: Pam Augspurger
Composition: Tamarack Software
Printer: Phoenix Color Book Tech Park

ISBN 0-8053-7154-0

2 3 4 5 6 7 8 9 10   BRR   07 06 05

www.aw-bc.com

# Preface

The test bank for the Seventh Edition of Campbell and Reece's *BIOLOGY* is a thorough revision based on the solid foundation established by the six previous editions. Each test bank contributor, along with editors, reviewed every question carefully to ensure that the content and terminology of that question accurately reflects the material in the new edition of *BIOLOGY*. The contributors and editors revised each chapter of the test bank with the goal of replacing or significantly altering 30% of the questions.

Each chapter of the test bank also includes Media Activity Questions. These questions are taken directly from the Activity Quizzes on the Campbell website and CD-ROM and can be used on tests to reward students for performing assigned Media Activities. Note that in some cases the titles of these activities had to be altered to fit in our two-column test bank format. The Self-Quiz questions found in the review section of each textbook chapter have also been added to the test bank. It should be noted that the answers to these Self-Quiz questions are in the textbook.

We have tried to classify each question according to the complexity of the mental processes involved. The model we used is modified from Bloom, Benjamin et al., *Taxonomy of Educational Objectives: The Classification of Educational Goals, Handbook I: Cognitive Domain*. New York: Longmans, Green, 1956. The categories in the cognitive domain that we used to classify questions are:

1. **Knowledge:** recognizing or recalling information
2. **Comprehension:** grasping (understanding) the meaning of informational materials
3. **Application:** applying previously learned information in new situations to answer questions that have single or best answers

We recognize that you may interpret our classifications differently; therefore, these classifications should be considered only as a rough guide to the abilities required to answer each question.

The editing of prior questions and the writing of new questions was accomplished by the following group of biologists:

| | |
|---|---|
| Ch. 1 & Unit 1 | Conrad Firling, University of Minnesota, Duluth, MN |
| Unit 2 | Thomas Owens, Cornell University, NY |
| | Mark Hens, University of North Carolina, Greensboro, NC |
| Unit 3 | Peter Follette, Science Writer |
| Units 4–5 | Michael Dini, Texas Tech University, Lubbock, TX |
| Unit 6 | Marshall Sundberg, Emporia State University, Emporia, KS |
| Unit 7 | Jean DeSaix, University of North Carolina, Chapel Hill, NC |
| | Robert Yost, Indiana State University Purdue University, Indianapolis, IN |
| | Edward Zalisko, Blackburn College, Carlinville, IL |
| Unit 8 | Janice Moore, Colorado State University, Fort Collins, CO |

The questions in the Seventh Edition Test Bank are built upon questions authored by others. I am grateful to the following biologists who have contributed questions to previous editions of the test bank (edition numbers are shown in parentheses): Neil Campbell, UC Riverside (3); Angela Cunningham, Baylor University (5); Richard Dohrkopf, Baylor University (4, 5); Gary Fabris, Red Deer College, Alberta Canada (4); Eugene Fenster, Longview Community College (6); Frank Keppner, University of Rhode Island (1); Walter MacDonald, Trenton State University (2); Rebecca Pyles, East Tennessee State University (4); Kurt Redborg, Coe College (4, 5, 6); Marc Snyder, Colorado College (5); Richard Storey, The Colorado College (4, 5); Martha Taylor, Cornell University (3); Margaret Waterman, Harvard Medical School (3); Dan Wivagg, Baylor University (3, 4, 5); Catherine Wilcoxson Ueckert, Northern Arizona University (5, 6); Betty Ann Wonderly, J. J. Pearce High School, Richardson, TX (3).

## Acknowledgments

I want to thank Beth Wilbur, Editor in Chief for Benjamin Cummings, for asking me to edit the questions, and to Amy Austin, Project Editor for Benjamin Cummings, for her immense help in coordinating the entire project. Amy was a joy to work with. This project would have been much more difficult if it were not for Amy's skill and attention to detail. I thank Vivian McDougal, Production Supervisor at Benjamin Cummings, and Carol Schultz and her staff at Tamarack for their expertise and hard work in translating our computer files to the printed page and to the cross-platform CD-ROM. A special thanks to Kim Brown who worked nights and weekends to word process many of the questions into our test generation program files. Thanks Beth, Amy, Vivian, Carol, and Kim.

I recognize that the questions in the test bank may have errors. Since I edited all the questions, I take full responsibility for any mistakes. If you find errors, I would appreciate hearing from you.

William Barstow
Associate Biology Division Chairman and
Director of the Undergraduate Biology Major
University of Georgia
Athens, GA 30602
Phone (706) 542-1688
Fax (706) 542-1695
Email: barstow@plantbio.uga.edu

# Contents

# Chapter 1  Exploring Life

1) Which of the following properties or processes do we associate with living things?
   A) evolutionary adaptations
   B) energy processing
   C) responding to the environment
   D) growth and reproduction
   E) all of the above

Answer: E
*Topic: Overview*
*Skill: Knowledge*

2) Which of the following sequences represents the hierarchy of biological organization from the least to the most complex level?
   A) organelle, tissue, biosphere, ecosystem, population, organism
   B) cell, community, population, organ system, molecule, organelle
   C) organism, community, biosphere, molecule, tissue, organ
   D) ecosystem, cell, population, tissue, organism, organ system
   E) molecule, cell, organ system, population, ecosystem, biosphere

Answer: E
*Topic: Concept 1.1*
*Skill: Knowledge*

3) Which of the following sequences represents the hierarchy of biological organization from the most to the least complex level?
   A) organelle, cell, organ system, population, community, ecosystem
   B) ecosystem, community, organism, tissue, cell, organelle
   C) biosphere, population, organism, cell, tissue, molecule
   D) biosphere, community, tissue, organ system, molecule, organelle
   E) organism, population, organ system, tissue, molecule, cell

Answer: B
*Topic: Concept 1.1*
*Skill: Knowledge*

4) What is a localized group of organisms that belong to the same species?
   A) biosystem
   B) community
   C) population
   D) ecosystem
   E) organ system

Answer: C
*Topic: Concept 1.1*
*Skill: Knowledge*

5) A maple leaf is at which level in the hierarchy of biological organization?
   A) tissue
   B) cell
   C) organelle
   D) organ
   E) organ system

Answer: D
*Topic: Concept 1.1*
*Skill: Knowledge*

6) Which of these is an example of an organelle?

    A) chloroplast

    B) muscle

    C) epidermis

    D) intestine

    E) maple leaf

Answer: A
*Topic: Concept 1.1*
*Skill: Knowledge*

7) In terms of the hierarchical organization of life, a bacterium is at the _____ level of organization, whereas a human is at the _____ level of organization.

    A) single-celled organism; multicellular organism

    B) single organelle; organism

    C) organelle; organ system

    D) single tissue; multicellular organism

    E) tissue; organism

Answer: A
*Topic: Concept 1.1*
*Skill: Knowledge*

8) Which of these is a correct representation of the hierarchy of biological organization from least to most complex?

    A) hydrogen, water, heart muscle cell, heart muscle cell nucleus, heart muscle tissue, heart, human

    B) hydrogen, water, muscle cell nucleus, heart muscle cell, heart, heart muscle tissue, human

    C) hydrogen, water, heart muscle cell nucleus, heart muscle cell, heart muscle tissue, heart, human

    D) water, hydrogen, heart muscle cell nucleus, heart muscle cell, heart muscle tissue, heart, human

    E) heart muscle cell nucleus, hydrogen, water, heart muscle cell, heart, heart muscle tissue, human

Answer: C
*Topic: Concept 1.1*
*Skill: Knowledge*

9) Which of these is a correct representation of the hierarchy of biological organization from least to most complex?

    A) organelle of a stomach cell, digestive system, large intestine, small intestine, intestinal tissue, organism

    B) organelle of an intestinal cell, digestive system, small intestine, large intestine, intestinal tissue, organism

    C) molecule, intestinal cell organelle, intestinal cell, intestinal tissue, digestive system, organism

    D) molecule, small intestine, large intestine, intestinal tissue, digestive system, organism

    E) molecule, digestive system, digestive cell organelle, small intestine, large intestine, intestinal cell, organism

Answer: C
*Topic: Concept 1.1*
*Skill: Knowledge*

10) Plants convert the energy of sunlight into
  A) the energy of motion.
  B) carbon dioxide and water.
  C) the potential energy of chemical bonds.
  D) minerals.
  E) kinetic energy.

Answer: C
*Topic: Concept 1.1*
*Skill: Knowledge*

11) As a result of photosynthesis, plants release _____ into the atmosphere.
  A) methane
  B) carbon dioxide
  C) water
  D) minerals
  E) oxygen

Answer: E
*Topic: Concept 1.1*
*Skill: Knowledge*

12) Which of the following is the main source of energy for producers such as plants and other photosynthetic organisms?
  A) sunlight or solar energy
  B) carbon dioxide or kinetic energy
  C) heat or thermal energy
  D) chemicals or chemical energy
  E) both B and D

Answer: A
*Topic: Concept 1.1*
*Skill: Knowledge*

13) The dynamics of any ecosystem include the following major processes:
  A) the flow of energy from sunlight to producers
  B) the flow of energy from sunlight to producers and then to consumers
  C) the recycling of chemical nutrients
  D) the flow of energy to producers and the recycling of nutrients
  E) the flow of energy from sunlight to producers and then to consumers, and the recycling of chemical nutrients.

Answer: E
*Topic: Concept 1.1*
*Skill: Knowledge*

14) For most ecosystems _____ is (are) the ultimate source of energy, and energy leaves the ecosystem in the form of _____.
  A) sunlight; heat
  B) heat; light
  C) plants; animals
  D) plants; heat
  E) producers; consumers

Answer: A
*Topic: Concept 1.1*
*Skill: Knowledge*

15) The lowest level of biological organization that can perform all the activities required for life is the
  A) organelle—for example, a chloroplast.
  B) cell—for example, a skin cell.
  C) tissue—for example, nervous tissue.
  D) organ system—for example, the reproductive system.
  E) organism—for example, an amoeba, dog, human, or maple tree.

Answer: B
*Topic: Concept 1.1*
*Skill: Knowledge*

16) Which of the following is *true* regarding deoxyribonucleic acid (DNA)?

    A) Each deoxyribonucleic acid molecule is composed of two long chains of nucleotides arranged in a double helix.

    B) Genes are composed of deoxyribonucleic acid.

    C) DNA is composed of chemical building blocks called nucleotides.

    D) Only A and C are correct.

    E) A, B, and C are correct.

Answer: E
*Topic: Concept 1.1*
*Skill: Knowledge*

17) What are the basic "building blocks" of deoxyribonucleic acid (DNA)?

    A) 100,000 different kinds of proteins

    B) 26 different kinds of chromosomes

    C) 20 different kinds of amino acids

    D) 4 different kinds of nucleotides

    E) 3 different kinds of genomes

Answer: D
*Topic: Concept 1.1*
*Skill: Knowledge*

18) Which of the following types of cells utilize deoxyribonucleic acid (DNA) as their genetic material?

    A) animal

    B) plant

    C) archaea

    D) A and B only

    E) A, B, and C

Answer: E
*Topic: Concept 1.1*
*Skill: Comprehension*

19) Which of the following statements concerning prokaryotic and eukaryotic cells is *not* correct?

    A) Prokaryotic cells lack a membrane-bound nucleus.

    B) Prokaryotic cells contain small membrane-enclosed organelles.

    C) Eukaryotic cells contain a membrane-bound nucleus.

    D) DNA, or deoxyribonucleic acid, is present in both prokaryotic cells and eukaryotic cells.

    E) DNA or deoxyribonucleic acid is present in the nucleus of eukaryotic cells.

Answer: B
*Topic: Concept 1.1*
*Skill: Knowledge*

20) Which of the following is reflective of the phrase "the whole is greater than the sum of its parts"?

    A) high-throughput technology

    B) emergent properties

    C) natural selection

    D) reductionism

    E) feedback regulations

Answer: B
*Topic: Concept 1.2*
*Skill: Knowledge*

21) In order to understand the chemical basis of inheritance, one must understand the molecular structure of DNA. This is an example of the application of _____ to the study of biology.

    A) evolution

    B) emergent properties

    C) reductionism

    D) the cell theory

    E) feedback regulation

Answer: C
*Topic: Concept 1.2*
*Skill: Comprehension*

22) The chemical reactions within cells are regulated by organic catalysts called

A) feedback activators.

B) feedback inhibitors.

C) enzymes.

D) metabolites.

E) nutrients.

Answer: C
*Topic: Concept 1.2*
*Skill: Knowledge*

23) Once labor begins in childbirth, contractions increase in intensity and frequency until delivery. The increasing labor contractions of childbirth are an example of

A) a bioinformatic system.

B) positive feedback.

C) negative feedback.

D) feedback inhibition.

E) both C and D

Answer: B
*Topic: Concept 1.2*
*Skill: Comprehension*

24) When blood glucose level rises, the pancreas secretes insulin, and as a result blood glucose level declines.  When blood glucose level is low, the pancreas secretes glucagon, and as a result blood glucose level rises.  Such regulation of blood glucose level is the result of

A) catalytic feedback.

B) positive feedback.

C) negative feedback.

D) bioinformatic regulation.

E) both A and B

Answer: C
*Topic: Concept 1.2*
*Skill: Comprehension*

25) There are approximately _____ identified and named species.

A) 1,800

B) 180,000

C) 1,800,000

D) 18,000,000

E) 180,000,000

Answer: C
*Topic: Concept 1.3*
*Skill: Knowledge*

26) Which branch of biology is concerned with the naming and classifying of organisms?

A) informatics

B) schematic biology

C) taxonomy

D) genomics

E) evolution

Answer: C
*Topic: Concept 1.3*
*Skill: Knowledge*

27) Prokaryotic and eukaryotic cells generally have which of the following features in common?

A) a membrane-bounded nucleus

B) a cell wall made of cellulose

C) ribosomes

D) flagella or cilia that contain microtubules

E) linear chromosomes made of DNA and protein

Answer: C
*Topic: Concept 1.3*
*Skill: Knowledge*

28) Which of the following are characteristics shared by members of both domain Bacteria and domain Archaea?

A) cytosol

B) nucleus

C) DNA

D) A and C only

E) A, B, and C

Answer: D
*Topic: Concept 1.3*
*Skill: Knowledge*

29) What are the two classifications of prokaryotes?

A) domain Bacteria and domain Eukarya

B) domain Archaea and kingdom Monera

C) domain Eukarya and kingdom Monera

D) domain Bacteria and kingdom Monera

E) domain Bacteria and domain Archaea

Answer: E
*Topic: Concept 1.3*
*Skill: Knowledge*

30) All eukaryotes belong to which group(s)?

A) domain Bacteria

B) domain Archaea

C) domain Eukarya

D) kingdom Protista

E) both C and D

Answer: C
*Topic: Concept 1.3*
*Skill: Knowledge*

31) Species that are in the same _____ are more closely related than species that are only in the same _____.

A) phylum; class

B) family; order

C) class; order

D) family; genus

E) kingdom; phylum

Answer: B
*Topic: Concept 1.3*
*Skill: Comprehension*

32) Two species belonging to the same genus must also belong to the same

A) kingdom.

B) phylum.

C) class.

D) order.

E) all of the above

Answer: E
*Topic: Concept 1.3*
*Skill: Comprehension*

33) Which of these is reflective of the hierarchical organization of life from most to least inclusive?

A) kingdom, order, family, phylum, class, genus, species

B) phylum, class, order, kingdom, family, genus, species

C) kingdom, phylum, class, order, family, genus, species

D) genus, species, kingdom, phylum, class, order, family

E) class, order, kingdom, phylum, family, genus, species

Answer: C
*Topic: Concept 1.3*
*Skill: Knowledge*

34) A water sample from a hot thermal vent contained a single-celled organism that lacked a nucleus. What is its most likely classification?
   A) domain Eukarya
   B) domain Archaea
   C) kingdom Animalia
   D) kingdom Protista
   E) kingdom Fungi

Answer: B
*Topic: Concept 1.3*
*Skill: Comprehension*

35) A maple tree is classified into domain _____ and kingdom _____.
   A) Eukarya; Animalia
   B) Eukarya; Fungi
   C) Eukarya; Plantae
   D) Eukarya; Protista
   E) Bacteria; Archaea

Answer: C
*Topic: Concept 1.3*
*Skill: Comprehension*

36) A new species has been discovered. Individuals of this species are multicellular eukaryotes that obtain nutrients from decomposing organic matter. How should this species be classified?
   A) domain Bacteria, kingdom Prokaryota
   B) domain Archaea, kingdom Bacteria
   C) domain Eukarya, kingdom Plantae
   D) domain Eukarya, kingdom Protista
   E) domain Eukarya, kingdom Fungi

Answer: E
*Topic: Concept 1.3*
*Skill: Comprehension*

37) A new species has been discovered. Individuals of this species are multicellular eukaryotes that obtain their energy-providing nutrients by ingesting other organisms. How should this species be classified?
   A) kingdom Archaea
   B) kingdom Bacteria
   C) kingdom Plantae
   D) kingdom Protista
   E) kingdom Animalia

Answer: E
*Topic: Concept 1.3*
*Skill: Comprehension*

38) You have just discovered a new species that has starch, rather than DNA, as its genetic material. You are elated because you may have just discovered a new
   A) member of kingdom Protista.
   B) member of domain Bacteria.
   C) member of domain Archaea.
   D) member of domain Eukarya.
   E) domain of life.

Answer: E
*Topic: Concept 1.3*
*Skill: Comprehension*

39) Which of these provides evidence of the common ancestry of all life?
   A) the ubiquitous use of catalysts by living systems
   B) the universality of the genetic code
   C) the structure of the nucleus
   D) the structure of cilia
   E) the structure of chloroplasts

Answer: B
*Topic: Concept 1.3*
*Skill: Comprehension*

40) Which of the following is (are) true of natural selection?

A) requires genetic variation

B) results in descent with modification

C) involves differential reproductive success

D) B and C only

E) A, B, and C

Answer: E
*Topic: Concept 1.4*
*Skill: Knowledge*

41) According to Charles Darwin, organisms of a particular species are adapted to their environment when they

A) possess non–inheritable traits that enhance their survival in the local environment.

B) possess non–inheritable traits that enhance their reproductive success in the local environment.

C) possess non–inheritable traits that enhance their survival and reproductive success in the local environment.

D) possess inheritable traits that enhance their survival and reproductive success in the local environment.

E) possess inheritable traits that decrease their survival and reproductive success in the local environment.

Answer: D
*Topic: Concept 1.4*
*Skill: Comprehension*

42) Which of the following statements is *not* part of Charles Darwin's concept of natural selection?

A) Slight inheritable variations within a population may make an individual significantly more or less likely to survive in its environment, and thus to reproduce.

B) Every organism has the potential to produce more offspring than the local environment can support.

C) Characteristics of organisms are inherited as genes on chromosomes.

D) Better adapted members of a species will survive and reproduce more successfully.

E) Most individuals in a species do not survive to reproduce.

Answer: C
*Topic: Concept 1.4*
*Skill: Comprehension*

43) Which of these individuals is most likely to be successful in an evolutionary sense?

A) a reproductively sterile individual who never falls ill

B) an organism that dies after 5 days of life but leaves 10 offspring, all of whom survive to reproduce

C) a male who mates with 20 females and fathers 1 offspring

D) an organism that lives 100 years and leaves 2 offspring, both of whom survive to reproduce

E) a female who mates with 20 males and produces 1 offspring

Answer: B
*Topic: Concept 1.4*
*Skill: Comprehension*

44) In a hypothetical world, every 50 years people over 6 feet tall are eliminated from the population. Based on your knowledge of natural selection, you would predict that the average height of the human population will

A) remain unchanged.

B) gradually decline.

C) rapidly decline.

D) gradually increase.

E) rapidly increase.

Answer: B
*Topic: Concept 1.4*
*Skill: Comprehension*

45) Through time, the lineage that led to modern whales shows a change from four-limbed land animals to aquatic animals with two limbs that function as flippers. This change is best explained by

A) natural philosophy.

B) creationism.

C) the hierarchy of the biological organization of life.

D) natural selection.

E) feedback inhibition.

Answer: D
*Topic: Concept 1.4*
*Skill: Comprehension*

46) Evolution is biology's core theme that ties together all the other themes. This is because evolution

A) explains the unity and diversity of life.

B) explains how organisms become adapted to their environment through the differential reproductive success of varying individuals.

C) explains why distantly related organisms sometimes resemble each other.

D) explains why some organisms have traits in common.

E) all of the above

Answer: E
*Topic: Concept 1.4*
*Skill: Comprehension*

47) The method of scientific inquiry that describes natural structures and processes as accurately as possible through careful observation and the analysis of data is known as

A) hypothesis–based science.

B) discovery science.

C) experimental science.

D) quantitative science.

E) qualitative science.

Answer: B
*Topic: Concept 1.5*
*Skill: Knowledge*

48) Collecting data based on observation is an example of _____; analyzing this data to reach a conclusion is an example of _____ reasoning.

A) hypothesis–based science; inductive

B) the process of science; deductive

C) discovery science; inductive

D) descriptive science; deductive

E) hypothesis–based science; deductive

Answer: C
*Topic: Concept 1.5*
*Skill: Comprehension*

49) What is a hypothesis?

A) the same thing as an unproven theory

B) a tentative explanation that can be tested and is falsifiable

C) a verifiable observation sensed directly, or sensed indirectly with the aid of scientific instrumentation

D) a fact based on qualitative data that is testable

E) a fact based on quantitative data that is falsifiable

Answer: B
*Topic: Concept 1.5*
*Skill: Knowledge*

50) Which of these is a deduction?

A) My car won't start.

B) My car's battery is dead.

C) My car is out of gas.

D) I lost my car key.

E) If I turn the key in the ignition while stepping on the gas pedal, then my car will start.

Answer: E
*Topic: Concept 1.5*
*Skill: Comprehension*

51) When applying the process of science, which of these is tested?

A) a question

B) a result

C) an observation

D) a prediction

E) a hypothesis

Answer: D
*Topic: Concept 1.5*
*Skill: Comprehension*

52) The statement "If you show your dog affection, then your dog will seek your company" is an example of

A) a statement that can be tested.

B) a statement derived from a hypothesis.

C) a prediction.

D) deductive reasoning.

E) all of the above

Answer: E
*Topic: Concept 1.5*
*Skill: Comprehension*

53) A controlled experiment is one in which

A) the experiment is repeated many times to ensure that the results are accurate.

B) the experiment proceeds at a slow pace to guarantee that the scientist can carefully observe all reactions and process all experimental data.

C) there are at least two groups, one of which does not receive the experimental treatment.

D) there are at least two groups, one differing from the other by two or more variables.

E) there is one group for which the scientist controls all variables.

Answer: C
*Topic: Concept 1.5*
*Skill: Comprehension*

54) Why is it important that an experiment include a control group?

A) The control group is the group that the reseacher is in control of; it is the group in which the researcher predetermines the nature of the results.

B) The control group provides a reserve of experimental subjects.

C) A control group is required for the development of an "if; then" statement.

D) A control group assures that an experiment will be repeatable.

E) Without a control group, there is no basis for knowing if a particular result is due to the variable being tested or to some other factor.

Answer: E
*Topic: Concept 1.5*
*Skill: Comprehension*

55) What is the primary reason for including a control group within the design of an experiment?

A) To ensure that the results obtained are due to a difference in only one variable

B) To ensure that the experimenter can perform a more complete statistical analysis

C) To demonstrate in what way the experiment was performed incorrectly

D) To accumulate additional facts that can be reported to other scientists

E) To test the effect of more than one variable

Answer: A
*Topic: Concept 1.5*
*Skill: Comprehension*

56) The application of scientific knowledge for some specific purpose is known as

A) technology.

B) deductive science.

C) inductive science.

D) anthropologic science.

E) pure science.

Answer: A
*Topic: Concept 1.5*
*Skill: Knowledge*

57) Which of the following is *not* a theme that unifies biology?

A) interaction with the environment

B) emergent properties

C) evolution

D) reductionism

E) structure and function

Answer: D
*Topic: Concept 1.6*
*Skill: Knowledge*

# Media Activity Questions

1) DNA is composed of building blocks called
   A) nucleic acids.
   B) Gs.
   C) nucleotides.
   D) adenines.
   E) amino acids.

   Answer: C
   *Topic: Web/CD Activity: Heritable Information*

2) In eukaryotic cells DNA has the appearance of a
   A) single strand.
   B) letter U.
   C) double helix.
   D) triple helix.
   E) circle.

   Answer: C
   *Topic: Web/CD Activity: Heritable Information*

3) Which of the following is a correct match of cell type with structure?
   A) nerve cell—closely joined
   B) skin cell—has a large volume
   C) intestinal cell—has a large volume
   D) intestinal cell—closely joined
   E) muscle cell—has proteins that slide back and forth

   Answer: E
   *Topic: Web/CD Activity: Form Fits Function: Cells*

4) What element is found in all organic compounds?
   A) carbon
   B) oxygen
   C) helium
   D) iron
   E) nitrogen

   Answer: A
   *Topic: Activity: Energy Flow and Chemical Cycling*

5) What name is given to organisms that convert the carbon in organic compounds into carbon in carbon dioxide?
   A) autotrophs
   B) heterotrophs
   C) plants
   D) recyclers
   E) decomposers

   Answer: D
   *Topic: Activity: Energy Flow and Chemical Cycling*

# Self-Quiz Questions

1) All organisms on your campus make up
   A) an ecosystem.
   B) a community.
   C) a population.
   D) an experimental group.
   E) a taxonomic domain.

   Answer: B

2) Which of the following is a correct sequence of levels in life's hierarchy, proceeding downward from an individual animal?
   A) brain, organ system, nerve cell, nervous tissue
   B) organ system, population of cells, nervous tissue, brain
   C) organism, organ system, tissue, cell, organ
   D) nervous system, brain, nervous tissue, nerve cell
   E) organ system, tissue, molecule, cell

   Answer: D

3) Which of the following is *not* an observation or inference on which Darwin's theory of natural selection is based?
   A) Poorly adapted individuals never produce offspring.
   B) There is heritable variation among individuals.
   C) Because of overproduction of offspring, there is competition for limited resources.
   D) Individuals whose inherited characteristics best fit them to the environment will generally produce more offspring.
   E) A population can become adapted to its environment.

   Answer: A

4) Systems biology is mainly an attempt to
   A) understand the integration of all levels of biological organization from molecules to the biosphere.
   B) simplify complex problems by reducing the system into smaller, less complex units.
   C) model one level of biological organization based on an understanding of the lower levels of organization.
   D) provide a systematic method for interpretation of large amounts of biological data.
   E) speed up the technological application of scientific knowledge.

   Answer: C

5) Protists and bacteria are grouped into different domains because
   A) protists eat bacteria.
   B) bacteria are not made of cells.
   C) bacterial cells lack a nucleus.
   D) bacteria decompose protists.
   E) protists are photosynthetic.

   Answer: C

6) Which of the following best demonstrates the unity among all organisms?
   A) matching DNA nucleotide sequences
   B) descent with modification
   C) the structure and function of DNA
   D) natural selection
   E) emergent properties

   Answer: C

7) Which of the following is an example of qualitative data?

A) The temperature decreased from 20°C to 15°C.

B) The plant's height is 25 centimeters.

C) The fish swam in a zig-zag motion.

D) The six pairs of robins hatched an average of three chicks.

E) The contents of the human stomach are mixed about every 20 seconds.

Answer: C

8) Which of the following best describes the logic of hypothesis-based science?

A) If I generate a testable hypothesis, tests and observations will support it.

B) If my prediction is correct, it will lead to a testable hypothesis.

C) If my observations are accurate, they will support my hypothesis.

D) If my hypothesis is correct, I can expect certain test results.

E) If my experiments are set up right, they will lead to a testable hypothesis.

Answer: D

9) A controlled experiment is one that

A) proceeds slowly enough that a scientist can make careful records of the results.

B) may include experimental groups and control groups tested in parallel.

C) is repeated many times to make sure the results are accurate.

D) keeps all environmental variables constant.

E) is supervised by an experienced scientist.

Answer: B

10) Which of the following statements best distinguishes hypotheses from theories in science?

A) Theories are hypotheses that have been proved.

B) Hypotheses are guesses; theories are correct answers.

C) Hypotheses usually are relatively narrow in scope; theories have broad explanatory power.

D) Hypotheses and theories are essentially the same thing.

E) Theories are proved true in all cases; hypotheses are usually falsified by tests.

Answer: C

# Chapter 2  The Chemical Context of Life

1) About 25 of the 92 natural elements are known to be essential to life. Which four of these 25 elements make up approximately 96% of living matter?

A) carbon, sodium, chlorine, nitrogen

B) carbon, sulfur, phosphorus, hydrogen

C) oxygen, hydrogen, calcium, sodium

D) carbon, hydrogen, nitrogen, oxygen

E) carbon, oxygen, sulfur, calcium

Answer: D
*Topic: Concept 2.1*
*Skill: Knowledge*

2) Trace elements are those required by an organism in only minute quantities. Which of the following is a trace element that is required by humans and other vertebrates?

A) nitrogen

B) calcium

C) iodine

D) sodium

E) phosphorus

Answer: C
*Topic: Concept 2.1*
*Skill: Knowledge*

3) Which of the following statements is *false*?

A) Atoms of the various elements differ in their number of subatomic particles.

B) All atoms of a particular element have the same number of protons in their nuclei.

C) The neutrons and protons present in the nucleus of an atom are almost identical in mass; each has a mass of about 1 dalton.

D) An atom is the smallest unit of an element that still retains the properties of the element.

E) Protons and electrons are electrically charged particles. Protons have one unit of negative charge, and electrons have one unit of positive charge.

Answer: E
*Topic: Concept 2.2*
*Skill: Knowledge*

4) Each element is unique and different from other elements because of the number of protons in the nuclei of its atoms. Which of the following indicates the number of protons in an atom's nucleus?

A) atomic mass

B) atomic weight

C) atomic number

D) mass weight

E) mass number

Answer: C
*Topic: Concept 2.2*
*Skill: Knowledge*

5) The mass number of an element can be easily approximated by adding together the number of _____ in an atom of that element.

A) protons and neutrons

B) energy levels

C) protons and electrons

D) neutrons and electrons

E) isotopes

Answer: A
*Topic: Concept 2.2*
*Skill: Comprehension*

6) What is the approximate atomic mass of an atom with 16 neutrons, 15 protons, and 15 electrons?

A) 15 daltons

B) 16 daltons

C) 30 daltons

D) 31 daltons

E) 46 daltons

Answer: D
*Topic: Concept 2.2*
*Skill: Comprehension*

7) Oxygen has an atomic number of 8 and a mass number of 16. Thus, the atomic mass of an oxygen atom is

A) exactly 8 grams.

B) exactly 8 daltons.

C) approximately 16 grams.

D) approximately 16 daltons.

E) 24 amu (atomic mass units).

Answer: D
*Topic: Concept 2.2*
*Skill: Comprehension*

8) The nucleus of a nitrogen atom contains 7 neutrons and 7 protons. Which of the following is a *correct* statement concerning nitrogen?

A) The nitrogen atom has a mass number of approximately 7 daltons and an atomic mass of 14.

B) The nitrogen atom has a mass number of approximately 14 daltons and an atomic mass of 7.

C) The nitrogen atom has a mass number of 14 and an atomic mass of 7 grams.

D) The nitrogen atom has a mass number of 7 grams and an atomic number of 14.

E) The nitrogen atom has a mass number of 14 and an atomic mass of approximately 14 daltons.

Answer: E
*Topic: Concept 2.2*
*Skill: Comprehension*

9) Calcium has an atomic number of 20 and an atomic mass of 40. Therefore, a calcium atom must have

A) 20 protons.

B) 40 electrons.

C) 40 neutrons.

D) A and B only

E) A, B, and C

Answer: A
*Topic: Concept 2.2*
*Skill: Comprehension*

10) An atom with an atomic number of 9 and a mass number of 19 would have an atomic mass of approximately

A) 9 daltons.

B) 9 grams.

C) 10 daltons.

D) 20 grams.

E) 19 daltons.

Answer: E
*Topic: Concept 2.2*
*Skill: Comprehension*

11) Different atomic forms of an element contain the same number of protons but a different number of neutrons. What are these different atomic forms called?

A) ions

B) isotopes

C) neutronic atoms

D) isomers

E) radioactive atoms

Answer: B
*Topic: Concept 2.2*
*Skill: Knowledge*

12) How do isotopes of the same element differ from each other?

A) number of protons

B) number of electrons

C) number of neutrons

D) valence electron distribution

E) amount of radioactivity

Answer: C
*Topic: Concept 2.2*
*Skill: Knowledge*

13) Which of the following best describes the relationship between the atoms described below?

| Atom 1 | Atom 2 |
|--------|--------|
| $_{1}^{1}\text{H}$ | $_{1}^{3}\text{H}$ |

A) They are isomers.

B) They are polymers.

C) They are isotopes.

D) They contain 1 and 3 protons, respectively.

E) They each contain 1 neutron.

Answer: C
*Topic: Concept 2.2*
*Skill: Comprehension*

14) Which of the following best describes the relationship between the atoms described below?

| Atom 1 | Atom 2 |
|--------|--------|
| $_{15}^{31}\text{P}$ | $_{15}^{32}\text{P}$ |

A) They are both radioactive.

B) They are both phosphorus cations.

C) They are both phosphorus anions.

D) They are both isotopes of phosphorus.

E) They contain 31 and 32 protons, respectively.

Answer: D
*Topic: Concept 2.2*
*Skill: Comprehension*

15) One difference between carbon-12 $\left( {}^{12}_{6}C \right)$

and carbon-14 $\left( {}^{14}_{6}C \right)$ is that carbon-14

has

   A) two more protons than carbon-12.

   B) two more electrons than carbon-12.

   C) two more neutrons than carbon-12.

   D) A and C only

   E) B and C only

Answer: C
*Topic: Concept 2.2*
*Skill: Comprehension*

16) ${}^{3}H$ is a radioactive isotope of hydrogen.

One difference between hydrogen-1 $({}^{1}_{1}H)$

and hydrogen-3 $({}^{3}_{1}H)$ is that hydrogen-3

has

   A) one more neutron and one more
      proton than hydrogen-1.

   B) one more proton and one more
      electron than hydrogen-1.

   C) one more electron and one more
      neutron than hydrogen-1.

   D) two more neutrons than hydrogen-1.

   E) two more protons than hydrogen-1.

Answer: D
*Topic: Concept 2.2*
*Skill: Comprehension*

17) The atomic number of carbon is 6.
    Carbon-14 is heavier than carbon-12
    because the atomic nucleus of carbon-14
    contains _____ neutrons.

   A) 6

   B) 7

   C) 8

   D) 12

   E) 14

Answer: C
*Topic: Concept 2.2*
*Skill: Comprehension*

18) Two isotopes of the same element will
    have different numbers of

   A) protons.

   B) neutrons.

   C) electrons.

   D) protons and neutrons.

   E) neutrons and electrons.

Answer: B
*Topic: Concept 2.2*
*Skill: Comprehension*

19) Electrons exist only at fixed levels of
    potential energy.  However, if an atom
    absorbs sufficient energy, a possible result
    is that

   A) an electron may move to an electron
      shell farther out from the nucleus.

   B) an electron may move to an electron
      shell closer to the nucleus.

   C) the atom may become a radioactive
      isotope.

   D) the atom would become a positively
      charged ion, or cation.

   E) the atom would become a negatively
      charged ion, or anion.

Answer: A
*Topic: Concept 2.2*
*Skill: Knowledge*

20) The atomic number of neon is 10. Therefore, which of the following is *correct* about an atom of neon?

A) It has 8 electrons in its outer electron shell.

B) It is inert.

C) It has an atomic mass of 10 daltons.

D) A and B only

E) A, B, and C are correct.

Answer: D
*Topic: Concept 2.2*
*Skill: Comprehension*

21) From its atomic number of 15, it is possible to predict that the phosphorus atom has

A) 15 neutrons.

B) 15 protons.

C) 15 electrons.

D) 8 electrons in its outermost electron shell.

E) B and C only

Answer: E
*Topic: Concept 2.2*
*Skill: Comprehension*

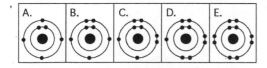

**Figure 2.1**

22) Which drawing depicts the electron configuration of neon ($^{20}_{10}$Ne)?

Answer: E
*Topic: Concept 2.2*
*Skill: Comprehension*

23) Which drawing depicts the electron configuration of oxygen ($^{16}_{8}$O)?

Answer: C
*Topic: Concept 2.2*
*Skill: Comprehension*

24) Which drawing depicts the electron configuration of nitrogen ($^{14}_{7}$N)?

Answer: B
*Topic: Concept 2.2*
*Skill: Comprehension*

25) Which drawing is of an atom with the atomic number of 6?

Answer: A
*Topic: Concept 2.2*
*Skill: Comprehension*

26) Which drawing depicts an atom that is inert or chemically unreactive?

Answer: E
*Topic: Concept 2.2*
*Skill: Comprehension*

27) Which drawing depicts an atom with a valence of 3?

Answer: B
*Topic: Concept 2.2*
*Skill: Comprehension*

28) Which drawing depicts an atom with a valence of 2?

Answer: C
*Topic: Concept 2.2*
*Skill: Comprehension*

29) What does the reactivity of an atom depend on?

    A) number of valence shells in the atom

    B) number of orbitals found in the atom

    C) number of electrons in each orbital in the atom

    D) presence of unpaired electrons in the outer valence shell of the atom

    E) presence of hybridized orbitals in the atom

Answer: D
*Topic: Concept 2.2*
*Skill: Knowledge*

30) Atoms whose outer electron shells contain eight electrons tend to

    A) form ionic bonds in aqueous solutions.

    B) form covalent bonds in aqueous solutions.

    C) be stable and chemically nonreactive, or inert.

    D) be unstable and chemically very reactive.

    E) be isotopes and very radioactive.

Answer: C
*Topic: Concept 2.2*
*Skill: Knowledge*

31) What are the chemical properties of atoms whose valence shells are filled with electrons?

    A) They form ionic bonds in aqueous solutions.

    B) They form covalent bonds in aqueous solutions.

    C) They are stable and chemically unreactive or inert.

    D) They exhibit similar chemical behaviors.

    E) C and D only

Answer: E
*Topic: Concept 2.2*
*Skill: Knowledge*

*Use the information extracted from the periodic table in Figure 2.2 to answer the following questions.*

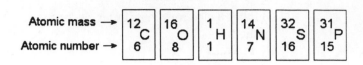

**Figure 2.2**

32) How many electrons does nitrogen have in its valence shell?

    A) 2

    B) 5

    C) 7

    D) 8

    E) 14

Answer: B
*Topic: Concept 2.2*
*Skill: Comprehension*

33) How many electrons does phosphorus have in its valence shell?

    A) 1

    B) 2

    C) 3

    D) 4

    E) 5

Answer: E
*Topic: Concept 2.2*
*Skill: Comprehension*

34) How many neutrons are present in the nucleus of a phosphorus atom?

    A) 8

    B) 15

    C) 16

    D) 31

    E) 46

Answer: C
*Topic: Concept 2.2*
*Skill: Comprehension*

35) How many electrons does an atom of sulfur have in its valence shell?

A) 4

B) 6

C) 8

D) 16

E) 32

Answer: B
*Topic: Concept 2.2*
*Skill: Comprehension*

36) Based on electron configuration, which of these elements would exhibit chemical behavior most like that of oxygen?

A) carbon

B) hydrogen

C) nitrogen

D) sulfur

E) phosphorus

Answer: D
*Topic: Concept 2.2*
*Skill: Application*

37) How many electrons would be expected in the outermost electron shell of an atom with atomic number 12?

A) 1

B) 2

C) 4

D) 6

E) 8

Answer: B
*Topic: Concept 2.2*
*Skill: Comprehension*

38) The atomic number of each atom is given to the left of each of the elements below. Which of the atoms has the same valence as carbon ($_{6}^{12}$C)?

A) $_7$nitrogen

B) $_9$fluorine

C) $_{10}$neon

D) $_{12}$magnesium

E) $_{14}$silicon

Answer: E
*Topic: Concept 2.2*
*Skill: Application*

39) What is the valence of an atom with six electrons in its outer electron shell?

A) 1

B) 2

C) 3

D) 4

E) 5

Answer: B
*Topic: Concept 2.2*
*Skill: Comprehension*

40) Fluorine has an atomic number of 9 and a mass number of 19. How many electrons are needed to complete the valence shell of a fluorine atom?

A) 1

B) 3

C) 5

D) 7

E) 9

Answer: A
*Topic: Concept 2.2*
*Skill: Comprehension*

41) What is the maximum number of electrons in the 1s orbital of an atom?

A) 1

B) 2

C) 3

D) 4

E) 5

Answer: B
*Topic: Concept 2.2*
*Skill: Knowledge*

42) What is the maximum number of electrons in a 2p orbital of an atom?

A) 1

B) 2

C) 3

D) 4

E) 5

Answer: B
*Topic: Concept 2.2*
*Skill: Knowledge*

43) A covalent chemical bond is one in which

A) electrons are removed from one atom and transferred to another atom so that the two atoms become oppositely charged.

B) protons and neutrons are shared by two atoms so as to satisfy the requirements of both atoms.

C) outer-shell electrons of two atoms are shared so as to satisfactorily fill the outer electron shells of both atoms.

D) outer-shell electrons of one atom are transferred to the inner electron shells of another atom.

E) the inner-shell electrons of one atom are transferred to the outer shell of another atom.

Answer: C
*Topic: Concept 2.3*
*Skill: Knowledge*

44) What do atoms form when they share electron pairs?

A) elements

B) ions

C) aggregates

D) isotopes

E) molecules

Answer: E
*Topic: Concept 2.3*
*Skill: Knowledge*

45) If an atom of sulfur (atomic number 16) were allowed to react with atoms of hydrogen (atomic number 1), which of the molecules below would be formed?

A) S–H

B) H–S–H

C) H–S–H
     |
     H

D)    H
     |
  H–S–H
     |
     H

E) H=S=H

Answer: B
*Topic: Concept 2.3*
*Skill: Application*

46) What is the maximum number of covalent bonds an element with atomic number 8 can make with hydrogen?

A) 1

B) 2

C) 3

D) 4

E) 6

Answer: B
*Topic: Concept 2.3*
*Skill: Comprehension*

47) A molecule of carbon dioxide ($CO_2$) is formed when one atom of carbon (atomic number 6) is covalently bonded with two atoms of oxygen (atomic number 8). What is the total number of electrons that must be shared between the carbon atom and the oxygen atoms in order to complete the outer electron shell of all three atoms?

A) 1

B) 2

C) 3

D) 4

E) 5

Answer: D
*Topic: Concept 2.3*
*Skill: Application*

48) Nitrogen (N) is much more electronegative than hydrogen (H). Which of the following statements is *correct* about the atoms in ammonia ($NH_3$)?

A) Each hydrogen atom has a partial positive charge.

B) The nitrogen atom has a strong positive charge.

C) Each hydrogen atom has a slight negative charge.

D) The nitrogen atom has a partial positive charge.

E) There are covalent bonds between the hydrogen atoms.

Answer: A
*Topic: Concept 2.3*
*Skill: Comprehension*

49) What do the four elements most abundant in life—carbon, oxygen, hydrogen, and nitrogen—have in common?

A) They all have the same number of valence electrons.

B) Each element exists in only one isotopic form.

C) They are equal in electronegativity.

D) They are elements produced only by living cells.

E) They all have unpaired electrons in their valence shells.

Answer: E
*Topic: Concept 2.3*
*Skill: Comprehension*

50) When two atoms are equally electronegative, they will interact to form

A) equal numbers of isotopes.

B) ions.

C) polar covalent bonds.

D) nonpolar covalent bonds.

E) ionic bonds.

Answer: D
*Topic: Concept 2.3*
*Skill: Comprehension*

51) What results from an unequal sharing of electrons between atoms?

A) a nonpolar covalent bond

B) a polar covalent bond

C) an ionic bond

D) a hydrogen bond

E) a hydrophobic interaction

Answer: B
*Topic: Concept 2.3*
*Skill: Knowledge*

52) A covalent bond is likely to be polar when

A) one of the atoms sharing electrons is much more electronegative than the other atom.

B) the two atoms sharing electrons are equally electronegative.

C) the two atoms sharing electrons are of the same element.

D) it is between two atoms that are both very strong electron acceptors.

E) the two atoms sharing electrons are different elements.

Answer: A
*Topic: Concept 2.3*
*Skill: Comprehension*

53) A polar covalent bond can form when

A) there is the loss of one or more electrons from one atom to another atom of the same molecule.

B) there is the gain of one or more electrons from one atom to another atom of the same molecule.

C) one of the atoms has a greater affinity for electrons than the other atom of the same molecule.

D) one of the atoms has a greater affinity for neutrons than the other atom of the same molecule.

E) two atoms of a molecule attract electrons equally.

Answer: C
*Topic: Concept 2.3*
*Skill: Comprehension*

54) Which of the following molecules contains the strongest polar covalent bond?

A) $H_2$

B) $O_2$

C) $CO_2$

D) $H_2O$

E) $CH_4$

Answer: D
*Topic: Concept 2.3*
*Skill: Comprehension*

*The following questions refer to Figure 2.3.*

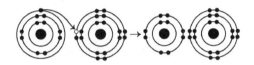

**Figure 2.3**

55) What results from the chemical reaction illustrated in Figure 2.3?

A) a cation with a net charge of +1

B) a cation with a net charge of –1

C) an anion with a net charge of +1

D) an anion with a net charge of –1

E) A and D

Answer: E
*Topic: Concept 2.3*
*Skill: Comprehension*

56) What is the atomic number of the cation formed in the reaction illustrated in Figure 2.3?

A) 1

B) 8

C) 10

D) 11

E) 16

Answer: D
*Topic: Concept 2.3*
*Skill: Application*

57) The ionic bond of sodium chloride is formed when
    A) chlorine gains an electron from sodium.
    B) sodium and chlorine share an electron pair.
    C) sodium and chlorine both lose electrons from their outer valence shells.
    D) sodium gains an electron from chlorine.
    E) chlorine gains a proton from sodium.

Answer: A
*Topic: Concept 2.3*
*Skill: Comprehension*

58) What is the difference between covalent bonds and ionic bonds?
    A) Covalent bonds involve the sharing of protons between atoms, and ionic bonds involve the sharing of electrons between atoms.
    B) Covalent bonds involve the sharing of neutrons between atoms, and ionic bonds involve the sharing of electrons between atoms.
    C) Covalent bonds involve the sharing of electrons between atoms, and ionic bonds involve the electrical attraction between atoms.
    D) Covalent bonds involve the sharing of protons between atoms, and ionic bonds involve the sharing of neutrons between atoms.
    E) Covalent bonds involve the transfer of electrons between atoms, and ionic bonds involve the sharing of neutrons between atoms.

Answer: C
*Topic: Concept 2.3*
*Skill: Comprehension*

59) What kind of a bond does $NH_4^+$ form with $Cl^-$ to make ammonium chloride salt ($NH_4Cl$)?
    A) nonpolar covalent
    B) polar covalent
    C) ionic
    D) hydrogen
    E) C and D only

Answer: C
*Topic: Concept 2.3*
*Skill: Comprehension*

60) In ammonium chloride salt ($NH_4Cl$) the anion is a single chloride ion, $Cl^-$. What is the cation of $NH_4Cl$?
    A) N, with a charge of +3
    B) H, with a charge of +1
    C) $H_4$ with a charge of +4
    D) $NH_4$ with a charge of +1
    E) $NH_4$ with a charge of +4

Answer: D
*Topic: Concept 2.3*
*Skill: Comprehension*

61) The atomic number of chlorine is 17. The atomic number of magnesium is 12. What is the formula for magnesium chloride?
    A) MgCl
    B) $MgCl_2$
    C) $Mg_2Cl$
    D) $Mg_2Cl_2$
    E) $MgCl_3$

Answer: B
*Topic: Concept 2.3*
*Skill: Application*

*Use these choices to answer the following questions.*

    A. nonpolar covalent bond
    B. polar covalent bond
    C. ionic bond
    D. hydrogen bond
    E. hydrophobic interaction

62) Results from a transfer of electron(s) between atoms.

Answer: C
*Topic: Concept 2.3*
*Skill: Knowledge*

63) Explains most specifically the attraction of water molecules to one another.

Answer: D
*Topic: Concept 2.3*
*Skill: Knowledge*

64) Van der Waals interactions result when

    A) hybrid orbitals overlap.

    B) electrons are not symmetrically distributed in a molecule.

    C) molecules held by ionic bonds react with water.

    D) two polar covalent bonds react.

    E) a hydrogen atom loses an electron.

Answer: B
*Topic: Concept 2.3*
*Skill: Knowledge*

65) A van der Waals interaction is the weak attraction between

    A) the electrons of one molecule and the electrons of a nearby molecule.

    B) the nucleus of one molecule and the electrons of a nearby molecule.

    C) a polar molecule and a nearby nonpolar molecule.

    D) a polar molecule and a nearby molecule that is also polar.

    E) a nonpolar molecule and a nearby molecule that is also nonpolar.

Answer: B
*Topic: Concept 2.3*
*Skill: Comprehension*

66) Which of the following is *not* considered to be a weak molecular interaction?

    A) a covalent bond

    B) a van der Waals interaction

    C) an ionic bond in the presence of water

    D) a hydrogen bond

    E) A and B only

Answer: A
*Topic: Concept 2.3*
*Skill: Comprehension*

67) Which of the following is true for this reaction? $3 H_2 + N_2 \Leftrightarrow 2 NH_3$

    A) The reaction is nonreversible.

    B) Hydrogen and nitrogen are the reactants of the reverse reaction.

    C) Hydrogen and nitrogen are the products of the forward reaction.

    D) Ammonia is being formed and decomposed.

    E) Hydrogen and nitrogen are being decomposed.

Answer: D
*Topic: Concept 2.4*
*Skill: Comprehension*

68) Which of the following best describes chemical equilibrium?

A) Forward and reverse reactions continue with no effect on the concentrations of the reactants and products.

B) Concentrations of products are higher than the concentrations of the reactants.

C) Forward and reverse reactions have stopped so that the concentration of the reactants equals the concentration of the products.

D) Reactions stop only when all reactants have been converted to products.

E) There are equal concentrations of reactants and products, and the reactions have stopped.

Answer: A
*Topic: Concept 2.4*
*Skill: Comprehension*

69) Which of the following describes any reaction that has attained chemical equilibrium?

A) The concentration of the reactants equals the concentration of the products.

B) The rate of the forward reaction is equal to the rate of the reverse reaction.

C) All of the reactants have been converted to the products of the reaction.

D) All of the products have been converted to the reactants of the reaction.

E) Both the forward and the reverse reactions have stopped with no net effect on the concentration of the reactants and the products.

Answer: B
*Topic: Concept 2.4*
*Skill: Comprehension*

# Media Activity Questions

1) What is the atomic mass of an atom that has 6 protons, 6 neutrons, and 6 electrons?

   A) 6

   B) 8

   C) +1

   D) 12

   E) 18

   Answer: D
   *Topic: Activity: Structure of the Atomic Nucleus*

2) An uncharged atom of boron has an atomic number of 5 and an atomic mass of 11. How many electrons does boron have?

   A) 11

   B) 15

   C) 0

   D) 5

   E) 2

   Answer: D
   *Topic: Web/CD Activity: Electron Arrangement*

3) A(n) _____ refers to two or more atoms held together by covalent bonds.

   A) ion

   B) isotope

   C) community

   D) shell

   E) molecule

   Answer: E
   *Topic: Web/CD Activity: Covalent Bonds*

4) In salt, what is the nature of the bond between sodium and chlorine?

   A) polar covalent

   B) nonpolar covalent

   C) hydrogen

   D) hydrophobic

   E) ionic

   Answer: E
   *Topic: Web/CD Activity: Ionic Bonds*

5) What name is given to the bond between water molecules?

   A) hydrogen

   B) hydrophobic

   C) ionic

   D) polar covalent

   E) nonpolar covalent

   Answer: A
   *Topic: Web/CD Activity: Hydrogen Bonds*

# Self-Quiz Questions

1) An element is to a (an) _____ as an organ is to a (an) _____.
   A) atom; organism
   B) compound; organism
   C) molecule; cell
   D) atom; cell
   E) compound; organelle

   Answer: B

2) In the term *trace element,* the modifier *trace* means
   A) the element is required in very small amounts.
   B) the element can be used as a label to trace atoms through an organism's metabolism.
   C) the element is very rare on Earth.
   D) the element enhances health but is not essential for the organism's long-term survival.
   E) the element passes rapidly through the organism.

   Answer: A

3) Compared to $^{31}P$, the radioactive isotope $^{32}P$ has
   A) a different atomic number.
   B) one more neutron.
   C) one more proton.
   D) one more electron.
   E) a different charge.

   Answer: B

4) Atoms can be represented by simply listing the number of protons, neutrons, and electrons—for example, $2p^+$; $2n^0$; $2e^-$ for helium. Which atom represents the $^{18}O$ isotope of oxygen?
   A) $6p^+$; $8n^0$; $6e^-$
   B) $8p^+$; $10n^0$; $8e^-$
   C) $9p^+$; $9n^0$; $9e^-$
   D) $7p^+$; $2n^0$; $9e^-$
   E) $10p^+$; $8n^0$; $9e^-$

   Answer: B

5) The atomic number of sulfur is 16. Sulfur combines with hydrogen by covalent bonding to form a compound, hydrogen sulfide. Based on the electron configuration of sulfur, we can predict that the molecular formula of the compound will be _____.
   A) HS
   B) $HS_2$
   C) $H_2S$
   D) $H_3S_2$
   E) $H_4S$

   Answer: C

6) Review the valences of carbon, oxygen, hydrogen, and nitrogen, and then determine which of the following molecules is most likely to exist.

A) O = C-H

B)
```
          H   H
          |   |
    H - O - C - C = O
              |
              H
```

C)
```
      H       H
      |       |
    H - C - H - C = O
      |
      H
```

D)
```
      O
      |
    H - N = H
```

Answer: B

7) The reactivity of an atom arises from
   A) the average distance of the outermost electron shell from the nucleus.
   B) the existence of unpaired electrons in the valence shell.
   C) the sum of the potential energies of all the electron shells.
   D) the potential energy of the valence shell.
   E) the energy difference between the $s$ and $p$ orbitals.

Answer: B

8) Which of these statements is true of all anionic atoms?
   A) The atom has more electrons than protons.
   B) The atom has more protons than electrons.
   C) The atom has fewer protons than does a neutral atom of the same element.
   D) The atom has more neutrons than protons.
   E) The net charge is 1–.

Answer: A

9) What coefficients must be placed in the blanks so that all atoms are accounted for in the product?

$$C_6H_{12}O_6 \rightarrow \underline{\quad}C_2H_6O + \underline{\quad}CO_2$$

   A) 1; 2
   B) 2; 2
   C) 1; 3
   D) 1; 1
   E) 3; 1

Answer: B

10) Which of the following statements correctly describes any chemical reaction that has reached equilibrium?
   A) The concentration of products equals the concentration of reactants.
   B) The rate of the forward reaction equals the rate of the reverse reaction.
   C) Both forward and reverse reactions have halted.
   D) The reaction is now irreversible.
   E) No reactants remain.

Answer: B

# Chapter 3  Water and the Fitness of the Environment

1) In a single molecule of water, the two hydrogen atoms are bonded to a single oxygen atom by
   A) hydrogen bonds.
   B) nonpolar covalent bonds.
   C) polar covalent bonds.
   D) ionic bonds.
   E) van der Waals interactions.

Answer: C
*Topic: Concept 3.1*
*Skill: Knowledge*

2) The slight negative charge at one end of one water molecule is attracted to the slight positive charge of another water molecule. What is this attraction called?
   A) a covalent bond
   B) a hydrogen bond
   C) an ionic bond
   D) a hydrophilic bond
   E) a hydrophobic bond

Answer: B
*Topic: Concept 3.1*
*Skill: Knowledge*

3) An example of a hydrogen bond is the bond between
   A) C and H in methane ($CH_4$).
   B) the H of one water molecule and the O of another water molecule.
   C) $Na^+$ and $Cl^-$ in salt.
   D) the two hydrogen atoms in a molecule of hydrogen gas ($H_2$).
   E) $Mg^+$ and $Cl^-$ in $MgCl_2$.

Answer: B
*Topic: Concept 3.1*
*Skill: Comprehension*

4) Water is able to form hydrogen bonds because
   A) oxygen has a valence of 2.
   B) the water molecule is shaped like a tetrahedron.
   C) the bonds that hold together the atoms in a water molecule are polar covalent bonds.
   D) the oxygen atom in a water molecule has a weak positive charge.
   E) each of the hydrogen atoms in a water molecule is weakly negative in charge.

Answer: C
*Topic: Concept 3.1*
*Skill: Knowledge*

5) What determines the cohesiveness of water molecules?
   A) hydrophobic interactions
   B) nonpolar covalent bonds
   C) ionic bonds
   D) hydrogen bonds
   E) both A and C

Answer: D
*Topic: Concept 3.2*
*Skill: Knowledge*

6) What do cohesion, surface tension, and adhesion have in common with reference to water?
   A) All increase when temperature increases.
   B) All are produced by ionic bonding.
   C) All are properties related to hydrogen bonding.
   D) All have to do with nonpolar covalent bonds.
   E) C and D only

Answer: C
*Topic: Concept 3.2*
*Skill: Knowledge*

7) Which of the following is possible due to the high surface tension of water?

A) Lakes don't freeze solid in winter, despite low temperatures.

B) A water strider can walk across the surface of a small pond.

C) Organisms resist temperature changes, although they give off heat due to chemical reactions.

D) Water can act as a solvent.

E) The pH of water remains exactly neutral.

Answer: B
*Topic: Concept 3.2*
*Skill: Comprehension*

8) Which of the following is true when an ice cube cools a drink?

A) Molecule collisions in the drink increase.

B) Kinetic energy in the drink decreases.

C) A calorie of heat energy is transferred from the ice to the water of the drink.

D) The specific heat of the water in the drink decreases.

E) Evaporation of the water in the drink increases.

Answer: B
*Topic: Concept 3.2*
*Skill: Comprehension*

9) Which of the following is a *correct* definition of a kilocalorie?

A) the amount of heat required to raise the temperature of 1 g of water by 1°F

B) the amount of heat required to raise the temperature of 1 g of water by 1°C

C) the amount of heat required to raise the temperature of 1 kg of water by 1°F

D) the amount of heat required to raise the temperature of 1 kg of water by 1°C

E) the amount of heat required to raise the temperature of 1,000 g of water by 1°F

Answer: D
*Topic: Concept 3.2*
*Skill: Knowledge*

10) The nutritional information on a cereal box shows that one serving of a dry cereal has 200 kilocalories. If one were to burn one serving of the cereal, the amount of heat given off would be sufficient to raise the temperature of 20 kg of water how many degrees Celsius?

A) 0.2°C

B) 1.0°C

C) 2.0°C

D) 10.0°C

E) 20.0°C

Answer: D
*Topic: Concept 3.2*
*Skill: Application*

11) Water's high specific heat is mainly a consequence of the

    A) small size of the water molecules.

    B) high specific heat of oxygen and hydrogen atoms.

    C) absorption and release of heat when hydrogen bonds break and form.

    D) fact that water is a poor heat conductor.

    E) inability of water to dissipate heat into dry air.

Answer: C
*Topic: Concept 3.2*
*Skill: Comprehension*

12) Which bonds must be broken for water to vaporize?

    A) ionic bonds

    B) nonpolar covalent bonds

    C) polar covalent bonds

    D) hydrogen bonds

    E) covalent bonds

Answer: D
*Topic: Concept 3.2*
*Skill: Knowledge*

13) Desert rabbits are adapted to the warm climate because their large ears aid in the removal of heat due to the

    A) high surface tension of water.

    B) high heat of vaporization of water.

    C) high specific heat of water.

    D) buffering capacity of water.

    E) dissociation of water molecules.

Answer: B
*Topic: Concept 3.2*
*Skill: Comprehension*

14) The formation of ice during colder weather helps moderate the seasonal transition to winter. This is mainly because

    A) the breaking of hydrogen bonds absorbs heat.

    B) the formation of hydrogen bonds releases heat.

    C) the formation of hydrogen bonds absorbs heat.

    D) there is greater evaporative cooling of lakes.

    E) ice is denser than liquid water.

Answer: B
*Topic: Concept 3.2*
*Skill: Comprehension*

15) Temperature usually increases when water condenses. Which behavior of water is most directly responsible for this phenomenon?

    A) the change in density when it condenses to form a liquid or solid

    B) reactions with other atmospheric compounds

    C) the release of heat by the formation of hydrogen bonds

    D) the release of heat by the breaking of hydrogen bonds

    E) the high surface tension of water

Answer: C
*Topic: Concept 3.2*
*Skill: Comprehension*

16) At what temperature is water at its densest?

    A) 0°C

    B) 4°C

    C) 32°C

    D) 100°C

    E) 212°C

Answer: B
*Topic: Concept 3.2*
*Skill: Knowledge*

17) Ice is lighter and floats in water because it is a crystalline structure in which each water molecule is bonded to a maximum of four other water molecules by which kind of bond?

  A) ionic

  B) hydrogen

  C) covalent

  D) A and C only

  E) A, B, and C

Answer: B
*Topic: Concept 3.2*
*Skill: Knowledge*

18) Why does ice float in liquid water?

  A) The liquid water molecules have more kinetic energy and thus support the ice.

  B) The ionic bonds between the molecules in ice prevent the ice from sinking.

  C) Ice always has air bubbles that keep it afloat.

  D) Hydrogen bonds stabilize and keep the molecules of ice farther apart than the water molecules of liquid water.

  E) The crystalline lattice of ice causes it to be denser than liquid water.

Answer: D
*Topic: Concept 3.2*
*Skill: Comprehension*

*The following question is based on Figure 3.1: solute molecule surrounded by a hydration shell of water.*

**Figure 3.1**

19) Based on your knowledge of the polarity of water molecules, the solute molecule is most likely

  A) positively charged.

  B) negatively charged.

  C) without charge.

  D) hydrophobic.

  E) nonpolar.

Answer: A
*Topic: Concept 3.2*
*Skill: Application*

20) Hydrophobic substances such as vegetable oil are

  A) nonpolar substances that repel water molecules.

  B) nonpolar substances that have an attraction for water molecules.

  C) polar substances that repel water molecules.

  D) polar substances that have an affinity for water.

  E) charged molecules that hydrogen–bond with water molecules.

Answer: A
*Topic: Concept 3.2*
*Skill: Knowledge*

21) One mole (mol) of a substance is

A) $6.02 \times 10^{23}$ molecules of the substance.

B) 1 g of the substance dissolved in 1 L of solution.

C) the largest amount of the substance that can be dissolved in 1 L of solution.

D) the molecular mass of the substance expressed in grams.

E) A and D only

Answer: E
*Topic: Concept 3.2*
*Skill: Knowledge*

22) How many molecules of glucose ($C_6H_{12}O_6$, molecular mass =180 daltons) would be present in one mole of glucose?

A) 24

B) 342

C) $23 \times 10^{14}$

D) $180 \times 10^{14}$

E) $6.02 \times 10^{23}$

Answer: E
*Topic: Concept 3.2*
*Skill: Knowledge*

23) How many molecules of glycerol ($C_3H_8O_3$) would be present in 1 L of a 1 *M* glycerol solution?

A) 1

B) 14

C) 92

D) $1 \times 10^7$

E) $6.02 \times 10^{23}$

Answer: E
*Topic: Concept 3.2*
*Skill: Knowledge*

24) Recall that when sodium chloride (NaCl) is placed in water the component atoms of the NaCl crystal dissociate into individual sodium ions ($Na^+$) and chloride ions ($Cl^-$). In contrast, the atoms of covalently bonded molecules (e.g., glucose, sucrose, glycerol) do not generally dissociate when placed in aqueous solution. Which of the following solutions would be expected to contain the greatest concentration of particles (molecules or ions)?

A) 0.5 *M* NaCl

B) 0.5 *M* glucose

C) 1.0 *M* NaCl

D) 1.0 *M* glucose

E) 1.0 *M* $MgCl_2$

Answer: E
*Topic: Concept 3.2*
*Skill: Application*

25) When sodium chloride (NaCl) is placed in water the component atoms of the NaCl crystal dissociate into individual sodium ions ($Na^+$) and chloride ions ($Cl^-$). In contrast, the atoms of covalently bonded molecules (e.g., glucose, sucrose, glycerol) do not generally dissociate when placed in aqueous solution. Which of the following solutions would be expected to contain the greatest number of particles (molecules or ions)?

A) 1 L of 0.5 *M* NaCl

B) 1 L 0.5 *M* glucose

C) 1 L of 1.0 *M* NaCl

D) 1 L of 1.0 *M* glucose

E) C and D only

Answer: C
*Topic: Concept 3.2*
*Skill: Application*

26) The molecular mass of glucose is 180 g. To make a 1 $M$ solution of glucose, you should do which of the following?

A) Dissolve 1 g of glucose in 1 L of water.

B) Dissolve 180 g of glucose in 1 L of water.

C) Dissolve 180 g of glucose in 100 g of water.

D) Dissolve 180 mg (milligrams) of glucose in 1 L of water.

E) Dissolve 180 g of glucose in water, and then add more water until the total volume of the solution is 1 L.

Answer: E
*Topic: Concept 3.2*
*Skill: Application*

27) The molecular mass of glucose ($C_6H_{12}O_6$) is 180 g. To make a 0.5 $M$ solution of glucose, you should do which of the following?

A) Dissolve 0.5 g of glucose in a small volume of water, and then add more water until the total volume of solution is 1 L.

B) Dissolve 90 g of glucose in a small volume of water, and then add more water until the total volume of the solution is 1 L.

C) Dissolve 180 g of glucose in a small volume of water, and then add more water until the total volume of the solution is 1 L.

D) Dissolve 0.5 g of glucose in 1 L of water.

E) Dissolve 180 g of glucose in 1 L of water.

Answer: B
*Topic: Concept 3.2*
*Skill: Application*

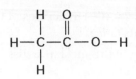

**Figure 3.2**

28) How many grams of the molecule in Figure 3.2 would be equal to 1 mol of the molecule?
(Carbon = 12, Oxygen = 16, Hydrogen = 1)

A) 29

B) 30

C) 60

D) 150

E) 342

Answer: C
*Topic: Concept 3.2*
*Skill: Application*

29) How many grams of the molecule in Figure 3.2 would be required to make 1 L of a 0.5 $M$ solution of the molecule?
(Carbon = 12, Oxygen = 16, Hydrogen = 1)

A) 29

B) 30

C) 60

D) 150

E) 342

Answer: B
*Topic: Concept 3.2*
*Skill: Application*

30) How many grams of the molecule in Figure 3.2 would be required to make 2.5 L of a 1 $M$ solution of the molecule? (Carbon = 12, Oxygen = 16, Hydrogen = 1)

A) 29

B) 30

C) 60

D) 150

E) 342

Answer: D
*Topic: Concept 3.2*
*Skill: Application*

31) Which of the following ionizes completely in solution and is considered to be a strong acid?

A) NaOH

B) HCl

C) $NH_3$

D) $H_2CO_3$

E) $CH_3COOH$

Answer: B
*Topic: Concept 3.3*
*Skill: Knowledge*

32) Which of the following ionizes completely in solution and is considered to be a strong base?

A) NaCl

B) HCl

C) $NH_3$

D) $H_2CO_3$

E) NaOH

Answer: E
*Topic: Concept 3.3*
*Skill: Knowledge*

33) Which of the following statements is *completely* correct?

A) $H_2CO_3$ is a weak acid, and NaOH is a weak base.

B) $H_2CO_3$ is a strong acid, and NaOH is a strong base.

C) $NH_3$ is a weak base, and $H_2CO_3$ is a strong acid.

D) $NH_3$ is a weak base, and HCl is a strong acid.

E) $NH_3$ is a strong base, and HCl is a weak acid.

Answer: D
*Topic: Concept 3.3*
*Skill: Knowledge*

34) A given solution contains $0.0001 (10^{-4})$ moles of hydrogen ions [$H^+$] per liter. Which of the following best describes this solution?

A) acidic: $H^+$ acceptor

B) basic: $H^+$ acceptor

C) acidic: $H^+$ donor

D) basic: $H^+$ donor

E) neutral

Answer: C
*Topic: Concept 3.3*
*Skill: Comprehension*

35) A solution contains $0.0000001 (10^{-7})$ moles of hydroxide ions [$OH^-$] per liter. Which of the following best describes this solution?

A) acidic: $H^+$ acceptor

B) basic: $H^+$ acceptor

C) acidic: $H^+$ donor

D) basic: $H^+$ donor

E) neutral

Answer: E
*Topic: Concept 3.3*
*Skill: Comprehension*

36) What would be the pH of a solution with a hydroxide ion [OH⁻] concentration of $10^{-12}$ M?

    A) pH 2

    B) pH 4

    C) pH 10

    D) pH 12

    E) pH 14

Answer: A
*Topic: Concept 3.3*
*Skill: Comprehension*

37) What would be the pH of a solution with a hydrogen ion [H⁺] concentration of $10^{-8}$ M?

    A) pH 2

    B) pH 4

    C) pH 6

    D) pH 8

    E) pH 10

Answer: D
*Topic: Concept 3.3*
*Skill: Comprehension*

38) Which of the following solutions has the greatest concentration of hydrogen ions [H⁺]?

    A) gastric juice at pH 2

    B) vinegar at pH 3

    C) tomato juice at pH 4

    D) black coffee at pH 5

    E) household bleach at pH 12

Answer: A
*Topic: Concept 3.3*
*Skill: Knowledge*

39) Which of the following solutions has the greatest concentration of hydroxide ions [OH⁻]?

    A) lemon juice at pH 2

    B) vinegar at pH 3

    C) tomato juice at pH 4

    D) urine at pH 6

    E) seawater at pH 8

Answer: E
*Topic: Concept 3.3*
*Skill: Comprehension*

40) If the pH of a solution is decreased from 9 to 8, it means that the

    A) concentration of H⁺ has decreased 10 times what it was at pH 9.

    B) concentration of H⁺ has increased 10 times what it was at pH 9.

    C) concentration of OH⁻ has increased 10 times what it was at pH 9.

    D) concentration of OH⁻ has decreased 10 times what it was at pH 9.

    E) B and D are correct.

Answer: E
*Topic: Concept 3.3*
*Skill: Comprehension*

41) If the pH of a solution is increased from pH 5 to pH 7, it means that the

    A) concentration of H⁺ is 2 times greater than what it was at pH 5.

    B) concentration of H⁺ is 2 times less than what it was at pH 5.

    C) concentration of OH⁻ is 100 times greater than what it was at pH 5.

    D) concentration of OH⁻ is 100 times less than what it was at pH 5.

    E) concentration of H⁺ is 100 times greater and the concentration of OH⁻ is 100 times less than what they were at pH 5.

Answer: C
*Topic: Concept 3.3*
*Skill: Comprehension*

42) One liter of a solution of pH 2 has how many more hydrogen ions ($H^+$) than 1 L of a solution of pH 6?

A) 4 times more

B) 400 times more

C) 4,000 times more

D) 10,000 times more

E) 100,000 times more

Answer: D
*Topic: Concept 3.3*
*Skill: Comprehension*

43) One liter of a solution pH 9 has how many more hydroxide ions ($OH^-$) than 1 L of a solution of pH 4?

A) 5 times more

B) 100 times more

C) 1,000 times more

D) 10,000 times more

E) 100,000 times more

Answer: E
*Topic: Concept 3.3*
*Skill: Comprehension*

44) Which of the following statements is *true* about buffer solutions?

A) They maintain a constant pH when bases are added to them but not when acids are added to them.

B) They maintain a constant pH when acids are added to them but not when bases are added to them.

C) They maintain a constant pH of exactly 7 in all living cells and biological fluids.

D) They maintain a relatively constant pH.

E) They are found only in living systems and biological fluids.

Answer: D
*Topic: Concept 3.3*
*Skill: Knowledge*

45) Buffers are substances that help resist shifts in pH by

A) releasing $H^+$ in acidic solutions.

B) donating $H^+$ to a solution when they have been depleted.

C) releasing $OH^-$ in basic solutions.

D) accepting $H^+$ when the are in excess.

E) both B and D

Answer: E
*Topic: Concept 3.3*
*Skill: Knowledge*

46) One of the buffers that contribute to pH stability in human blood is carbonic acid ($H_2CO_3$). Carbonic acid is a weak acid that dissociates into a bicarbonate ion ($HCO_3^-$) and a hydrogen ion ($H^+$). Thus,

$$H_2CO_3 \Leftrightarrow HCO_3^- + H^+$$

If the pH of the blood drops, one would expect

A) a decrease in the concentration of $H_2CO_3$ and an increase in the concentration of $HCO_3^-$.

B) the concentration of hydroxide ion ($OH^-$) to increase.

C) the concentration of bicarbonate ion ($HCO_3^-$) to increase.

D) the $HCO_3^-$ to act as a base and remove excess $H^+$ with the formation of $H_2CO_3$.

E) the $HCO_3^-$ to act as an acid and remove excess $H^+$ with the formation of $H_2CO_3$.

Answer: D
*Topic: Concept 3.3*
*Skill: Application*

47) One of the buffers that contribute to pH stability in human blood is carbonic acid ($H_2CO_3$). Carbonic acid is a weak acid that when placed in an aqueous solution dissociates into a bicarbonate ion ($HCO_3^-$) and a hydrogen ion ($H^+$). Thus,
$$H_2CO_3 \Leftrightarrow HCO_3^- + H^+$$
If the pH of the blood increases, one would expect

A) a decrease in the concentration of $H_2CO_3$ and an increase in the concentration of $H_2O$.

B) an increase in the concentration of $H_2CO_3$ and a decrease in the concentration of $H_2O$.

C) a decrease in the concentration of $HCO_3^-$ and an increase in the concentration of $H_2O$.

D) an increase in the concentration of $HCO_3^-$ and a decrease in the concentration of $H_2O$.

E) a decrease in the concentration of $HCO_3^-$ and an increase in the concentration of both $H_2CO_3$ and $H_2O$.

Answer: A
*Topic: Concept 3.3*
*Skill: Application*

48) Assume that acid rain has lowered the pH of a particular lake to pH 4.0. What is the hydroxide ion concentration of this lake?

A) $1 \times 10^{-10}$ mol of hydroxide ion per liter of lake water

B) $1 \times 10^{-4}$ mol of hydroxide ion per liter of lake water

C) 10.0 $M$ with regard to hydroxide ion concentration

D) 4.0 $M$ with regard to hydroxide ion concentration

E) both B and D

Answer: A
*Topic: Concept 3.3*
*Skill: Application*

49) Research indicates that acid precipitation can damage living organisms by

A) buffering aquatic systems such as lakes and streams.

B) decreasing the $H^+$ concentration of lakes and streams.

C) increasing the $OH^-$ concentration of lakes and streams.

D) washing away certain mineral ions that help buffer soil solution and are essential nutrients for plant growth.

E) both B and C

Answer: D
*Topic: Concept 3.3*
*Skill: Knowledge*

# Media Activity Questions

1) Water's surface tension and heat storage capacity is accounted for by its

   A) orbitals.

   B) weight.

   C) hydrogen bonds.

   D) mass.

   E) size.

Answer: C
*Topic: Web/CD Activity: The Polarity of Water*

2) What property of water is responsible for water transport in plants?

   A) moderation of temperature

   B) insulation

   C) its versatility as a solvent

   D) cohesion

   E) its role as a buffer

Answer: D
*Topic: Web/CD Activity: Cohesion of Water*

3) When does a hydronium ion form?

   A) when two water molecules bind

   B) when a water molecule gains an hydrogen ion from another water molecule

   C) as a product of evaporation

   D) when a hydrogen ion binds with a hydroxide ion

   E) when a water molecule splits in half

Answer: B
*Topic: Web/CD Activity: Dissociation of Water*

4) About _____ molecules in a glass of water are dissociated.

   A) 1 in 1,000,000,000

   B) 1 in 1,000,000

   C) 1 in 5,000,000

   D) 1 in 2

   E) 1 in 500,000,000

Answer: E
*Topic: Web/CD Activity: Dissociation of Water*

5) In a neutral solution the concentration of

   A) hydrogen ions is equal to the concentration of hydroxide ions.

   B) water molecules is less than the concentration of hydrogen ions.

   C) hydrogen ions is less than the concentration of hydroxide ions.

   D) water molecules is less than the concentration of hydroxide ions.

   E) hydrogen ions is greater than the concentration of hydroxide ions.

Answer: A
*Topic: Web/CD Activity: Acids, Bases, and pH*

# Self-Quiz Questions

1) What is the best explanation of the phrase "fitness of the environment" as used in this chapter?

   A) Earth's environment is constant.

   B) It is the physical environment, not life, that has changed.

   C) The environment of Earth has adapted to life.

   D) Life as we know it depends on certain environmental qualities on Earth.

   E) Water and other aspects of Earth's environment exist because they make the planet more suitable for life.

   Answer: D

2) Many mammals control their body temperature by sweating. Which behavior of water is most directly responsible for the ability of sweat to lower body temperature?

   A) water's change in density when it condenses

   B) water's ability to dissolve molecules in the air

   C) the release of heat by the formation of hydrogen bonds

   D) the absorption of heat by the breaking of hydrogen bonds

   E) water's high surface tension

   Answer: D

3) For two bodies of matter in contact, heat always flows from

   A) the body with greater heat to the one with less heat.

   B) the body of higher temperature to the one of lower temperature.

   C) the denser body to the less dense body.

   D) the body with more water to the one with less water.

   E) the larger body to the smaller body.

   Answer: B

4) A slice of pizza has 500 kcal. If we could burn the pizza and use all the heat to warm a 50-L container of cold water, what would be the approximate increase in the temperature of the water? (*Note*: A liter of cold water weighs about 1 kg.)

   A) 50°C

   B) 5°C

   C) 10°C

   D) 100°C

   E) 1°C

   Answer: C

5) The bonds that are broken when water vaporizes are

   A) ionic bonds.

   B) bonds between water molecules.

   C) bonds between atoms within individual water molecules.

   D) polar covalent bonds.

   E) nonpolar covalent bonds.

   Answer: B

6) Which of the following is an example of a
hydrophobic material?

   A) paper

   B) table salt

   C) wax

   D) sugar

   E) pasta

   Answer: C

7) We can be sure that a mole of table sugar
and a mole of vitamin C are equal in their

   A) mass in daltons.

   B) mass in grams.

   C) number of molecules.

   D) number of atoms.

   E) volume.

   Answer: C

8) How many grams of acetic acid ($C_2H_4O_2$)
would you use to make 10 L of a 0.1 $M$
aqueous solution of acetic acid? (*Note:* The
atomic masses, in daltons, are
approximately 12 for carbon, 1 for
hydrogen, and 16 for oxygen.)

   A) 10.0 g

   B) 0.1 g

   C) 6.0 g

   D) 60.0 g

   E) 0.6 g

   Answer: D

9) Acid precipitation has lowered the pH of a
particular lake to 4.0. What is the
hydrogen ion concentration of the lake?

   A) 4.0 $M$

   B) $10^{-10} M$

   C) $10^{-4} M$

   D) $10^4 M$

   E) 4%

   Answer: C

10) What is the *hydroxide* ion concentration of
the lake described in question 9?

   A) $10^{-7} M$

   B) $10^{-4} M$

   C) $10^{-10} M$

   D) $10^{-14} M$

   E) 10 $M$

   Answer: C

# Chapter 4  Carbon and the Molecular Diversity of Life

1) Organic chemistry is a science based on the study of
   A) functional groups.
   B) vital forces interacting with matter.
   C) carbon compounds.
   D) water and its interaction with other kinds of molecules.
   E) inorganic compounds.

Answer: C
*Topic: Concept 4.1*
*Skill: Knowledge*

2) Early 19th-century scientists believed that living organisms differed from nonliving things as a result of possessing a "life force" that could create organic molecules from inorganic matter. The term given to this belief is
   A) organic synthesis.
   B) vitalism.
   C) mechanism.
   D) organic evolution.
   E) inorganic synthesis.

Answer: B
*Topic: Concept 4.1*
*Skill: Knowledge*

3) The concept of vitalism is based on a belief in a life force outside the jurisdiction of physical and chemical laws. According to this belief, organic compounds can arise only within living organisms. Which of the following did the most to refute the concept of vitalism?
   A) Wöhler's synthesis of urea
   B) Berzelius's distinction between organic and inorganic compounds
   C) Miller's experiments with ancient atmospheres
   D) Rodriguez's studies of phytochemicals
   E) Kolbe's synthesis of acetic acid

Answer: C
*Topic: Concept 4.1*
*Skill: Comprehension*

4) The experimental approach taken in current biological investigations presumes that

A) simple organic compounds can be synthesized in the laboratory from inorganic precursors, but complex organic compounds like carbohydrates and proteins can only be synthesized by living organisms.

B) a life force ultimately controls the activities of living organisms and this life force cannot be studied by physical or chemical methods.

C) although a life force, or vitalism, exists in living organisms, this life force cannot be studied by physical or chemical methods.

D) living organisms are composed of the same elements present in nonliving things, plus a few special trace elements found in only living organisms or their products.

E) living organisms can be understood in terms of the same physical and chemical laws that can be used to explain all natural phenomena.

Answer: E
*Topic: Concept 4.1*
*Skill: Comprehension*

5) Which property of the carbon atom gives it compatibility with a greater number of different elements than any other type of atom?

A) Carbon has 6 to 8 neutrons.

B) Carbon has a valence of 4.

C) Carbon forms ionic bonds.

D) A and C only

E) A, B, and C

Answer: B
*Topic: Concept 4.2*
*Skill: Knowledge*

6) How many electron pairs does carbon share in order to complete its valence shell?

A) 1

B) 2

C) 3

D) 4

E) 8

Answer: D
*Topic: Concept 4.2*
*Skill: Comprehension*

7) What type(s) of bond(s) does carbon have a tendency to form?

A) ionic

B) hydrogen

C) covalent

D) A and B only

E) A, B, and C

Answer: C
*Topic: Concept 4.2*
*Skill: Knowledge*

8) Which of the following is (are) true about the carbon atoms present in all organic molecules?

A) They were incorporated into organic molecules by plants.

B) They were processed into sugars through photosynthesis.

C) They are ultimately derived from carbon dioxide.

D) Only A and C are correct.

E) A, B, and C are correct.

Answer: E
*Topic: Concept 4.2*
*Skill: Comprehension*

9) What is the reason why hydrocarbons are not soluble in water?

    A) The majority of their bonds are polar covalent carbon to hydrogen linkages.

    B) The majority of their bonds are nonpolar covalent carbon-to-hydrogen linkages.

    C) They are hydrophilic.

    D) They exhibit considerable molecular complexity and diversity.

    E) They are lighter than water.

Answer: B
*Topic: Concept 4.2*
*Skill: Comprehension*

10) How many structural isomers are possible for a substance having the molecular formula $C_4H_{10}$?

    A) 1

    B) 2

    C) 4

    D) 3

    E) 11

Answer: B
*Topic: Concept 4.2*
*Skill: Application*

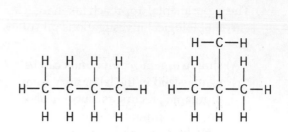

**Figure 4.1**

11) The two molecules shown in Figure 4.1 are best described as

    A) optical isomers.

    B) radioactive isotopes.

    C) structural isomers.

    D) nonradioactive isotopes.

    E) geometric isomers.

Answer: C
*Topic: Concept 4.2*
*Skill: Comprehension*

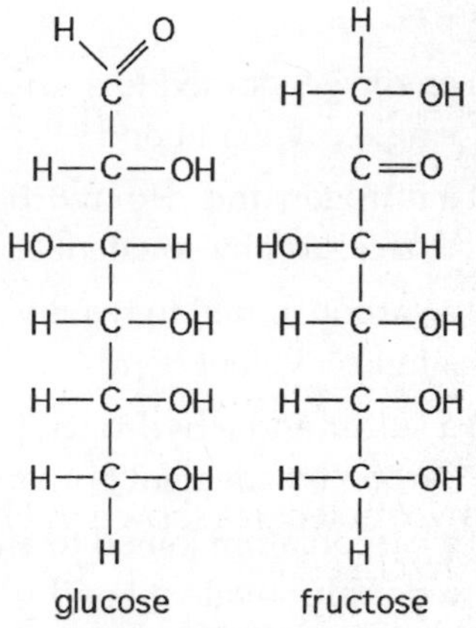

**Figure 4.2**

12) Observe the structures of glucose and fructose in Figure 4.2. These two molecules differ in the
    A) number of carbon, hydrogen, and oxygen atoms.
    B) types of carbon, hydrogen, and oxygen atoms.
    C) arrangement of carbon, hydrogen, and oxygen atoms.
    D) number of oxygen atoms joined to carbon atoms by double covalent bonds.
    E) answers A, B, and C

Answer: C
*Topic: Concept 4.2*
*Skill: Comprehension*

13) Observe the structures of glucose and fructose in Figure 4.2. These two molecules are
    A) geometric isotopes.
    B) enantiomers.
    C) geometric isomers.
    D) structural isomers.
    E) nonisotopic isomers.

Answer: D
*Topic: Concept 4.2*
*Skill: Comprehension*

14) Which of the following is *true* of geometric isomers?
    A) They have variations in arrangement around a double bond.
    B) They have an asymmetric carbon that makes them mirror images.
    C) They have the same chemical properties.
    D) They have different molecular formulas.
    E) Their atoms and bonds are arranged in different sequences.

Answer: A
*Topic: Concept 4.2*
*Skill: Knowledge*

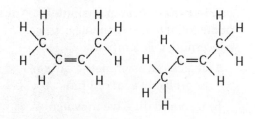

**Figure 4.3**

15) The two molecules shown in Figure 4.3 are best described as
    A) enantiomers.
    B) radioactive isotopes.
    C) structural isomers.
    D) nonisotopic isomers.
    E) geometric isomers.

Answer: E
*Topic: Concept 4.2*
*Skill: Comprehension*

16) Research suggests that side effects from Ritalin, the drug used to treat attention deficit disorder, may be caused by contamination of enantiomers, or molecules that

A) have identical three-dimensional shapes.

B) are mirror images of one another.

C) lack an asymmetric carbon.

D) differ in the location of their double bonds.

E) differ in their electrical charge.

Answer: B
*Topic: Concept 4.2*
*Skill: Knowledge*

17) A compound contains hydroxyl groups as its predominant functional group. Which of the following statements is *true* concerning this compound?

A) It lacks an asymmetric carbon, and it is probably a fat or lipid.

B) It should dissolve in water.

C) It should dissolve in a nonpolar solvent.

D) It won't form hydrogen bonds with water.

E) It is hydrophobic.

Answer: B
*Topic: Concept 4.3*
*Skill: Comprehension*

18) Which is the best description of a carbonyl group?

A) an oxygen joined to a carbon by a single covalent bond

B) a nitrogen and two hydrogens joined to a carbon by covalent bonds

C) a carbon joined to two hydrogens by single covalent bonds

D) a sulfur and a hydrogen joined to a carbon by covalent bonds

E) a carbon atom joined to an oxygen by a double covalent bond

Answer: E
*Topic: Concept 4.3*
*Skill: Knowledge*

$$R-C\overset{\displaystyle O}{\underset{\displaystyle O-H}{\big\|}}$$

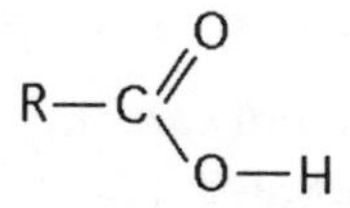

**Figure 4.4**

19) What is the name of the functional group shown in Figure 4.4?

A) carbonyl

B) ketone

C) aldehyde

D) carboxyl

E) hydroxyl

Answer: D
*Topic: Concept 4.3*
*Skill: Knowledge*

20) Which of the following contains nitrogen in addition to carbon, oxygen, and hydrogen?

    A) an alcohol such as ethanol

    B) a monosaccharide such as glucose

    C) a steroid such as testosterone

    D) an amino acid such as glycine

    E) a hydrocarbon such as benzene

Answer: D
*Topic: Concept 4.3*
*Skill: Comprehension*

21) Which of the following is a *false* statement concerning amino groups?

    A) They are basic in pH.

    B) They are found in amino acids.

    C) They contain nitrogen.

    D) They are nonpolar.

    E) They are components of urea.

Answer: D
*Topic: Concept 4.3*
*Skill: Comprehension*

22) Which two functional groups are *always* found in amino acids?

    A) ketone and aldehyde

    B) carbonyl and carboxyl

    C) carboxyl and amino

    D) phosphate and sulfhydryl

    E) hydroxyl and aldehyde

Answer: C
*Topic: Concept 4.3*
*Skill: Knowledge*

23) Amino acids are acids because they always possess which functional group?

    A) amino

    B) carbonyl

    C) carboxyl

    D) sulfhydryl

    E) aldehyde

Answer: C
*Topic: Concept 4.3*
*Skill: Knowledge*

24) A carbon skeleton is covalently bonded to both an amino group and a carboxyl group. When placed in water it

    A) would function only as an acid because of the carboxyl group.

    B) would function only as a base because of the amino group.

    C) would function as neither an acid nor a base.

    D) would function as both an acid and a base.

    E) is impossible to determine how it would function.

Answer: D
*Topic: Concept 4.3*
*Skill: Application*

25) A chemist wishes to make an organic molecule less acidic. Which of the following functional groups should be added to the molecule in order to do so?

    A) carboxyl

    B) sulfhydryl

    C) hydroxyl

    D) amino

    E) phosphate

Answer: D
*Topic: Concept 4.3*
*Skill: Application*

26) Which functional groups can act as acids?

   A) amine and sulfhydryl

   B) carbonyl and carboxyl

   C) carboxyl and phosphate

   D) hydroxyl and aldehyde

   E) ketone and amino

Answer: C
*Topic: Concept 4.3*
*Skill: Comprehension*

*The following questions refer to the structures shown in Figure 4.5.*

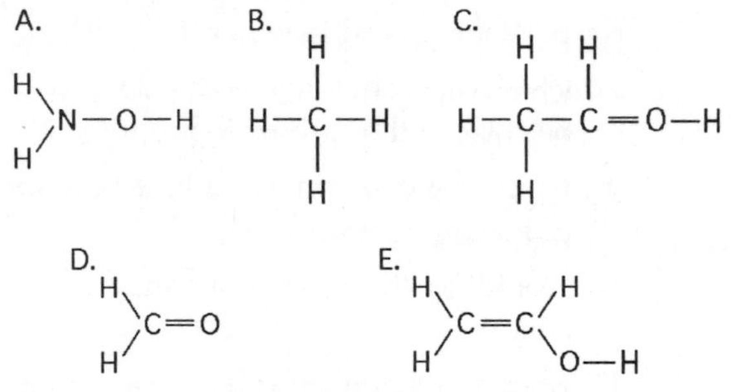

**Figure 4.5**

27) Which of the structures is an impossible covalently bonded molecule?

Answer: C
*Topic: Concept 4.3*
*Skill: Comprehension*

28) Which of the structures contain(s) a carboxyl functional group?

   A) A

   B) B

   C) C

   D) C and E

   E) none of the structures

Answer: E
*Topic: Concept 4.3*
*Skill: Comprehension*

29) In which of the structures are the atoms bonded by ionic bonds?

   A) A

   B) B

   C) C

   D) C, D, and E only

   E) none of the structures

Answer: E
*Topic: Concept 4.3*
*Skill: Comprehension*

*The following questions refer to the functional groups shown in Figure 4.6.*

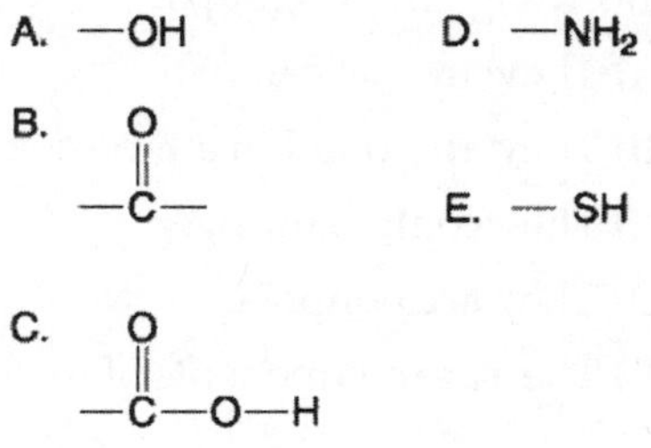

**Figure 4.6**

30) Which is a hydroxyl functional group?

Answer: A
*Topic: Concept 4.3*
*Skill: Knowledge*

31) Which is an amino functional group?

Answer: D
*Topic: Concept 4.3*
*Skill: Knowledge*

32) Which is a carbonyl functional group?

Answer: B
*Topic: Concept 4.3*
*Skill: Knowledge*

33) Which is a functional group that helps
stabilize proteins by forming covalent
cross-links within or between protein
molecules?

Answer: E
*Topic: Concept 4.3*
*Skill: Knowledge*

34) Which is a carboxyl functional group?

Answer: C
*Topic: Concept 4.3*
*Skill: Knowledge*

35) Which is an acidic functional group that
can dissociate and release $H^+$ into a
solution?

Answer: C
*Topic: Concept 4.3*
*Skill: Knowledge*

36) Which is a basic functional group that can
accept $H^+$ and become positively charged?

Answer: D
*Topic: Concept 4.3*
*Skill: Knowledge*

*The following questions refer to the molecules shown in Figure 4.7.*

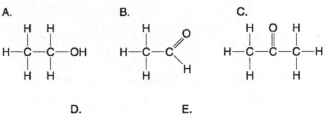

**Figure 4.7**

37) Which molecule is water–soluble because
it has a hydroxyl functional group?

Answer: A
*Topic: Concept 4.3*
*Skill: Knowledge*

38) Which molecule is an alcohol?

Answer: A
*Topic: Concept 4.3*
*Skill: Knowledge*

39) Which molecules contain a carbonyl
group?
  A) A and B
  B) B and C
  C) C and D
  D) D and E
  E) E and A

Answer: B
*Topic: Concept 4.3*
*Skill: Knowledge*

40) Which molecule has a carbonyl functional
group in the form of a ketone?

Answer: C
*Topic: Concept 4.3*
*Skill: Knowledge*

41) Which molecule has a carbonyl functional group in the form of an aldehyde?

Answer: B
*Topic: Concept 4.3*
*Skill: Knowledge*

42) Which molecule contains a carboxyl group?

Answer: D
*Topic: Concept 4.3*
*Skill: Knowledge*

43) Which molecule can increase the concentration of hydrogen ions in a solution and is therefore an organic acid?

Answer: D
*Topic: Concept 4.3*
*Skill: Comprehension*

*The following questions refer to the molecules shown in Figure 4.8.*

A.
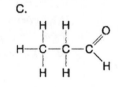

D.

**Figure 4.8**

44) Which molecule contains a sulfhydryl functional group?

Answer: B
*Topic: Concept 4.3*
*Skill: Knowledge*

45) Which molecule functions to transfer energy between organic molecules?

Answer: D
*Topic: Concept 4.3*
*Skill: Knowledge*

46) Which molecule contains an amino functional group, but is not an amino acid?

Answer: A
*Topic: Concept 4.3*
*Skill: Knowledge*

47) Which molecule is a thiol?

Answer: B
*Topic: Concept 4.3*
*Skill: Knowledge*

48) Which molecule is an organic phosphate?

Answer: D
*Topic: Concept 4.3*
*Skill: Knowledge*

49) Which molecule can function as a base?

Answer: A
*Topic: Concept 4.3*
*Skill: Comprehension*

50) Which of the following statements is (are) *true* about the phosphate ion?
   A) It is negatively charged.
   B) It has acid properties.
   C) It is hydrophobic.
   D) Only A and B are true.
   E) A, B, and C are true.

Answer: D
*Topic: Concept 4.3*
*Skill: Comprehension*

# Media Activity Questions

1) Hydrocarbons
   A) are polar.
   B) are held together by ionic bonds.
   C) contain nitrogen.
   D) contain only hydrogen and carbon atoms.
   E) are held together by hydrogen bonds.

   Answer: D
   *Topic: Web/CD Activity: Carbon–Based Molecules*

2) What kind of effect does R–dopa have on Parkinson's disease?
   A) It alleviates the symptoms.
   B) It makes the symptoms worse.
   C) At first it makes the symptoms worse but over the long term it alleviates the symptoms.
   D) At first it alleviates the symptoms but over the long term it makes the symptoms worse.
   E) R–dopa has no effect on Parkinson's disease.

   Answer: E
   *Topic: Web/CD Activity: Isomers*

3) Structural isomers are molecules that
   A) are enantiomers.
   B) are hydrocarbons.
   C) have a ring structure.
   D) are mirror images.
   E) differ in the covalent arrangements of their atoms.

   Answer: E
   *Topic: Web/CD Activity: Isomers*

4) Which of these functional groups does not contain oxygen?
   A) carboxyl
   B) sulfhydryl
   C) hydroxyl
   D) carbonyl
   E) phosphate

   Answer: B
   *Topic: Web/CD Activity: Functional Groups*

5) If this functional group is at the end of a carbon skeleton, the molecule is called an aldehyde.
   A) amino
   B) sulfhydryl
   C) carbonyl
   D) carboxyl
   E) hydroxyl

   Answer: C
   *Topic: Web/CD Activity: Functional Groups*

# Self–Quiz Questions

1) Organic chemistry is currently defined as
    A) the study of compounds that can be made only by living cells.
    B) the study of carbon compounds.
    C) the study of vital forces.
    D) the study of natural (as opposed to synthetic) compounds.
    E) the study of hydrocarbons.

    Answer: B

2) Choose the pair of terms that correctly completes this sentence: Hydroxyl is to _____ as _____ is to aldehyde.
    A) carbonyl; ketone
    B) oxygen; carbon
    C) alcohol; carbonyl
    D) amine; carboxyl
    E) alcohol; ketone

    Answer: C

3) Which of the following hydrocarbons has a double bond in its carbon skeleton?
    A) $C_3H_8$
    B) $C_2H_6$
    C) $CH_4$
    D) $C_2H_4$
    E) $C_2H_2$

    Answer: D

4) The gasoline consumed by an automobile is a fossil fuel consisting mostly of
    A) aldehydes.
    B) amino acids.
    C) alcohols.
    D) hydrocarbons.
    E) thiols.

    Answer: D

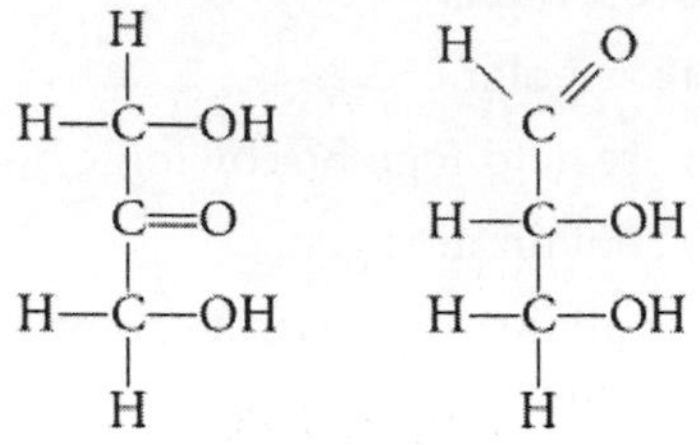

Figure 4.9

5) Choose the term that correctly describes the relationship between the two sugar molecules shown in Figure 4.9.
    A) structural isomers
    B) geometric isomers
    C) enantiomers
    D) isotopes

    Answer: A

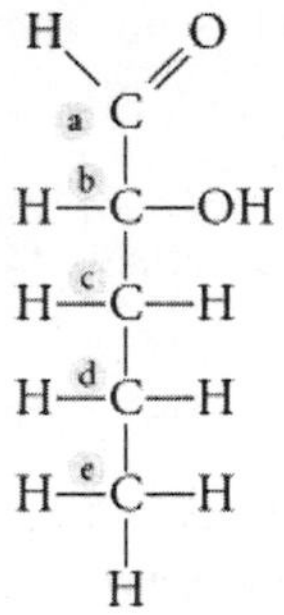

Figure 4.10

6) Identify the asymmetric carbon in the molecule shown in Figure 4.10.

    Answer: B

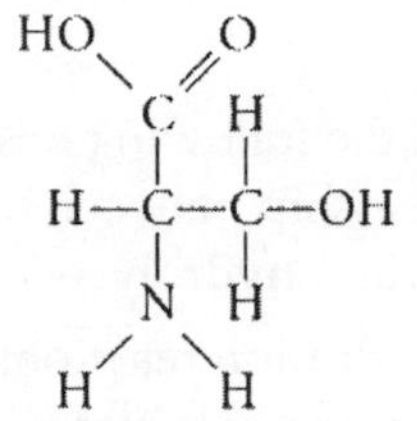

**Figure 4.11**

**Figure 4.12**

7) Which functional group is *not* present in the molecule shown in Figure 4.11?

   A) carboxyl        B) sulfhydryl

   C) hydroxyl        D) amino

   Answer: B

8) Which action could produce a carbonyl group?

   A) the replacement of the hydroxyl of a carboxyl group with hydrogen

   B) the addition of a thiol to a hydroxyl

   C) the addition of a hydroxyl to a phosphate

   D) the replacement of the nitrogen of an amine with oxygen

   E) the addition of a sulfhydryl to a carboxyl

   Answer: A

9) Which functional group is most likely to be responsible for an organic molecule behaving as a base?

   A) hydroxyl

   B) carbonyl

   C) carboxyl

   D) amino

   E) phosphate

   Answer: D

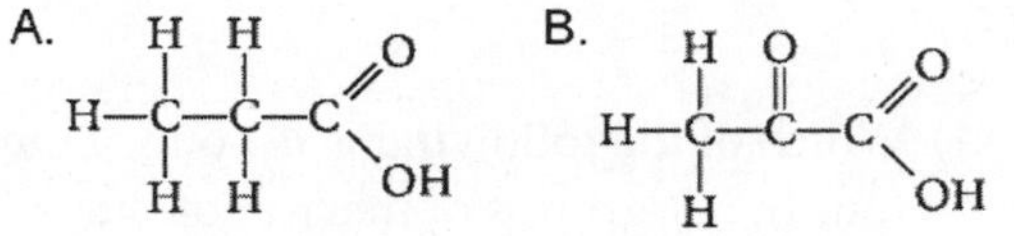

10) Given what you know about the electronegativity of oxygen, predict which of the molecules shown in Figure 4.12 would be the strongest acid?

   Answer: B

# Chapter 5  Carbon and the Molecular Diversity of Life

1) Which of the following is *not* one of the four major groups of macromolecules found in living organisms?

A) glucose

B) carbohydrates

C) lipids

D) proteins

E) nucleic acids

Answer: A
*Topic: Overview*
*Skill: Knowledge*

2) Polymers of polysaccharides, fats, and proteins are all synthesized from monomers by which process?

A) connecting monosaccharides together (condensation reactions)

B) the addition of water to each monomer (hydrolysis)

C) the removal of water (dehydration reactions)

D) ionic bonding of the monomers

E) the formation of disulfide bridges between monomers

Answer: C
*Topic: Concept 5.1*
*Skill: Comprehension*

3) Which of the following best summarizes the relationship between dehydration reactions and hydrolysis?

A) Dehydration reactions assemble polymers, and hydrolysis breaks down polymers.

B) Hydrolysis only occurs in the urinary system, and dehydration reactions only occur in the digestive tract.

C) Dehydration reactions can occur only after hydrolysis.

D) Hydrolysis creates monomers, and dehydration reactions break down polymers.

E) A and C are correct.

Answer: A
*Topic: Concept 5.2*
*Skill: Comprehension*

4) A molecule with the chemical formula $C_{16}H_{32}O_{16}$ is probably a

A) carbohydrate.

B) lipid.

C) protein.

D) nucleic acid.

E) hydrocarbon.

Answer: A
*Topic: Concept 5.2*
*Skill: Comprehension*

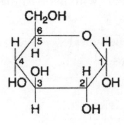

**Figure 5.1**

5) If 128 molecules of the general type shown in Figure 5.1 were covalently joined together in sequence, the single molecule that would result would be a

A) polysaccharide.

B) polypeptide.

C) polyunsaturated lipid.

D) monosaccharide.

E) disaccharide.

Answer: A
*Topic: Concept 5.2*
*Skill: Comprehension*

6) Consider a polysaccharide consisting of 576 glucose molecules. The total hydrolysis of the polysaccharide would result in the production of

A) 575 glucose molecules.

B) 575 water molecules.

C) 576 glucose molecules.

D) A and B only

E) B and C only

Answer: C
*Topic: Concept 5.2*
*Skill: Comprehension*

7) Lactose, a sugar in milk, is composed of one glucose molecule joined by a glycosidic linkage to one galactose molecule. How is lactose classified?

A) as a pentose

B) as a hexose

C) as a monosaccharide

D) as a disaccharide

E) as a polysaccharide

Answer: D
*Topic: Concept 5.2*
*Skill: Comprehension*

8) Which of the following are polysaccharides?

A) glycogen

B) starch

C) chitin

D) A and B only

E) A, B, and C

Answer: E
*Topic: Concept 5.2*
*Skill: Knowledge*

9) Which of the following is *true* of both starch and cellulose?

A) They are both polymers of glucose.

B) They are geometric isomers of each other.

C) They can both be digested by humans.

D) They are both used for energy storage in plants.

E) They are both structural components of the plant cell wall.

Answer: A
*Topic: Concept 5.2*
*Skill: Knowledge*

10) Which of the following is *true* of cellulose?

A) It is a polymer composed of sucrose monomers.

B) It is a storage polysaccharide for energy in plant cells.

C) It is a storage polysaccharide for energy in animal cells.

D) It is a major structural component of plant cell walls.

E) It is a major structural component of animal cell plasma membranes.

Answer: D
*Topic: Concept 5.2*
*Skill: Knowledge*

11) Humans can digest starch but not cellulose because

A) the monomer of starch is glucose, while the monomer of cellulose is galactose.

B) humans have enzymes that can hydrolyze the beta (β) glycosidic linkages of starch but not the alpha (α) glycosidic linkages of cellulose.

C) humans have enzymes that can hydrolyze the alpha (α) glycosidic linkages of starch but not the beta (β) glycosidic linkages of cellulose.

D) humans harbor starch–digesting bacteria in the digestive tract.

E) the monomer of starch is glucose, while the monomer of cellulose is maltose.

Answer: C
*Topic: Concept 5.2*
*Skill: Comprehension*

12) A molecule with the formula $C_{18}H_{36}O_2$ is probably a

A) carbohydrate.

B) lipid.

C) protein.

D) nucleic acid.

E) hydrocarbon.

Answer: B
*Topic: Concept 5.3*
*Skill: Comprehension*

13) Which of the following is (are) *true* for the class of large biological molecules known as lipids?

A) They are insoluble in water.

B) They are an important constituent of cell membranes.

C) They contain twice as much energy as an equivalent weight of polysaccharide.

D) Only A and B are correct.

E) A, B, and C are correct.

Answer: E
*Topic: Concept 5.3*
*Skill: Knowledge*

14) Triacylglycerol is a

A) protein with tertiary structure.

B) lipid made with three fatty acids and glycerol.

C) lipid that makes up much of the plasma membrane.

D) molecule formed from three alcohols by dehydration reactions.

E) carbohydrate with three sugars joined together by glycosidic linkages.

Answer: B
*Topic: Concept 5.3*
*Skill: Knowledge*

15) Saturated fatty acids
   A) are the predominant fatty acid in corn oil.
   B) have double bonds between carbon atoms of the fatty acids.
   C) have a higher ratio of hydrogen to carbon than do unsaturated fatty acids.
   D) are usually liquid at room temperature.
   E) are usually produced by plants.

Answer: C
*Topic: Concept 5.3*
*Skill: Knowledge*

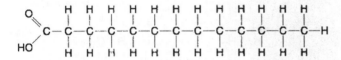

**Figure 5.2**

16) What is the molecule illustrated in Figure 5.2?
   A) a saturated fatty acid
   B) an unsaturated fatty acid
   C) a polyunsaturated triacylglyceride
   D) a trans polyunsaturated triacylglyceride
   E) a steroid similar to cholesterol

Answer: A
*Topic: Concept 5.3*
*Skill: Knowledge*

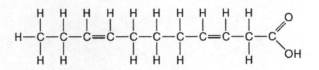

**Figure 5.3**

17) The molecule shown in Figure 5.3 is a
   A) polysaccharide.
   B) polypeptide.
   C) saturated fatty acid.
   D) triacylglycerol.
   E) unsaturated fatty acid.

Answer: E
*Topic: Concept 5.3*
*Skill: Knowledge*

18) The hydrogenation of vegetable oil would result in which of the following?
   A) a decrease in the number of carbon–carbon double bonds in the oil (fat) molecules
   B) an increase in the number of hydrogen atoms in the oil (fat) molecule
   C) the oil (fat) being a solid at room temperature
   D) A and C only
   E) A, B, and C

Answer: E
*Topic: Concept 5.3*
*Skill: Comprehension*

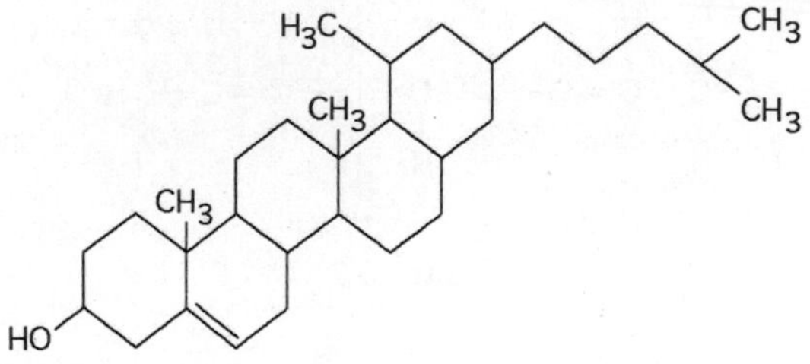

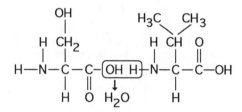

**Figure 5.4**

19) What is the structure shown in Figure 5.4?

    A) starch molecule

    B) protein molecule

    C) steroid molecule

    D) cellulose molecule

    E) phospholipid molecule

Answer: C
*Topic: Concept 5.3*
*Skill: Knowledge*

20) A polypeptide can best be described as a

    A) monomer of a protein polymer.

    B) polymer containing 20 amino acid molecules.

    C) polymer containing 19 peptide bonds.

    D) polymer containing 20 peptide bonds.

    E) polymer of amino acids.

Answer: E
*Topic: Concept 5.4*
*Skill: Knowledge*

21) The 20 different amino acids found in polypeptides exhibit different chemical and physical properties because of different

    A) carboxyl groups attached to an alpha (α) carbon.

    B) amino groups attached to an alpha (α) carbon.

    C) side chains (R groups).

    D) alpha (α) carbons.

    E) asymmetric carbons.

Answer: C
*Topic: Concept 5.4*
*Skill: Knowledge*

**Figure 5.5**

22) The chemical reaction illustrated in Figure 5.5 results in the formation of a (an)

    A) ionic bond.

    B) peptide bond.

    C) glycosidic linkage.

    D) ester linkage.

    E) phosphodiester linkage.

Answer: B
*Topic: Concept 5.4*
*Skill: Comprehension*

23) The bonding of two amino acid molecules to form a larger molecule requires which of the following?

    A) removal of a water molecule

    B) addition of a water molecule

    C) formation of an ionic bond

    D) formation of a hydrogen bond

    E) both A and C

Answer: A
*Topic: Concept 5.4*
*Skill: Comprehension*

24) Polysaccharides, lipids, and proteins are similar in that they

    A) are synthesized from monomers by the process of hydrolysis.

    B) are synthesized from monomers by dehydration reactions.

    C) are synthesized as a result of peptide bond formation between monomers.

    D) are decomposed into their subunits by dehydration reactions.

    E) all contain nitrogen in their monomer building blocks.

Answer: B
*Topic: Concepts 5.1–5.4*
*Skill: Knowledge*

25) Dehydration reactions are used in forming which of the following compounds?

    A) triacylglycerides

    B) polysaccharides

    C) proteins

    D) A and C only

    E) A, B, and C

Answer: E
*Topic: Concepts 5.1–5.4*
*Skill: Knowledge*

26) Upon chemical analysis, a particular protein was found to contain 556 amino acids. How many peptide bonds are present in this protein?

    A) 139

    B) 554

    C) 555

    D) 556

    E) 558

Answer: C
*Topic: Concept 5.4*
*Skill: Comprehension*

*Refer to Figure 5.6 to answer the following questions.*

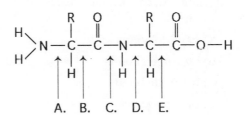

**Figure 5.6**

27) At which bond would water need to be added to achieve hydrolysis of the peptide, back to its component amino acid?

Answer: C
*Topic: Concept 5.4*
*Skill: Comprehension*

28) Which bond is closest to the N-terminus of the molecule?

Answer: A
*Topic: Concept 5.4*
*Skill: Comprehension*

29) Which bond is closest to the C–terminus of the molecule?

Answer: E
*Topic: Concept 5.4*
*Skill: Comprehension*

30) How many different kinds of polypeptides, each composed of 12 amino acids, could be synthesized using the 20 common amino acids?

A) $4^{12}$

B) $12^{20}$

C) $12^5$

D) 20

E) $20^{12}$

Answer: E
*Topic: Concept 5.4*
*Skill: Application*

31) Which bonds are created during the formation of the primary structure of a protein?

A) peptide bonds

B) hydrogen bonds

C) disulfide bonds

D) phosphodiester bonds

E) A, B, and C

Answer: A
*Topic: Concept 5.4*
*Skill: Knowledge*

32) What maintains the secondary structure of a protein?

A) peptide bonds

B) hydrogen bonds

C) disulfide bonds

D) ionic bonds

E) phosphodiester bonds

Answer: B
*Topic: Concept 5.4*
*Skill: Knowledge*

33) Which type of interaction stabilizes the alpha (α) helix and the beta (β) pleated sheet structures of proteins?

A) hydrophobic interactions

B) nonpolar covalent bonds

C) ionic bonds

D) hydrogen bonds

E) peptide bonds

Answer: D
*Topic: Concept 5.4*
*Skill: Knowledge*

34) The α helix and the β pleated sheet are both common polypeptide forms found in which level of protein structure?

A) primary

B) secondary

C) tertiary

D) quaternary

E) all of the above

Answer: B
*Topic: Concept 5.4*
*Skill: Knowledge*

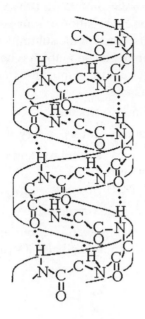

**Figure 5.7**

35) Figure 5.7 shows the
   A) 1–4 linkage of the α glucose monomers of starch.
   B) 1–4 linkage of the β glucose monomers of cellulose.
   C) double helical structure of a DNA molecule.
   D) α helix secondary structure of a polypeptide.
   E) β pleated sheet secondary structure of a polypeptide.

Answer: D
*Topic: Concept 5.4*
*Skill: Comprehension*

36) Figure 5.7 best illustrates the
   A) secondary structure of a polypeptide.
   B) tertiary structure of a polypeptide.
   C) quaternary structure of a protein.
   D) double helix structure of DNA.
   E) primary structure of a polysaccharide.

Answer: A
*Topic: Concept 5.4*
*Skill: Comprehension*

37) The tertiary structure of a protein is the
   A) bonding together of several polypeptide chains by weak bonds.
   B) order in which amino acids are joined in a polypeptide chain.
   C) unique three–dimensional shape of the fully folded polypeptide.
   D) organization of a polypeptide chain into an α helix or β pleated sheet.
   E) overall protein structure resulting from the aggregation of two or more polypeptide subunits.

Answer: C
*Topic: Concept 5.4*
*Skill: Knowledge*

38) A strong covalent bond between amino acids that functions in maintaining a polypeptide's specific three–dimensional shape is a (an)
   A) ionic bond.
   B) hydrophobic interaction.
   C) van der Waals interaction.
   D) disulfide bond.
   E) hydrogen bond.

Answer: D
*Topic: Concept 5.4*
*Skill: Knowledge*

39) At which level of protein structure are interactions between the side chains (R groups) *most* important?

    A) primary

    B) secondary

    C) tertiary

    D) quaternary

    E) all of the above

Answer: C
*Topic: Concept 5.4*
*Skill: Knowledge*

40) The R group or side chain of the amino acid serine is $-CH_2-OH$. The R group or side chain of the amino acid alanine is $-CH_3$. Where would you expect to find these amino acids in a globular protein in aqueous solution?

    A) Serine would be in the interior, and alanine would be on the exterior of the globular protein.

    B) Alanine would be in the interior, and serine would be on the exterior of the globular protein.

    C) Both serine and alanine would be in the interior of the globular protein.

    D) Both serine and alanine would be on the exterior of the globular protein.

    E) Both serine and alanine would be in the interior and on the exterior of the globular protein.

Answer: B
*Topic: Concept 5.4*
*Skill: Application*

41) The globular protein transthyretin results from the aggregation of four polypeptide subunits. Each of the subunits is a polypeptide chain with an α helix region. Which structure(s) must the transthyretin protein have?

    A) primary structure

    B) primary and secondary structure

    C) primary, secondary, and tertiary structure

    D) primary, secondary, tertiary, and quaternary structure

    E) primary, secondary, tertiary, quaternary, and alpha structure

Answer: D
*Topic: Concept 5.4*
*Skill: Comprehension*

42) What would be an unexpected consequence of changing one amino acid in a protein consisting of 325 amino acids?

    A) The primary structure of the protein would be changed.

    B) The tertiary structure of the protein might be changed.

    C) The biological activity or function of the protein might be altered.

    D) Only A and C are correct.

    E) A, B, and C are correct.

Answer: E
*Topic: Concept 5.4*
*Skill: Comprehension*

43) Altering which of the following levels of structural organization could change the function of a protein?

    A) primary

    B) secondary

    C) tertiary

    D) quaternary

    E) all of the above

Answer: E
*Topic: Concept 5.4*
*Skill: Comprehension*

44) All of the following molecules are proteins *except*

A) hemoglobin.

B) transthyretin.

C) collagen.

D) lysozyme.

E) glycogen.

Answer: E
*Topic: Concept 5.4*
*Skill: Knowledge*

45) What is the term used for a change in a protein's three-dimensional shape or conformation due to disruption of hydrogen bonds, disulfide bridges, or ionic bonds?

A) hydrolysis

B) stabilization

C) destabilization

D) renaturation

E) denaturation

Answer: E
*Topic: Concept 5.4*
*Skill: Knowledge*

46) What is the term used for a protein molecule that assists in the proper folding of other proteins?

A) tertiary protein

B) chaperonin

C) enzyme protein

D) renaturing protein

E) denaturing protein

Answer: B
*Topic: Concept 5.4*
*Skill: Knowledge*

47) Of the following functions, the major purpose of RNA is to

A) transmit genetic information to offspring.

B) function in the synthesis of protein.

C) make a copy of itself, thus ensuring genetic continuity.

D) act as a pattern or blueprint to form DNA.

E) form the genes of higher organisms.

Answer: B
*Topic: Concept 5.5*
*Skill: Comprehension*

48) Which of the following *best* describes the flow of information in eukaryotic cells?

A) DNA → RNA → proteins

B) RNA → proteins → DNA

C) proteins → DNA → RNA

D) RNA → DNA → proteins

E) DNA → proteins → RNA

Answer: A
*Topic: Concept 5.5*
*Skill: Comprehension*

49) Which of the following descriptions *best* fits the class of molecules known as nucleotides?

A) a nitrogenous base and a phosphate group

B) a nitrogenous base and a pentose sugar

C) a nitrogenous base, a phosphate group, and a pentose sugar

D) a phosphate group and an adenine or uracil

E) a pentose sugar and a purine or pyrimidine

Answer: C
*Topic: Concept 5.5*
*Skill: Knowledge*

50) Which of the following are nitrogenous bases of the pyrimidine type?

A) guanine and adenine

B) cytosine and uracil

C) thymine and guanine

D) ribose and deoxyribose

E) adenine and thymine

Answer: B
*Topic: Concept 5.5*
*Skill: Knowledge*

51) Which of the following are nitrogenous bases of the purine type?

A) cytosine and guanine

B) guanine and adenine

C) adenine and thymine

D) thymine and uracil

E) uracil and cytosine

Answer: B
*Topic: Concept 5.5*
*Skill: Knowledge*

52) All of the following nitrogenous bases are found in DNA *except*

A) thymine.

B) adenine.

C) uracil.

D) guanine.

E) cytosine.

Answer: C
*Topic: Concept 5.5*
*Skill: Knowledge*

53) A double-stranded DNA molecule contains a total of 120 purines and 120 pyrimidines. This DNA molecule could be comprised of

A) 120 adenine and 120 uracil molecules.

B) 120 thymine and 120 adenine molecules.

C) 120 cytosine and 120 thymine molecules.

D) 240 adenine and 240 cytosine molecules.

E) 240 guanine and 240 thymine molecules.

Answer: B
*Topic: Concept 5.5*
*Skill: Application*

54) The difference between the sugar in DNA and the sugar in RNA is that the sugar in DNA

A) is a six-carbon sugar and the sugar in RNA is a five-carbon sugar.

B) can form a double-stranded molecule.

C) has a six-membered ring of carbon and nitrogen atoms.

D) can attach to a phosphate.

E) contains one less oxygen atom.

Answer: E
*Topic: Concept 5.5*
*Skill: Knowledge*

55) Which of the following statements *best* summarizes the structural differences between DNA and RNA?

A) RNA is a protein, whereas DNA is a nucleic acid.

B) DNA is a protein, whereas RNA is a nucleic acid.

C) DNA nucleotides contain a different sugar than RNA nucleotides.

D) RNA is a double helix, but DNA is single-stranded.

E) A and D are correct.

Answer: C
*Topic: Concept 5.5*
*Skill: Knowledge*

56) In the double helix structure of nucleic acids, cytosine hydrogen bonds to

A) deoxyribose.

B) ribose.

C) adenine.

D) thymine.

E) guanine.

Answer: E
*Topic: Concept 5.5*
*Skill: Knowledge*

57) The two strands making up the DNA double helix molecule

A) cannot be separated.

B) contain ribose and deoxyribose in opposite strands.

C) are held together by hydrogen bonds.

D) are attached through a phosphate to hold the strands together.

E) contain uracil but not thymine.

Answer: C
*Topic: Concept 5.5*
*Skill: Knowledge*

58) If one strand of a DNA molecule has the sequence of bases 5'ATTGCA3', the other complementary strand would have the sequence

A) 5'TAACGT3'.

B) 3'TAACGT5'.

C) 5'UAACGU3'.

D) 3'UAACGU5'.

E) 5'UGCAAU3'.

Answer: B
*Topic: Concept 5.5*
*Skill: Knowledge*

59) The structural feature that allows DNA to replicate is the

A) sugar–phosphate backbone.

B) complementary pairing of the nitrogenous bases.

C) disulfide bonding (bridging) of the two helixes.

D) twisting of the molecule to form an α helix.

E) three–component structure of the nucleotides.

Answer: B
*Topic: Concept 5.5*
*Skill: Knowledge*

60) A new organism is discovered in the forests of Costa Rica. Scientists there determine that the polypeptide sequence of hemoglobin from the new organism has 72 amino acid differences from humans, 65 differences from a gibbon, 49 differences from a rat, and 5 differences from a frog. These data suggest that the new organism

A) is more closely related to humans than to frogs.

B) is more closely related to frogs than to humans.

C) may have evolved from gibbons but not rats.

D) is more closely related to humans than to rats.

E) may have evolved from rats but not from humans and gibbons.

Answer: B
*Topic: Concept 5.5*
*Skill: Application*

61) Which of the following is an example of hydrolysis?

A) the reaction of two monosaccharides, forming a disaccharide with the release of water

B) the synthesis of two amino acids, forming a peptide with the release of water

C) the reaction of a fat, forming glycerol and fatty acids with the release of water

D) the reaction of a fat, forming glycerol and fatty acids with the utilization of water

E) the synthesis of a nucleotide from a phosphate, a pentose sugar, and a nitrogenous base with the production of a molecule of water

Answer: D
*Topic: Concepts 5.1–5.4*
*Skill: Comprehension*

62) Large organic molecules are usually assembled by polymerization of a few kinds of simple subunits. Which of the following is an *exception* to this statement?

A) a steroid

B) cellulose

C) DNA

D) an enzyme

E) a contractile protein

Answer: A
*Topic: Concepts 5.1–5.4*
*Skill: Comprehension*

63) The element nitrogen is present in all of the following *except*

A) proteins.

B) nucleic acids.

C) amino acids.

D) DNA.

E) monosaccharides.

Answer: E
*Topic: Concepts 5.1–5.4*
*Skill: Knowledge*

*The following questions are based on the 15 molecules illustrated in Figure 5.8. Each molecule may be used once, more than once, or not at all.*

*(Figure 5.8 appears on page 72.)*

64) Which of the following molecules are structural isomers?

A) 1 and 4

B) 5 and 14

C) 6 and 12

D) 12 and 13

E) 14 and 15

Answer: A
*Topic: Concept 5.2*
*Skill: Comprehension*

65) Which of the following combinations could be linked together to form a nucleotide?

A) 1, 2, and 11

B) 3, 7, and 8

C) 5, 9, and 10

D) 11, 12, and 13

E) 12, 14, and 15

Answer: D
*Topic: Concept 5.5*
*Skill: Comprehension*

66) Which of the following molecules contain(s) an aldehyde type of carbonyl functional group?

A) 1

B) 4

C) 8

D) 10

E) 1 and 4

Answer: E
*Topic: Concept 5.2*
*Skill: Comprehension*

67) Which of the following molecules is (are) a carbohydrate?

A) 1 and 4

B) 6

C) 12

D) 5 and 14

E) all of the above

Answer: E
*Topic: Concept 5.2*
*Skill: Comprehension*

68) Which of the following molecules is a saturated fatty acid?

A) 1

B) 5

C) 6

D) 8

E) 9

Answer: E
*Topic: Concept 5.3*
*Skill: Knowledge*

69) Which of the following molecules is a purine type of nitrogenous base?

A) 2

B) 3

C) 5

D) 12

E) 13

Answer: E
*Topic: Concept 5.5*
*Skill: Knowledge*

70) Which of the following molecules act as building blocks (monomers) of polypeptides?

A) 1, 4, and 6

B) 2, 7, and 8

C) 7, 8, and 13

D) 11, 12, and 13

E) 12, 13, and 15

Answer: B
*Topic: Concept 5.4*
*Skill: Knowledge*

71) Which of the following molecules is an amino acid with a hydrophobic R group or side chain?

 A) 3

 B) 5

 C) 7

 D) 8

 E) 12

Answer: C
*Topic: Concept 5.4*
*Skill: Comprehension*

72) Which of the following molecules could be joined together by a peptide bond as a result of a dehydration reaction?

 A) 2 and 3

 B) 3 and 7

 C) 7 and 8

 D) 8 and 9

 E) 12 and 13

Answer: C
*Topic: Concept 5.4*
*Skill: Comprehension*

73) A fat (or triacylglycerol) would be formed as a result of a dehydration reaction between

 A) one molecule of 9 and three molecules of 10.

 B) three molecules of 9 and one molecule of 10.

 C) one molecule of 5 and three molecules of 9.

 D) three molecules of 5 and one molecule of 9.

 E) one molecule of 5 and three molecules of 10.

Answer: B
*Topic: Concept 5.3*
*Skill: Comprehension*

74) Which of the following molecules could be joined together by a phosphodiester type of covalent bond?

 A) 3 and 4

 B) 3 and 8

 C) 6 and 15

 D) 11 and 12

 E) 11 and 13

Answer: D
*Topic: Concept 5.3*
*Skill: Comprehension*

75) Which of the following molecules is the pentose sugar found in RNA?

 A) 1

 B) 4

 C) 6

 D) 12

 E) 13

Answer: D
*Topic: Concept 5.5*
*Skill: Knowledge*

76) Which of the following molecules contains a glycosidic linkage type of covalent bond?

 A) 4

 B) 6

 C) 12

 D) 13

 E) 15

Answer: E
*Topic: Concept 5.2*
*Skill: Comprehension*

77) Which of the following molecules has (have) a functional group that frequently is involved in maintaining the tertiary structure of a protein?

   A) 2

   B) 3

   C) 9

   D) 11

   E) 9 and 11

Answer: A
*Topic: Concept 5.4*
*Skill: Comprehension*

78) Which of the following molecules consists of a hydrophilic "head" region and a hydrophobic "tail" region?

   A) 2

   B) 5

   C) 7

   D) 9

   E) 11

Answer: B
*Topic: Concept 5.3*
*Skill: Knowledge*

79) Which of the following statements is *false*?

   A) 1 and 4 could be joined together by a glycosidic linkage to form a disaccharide.

   B) 9 and 10 could be joined together by ester bonds to form a triacylglycerol.

   C) 2 and 7 could be joined together to form a short peptide.

   D) 2, 7, and 8 could be joined together to form a short peptide.

   E) 14 and 15 could be joined together to form a polypeptide.

Answer: E
*Topic: Concepts 5.2–5.4*
*Skill: Comprehension*

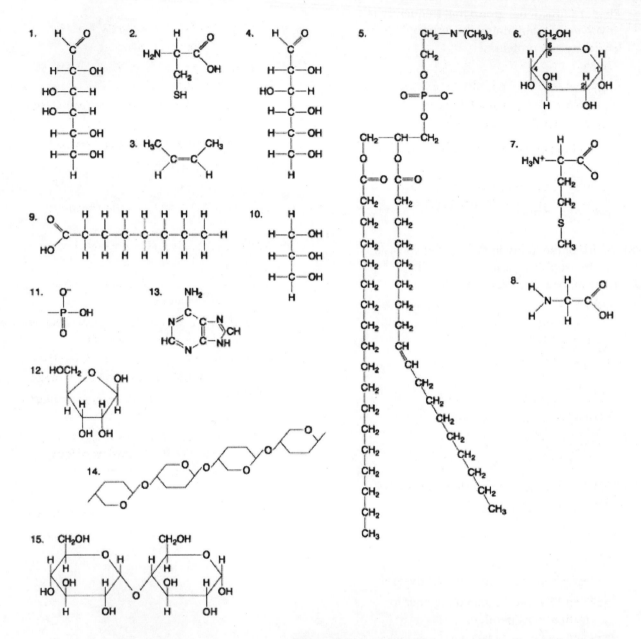

**Figure 5.8**

# Media Activity Questions

1) Carbohydrates generally have a molecular formula

   A) that includes a –SH group.

   B) in which carbon, hydrogen, and oxygen are present in a ratio of 1:2:1.

   C) that includes a –NH$_2$ group.

   D) that includes at least one hydrocarbon tail.

   E) in which carbon, hydrogen, and oxygen are present in a 2:1:2 ratio.

   Answer: B
   *Topic: Web/CD Activity: Carbohydrates*

2) A function of cholesterol that does not harm health is its role

   A) in calcium and phosphate metabolism.

   B) as a component of animal cell membranes.

   C) as the primary female sex hormone.

   D) as the primary male sex hormone.

   E) None of the above; all of cholesterol's effects on the body are harmful.

   Answer: B
   *Topic: Web/CD Activity: Lipids*

3) Which of these does not contain a structural protein?

   A) muscles

   B) tendons

   C) ovalbumin

   D) spider silk

   E) ligaments

   Answer: C
   *Topic: Web/CD Activity: Protein Functions*

4) The primary structure of a protein is

   A) an α helix or a pleated sheet.

   B) the amino acid sequence of the polypeptide chain.

   C) composed of two or more polypeptide chains.

   D) maintained by hydrogen bonds.

   E) irregular folding.

   Answer: B
   *Topic: Web/CD Activity: Protein Structure*

5) Which of these is a difference between DNA and RNA?

   A) RNA is double-stranded; DNA is single-stranded.

   B) DNA is found in the nucleus; RNA is never found in the nucleus.

   C) In DNA, adenine pairs with guanine; in RNA, adenine pairs with thymine.

   D) DNA contains thymine; RNA contains uracil.

   E) DNA consists of five different nucleotides; RNA consists of four different nucleotides.

   Answer: D
   *Topic: Web/CD Activity: Nucleic Acid Structure*

# Self–Quiz Questions

1) Which term includes all others in the list?

   A) monosaccharide

   B) disaccharide

   C) starch

   D) carbohydrate

   E) polysaccharide

   Answer: D

2) The molecular formula for glucose is $C_6H_{12}O_6$. What would be the molecular formula for a polymer made by linking ten glucose molecules together by dehydration reactions?

   A) $C_{60}H_{120}O_{60}$

   B) $C_6H_{12}O_6$

   C) $C_{60}H_{102}O_{51}$

   D) $C_{60}H_{100}O_{50}$

   E) $C_{60}H_{111}O_{51}$

   Answer: C

3) The enzyme amylase can break glycosidic linkages between glucose monomers only if the monomers are the $\alpha$ form. Which of the following could amylase break down? (Choose all that apply.)

   A) cellulose

   B) chitin

   C) glycogen

   D) starch

   E) amylopectin

   Answer: C, D, E

4) Choose the pair of terms that correctly completes this sentence: Nucleotides are to _____ as _____ are to proteins.

   A) nucleic acids; amino acids

   B) amino acids; polypeptides

   C) glycosidic linkages; polypeptide linkages

   D) genes; enzymes

   E) polymers; polypeptides

   Answer: A

5) Which of the following statements concerning *unsaturated* fats is true?

   A) They are more common in animals than in plants.

   B) They have double bonds in the carbon chains of their fatty acids.

   C) They generally solidify at room temperature.

   D) They contain more hydrogen than saturated fats having the same number of carbon atoms.

   E) They have fewer fatty acid molecules per fat molecule.

   Answer: B

6) The structural level of a protein least affected by a disruption in hydrogen bonding is the

   A) primary level.

   B) secondary level.

   C) tertiary level.

   D) quaternary level.

   E) All structural levels are equally affected.

   Answer: D

7) Which of the following pairs of base sequences could form a short stretch of a normal double helix of DNA?

A) 5'-purine-pyrimidine-purine-pyrimidine-3' with
3'-purine-pyrimidine-purine-pyrimidine-5'

B) 5'-A-G-C-T-3' with 5'-T-C-G-A-3'

C) 5'-G-C-G-C-3' with 5'-T-A-T-A-3'

D) 5'-A-T-G-C-3' with 5'-G-C-A-T-3'

E) A, B, and D are all correct.

Answer: D

8) Enzymes that break down DNA catalyze the hydrolysis of the covalent bonds that join nucleotides together. What would happen to DNA molecules treated with these enzymes?

A) The two strands of the double helix would separate.

B) The phosphodiester bonds between deoxyribose sugars would be broken.

C) The purines would be separated from the deoxyribose sugars.

D) The pyrimidines would be separated from the deoxyribose sugars.

E) All bases would be separated from the deoxyribose sugars.

Answer: B

9) Which of the following is *not* a protein?

A) hemoglobin

B) cholesterol

C) an antibody

D) an enzyme

E) insulin

Answer: B

10) Which of the following statements about the 5' end of a polynucleotide strand is correct?

A) The 5' end has a hydroxyl group.

B) The 5' end has a phosphate group.

C) The 5' end is identical to the 3' end.

D) The 5' end is antiparallel to the 3' end.

E) The 5' end is the fifth position on one of the nitrogenous bases.

Answer: B

# Chapter 6   A Tour of the Cell

1) What limits the resolving power of a light microscope?
   A) the type of lens used to magnify the object under study
   B) the shortest wavelength of light used to illuminate the specimen
   C) the type of lens that focuses a beam of electrons through the specimen
   D) the type of heavy metal or dye that is used to stain the specimen
   E) the ratio of an object's image to its real size

Answer: B
*Topic: Concept 6.1*
*Skill: Knowledge*

2) When biologists wish to study the internal ultrastructure of cells, they most likely would use
   A) a light microscope.
   B) a scanning electron microscope.
   C) a transmission electronic microscope.
   D) A and C only
   E) A, B, and C

Answer: C
*Topic: Concept 6.1*
*Skill: Knowledge*

3) The advantage of light microscopy over electron microscopy is that
   A) light microscopy provides for higher magnification than electron microscopy.
   B) light microscopy provides for higher resolving power than electron microscopy.
   C) light microscopy allows one to view dynamic processes in living cells.
   D) both A and B
   E) both B and C

Answer: C
*Topic: Concept 6.1*
*Skill: Knowledge*

4) A primary objective of cell fractionation is to
   A) view the structure of cell membranes.
   B) identify the enzymes outside the organelles.
   C) determine the size of various organelles.
   D) separate the major organelles so their particular functions can be determined.
   E) crack the cell wall so the cytoplasmic contents can be released.

Answer: D
*Topic: Concept 6.1*
*Skill: Knowledge*

5) In the fractionation of homogenized cells using centrifugation, the primary factor that determines whether a specific cellular component ends up in the supernatant or the pellet is

A) the relative solubility of the component.

B) the size and weight of the component.

C) the percentage of carbohydrates in the component.

D) the number of enzymes in the fraction.

E) the presence or-absence of lipids in the component.

Answer: B
*Topic: Concept 6.1*
*Skill: Knowledge*

6) Which of the following *correctly* lists the order in which cellular components will be found in the pellet when homogenized cells are treated with increasingly rapid spins in a centrifuge?

A) ribosomes, nucleus, mitochondria

B) chloroplasts, ribosomes, vacuoles

C) nucleus, ribosomes, chloroplasts

D) vacuoles, ribosomes, nucleus

E) nucleus, mitochondria, ribosomes

Answer: E
*Topic: Concept 6.1*
*Skill: Comprehension*

7) Quantum dots are small (15–30 nm diameter), bright particles visible using light microscopy. If the dots can be specifically bound to individual proteins on a plasma membrane of a cell, which of the following *correctly* describes the advantage of using quantum dots in examining proteins?

A) The dots permit the position of the proteins to be determined more precisely.

B) The dots permit the average distance between the proteins to be determined more precisely.

C) The dots permit the size of the proteins to be determined more precisely.

D) The dots permit the motion of the proteins to be determined more precisely.

E) All of the above are correct.

Answer: D
*Topic: Concept 6.1*
*Skill: Application*

8) Which of the following are prokaryotic cells?

A) plants

B) fungi

C) bacteria

D) animals

E) B and C only

Answer: C
*Topic: Concept 6.2*
*Skill: Knowledge*

9) All of the following are part of a prokaryotic cell *except*

    A) DNA.

    B) a cell wall.

    C) a plasma membrane.

    D) ribosomes.

    E) an endoplasmic reticulum.

Answer: E
*Topic: Concept 6.2*
*Skill: Knowledge*

10) The volume enclosed by the plasma membrane of plant cells is often much larger than the corresponding volume in animal cells. The most reasonable explanation for this observation is that

    A) plant cells are capable of having a much higher surface-to-volume ratio than animal cells.

    B) plant cells have a much more highly convoluted (folded) plasma membrane than animal cells.

    C) plant cells contain a large vacuole that reduces the volume of the cytoplasm.

    D) animal cells are more spherical, while plant cells are elongated.

    E) the basic functions of plant cells are very different from those of animal cells.

Answer: C
*Topic: Concept 6.2*
*Skill: Comprehension*

11) Which of the following comparisons between prokaryotic and eukaryotic cells is *incorrect*?

    A) The lack of organelles in prokaryotes means that they are structurally less complex than eukaryotes.

    B) The lack of internal membranes means that prokaryotes cannot compartmentalize function to the same extent as eukaryotes.

    C) All membrane function in prokaryotes is accomplished in the plasma membrane, while in eukaryotes, these functions are more distributed among the organelles.

    D) The specialization of function in organelles suggests that eukaryotes will contain a wider variety of phospholipids than prokaryotes.

    E) The lack of organelles in prokaryotes means that the basic cellular functions are different in prokaryotes than in eukaryotes.

Answer: E
*Topic: Concept 6.2*
*Skill: Application*

*For the following questions, use the lettered answers to match the structure to its proper cell type. Choose the most inclusive category. Each answer may be used once, more than once, or not at all.*

    A.  a feature of all cells
    B.  found in prokaryotic cells only
    C.  found in eukaryotic cells only
    D.  found in plant cells only
    E.  found in animal cells only

12) plasma membrane

Answer: A
*Topic: Concept 6.2*
*Skill: Knowledge*

13) tonoplast

Answer: D
*Topic: Concept 6.4*
*Skill: Knowledge*

14) nucleoid

Answer: B
*Topic: Concept 6.3*
*Skill: Knowledge*

15) Which of the following does *not* contain functional ribosomes?

A) a prokaryotic cell

B) a plant mitochondrion

C) a chloroplast

D) an animal mitochondrion

E) a nucleolus

Answer: E
*Topic: Concept 6.3*
*Skill: Knowledge*

16) Large numbers of ribosomes are present in cells that specialize in producing which of the following molecules?

A) lipids

B) starches

C) proteins

D) steroids

E) glucose

Answer: C
*Topic: Concept 6.3*
*Skill: Knowledge*

17) Which of the following compounds require the presence of the nuclear pores to move between the cytoplasm and the interior of the nucleus?

A) ribosomal RNA

B) messenger RNA

C) proteins synthesized in the cytoplasm that are part of ribosomes

D) A and B only

E) A, B, and C

Answer: E
*Topic: Concept 6.3*
*Skill: Comprehension*

18) Which of the following organelles is not a common destination for small vesicles that bud off the Golgi apparatus?

A) plasma membrane

B) lysosomes

C) vacuole

D) endoplasmic reticulum

E) all of the above

Answer: D
*Topic: Concept 6.3*
*Skill: Comprehension*

19) Which of the following *incorrectly* matches the type of cell, type of protein, and site of the protein's synthesis?

A) prokaryote, cytoplasmic protein, free cytoplasmic ribosome

B) eukaryote, plasma membrane protein, rough ER

C) prokaryote, plasma membrane protein, ribosome bound to plasma membrane

D) eukaryote, cytoplasmic protein, free cytoplasmic ribosome

E) prokaryote, secreted protein, free cytoplasmic ribosome

Answer: E
*Topic: Concept 6.3*
*Skill: Comprehension*

20) Under which of the following conditions would you expect to find a cell with a predominance of free ribosomes?

A) a cell that is secreting proteins

B) a cell that is producing cytoplasmic enzymes

C) a cell that is constructing its cell wall or extracellular matrix

D) a cell that is digesting food particles

E) a cell that is enlarging its vacuole

Answer: B
*Topic: Concepts 6.3, 6.4*
*Skill: Application*

21) Which type of organelle is primarily involved in the synthesis of oils, phospholipids, and steroids?

A) ribosome

B) lysosome

C) smooth endoplasmic reticulum

D) mitochondrion

E) contractile vacuole

Answer: C
*Topic: Concept 6.4*
*Skill: Knowledge*

22) Which structure is the site of the synthesis of proteins that may be exported from the cell?

A) rough ER

B) lysosomes

C) plasmodesmata

D) Golgi vesicles

E) tight junctions

Answer: A
*Topic: Concept 6.4*
*Skill: Knowledge*

23) Which of the following structures is most directly associated with the secretion of compounds that will become part of the plant cell wall?

A) smooth ER

B) rough ER

C) plasmodesmata

D) Golgi-derived vesicles

E) Golgi apparatus

Answer: D
*Topic: Concept 6.4*
*Skill: Comprehension*

24) The Golgi apparatus has a polarity or sidedness to its structure and function. Which of the following statements *correctly* describes this polarity?

A) Transport vesicles fuse with one side of the Golgi and leave from the opposite side.

B) Proteins in the membrane of the Golgi may be sorted and modified as they move from one side of the Golgi to the other.

C) Lipids in the membrane of the Golgi may be sorted and modified as they move from one side of the Golgi to the other.

D) Soluble proteins in the cisternae (interior) of the Golgi may be sorted and modified as they move from one side of the Golgi to the other.

E) All of the above correctly describe polar characteristics of the Golgi function.

Answer: E
*Topic: Concept 6.4*
*Skill: Comprehension*

25) Of the following, which is probably the most common route for membrane flow in the endomembrane system?

A) Golgi → lysosome → ER → plasma membrane

B) tonoplast → plasma membrane → nuclear envelope → smooth ER

C) nuclear envelope → lysosome → Golgi → plasma membrane

D) rough ER → vesicles → Golgi → plasma membrane

E) ER → chloroplasts → mitochondrion – cell membrane

Answer: D
*Topic: Concept 6.4*
*Skill: Knowledge*

26) Which of the following cell components is *not* directly involved in synthesis or secretion?

A) ribosome

B) rough endoplasmic reticulum

C) Golgi body

D) smooth endoplasmic reticulum

E) lysosome

Answer: E
*Topic: Concept 6.4*
*Skill: Comprehension*

27) The fact that the outer membrane of the nuclear envelope has bound ribosomes allows one to *most reliably* conclude that

A) at least some of the proteins that function in the nuclear envelope are made by the ribosomes on the nuclear envelope.

B) the nuclear envelope is not part of the endomembrane system.

C) the nuclear envelope is physically continuous with the endoplasmic reticulum.

D) small vesicles from the Golgi fuse with the nuclear envelope.

E) nuclear pore complexes contain proteins.

Answer: A
*Topic: Concept 6.4*
*Skill: Comprehension*

28) The difference in lipid and protein composition between the membranes of the endomembrane system is largely determined by

A) the physical separation of most membranes from each other.

B) the transportation of membrane among the endomembrane system by small membrane vesicles.

C) the function of the Golgi apparatus in sorting membrane components.

D) the modification of the membrane components once they reach their final destination.

E) the synthesis of lipids and proteins in each of the organelles of the endomembrane system.

Answer: C
*Topic: Concept 6.4*
*Skill: Comprehension*

29) In animal cells, hydrolytic enzymes are packaged to prevent general destruction of cellular components. Which of the following organelles functions in this compartmentalization?

A) chloroplast

B) lysosome

C) central vacuole

D) peroxisome

E) glyoxysome

Answer: B
*Topic: Concept 6.4*
*Skill: Knowledge*

30) Which of the following statements *correctly* describes some aspect of protein excretion in prokaryotic cells?

   A) Prokaryotes are unlikely to be able to excrete proteins because they lack an endomembrane system.

   B) The mechanism of protein excretion in prokaryotes is probably the same as that in eukaryotes.

   C) Proteins that are excreted by prokaryotes are synthesized on ribosomes that are bound to the cytoplasmic surface of the plasma membrane.

   D) In prokaryotes, the ribosomes that are used for the synthesis of secreted proteins are located outside of the cell.

   E) Prokaryotes contain large pores in their plasma membrane that permit the movement of proteins out of the cell.

Answer: C
*Topic: Concept 6.4*
*Skill: Application*

*Refer to the following five terms to answer the following questions. Choose the most appropriate term for each phrase. Each term may be used once, more than once, or not at all.*

   A. lysosome
   B. vacuole
   C. mitochondrion
   D. Golgi apparatus
   E. peroxisome

31) produces and modifies polysaccharides that will be secreted

Answer: D
*Topic: Concept 6.4*
*Skill: Knowledge*

32) contains hydrolytic enzymes

Answer: A
*Topic: Concept 6.4*
*Skill: Knowledge*

33) helps to recycle the cell's organic material

Answer: A
*Topic: Concept 6.4*
*Skill: Knowledge*

34) one of the main energy transformers of cells

Answer: C
*Topic: Concept 6.5*
*Skill: Knowledge*

35) contains its own DNA and ribosomes

Answer: C
*Topic: Concept 6.5*
*Skill: Knowledge*

36) a compartment that often takes up much of the volume of a plant cell

Answer: B
*Topic: Concept 6.4*
*Skill: Knowledge*

37) contains enzymes that transfer hydrogen from various substrates to oxygen, producing $H_2O_2$

Answer: E
*Topic: Concept 6.5*
*Skill: Knowledge*

38) a versatile plant compartment that may hold reserves of organic compounds or inorganic ions

Answer: B
*Topic: Concept 6.4*
*Skill: Knowledge*

39) Of the following, what do both mitochondria and chloroplasts have in common?

A) ATP is produced.

B) DNA is present.

C) Ribosomes are present.

D) B and C only

E) A, B, and C are correct.

Answer: E
*Topic: Concept 6.5*
*Skill: Knowledge*

40) Grana, thylakoids, and stroma are all components found in

A) vacuoles.

B) chloroplasts.

C) mitochondria.

D) lysosomes.

E) nuclei.

Answer: B
*Topic: Concept 6.5*
*Skill: Knowledge*

41) Organelles other than the nucleus that contain DNA include

A) ribosomes.

B) mitochondria.

C) chloroplasts.

D) B and C only

E) A, B, and C

Answer: D
*Topic: Concept 6.5*
*Skill: Knowledge*

42) Which of the following statements *incorrectly* describes common structural features of an animal secretory cell and a photosynthetic plant cell?

A) Both cells have Golgi apparatus.

B) Both cells have mitochondria.

C) Both cells have chloroplasts.

D) Both cells have a plasma membrane.

E) Both cells have a nucleus.

Answer: C
*Topic: Concept 6.5*
*Skill: Comprehension*

43) The chemical reactions involved in respiration are virtually identical between prokaryotic and eukaryotic cells. In eukaryotic cells, ATP is synthesized primarily on the inner membrane of the mitochondria. Where are the corresponding reactions likely to occur in prokaryotic respiration?

A) in the cytoplasm

B) on the inner mitochondrial membrane

C) on the endoplasmic reticulum

D) on the plasma membrane

E) on the nuclear envelope

Answer: D
*Topic: Concept 6.5*
*Skill: Comprehension*

44) A biologist ground up some plant leaf cells and then centrifuged the mixture to fractionate the organelles. Organelles in one of the heavier fractions could produce ATP in the light, while organelles in the lighter fraction could produce ATP in the dark. The heavier and lighter fractions are most likely to contain, respectively,

A) mitochondria and chloroplasts.

B) chloroplasts and peroxisomes.

C) peroxisomes and chloroplasts.

D) chloroplasts and mitochondria.

E) mitochondria and peroxisomes.

Answer: D
*Topic: Concept 6.5*
*Skill: Comprehension*

45) Which of the following is a place where both DNA and ribosomes are *unlikely* to be found in *any* type of cell?

A) stroma of chloroplasts

B) mitochondrial matrix

C) nucleus

D) cytoplasm

E) Golgi apparatus

Answer: E
*Topic: Concept 6.5*
*Skill: Comprehension*

46) All of the following are correct matches of the location of a protein and the location of its synthesis *except*

A) plasma membrane protein—rough ER.

B) mitochondrial membrane protein—free cytoplasmic ribosomes.

C) cytoplasmic proteins—free cytoplasmic ribosomes.

D) chloroplast stromal protein—chloroplast ribosomes.

E) mitochondrial matrix protein—rough ER.

Answer: E
*Topic: Concept 6.5*
*Skill: Application*

47) Which of the following are capable of converting light energy to chemical energy?

A) chloroplasts

B) mitochondria

C) leucoplasts

D) peroxisomes

E) Golgi bodies

Answer: A
*Topic: Concept 6.5*
*Skill: Knowledge*

48) A cell has the following molecules and structures: enzymes, DNA, ribosomes, plasma membrane, and mitochondria. It could be a cell from

A) a bacterium.

B) an animal, but not a plant.

C) a plant, but not an animal.

D) a plant or an animal.

E) any kind of organism.

Answer: D
*Topic: Concept 6.5*
*Skill: Comprehension*

49) Which of the following is *not* a known function of the cytoskeleton?

A) to maintain a critical limit on cell size

B) to provide mechanical support to the cell

C) to maintain the characteristic shape of the cell

D) to hold mitochondria and other organelles in place within the cytosol

E) to assist in cell motility by interacting with specialized motor proteins

Answer: A
*Topic: Concept 6.6*
*Skill: Comprehension*

50) Motor proteins provide for molecular motion in cells by interacting with what types of cellular structures?

A) sites of energy production in cellular respiration

B) membrane proteins

C) ribosomes

D) cytoskeletons

E) cellulose fibers in the cell wall

Answer: D
*Topic: Concept 6.6*
*Skill: Knowledge*

51) Cells can be described as having a cytoskeleton of internal structures that contribute to the shape, organization, and movement of the cell. All of the following are part of the cytoskeleton *except*

A) the nuclear envelope.

B) microtubules.

C) microfilaments.

D) intermediate filaments.

E) actin.

Answer: A
*Topic: Concept 6.6*
*Skill: Knowledge*

52) Which of the following pairs is mismatched?

A) nucleolus—ribosomal RNA

B) nucleus—DNA replication

C) lysosome—protein synthesis

D) cell membrane—lipid bilayer

E) cytoskeleton—microtubules

Answer: C
*Topic: Concept 6.6*
*Skill: Comprehension*

53) Of the following, which cell structure would most likely be visible with a light microscope that has been manufactured to the maximum resolving power possible?

A) mitochondrion

B) microtubule

C) ribosome

D) largest microfilament

E) nuclear pore

Answer: A
*Topic: Concept 6.6*
*Skill: Comprehension*

54) Which of the following contain the 9 + 2 arrangement of microtubules?

A) cilia

B) centrioles

C) flagella

D) A and C only

E) A, B, and C

Answer: D
*Topic: Concept 6.6*
*Skill: Knowledge*

55) Cells would be unable to form cilia or flagella if they did not have

A) centrosomes.

B) ribosomes.

C) actin.

D) A and B only

E) A, B, and C

Answer: D
*Topic: Concept 6.7*
*Skill: Comprehension*

56) Which of the following possesses a microtubular structure similar to a basal body?

A) centriole

B) lysosome

C) nucleolus

D) peroxisome

E) ribosome

Answer: A
*Topic: Concept 6.6*
*Skill: Knowledge*

57) Microfilaments are well known for their role in which of the following?

A) ameboid movement

B) formation of cleavage furrows

C) contracting of muscle cells

D) A and B only

E) A, B, and C

Answer: E
*Topic: Concept 6.6*
*Skill: Comprehension*

58) Which of the following statements about the cytoskeleton is *incorrect*?

A) The dynamic aspect of cytoskeletal function is made possible by the assembly and disassembly of a few simple types of proteins into large aggregates.

B) Microfilaments are structurally rigid and resist compression, while microtubules resist tension (stretching).

C) Movement of cilia and flagella is the result of motor proteins causing microtubules to move relative to each other.

D) Chemicals that block the assembly of the cytoskeleton would prevent many different processes in cells.

E) Transport vesicles among the membranes of the endomembrane system depend on the function of the cytoskeleton.

Answer: B
*Topic: Concept 6.6*
*Skill: Application*

59) All of the following structures and proteins are directly associated with movement in cells or by cells *except*

A) cilia.

B) dynein.

C) actin.

D) flagella.

E) centrosomes.

Answer: E
*Topic: Concept 6.6*
*Skill: Knowledge*

60) All of the following serve an important role in determining or maintaining the structure of plant cells. Which of the following are distinct from the others in terms of composition?

   A) microtubules

   B) microfilaments

   C) plant cell walls

   D) intermediate filaments

   E) nuclear lamina

Answer: C
Topic: Concept 6.7
Skill: Comprehension

61) Which of the following relationships between cell structures and their respective functions is *not* correct?

   A) cell wall: support, protection

   B) chloroplasts: chief sites of cellular respiration

   C) chromosomes: genetic control information

   D) ribosomes: site of protein synthesis

   E) mitochondria: formation of ATP

Answer: B
Topic: Concept 6.7
Skill: Comprehension

62) The cell walls of bacteria, fungi, and plant cells and the extracellular matrix of animal cells are all external to the plasma membrane. Which of the following is *not* a characteristic of all of these extracellular structures?

   A) They must be highly permeable to water and small molecules in order to allow cells to exchange matter and energy with their environment.

   B) They must permit information transfer between the cell's external environment and the cytoplasm.

   C) They must provide a rigid structure that maintains an appropriate ratio of cell surface area to volume.

   D) They are constructed of materials that are largely synthesized in the cytoplasm and then transported out of the cell.

   E) They are composed of a mixture of proteins and carbohydrates.

Answer: C
Topic: Concept 6.7
Skill: Application

63) When a potassium ion ($K^+$) moves from the soil into the vacuole of a cell on the surface of a root, it must pass through several cellular structures. Which of the following correctly describes the order in which these structures will be encountered by the ion?

A) plasma membrane → primary cell wall → cytoplasm → tonoplast

B) secondary cell wall → plasma membrane → primary cell wall → cytoplasm → tonoplast

C) primary cell wall → plasma membrane → cytoplasm → tonoplast

D) primary cell wall → plasma membrane → tonoplast → cytoplasm → vacuole

E) tonoplast → primary cell wall → plasma membrane → cytoplasm

Answer: C
*Topic: Concept 6.7*
*Skill: Comprehension*

64) A cell lacking the ability to make and secrete glycoproteins would most likely be deficient in its

A) nuclear DNA.

B) extracellular matrix.

C) Golgi apparatus.

D) B and C only

E) A, B, and C

Answer: D
*Topic: Concept 6.7*
*Skill: Comprehension*

65) The extracellular matrix is thought to participate in the regulation of animal cell behavior by communicating information from the outside to the inside of the cell via

A) gap junctions.

B) the nucleus.

C) DNA and RNA.

D) integrins.

E) plasmodesmata.

Answer: D
*Topic: Concept 6.7*
*Skill: Knowledge*

66) Plasmodesmata in plant cells are *most* similar in function to which of the following structures in animal cells?

A) peroxisomes

B) desmosomes

C) gap junctions

D) extracellular matrix

E) tight junctions

Answer: C
*Topic: Concept 6.7*
*Skill: Comprehension*

67) Ions can travel directly from the cytoplasm of one animal cell to the cytoplasm of an adjacent cell through

A) plasmodesmata.

B) intermediate filaments.

C) tight junctions.

D) desmosomes.

E) gap junctions.

Answer: E
*Topic: Concept 6.7*
*Skill: Knowledge*

# Media Activity Questions

1) _____ are surface appendages that allow a bacterium to stick to a surface.

A) Cell walls

B) Flagella

C) Ribosomes

D) Mitochondria

E) Pili

Answer: E
*Topic: Web/CD Activity: Prokaryotic Cell*

2) In eukaryotic cells, the first step in protein synthesis is the

A) translation of an RNA nucleotide sequence into a sequence of amino acids.

B) linking of nucleotides to form a polypeptide.

C) translation of a DNA nucleotide sequence into a sequence of amino acids.

D) transferring of information from DNA to messenger RNA

E) removal of introns from RNA and the stitching together of exons

Answer: D
*Topic: Web/CD Activity: Role of the Nucleus . . .*

3) _____ is composed of DNA and protein.

A) A mitochondrion

B) A flagellum

C) A centriole

D) Chromatin

E) A ribosome

Answer: D
*Topic: Activity: Animal Cell Structure and Function*

4) Where is calcium stored?

A) mitochondria

B) smooth endoplasmic reticulum

C) centrioles

D) rough endoplasmic reticulum

E) microtubules

Answer: B
*Topic: Activity: Animal Cell Structure and Function*

5) Which of these structures is unique to plant cells?

A) mitochondrion

B) peroxisome

C) flagellum

D) central vacuole

E) nucleoid region

Answer: D
*Topic: Activity: Plant Cell Structure and Function*

# Self–Quiz Questions

1) The symptoms of a certain inherited disorder in humans include breathing problems and, in males, sterility. Which of the following is a reasonable hypothesis for the molecular basis of this disorder?

   A) a defective enzyme in the mitochondria

   B) defective actin molecules in cellular microfilaments

   C) defective dynein molecules in cilia and flagella

   D) abnormal hydrolytic enzymes in the lysosomes

   E) defective ribosome assembly in the nucleolus

   Answer: C

2) Choose the statement that correctly characterizes bound ribosomes.

   A) Bound ribosomes are enclosed in their own membrane.

   B) Bound and free ribosomes are structurally different.

   C) Bound ribosomes generally synthesize membrane proteins and secretory proteins.

   D) The most common location for bound ribosomes is the cytoplasmic surface of the plasma membrane.

   E) All of the above.

   Answer: C

3) Which of the following is not considered part of the endomembrane system?

   A) nuclear envelope

   B) chloroplast

   C) Golgi apparatus

   D) plasma membrane

   E) ER

   Answer: B

4) Cells of the pancreas will incorporate radioactively labeled amino acids into proteins. This "tagging" of newly synthesized proteins enables a researcher to track the location of these proteins in a cell. In this case, we are tracking an enzyme that is eventually secreted by pancreatic cells. Which of the following is the most likely pathway for movement of this protein in the cell?

   A) ER → Golgi → nucleus

   B) Golgi → ER → lysosome

   C) nucleus → ER → Golgi

   D) ER → Golgi → vesicles that fuse with plasma membrane

   E) ER → lysosomes → vesicles that fuse with plasma membrane

   Answer: D

5) Which of the following structures is common to plant *and* animal cells?

   A) chloroplast

   B) wall made of cellulose

   C) tonoplast

   D) mitochondrion

   E) centriole

   Answer: D

6) Which of the following is present in a prokaryotic cell?

   A) mitochondrion

   B) ribosome

   C) nuclear envelope

   D) chloroplast

   E) ER

   Answer: B

7) Which type of cell would probably provide the best opportunity to study lysosomes?

   A) muscle cell

   B) nerve cell

   C) phagocytic white blood cell

   D) leaf cell of a plant

   E) bacterial cell

Answer: C

8) Which of the following statements is a correct distinction between prokaryotic and eukaryotic cells attributable to the absence of a prokaryotic cytoskeleton?

   A) Organelles are found only in eukaryotic cells.

   B) Cytoplasmic streaming is not observed in prokaryotes.

   C) Only eukaryotic cells are capable of movement.

   D) Prokaryotic cells have cell walls.

   E) Only the eukaryotic cell concentrates its genetic material in a region separate from the rest of the cell.

Answer: B

9) Which of the following structure-function pairs is *mismatched*?

   A) nucleolus—ribosome production

   B) lysosome—intracellular digestion

   C) ribosome—protein synthesis

   D) Golgi—protein trafficking

   E) microtubule—muscle contraction

Answer: E

10) Cyanide binds with at least one of the molecules involved in the production of ATP. Following exposure of a cell to cyanide, most of the cyanide could be expected to be found within the

   A) mitochondria.

   B) ribosomes.

   C) peroxisomes.

   D) lysosomes.

   E) endoplasmic reticulum.

Answer: A

# Chapter 7  Membrane Structure and Function

For the following questions, match the membrane model or description with the scientist(s) who proposed the model. Each choice may be used once, more than once, or not at all.

A. H. Davson and J. Danielli
B. I. Langmuir
C. C. Overton
D. S. Singer and G. Nicolson
E. E. Gorter and F. Grendel

1) The first to propose that cell membranes are phospholipid bilayers.

Answer: E
*Topic: Concept 7.1*
*Skill: Knowledge*

2) Membranes are a phospholipid bilayer between two layers of hydrophilic proteins.

Answer: A
*Topic: Concept 7.1*
*Skill: Knowledge*

3) The membrane is a mosaic of protein molecules bobbing in a fluid bilayer of phospholipids.

Answer: D
*Topic: Concept 7.1*
*Skill: Knowledge*

4) Which of the following types of molecules are the major structural components of the cell membrane?
   A) phospholipids and cellulose
   B) nucleic acids and proteins
   C) phospholipids and proteins
   D) proteins and cellulose
   E) glycoproteins and cholesterol

Answer: C
*Topic: Concept 7.1*
*Skill: Knowledge*

For the following questions, match the labeled component of the cell membrane (Figure 7.1) with its description.

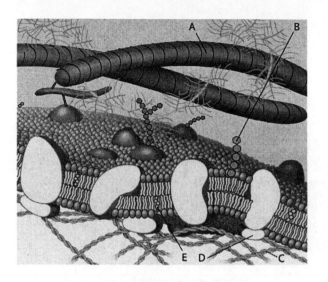

**Figure 7.1**

5) peripheral protein

Answer: D
*Topic: Concept 7.1*
*Skill: Knowledge*

6) cholesterol

Answer: E
*Topic: Concept 7.1*
*Skill: Knowledge*

7) fiber of the extracellular matrix

Answer: A
*Topic: Concept 7.1*
*Skill: Knowledge*

8) microfilament of the cytoskeleton

Answer: C
*Topic: Concept 7.1*
*Skill: Knowledge*

9) glycolipid

Answer: B
*Topic: Concept 7.1*
*Skill: Knowledge*

10) When biological membranes are frozen and then fractured, they tend to break along the middle of the bilayer. The best explanation for this is that

   A) the integral membrane proteins are not strong enough to hold the bilayer together.

   B) water that is present in the middle of the bilayer freezes and is easily fractured.

   C) hydrophilic interactions between the opposite membrane surfaces are destroyed on freezing.

   D) the carbon–carbon bonds of the phospholipid tails are easily broken.

   E) the hydrophobic interactions that hold the membrane together are weakest at this point.

Answer: E
*Topic: Concept 7.1*
*Skill: Application*

11) All of the following molecules are part of the cell membrane *except*

   A) lipids.

   B) nucleic acids.

   C) proteins.

   D) phosphate groups.

   E) steroids.

Answer: B
*Topic: Concept 7.1*
*Skill: Knowledge*

12) The original model for the bilayer structure of cell membranes, which was prepared in the 1920s, was based on which of the following?

   A) detailed electron micrographs of freeze-fractured membranes

   B) the presence of proteins as a functional component of biological membranes

   C) the observation that all membranes contain phospholipids and proteins

   D) the understanding that phospholipids are amphipathic molecules

   E) A and B only

Answer: D
*Topic: Concept 7.1*
*Skill: Comprehension*

13) The presence of cholesterol in the plasma membranes of some animals

   A) enables the membrane to stay fluid more easily when cell temperature drops.

   B) enables the animal to remove hydrogen atoms from saturated phospholipids.

   C) enables the animal to add hydrogen atoms to unsaturated phospholipids.

   D) makes the membrane less flexible, allowing it to sustain greater pressure from within the cell.

   E) makes the animal more susceptible to circulatory disorders.

Answer: A
*Topic: Concept 7.1*
*Skill: Comprehension*

14) According to the fluid mosaic model of cell membranes, which of the following is a *true* statement about membrane phospholipids?

    A) They can move laterally along the plane of the membrane.

    B) They frequently flip-flop from one side of the membrane to the other.

    C) They occur in an uninterrupted bilayer, with membrane proteins restricted to the surface of the membrane.

    D) They are free to depart from the membrane and dissolve in the surrounding solution.

    E) They have hydrophilic tails in the interior of the membrane.

Answer: A
*Topic: Concept 7.1*
*Skill: Comprehension*

15) The lateral mobility (fluidity) of lipids and proteins in membranes is a consequence of

    A) lack of covalent bonds between the lipid and protein components of the membrane.

    B) weak hydrophobic interactions among the components in the interior of the membrane.

    C) the presence of liquid water in the interior of the membrane.

    D) A and B only

    E) A, B, and C

Answer: D
*Topic: Concept 7.1*
*Skill: Comprehension*

16) What is one of the ways that the membranes of winter wheat are able to remain fluid when it is extremely cold?

    A) by increasing the percentage of unsaturated phospholipids in the membrane

    B) by increasing the percentage of cholesterol molecules in the membrane

    C) by decreasing the number of hydrophobic proteins in the membrane

    D) A and B only

    E) A, B, and C

Answer: A
*Topic: Concept 7.1*
*Skill: Comprehension*

17) The surface of an integral membrane protein would be best described as

    A) hydrophilic.

    B) hydrophobic.

    C) amphipathic.

    D) completely covered with phospholipids.

    E) exposed on only one surface of the membrane.

Answer: C
*Topic: Concept 7.1*
*Skill: Comprehension*

18) When a membrane is freeze-fractured, the bilayer splits down the middle between the two layers of phospholipids. In an electron micrograph of a freeze-fractured membrane, the bumps seen on the fractured surface of the membrane are

   A) peripheral proteins.

   B) phospholipids.

   C) carbohydrates.

   D) integral proteins.

   E) cholesterol molecules.

Answer: D
*Topic: Concept 7.1*
*Skill: Comprehension*

19) All of the following are functions of integral membrane proteins *except*

   A) protein synthesis.

   B) active transport.

   C) hormone reception.

   D) cell adhesion.

   E) cytoskeleton attachment.

Answer: A
*Topic: Concept 7.1*
*Skill: Knowledge*

20) Which of the following is a reasonable explanation for why unsaturated fatty acids help keep any membrane more fluid at lower temperatures?

   A) The double bonds form a kink in the fatty acid tail, forcing adjacent lipids to be further apart.

   B) Unsaturated fatty acids have a higher cholesterol content.

   C) Unsaturated fatty acids permit more water in the interior of the membrane.

   D) The double bonds block interaction among the hydrophilic head groups of the lipids.

   E) The double bonds result in a shorter fatty acid tail.

Answer: A
*Topic: Concept 7.1*
*Skill: Comprehension*

21) Which of the following is correct about integral membrane proteins?

   A) They lack tertiary structure.

   B) They are loosely bound to the surface of the bilayer.

   C) They are usually transmembrane proteins.

   D) They are not mobile within the bilayer.

   E) They serve only a structural role in membranes.

Answer: C
*Topic: Concept 7.1*
*Skill: Knowledge*

22) Of the following functions, which is most important for the glycoproteins and glycolipids of animal cell membranes?

A) facilitated diffusion of molecules down their concentration gradients

B) active transport of molecules against their concentration gradients

C) maintaining the integrity of a fluid mosaic membrane

D) maintaining membrane fluidity at low temperatures

E) a cell's ability to distinguish one type of neighboring cell from another

Answer: E
*Topic: Concept 7.1*
*Skill: Comprehension*

23) What is one of the functions of cholesterol in animal cell membranes?

A) facilitates transport of ions

B) stores energy

C) maintains membrane fluidity

D) speeds diffusion

E) phosphorylates ADP

Answer: C
*Topic: Concept 7.1*
*Skill: Knowledge*

24) What membrane–surface molecules are thought to be most important as cells recognize each other?

A) phospholipids

B) integral proteins

C) peripheral proteins

D) cholesterol

E) glycoproteins

Answer: E
*Topic: Concept 7.1*
*Skill: Knowledge*

25) An animal cell lacking oligosaccharides on the external surface of its plasma membrane would likely be impaired in which function?

A) transporting ions against an electrochemical gradient

B) cell–cell recognition

C) maintaining fluidity of the phospholipid bilayer

D) attaching to the cytoskeleton

E) establishing the diffusion barrier to charged molecules

Answer: B
*Topic: Concept 7.1*
*Skill: Application*

26) Which of the following adheres to the extracellular surface of animal cell plasma membranes?

A) fibers of the extracellular matrix

B) fibers of the cytoskeleton

C) the phospholipid bilayer

D) cholesterol

E) carrier proteins

Answer: A
*Topic: Concept 7.1*
*Skill: Knowledge*

27) What kinds of molecules pass through a cell membrane most easily?

A) large and hydrophobic

B) small and hydrophobic

C) large polar

D) ionic

E) monosaccharides such as glucose

Answer: B
*Topic: Concept 7.2*
*Skill: Comprehension*

28) Which of the following is a characteristic feature of a carrier protein in a plasma membrane?

 A) It is a peripheral membrane protein.

 B) It exhibits a specificity for a particular type of molecule.

 C) It requires the expenditure of cellular energy to function.

 D) It works against diffusion.

 E) It has few, if any, hydrophobic amino acids.

Answer: B
*Topic: Concept 7.2*
*Skill: Comprehension*

29) After a membrane freezes and then thaws, it often becomes leaky to solutes. The most reasonable explanation for this is that

 A) transport proteins become nonfunctional during freezing.

 B) the lipid bilayer loses its fluidity when it freezes.

 C) aquaporins can no longer function after freezing.

 D) the integrity of the lipid bilayer is broken when the membrane freezes.

 E) the solubility of most solutes in the cytoplasm decreases on freezing.

Answer: D
*Topic: Concept 7.2*
*Skill: Application*

30) Which of the following would likely move through the lipid bilayer of a plasma membrane most rapidly?

 A) $CO_2$

 B) an amino acid

 C) glucose

 D) $K^+$

 E) starch

Answer: A
*Topic: Concept 7.2*
*Skill: Comprehension*

31) The selective permeability of biological membranes is dependent on which of the following?

 A) the type of transport proteins that are present in the membrane

 B) the lipid bilayer being permeable to primarily small, nonpolar molecules

 C) the types of carbohydrates on the surface of the membrane

 D) A and B only

 E) A, B, and C

Answer: D
*Topic: Concept 7.2*
*Skill: Comprehension*

32) Which of the following statements is *correct* about diffusion?

 A) It is very rapid over long distances.

 B) It requires an expenditure of energy by the cell.

 C) It is a passive process in which molecules move from a region of higher concentration to a region of lower concentration.

 D) It is an active process in which molecules move from a region of lower concentration to one of higher concentration.

 E) It requires integral proteins in the cell membrane.

Answer: C
*Topic: Concept 7.2*
*Skill: Knowledge*

33) Water passes quickly through cell membranes because

    A) the bilayer is hydrophilic.

    B) it moves through hydrophobic channels.

    C) water movement is tied to ATP hydrolysis.

    D) it is a small, polar, charged molecule.

    E) it moves through aquaporins in the membrane.

Answer: E
*Topic: Concept 7.2*
*Skill: Knowledge*

*Use the diagram of the U–tube in Figure 7.2 to answer the questions that follow.*

The solutions in the two arms of this U–tube are separated by a membrane that is permeable to water and glucose but not to sucrose. Side A is half filled with a solution of 2 *M* sucrose and 1 *M* glucose. Side B is half filled with 1 *M* sucrose and 2 *M* glucose. Initially, the liquid levels on both sides are equal.

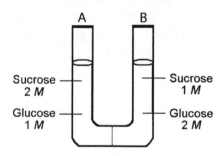

**Figure 7.2**

34) Initially, in terms of tonicity, the solution in side A with respect to that in side B is

    A) hypotonic.

    B) plasmolyzed.

    C) isotonic.

    D) saturated.

    E) hypertonic.

Answer: C
*Topic: Concept 7.3*
*Skill: Comprehension*

35) After the system reaches equilibrium, what changes are observed?

    A) The molarity of sucrose and glucose are equal on both sides.

    B) The molarity of glucose is higher in side A than in side B.

    C) The water level is higher in side A than in side B.

    D) The water level is unchanged.

    E) The water level is higher in side B than in side A.

Answer: C
*Topic: Concept 7.3*
*Skill: Application*

36) A patient has had a serious accident and lost a lot of blood. In an attempt to replenish body fluids, distilled water, equal to the volume of blood lost, is transferred directly into one of his veins. What will be the most probable result of this transfusion?

    A) It will have no unfavorable effect as long as the water is free of viruses and bacteria.

    B) The patient's red blood cells will shrivel up because the blood fluid is hypotonic compared to the cells.

    C) The patient's red blood cells will swell because the blood fluid is hypotonic compared to the cells.

    D) The patient's red blood cells will shrivel up because the blood fluid is hypertonic compared to the cells.

    E) The patient's red blood cells will burst because the blood fluid is hypertonic compared to the cells.

Answer: C
*Topic: Concept 7.3*
*Skill: Comprehension*

37) Celery stalks that are immersed in fresh water for several hours become stiff and hard. Similar stalks left in a salt solution become limp and soft. From this we can deduce that the cells of the celery stalks are

   A) hypotonic to both fresh water and the salt solution.

   B) hypertonic to both fresh water and the salt solution.

   C) hypertonic to fresh water but hypotonic to the salt solution.

   D) hypotonic to fresh water but hypertonic to the salt solution.

   E) isotonic with fresh water but hypotonic to the salt solution.

Answer: C
*Topic: Concept 7.3*
*Skill: Comprehension*

38) A cell whose cytoplasm has a concentration of 0.02 molar glucose is placed in a test tube of water containing 0.02 molar glucose. Assuming that glucose is not actively transported into the cell, which of the following terms describes the tonicity of the external solution relative to the cytoplasm of the cell?

   A) isotonic

   B) hypertonic

   C) hypotonic

   D) flaccid

   E) turgid

Answer: A
*Topic: Concept 7.3*
*Skill: Comprehension*

*Refer to Figure 7.3 to answer the following questions.*

The solutions in the arms of a U–tube are separated at the bottom of the tube by a selectively permeable membrane. The membrane is permeable to sodium chloride but not to glucose. Side A is filled with a solution of 0.4 *M* glucose and 0.5 *M* sodium chloride (NaCl), and side B is filled with a solution containing 0.8 *M* glucose and 0.4 *M* sodium chloride. Initially, the volume in both arms is the same.

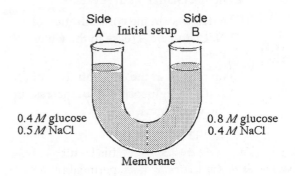

**Figure 7.3**

39) At the beginning of the experiment,

   A) side A is hypertonic to side B.

   B) side A is hypotonic to side B.

   C) side A is isotonic to side B.

   D) side A is hypertonic to side B with respect to glucose.

   E) side A is hypotonic to side B with respect to sodium chloride.

Answer: B
*Topic: Concept 7.3*
*Skill: Application*

40) If you examine side A after 3 days, you should find

A) a decrease in the concentration of NaCl and glucose and an increase in the water level.

B) a decrease in the concentration of NaCl, an increase in water level, and no change in the concentration of glucose.

C) no net change in the system.

D) a decrease in the concentration of NaCl and a decrease in the water level.

E) no change in the concentration of NaCl and glucose and an increase in the water level.

Answer: D
*Topic: Concept 7.3*
*Skill: Application*

41) Which of the following statements *correctly* describes the normal tonicity conditions for typical plant and animal cells?

A) The animal cell is in a hypotonic solution, and the plant cell is in an isotonic solution.

B) The animal cell is in an isotonic solution, and the plant cell is in a hypertonic solution.

C) The animal cell is in a hypertonic solution, and the plant cell is in an isotonic solution.

D) The animal cell is in an isotonic solution, and the plant cell is in a hypotonic solution.

E) The animal cell is in a hypertonic solution, and the plant cell is in a hypotonic solution.

Answer: D
*Topic: Concept 7.3*
*Skill: Comprehension*

*Read the following information and refer to Figure 7.4 to answer the following questions.*

Five dialysis bags, constructed from a semi–permeable membrane that is impermeable to sucrose, were filled with various concentrations of sucrose and then placed in separate beakers containing an initial concentration of 0.6 M sucrose solution. At 10–minute intervals, the bags were massed (weighed) and the percent change in mass of each bag was graphed.

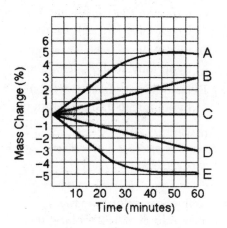

**Figure 7.4**

42) Which line represents the bag that contained a solution isotonic to the 0.6 molar solution at the beginning of the experiment?

Answer: C
*Topic: Concept 7.3*
*Skill: Application*

43) Which line represents the bag with the highest initial concentration of sucrose?

Answer: A
*Topic: Concept 7.3*
*Skill: Application*

44) Which line or lines represent(s) bags that contain a solution that is hypertonic at the end of 60 minutes?

A) A and B

B) B

C) C

D) D

E) D and E

Answer: B
*Topic: Concept 7.3*
*Skill: Application*

45) What is (are) the best explanation(s) for the shape of line E after 50 minutes?

A) The bag is isotonic with the solution around it.

B) Water is entering and leaving the bag at the same rate.

C) Sucrose is entering and leaving the bag at the same rate.

D) A and B only

E) A, B, and C

Answer: D
*Topic: Concept 7.3*
*Skill: Application*

46) You are working on a team that is designing a new drug. In order for this drug to work, it must enter the cytoplasm of specific target cells. Which of the following would *not* be a factor that determines whether the molecule enters the cell?

A) size of the drug molecule

B) polarity of the drug molecule

C) charge on the drug molecule

D) similarity of the drug molecule to other molecules transported by the target cells

E) lipid composition of the target cells' plasma membrane

Answer: E
*Topic: Concept 7.3*
*Skill: Application*

47) All of the following membrane activities require energy from ATP hydrolysis *except*

A) facilitated diffusion.

B) active transport.

C) $Na^+$ ions moving out of the cell.

D) proton pumps.

E) translocation of potassium into a cell.

Answer: A
*Topic: Concept 7.4*
*Skill: Knowledge*

48) What are the membrane structures that function in active transport?

A) peripheral proteins

B) carbohydrates

C) cholesterol

D) cytoskeleton filaments

E) integral proteins

Answer: E
*Topic: Concept 7.4*
*Skill: Knowledge*

49) The movement of a substance across a biological membrane against its concentration gradient with the help of energy input is

A) diffusion.

B) active transport.

C) osmosis.

D) facilitated diffusion.

E) exocytosis.

Answer: B
*Topic: Concept 7.4*
*Skill: Knowledge*

50) Carrier molecules in the membrane and metabolic energy are required for

 A) osmosis.

 B) facilitated diffusion.

 C) active transport.

 D) B and C only

 E) A, B, and C

Answer: C
*Topic: Concept 7.4*
*Skill: Knowledge*

51) Glucose diffuses slowly through artificial phospholipid bilayers. The cells lining the small intestine, however, rapidly move large quantities of glucose from the glucose-rich food into their glucose-poor cytoplasm. Using this information, which transport mechanism is most probably functioning in the intestinal cells?

 A) simple diffusion

 B) phagocytosis

 C) active transport pumps

 D) exocytosis

 E) facilitated diffusion

Answer: E
*Topic: Concept 7.4*
*Skill: Comprehension*

52) The main difference(s) between facilitated diffusion and active transport is (are)

 A) facilitated diffusion moves substances down their concentration gradient and active transport moves them against their gradient.

 B) facilitated diffusion does not rely on cellular energy and active transport does.

 C) facilitated diffusion uses channel or carrier proteins and active transport does not.

 D) A and B only

 E) A, B, and C

Answer: E
*Topic: Concept 7.4*
*Skill: Application*

53) What is the voltage across a membrane called?

 A) water potential

 B) chemical gradient

 C) membrane potential

 D) osmotic potential

 E) electrochemical gradient

Answer: C
*Topic: Concept 7.4*
*Skill: Knowledge*

54) In most cells, there are electrochemical gradients of many ions across the plasma membrane even though there are usually only one or two electrogenic pumps present in the membrane. The gradients of the other ions are most likely accounted for by

 A) cotransport proteins.

 B) ion channels.

 C) carrier proteins.

 D) B and C only

 E) A, B, and C

Answer: A
*Topic: Concept 7.4*
*Skill: Comprehension*

55) The sodium–potassium pump is called an electrogenic pump because it

 A) pumps equal quantities of Na$^+$ and K$^+$ across the membrane.

 B) pumps hydrogen ions out of the cell.

 C) contributes to the membrane potential.

 D) ionizes sodium and potassium atoms.

 E) is used to drive the transport of other molecules against a concentration gradient.

Answer: C
*Topic: Concept 7.4*
*Skill: Knowledge*

56) If a membrane protein in an animal cell is involved in the cotransport of glucose and sodium ions into the cell, which of the following is most likely *not* true?

 A) The sodium ions are moving down their electrochemical gradient.

 B) Glucose is entering the cell against its concentration gradient.

 C) Sodium ions can move down their electrochemical gradient through the cotransporter whether or not glucose is present outside the cell.

 D) The higher sodium ion concentration outside the cell is the result of an electrogenic pump.

 E) A substance that blocked sodium ions from binding to the cotransport protein would also block the transport of glucose.

Answer: C
*Topic: Concept 7.4*
*Skill: Application*

57) The movement of potassium into an animal cell requires

 A) low cellular concentrations of sodium.

 B) high cellular concentrations of potassium.

 C) an energy source such as ATP or a proton gradient.

 D) a cotransport protein.

 E) a gradient of protons across the plasma membrane.

Answer: C
*Topic: Concept 7.4*
*Skill: Comprehension*

58) Ions diffuse across membranes down their

 A) chemical gradients.

 B) concentration gradients.

 C) electrical gradients.

 D) electrochemical gradients.

 E) A and B are correct.

Answer: D
*Topic: Concept 7.4*
*Skill: Knowledge*

59) Which of the following characterizes the sodium–potassium pump?

 A) Sodium ions are pumped out of a cell against their gradient.

 B) Potassium ions are pumped into a cell against their gradient.

 C) The pump protein undergoes a conformational change.

 D) Only A and B are correct.

 E) A, B, and C are all correct.

Answer: E
*Topic: Concept 7.4*
*Skill: Comprehension*

60) What mechanisms do plants use to load sucrose produced by photosynthesis into specialized cells in the veins of leaves?

  A) an electrogenic pump

  B) a proton pump

  C) a contransport protein

  D) A and C only

  E) A, B, and C

Answer: E
*Topic: Concept 7.4*
*Skill: Comprehension*

61) The sodium–potassium pump in animal cells requires cytoplasmic ATP to pump ions across the plasma membrane. When the proteins of the pump are first synthesized in the rough ER, what side of the ER membrane will the ATP binding site be on?

  A) It will be on the cytoplasmic side of the ER.

  B) It will be on the side facing the interior of the ER.

  C) It could be facing in either direction because the orientation of proteins is scrambled in the Golgi apparatus.

  D) It doesn't matter, because the pump is not active in the ER.

  E) Not enough information is provided to answer this question.

Answer: A
*Topic: Concept 7.4*
*Skill: Application*

62) Which of the following statements about membrane structure and function is *false*?

  A) Diffusion of gases is faster in air than across membranes.

  B) Diffusion, osmosis, and facilitated diffusion do not require any direct energy input from the cell.

  C) The types of proteins that are exposed on one side of a membrane are nearly identical to those exposed on the other side of the membrane.

  D) Voltage across the membrane depends on an unequal distribution of ions across the plasma membrane.

  E) Special membrane proteins can cotransport two solutes by coupling diffusion down a concentration gradient to transport against the concentration gradient.

Answer: C
*Topic: Concept 7.4*
*Skill: Comprehension*

63) All of the following processes take material into cells *except*

  A) pinocytosis.

  B) endocytosis.

  C) exocytosis.

  D) active transport.

  E) carrier–facilitated diffusion.

Answer: C
*Topic: Concept 7.5*
*Skill: Knowledge*

64) An organism with a cell wall would have the most difficulty doing which process?

  A) diffusion

  B) osmosis

  C) active transport

  D) phagocytosis

  E) exocytosis

Answer: D
*Topic: Concept 7.5*
*Skill: Comprehension*

65) The membrane activity most nearly opposite to exocytosis is
   A) plasmolysis.
   B) osmosis.
   C) facilitated diffusion.
   D) phagocytosis.
   E) active transport.

Answer: D
*Topic: Concept 7.5*
*Skill: Knowledge*

66) White blood cells engulf bacteria through what process?
   A) exocytosis
   B) phagocytosis
   C) pinocytosis
   D) osmosis
   E) receptor-mediated exocytosis

Answer: B
*Topic: Concept 7.5*
*Skill: Knowledge*

67) What is the cause of familial hypercholesterolemia?
   A) defective LDL receptors on the cell membranes
   B) poor attachment of the cholesterol to the extracellular matrix of cells
   C) a poorly formed lipid bilayer that cannot incorporate cholesterol into cell membranes
   D) inhibition of the cholesterol active transport system in red blood cells
   E) a general lack of glycolipids in the blood cell membranes

Answer: A
*Topic: Concept 7.5*
*Skill: Knowledge*

68) In addition to exporting materials from the cytoplasm of the cell, the process of exocytosis is also important in
   A) the production of cell walls by plant cells.
   B) the increase in the size of cells.
   C) maintaining the osmotic balance between the cytoplasm and the cell exterior.
   D) A and B only
   E) A, B, and C

Answer: A
*Topic: Concept 7.5*
*Skill: Comprehension*

69) The difference between pinocytosis and receptor-mediated endocytosis is that
   A) pinocytosis brings only water into the cell, but receptor-mediated endocytosis brings in other molecules as well.
   B) pinocytosis increases the surface area of the plasma membrane whereas receptor-mediated endocytosis decreases the plasma membrane surface area.
   C) pinocytosis is nonselective in the molecules it brings into the cell, whereas receptor-mediated endocytosis offers more selectivity.
   D) pinocytosis requires cellular energy, but receptor-mediated endocytosis does not.
   E) pinocytosis can concentrate substances from the extracellular fluid, but receptor-mediated endocytosis cannot.

Answer: A
*Topic: Concept 7.5*
*Skill: Comprehension*

# Media Activity Questions

1) The interior of the phospholipid bilayer is

   A) composed of fatty acids.

   B) hydrophobic.

   C) composed of cholesterol.

   D) hydrophilic.

   E) water.

   Answer: B
   *Topic: Activity: Selective Permeability of Membranes*

2) Oxygen crosses a plasma membrane by

   A) osmosis.

   B) phagocytosis.

   C) active transport.

   D) pinocytosis.

   E) passive transport.

   Answer: E
   *Topic: Web/CD Activity: Diffusion*

3) In a hypotonic solution an animal cell will

   A) lyse.

   B) experience turgor.

   C) neither gain nor lose water.

   D) shrivel.

   E) lose water.

   Answer: A
   *Topic: Web/CD Activity: Osmosis and Water Balance*

4) Endocytosis moves materials _____ a cell via _____.

   A) into; facilitated diffusion

   B) into; membranous vesicles

   C) into; a transport protein

   D) out of; diffusion

   E) out of; membranous vesicles

   Answer: B
   *Topic: Web/CD Activity: Exocytosis and Endocytosis*

5) Cholesterol enters cells via

   A) phagocytosis.

   B) osmosis.

   C) receptor-mediated endocytosis.

   D) exocytosis.

   E) pinocytosis.

   Answer: C
   *Topic: Web/CD Activity: Exocytosis and Endocytosis*

# Self-Quiz Questions

1) In what way do the various membranes of a eukaryotic cell differ?

   A) Phospholipids are found only in certain membranes.

   B) Certain proteins are unique to each membrane.

   C) Only certain membranes of the cell are selectively permeable.

   D) Only certain membranes are constructed from amphipathic molecules.

   E) Some membranes have hydrophobic surfaces exposed to the cytoplasm, while others have hydrophilic surfaces facing the cytoplasm.

   Answer: B

2) According to the fluid mosaic model of membrane structure, proteins of the membrane are mostly

   A) spread in a continuous layer over the inner and outer surfaces of the membrane.

   B) confined to the hydrophobic core of the membrane.

   C) embedded in a lipid bilayer.

   D) randomly oriented in the membrane, with no fixed inside-outside polarity.

   E) free to depart from the fluid membrane and dissolve in the surrounding solution.

   Answer: C

3) Which of the following factors would tend to increase membrane fluidity?

   A) a greater proportion of unsaturated phospholipids

   B) a greater proportion of saturated phospholipids

   C) a lower temperature

   D) a relatively high protein content in the membrane

   E) a greater proportion of relatively large glycolipids compared to lipids having smaller molecular masses

   Answer: A

4) Which of the following processes includes all others?

   A) osmosis

   B) diffusion of a solute across a membrane

   C) facilitated diffusion

   D) passive transport

   E) transport of an ion down its electrochemical gradient

   Answer: D

5) Based on the model of sucrose uptake in Figure 7.19 (in the text), which of the following experimental treatments would increase the rate of sucrose transport into the cell?

   A) decreasing extracellular sucrose concentration

   B) decreasing extracellular pH

   C) decreasing cytoplasmic pH

   D) adding an inhibitor that blocks the regeneration of ATP

   E) adding a substance that makes the membrane more permeable to hydrogen ions

   Answer: B

# Chapter 8   An Introduction to Metabolism

1) Which of the following describe(s) some aspect of metabolism?
   A) synthesis of macromolecules
   B) breakdown of macromolecules
   C) control of enzyme activity
   D) A and B only
   E) A, B, and C

   Answer: E
   *Topic: Concept 8.1*
   *Skill: Knowledge*

2) Which term most precisely describes the cellular process of breaking down large molecules into smaller ones?
   A) catalysis
   B) metabolism
   C) anabolism
   D) dehydration
   E) catabolism

   Answer: E
   *Topic: Concept 8.1*
   *Skill: Knowledge*

3) Which of the following statements correctly describe(s) catabolic pathways?
   A) They do not depend on enzymes.
   B) They consume energy to build up polymers from monomers.
   C) They release energy as they degrade polymers to monomers.
   D) They lead to the synthesis of catabolic compounds.
   E) both A and B

   Answer: C
   *Topic: Concept 8.1*
   *Skill: Knowledge*

4) Which of the following is (are) *true* for anabolic pathways?
   A) They do not depend on enzymes.
   B) They are highly regulated sequences of chemical reactions.
   C) They consume energy to build up polymers from monomers.
   D) They release energy as they degrade polymers to monomers.
   E) both B and C

   Answer: E
   *Topic: Concept 8.1*
   *Skill: Knowledge*

5) Which of the following is a statement of the first law of thermodynamics?
   A) Energy cannot be created or destroyed.
   B) The entropy of the universe is decreasing.
   C) The entropy of the universe is constant.
   D) Kinetic energy is stored energy that results from the specific arrangement of matter.
   E) Energy cannot be transferred or transformed.

   Answer: A
   *Topic: Concept 8.1*
   *Skill: Knowledge*

6) The first law of thermodynamics states that energy can be neither created nor destroyed. For living organisms, which of the following is an important consequence of the first law?

A) The energy content of an organism is constant.

B) The organism ultimately must obtain all of the necessary energy for life from its environment.

C) The entropy of an organism decreases with time as the organism grows in complexity.

D) Organisms are unable to transform energy.

E) Life does not obey the first law of thermodynamics.

Answer: B
*Topic: Concept 8.1*
*Skill: Application*

7) According to the first law of thermodynamics,

A) the universe loses energy because of heat production.

B) systems rich in energy are intrinsically unstable and will give up energy with time.

C) energy can be neither created nor destroyed.

D) A and B only

E) A, B, and C

Answer: C
*Topic: Concept 8.1*
*Skill: Comprehension*

8) Living organisms increase in complexity as they grow, resulting in a decrease in the entropy of an organism. How does this relate to the second law of thermodynamics?

A) Living organisms do not obey the second law of thermodynamics, which states that entropy must increase with time.

B) Life obeys the second law of thermodynamics because the decrease in entropy as the organism grows is balanced by an increase in the entropy of the universe.

C) Living organisms do not follow the laws of thermodynamics.

D) As a consequence of growing, organisms create more disorder in their environment than the decrease in entropy associated with their growth.

E) Living organisms are able to transform energy into entropy.

Answer: D
*Topic: Concept 8.1*
*Skill: Application*

9) Which of the following statements about metabolism is *incorrect*?

A) Metabolism is an emergent property of life at the level of organisms.

B) Metabolism manages the utilization of materials and energy resources.

C) The uptake of water associated with the hydrolysis of biological polymers is part of metabolism.

D) Metabolism depends on a constant supply of energy.

E) None of these statements about metabolism is incorrect.

Answer: A
*Topic: Concept 8.1*
*Skill: Comprehension*

10) Whenever energy is transformed, there is always an increase in the

   A) free energy of the system.

   B) free energy of the universe.

   C) entropy of the system.

   D) entropy of the universe.

   E) enthalpy of the universe.

Answer: D
*Topic: Concept 8.1*
*Skill: Comprehension*

11) Which of the following statements is a logical consequence of the second law of thermodynamics?

   A) If the entropy of a system increases, there must be a corresponding decrease in the entropy of the universe.

   B) If there is an increase in the energy of a system, there must be a corresponding decrease in the energy of the rest of the universe.

   C) Every energy transfer requires activation energy from the environment.

   D) Every chemical reaction must increase the total entropy of the universe.

   E) Energy can be transferred or transformed, but it cannot be created or destroyed.

Answer: D
*Topic: Concept 8.1*
*Skill: Comprehension*

12) Which of the following statements correctly describe(s) some aspect of energy in living organisms?

   A) Living organisms can convert energy among several different forms.

   B) Living organisms can use energy to do work.

   C) Organisms expend energy in order to decrease their entropy

   D) A and B only

   E) A, B, and C

Answer: E
*Topic: Concept 8.1*
*Skill: Comprehension*

13) Which of the following statements is *not* representative of the second law of thermodynamics?

   A) Conversion of energy from one form to another is always accompanied by some loss of free energy.

   B) Heat represents a form of energy that cannot be used by most organisms to do work.

   C) Without an input of energy, organisms would tend towards increasing entropy.

   D) Cells require a constant input of energy to maintain their high level of organization.

   E) Every energy transformation by a cell decreases the entropy of the universe.

Answer: E
*Topic: Concept 8.1*
*Skill: Comprehension*

14) Which of the following forms of energy is least available to accomplish cellular work?

    A) light energy

    B) electrical energy

    C) thermal energy (heat)

    D) mechanical energy

    E) potential energy

Answer: C
*Topic: Concept 8.1*
*Skill: Knowledge*

15) Which of the following types of reactions would decrease the entropy within a cell?

    A) dehydration reactions

    B) hydrolysis

    C) respiration

    D) digestion

    E) catabolism

Answer: A
*Topic: Concept 8.1*
*Skill: Comprehension*

16) According to the second law of thermodynamics, which of the following statements is *incorrect*?

    A) The synthesis of large molecules from small molecules is exergonic.

    B) Earth is an open system.

    C) Life exists at the expense of energy derived from its environment.

    D) A living cell can never function as a closed system.

    E) Every chemical reaction in a cell results in a loss of free energy.

Answer: A
*Topic: Concept 8.1*
*Skill: Comprehension*

17) The organization of organisms has become increasingly complex with time. This statement

    A) is consistent with the second law of thermodynamics.

    B) requires that due to evolution, the entropy of the universe increased.

    C) is based on the fact that organisms function as closed systems.

    D) A and B only

    E) A, B, and C

Answer: A
*Topic: Concept 8.1*
*Skill: Comprehension*

18) The mathematical expression for the change in free energy of a system is: $\Delta G = \Delta H - T\Delta S$. Which of the following is (are) *incorrect*?

    A) $\Delta S$ is the change in entropy, a measure of randomness.

    B) $\Delta H$ is the change in enthalpy, the energy available to do work.

    C) $\Delta G$ is the change in free energy.

    D) $T$ is the absolute temperature.

    E) both A and B

Answer: B
*Topic: Concept 8.2*
*Skill: Knowledge*

19) What is the change in free energy of a system at chemical equilibrium?

    A) slightly increasing

    B) greatly increasing

    C) slightly decreasing

    D) greatly decreasing

    E) no net change

Answer: E
*Topic: Concept 8.2*
*Skill: Knowledge*

20) Which of the following is *true* for all exergonic reactions?

A) The products have more total energy than the reactants.

B) The reaction proceeds with a net release of free energy.

C) Some reactants will be converted to products.

D) A net input of energy from the surroundings is required for the reactions to proceed.

E) The reactions are nonspontaneous.

Answer: B
*Topic: Concept 8.2*
*Skill: Comprehension*

21) Chemical equilibrium is relatively rare in living cells. Which of the following *could* be an example of a reaction at chemical equilibrium in a cell?

A) a reaction in which the free energy at equilibrium is higher than the energy content at any point away from equilibrium

B) a chemical reaction in which the entropy change in the reaction is just balanced by an opposite entropy change in the cell's surroundings

C) an endergonic reaction in an active metabolic pathway where the energy for that reaction is supplied only by heat from the environment

D) a chemical reaction in which both the reactants and products are only used in a metabolic pathway that is completely inactive

E) There is no possibility of having chemical equilibrium in any living cell.

Answer: D
*Topic: Concept 8.2*
*Skill: Application*

22) Which of the following shows the correct changes in thermodynamic properties for a chemical reaction in which amino acids are linked to form a protein?

A) $+\Delta H, +\Delta S, +\Delta G$

B) $+\Delta H, -\Delta S, -\Delta G$

C) $+\Delta H, -\Delta S, +\Delta G$

D) $-\Delta H, -\Delta S, +\Delta G$

E) $-\Delta H, +\Delta S, +\Delta G$

Answer: C
*Topic: Concept 8.2*
*Skill: Comprehension*

23) When glucose monomers are joined together by glycosidic linkages to form a cellulose polymer, the changes in free energy, total energy, and entropy are as follows:

A) $+\Delta G, +\Delta H, +\Delta S$

B) $+\Delta G, +\Delta H, -\Delta S$

C) $+\Delta G, -\Delta H, -\Delta S$

D) $-\Delta G, +\Delta H, +\Delta S$

E) $-\Delta G, -\Delta H, -\Delta S$

Answer: B
*Topic: Concept 8.2*
*Skill: Comprehension*

24) A chemical reaction that has a positive $\Delta G$ is correctly described as

A) endergonic.

B) endothermic.

C) enthalpic.

D) spontaneous.

E) exothermic.

Answer: A
*Topic: Concept 8.2*
*Skill: Knowledge*

25) Why is ATP an important molecule in metabolism?

A) Its hydrolysis provides an input of free energy for exergonic reactions.

B) It provides energy coupling between exergonic and endergonic reactions.

C) Its terminal phosphate group contains a strong covalent bond that when hydrolyzed releases free energy.

D) A and B only

E) A, B and C

Answer: B
*Topic: Concept 8.3*
*Skill: Comprehension*

26) The hydrolysis of ATP to ADP and inorganic phosphate (ATP + $H_2O \rightarrow$ ADP + $P_i$)

A) has a $\Delta G$ of about –7 kcal/mol under standard conditions.

B) involves hydrolysis of a terminal phosphate bond of ATP.

C) can occur spontaneously under appropriate conditions.

D) Only A and B are correct.

E) A, B, and C are correct.

Answer: E
*Topic: Concept 8.3*
*Skill: Knowledge*

27) When 10,000 molecules of ATP are hydrolyzed to ADP and $P_i$ in a test tube, about twice as much heat is liberated as when a cell hydrolyzes the same amount of ATP. Which of the following is the best explanation for this observation?

A) Cells are open systems, but a test tube is a closed system.

B) Cells are less efficient at heat production than nonliving systems.

C) The hydrolysis of ATP in a cell produces different chemical products than does the reaction in a test tube.

D) The reaction in cells must be catalyzed by enzymes, but the reaction in a test tube does not need enzymes.

E) Cells convert some of the energy of ATP hydrolysis into other forms of energy besides heat.

Answer: E
*Topic: Concept 8.3*
*Skill: Application*

28) ATP generally energizes a cellular process by

A) releasing heat upon hydrolysis.

B) acting as a catalyst.

C) coupling free energy released by ATP hydrolysis to free energy needed by other reactions.

D) breaking a high–energy bond.

E) binding directly to the substrate(s) of the enzyme.

Answer: C
*Topic: Concept 8.3*
*Skill: Comprehension*

29) Which of the following reactions is most likely to be coupled to the reaction ATP + $H_2O \rightarrow ADP + P_i$ ($\Delta G = -7.3$ kcal/mol)?

A) $A + P_i \rightarrow AP$ ($\Delta G = +10$ kcal/mol)

B) $B + P_i \rightarrow BP$ ($\Delta G = +8$ kcal/mol)

C) $CP \rightarrow C + P_i$ ($\Delta G = -4$ kcal/mol)

D) $DP \rightarrow D + P_i$ ($\Delta G = -10$ kcal/mol)

E) $E + P_i \rightarrow EP$ ($\Delta G = +5$ kcal/mol)

Answer: E
*Topic: Concept 8.3*
*Skill: Comprehension*

30) Which of the following is most similar in structure to ATP?

A) an anabolic steroid

B) a DNA helix

C) RNA nucleotides

D) an amino acid with three phosphate groups attached

E) a phospholipid

Answer: C
*Topic: Concept 8.3*
*Skill: Comprehension*

31) What term is used to describe the transfer of free energy from catabolic pathways to anabolic pathways?

A) feedback regulation

B) bioenergetics

C) energy coupling

D) entropy

E) cooperativity

Answer: C
*Topic: Concept 8.3*
*Skill: Knowledge*

32) Which of the following statements is *true* concerning catabolic pathways?

A) They combine molecules into more energy–rich molecules.

B) They are usually coupled with anabolic pathways to which they supply energy in the form of ATP.

C) They are endergonic.

D) They are spontaneous and do not need enzyme catalysis.

E) They build up complex molecules such as protein from simpler compounds.

Answer: B
*Topic: Concept 8.3*
*Skill: Comprehension*

33) Which of the following statements regarding ATP is (are) correct?

A) ATP serves as a main energy shuttle inside cells.

B) ATP drives endergonic reactions in the cell by the enzymatic transfer of the phosphate group to specific reactants.

C) The regeneration of ATP from ADP and phosphate is an endergonic reaction.

D) A and B only

E) A, B, and C

Answer: E
*Topic: Concept 8.3*
*Skill: Knowledge*

34) Which of the following statements is (are) *true* about enzyme–catalyzed reactions?

A) The reaction is faster than the same reaction in the absence of the enzyme.

B) The free energy change of the reaction is the same as the reaction in the absence of the enzyme.

C) The reaction always goes in the direction toward chemical equilibrium.

D) A and B only

E) A, B, and C

Answer: A
*Topic: Concept 8.4*
*Skill: Comprehension*

35) How can one increase the rate of a chemical reaction?

A) Increase the activation energy needed.

B) Cool the reactants.

C) Decrease the concentration of the reactants.

D) Add a catalyst.

E) Increase the entropy of the reactants.

Answer: D
*Topic: Concept 8.4*
*Skill: Comprehension*

36) Sucrose is a disaccharide, composed of the monosaccharides glucose and fructose. The hydrolysis of sucrose by the enzyme sucrase results in

A) bringing glucose and fructose together to form sucrose.

B) the release of water from sucrose as the bond between glucose and fructose is broken.

C) breaking the bond between glucose and fructose and forming new bonds from the atoms of water.

D) production of water from the sugar as bonds are broken between the glucose monomers.

E) utilization of water as a covalent bond is formed between glucose and fructose to form sucrase.

Answer: C
*Topic: Concept 8.4*
*Skill: Application*

37) Reactants capable of interacting to form products in a chemical reaction must first overcome a thermodynamic barrier known as the reaction's

A) entropy.

B) activation energy.

C) endothermic level.

D) heat content.

E) free–energy content.

Answer: B
*Topic: Concept 8.4*
*Skill: Knowledge*

38) A solution of starch at room temperature does not readily decompose to form a solution of simple sugars because

A) the starch solution has less free energy than the sugar solution.

B) the hydrolysis of starch to sugar is endergonic.

C) the activation energy barrier for this reaction cannot be surmounted.

D) starch cannot be hydrolyzed in the presence of so much water.

E) starch hydrolysis is nonspontaneous.

Answer: C
*Topic: Concept 8.4*
*Skill: Comprehension*

39) Which of the following statements regarding enzymes is *true*?

A) Enzymes decrease the free energy change of a reaction.

B) Enzymes increase the rate of a reaction.

C) Enzymes change the direction of chemical reactions.

D) Enzymes are permanently altered by the reactions they catalyze.

E) Enzymes prevent changes in substrate concentrations.

Answer: B
*Topic: Concept 8.4*
*Skill: Knowledge*

40) Which of the following is *not* true of enzymes?

A) Enzyme catalysis is dependent on the pH and temperature of the reaction environment.

B) Enzyme catalysis is dependent on the three-dimensional structure or conformation of the enzyme.

C) Enzymes provide activation energy for the reaction they catalyze.

D) Enzymes are composed primarily of protein, but they may bind nonprotein cofactors.

E) Enzyme activity can be inhibited if the enzyme's allosteric site is bound with a noncompetitive inhibitor.

Answer: C
*Topic: Concept 8.4*
*Skill: Knowledge*

41) An enzyme catalyzes a reaction by

A) supplying the energy to speed up a reaction.

B) lowering the energy of activation of a reaction.

C) lowering the $\Delta G$ of a reaction.

D) changing the equilibrium of a spontaneous reaction.

E) increasing the amount of free energy of a reaction.

Answer: B
*Topic: Concept 8.4*
*Skill: Knowledge*

42) Which of these statements regarding enzymes is *false*?

   A) Enzymes are proteins that function as catalysts.

   B) Enzymes display specificity for certain molecules with which they interact.

   C) Enzymes provide activation energy for the reactions they catalyze.

   D) The activity of enzymes can be regulated by other molecules.

   E) An enzyme may be used many times over for a specific reaction.

Answer: C
*Topic: Concept 8.4*
*Skill: Knowledge*

43) During a laboratory experiment, you discover that an enzyme–catalyzed reaction has a ΔG of –20 kcal/mol. If you double the amount of enzyme in the reaction, what will be the ΔG for the new reaction?

   A) –40 kcal/mol

   B) –20 kcal/mol

   C) 0 kcal/mol

   D) +20 kcal/mol

   E) +40 kcal/mol

Answer: B
*Topic: Concept 8.4*
*Skill: Comprehension*

44) The active site of an enzyme is the region that

   A) binds allosteric regulators of the enzyme.

   B) is involved in the catalytic reaction of the enzyme.

   C) binds the products of the catalytic reaction.

   D) is inhibited by the presence of a coenzyme or a cofactor.

   E) both A and B

Answer: B
*Topic: Concept 8.4*
*Skill: Knowledge*

45) According to the induced fit hypothesis of enzyme catalysis, which of the following is *correct*?

   A) The binding of the substrate depends on the shape of the active site.

   B) Some enzymes change their structure when activators bind to the enzyme.

   C) A competitive inhibitor can outcompete the substrate for the active site.

   D) The binding of the substrate changes the shape of the enzyme's active site.

   E) The active site creates a microenvironment ideal for the reaction.

Answer: D
*Topic: Concept 8.4*
*Skill: Comprehension*

46) Many different things can alter enzyme activity. Which of the following underlie all types of enzyme regulation?

    A) changes in the activation energy of the reaction

    B) changes in the active site of the enzyme

    C) changes in the free energy of the reaction

    D) A and B only

    E) A, B, and C

Answer: D
*Topic: Concept 8.4*
*Skill: Application*

*Refer to Figure 8.1 to answer the following questions.*

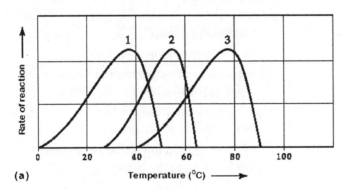

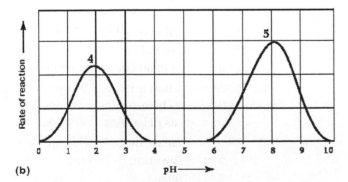

**Figure 8.1**

47) Which curve represents the behavior of an enzyme taken from a bacterium that lives in hot springs at temperatures of 70°C or higher?

    A) curve 1

    B) curve 2

    C) curve 3

    D) curve 4

    E) curve 5

Answer: C
*Topic: Concept 8.4*
*Skill: Knowledge*

48) Which curve was most likely generated from analysis of an enzyme from a human stomach where conditions are strongly acid?

    A) curve 1

    B) curve 2

    C) curve 3

    D) curve 4

    E) curve 5

Answer: D
*Topic: Concept 8.4*
*Skill: Knowledge*

49) Which curve was most likely generated from an enzyme that requires a cofactor?

    A) curve 1

    B) curve 2

    C) curve 4

    D) curve 5

    E) It is not possible to determine whether an enzyme requires a cofactor from these data.

Answer: E
*Topic: Concept 8.4*
*Skill: Comprehension*

50) As temperature decreases, the rate of an enzyme–catalyzed reaction also decreases. Which of the following explain(s) why this occurs?

A) Fewer substrates have sufficient energy to get over the activation energy barrier.

B) Motion in the active site of the enzyme is slowed, thus slowing the catalysis of the enzyme.

C) The motion of the substrate molecules decreases, allowing them to bind more easily to the active site.

D) A and B only

E) A, B, and C

Answer: D
*Topic: Concept 8.4*
*Skill: Application*

51) ATP is often an allosteric inhibitor of key enzymes in catabolic pathways. Which of the following statements is *inconsistent* with the role of ATP?

A) ATP couples energy production in catabolic pathways to energy demand in anabolic pathways.

B) When ATP levels are high in the cell, it is an indication that energy supply from catabolic reactions exceeds energy demand by anabolic reactions.

C) The binding of ATP to allosteric sites on enzymes of the catabolic pathway decreases the production of ATP by the pathway.

D) Increasing availability of ATP increases the energy available to drive endergonic reactions.

E) When ATP levels are low in the cell, there is no inhibition of the catabolic pathway and ATP production is at a maximum.

Answer: D
*Topic: Concept 8.4*
*Skill: Application*

52) Increasing the substrate concentration in an enzymatic reaction could overcome which of the following?

A) denaturization of the enzyme

B) allosteric inhibition

C) competitive inhibition

D) saturation of the enzyme activity

E) insufficient cofactors

Answer: C
*Topic: Concept 8.4*
*Skill: Comprehension*

53) What is a nonprotein "helper" of an enzyme molecule called?

A) accessory enzyme

B) allosteric group

C) coenzyme

D) functional group

E) enzyme activator

Answer: C
*Topic: Concept 8.4*
*Skill: Knowledge*

54) Which of the following is true of enzymes?

A) Enzymes may require a nonprotein cofactor or ion for catalysis to take place.

B) Enzyme function is reduced if the three-dimensional structure or conformation of an enzyme is altered.

C) Enzyme function is influenced by physical and chemical environmental factors such as pH and temperature.

D) Enzymes increase the rate of chemical reaction by lowering activation energy barriers.

E) All of the above are true of enzymes.

Answer: E
*Topic: Concept 8.4*
*Skill: Knowledge*

55) Zinc, an essential trace element for most organisms, is present in the active site of the enzyme carboxypeptidase. The zinc most likely functions as a(n)

A) competitive inhibitor of the enzyme.

B) noncompetitive inhibitor of the enzyme.

C) allosteric activator of the enzyme.

D) cofactor necessary for enzyme activity.

E) coenzyme derived from a vitamin.

Answer: D
*Topic: Concept 8.4*
*Skill: Knowledge*

56) Consider the following: Succinate dehydrogenase catalyzes the conversion of succinate to fumarate. The reaction is inhibited by malonic acid, which resembles succinate but cannot be acted upon by succinate dehydrogenase. Increasing the ratio of succinate to malonic acid reduces the inhibitory effect of malonic acid. Which of the following is correct?

A) Succinate dehydrogenase is the enzyme, and fumarate is the substrate.

B) Succinate dehydrogenase is the enzyme, and malonic acid is the substrate.

C) Succinate is the substrate, and fumarate is the product.

D) Fumarate is the product, and malonic acid is a noncompetitive inhibitor.

E) Malonic acid is the product, and fumarate is a competitive inhibitor.

Answer: C
*Topic: Concept 8.4*
*Skill: Comprehension*

*The following questions are based on the reaction A + B → C + D shown in Figure 8.2*

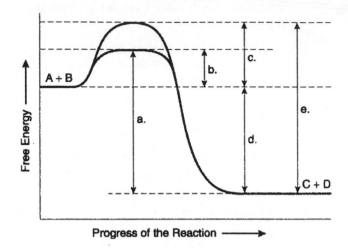

**Figure 8.2**

57) Which of the following terms best describes the reaction?

A) endergonic

B) exergonic

C) anabolic

D) allosteric

E) nonspontaneous

Answer: B
*Topic: Concept 8.4*
*Skill: Knowledge*

58) Which of the following represents the $\Delta G$ of the reaction?

A) a

B) b

C) c

D) d

E) e

Answer: D
*Topic: Concept 8.4*
*Skill: Knowledge*

59) Which of the following would be the same in an enzyme-catalyzed or noncatalyzed reaction?

    A) a

    B) b

    C) c

    D) d

    E) e

Answer: D
*Topic: Concept 8.4*
*Skill: Comprehension*

60) Which of the following bests describes the reaction?

    A) negative $\Delta G$, spontaneous

    B) positive $\Delta G$, nonspontaneous

    C) positive $\Delta G$, exergonic

    D) negative $\Delta G$, endergonic

    E) $\Delta G$ of zero, chemical equilibrium

Answer: A
*Topic: Concept 8.4*
*Skill: Comprehension*

61) Which of the following represents the difference between the free-energy content of the reaction and the free-energy content of the products?

    A) a

    B) b

    C) c

    D) d

    E) e

Answer: D
*Topic: Concept 8.4*
*Skill: Knowledge*

62) Which of the following represents the activation energy required for the enzyme-catalyzed reaction?

    A) a

    B) b

    C) c

    D) d

    E) e

Answer: B
*Topic: Concept 8.4*
*Skill: Comprehension*

63) Which of the following represents the activation energy required for a noncatalyzed reaction?

    A) a

    B) b

    C) c

    D) d

    E) e

Answer: C
*Topic: Concept 8.4*
*Skill: Knowledge*

64) Which *best* describes the reaction?

    A) The amount of free energy initially present in the reactants is indicated by "a."

    B) The amount of free energy present in the products is indicated by "e."

    C) The amount of free energy released as a result of the noncatalyzed reaction is indicated by "c."

    D) The amount of free energy released as a result of the catalyzed reaction is indicated by "d."

    E) The difference between "b" and "c" is the activation energy added by the presence of the enzyme.

Answer: D
*Topic: Concept 8.4*
*Skill: Comprehension*

65) Assume that the reaction has a $\Delta G$ of –5.6 kcal/mol. Which of the following would be true?

   A) The reaction could be coupled to power an endergonic reaction with a $\Delta G$ of +6.2 kcal/mol.

   B) The reaction could be coupled to power an exergonic reaction with a $\Delta G$ of +8.8 kcal/mol.

   C) The reaction would result in a decrease in entropy ($S$) and an increase in the total energy content ($H$) of the system.

   D) The reaction would result in an increase in entropy ($S$) and a decrease in the total energy content ($H$) of the system.

   E) The reaction would result in products ($C + D$) with a greater free–energy content than in the initial reactants ($A + B$).

Answer: D
*Topic: Concept 8.4*
*Skill: Comprehension*

*The next questions are based on the following information.*

A series of enzymes catalyze the reaction $X \rightarrow Y \rightarrow Z \rightarrow A$. Product A binds to the enzyme that converts X to Y at a position remote from its active site. This binding decreases the activity of the enzyme.

66) What is substance X?

   A) a coenzyme

   B) an allosteric inhibitor

   C) a substrate

   D) an intermediate

   E) the product

Answer: C
*Topic: Concept 8.5*
*Skill: Comprehension*

67) Substance A functions as

   A) a coenzyme.

   B) an allosteric inhibitor.

   C) the substrate.

   D) an intermediate.

   E) a competitive inhibitor.

Answer: B
*Topic: Concept 8.5*
*Skill: Comprehension*

68) The mechanism in which the end product of a metabolic pathway inhibits an earlier step in the pathway is known as

   A) metabolic inhibition.

   B) feedback inhibition.

   C) allosteric inhibition.

   D) noncooperative inhibition.

   E) reversible inhibition.

Answer: B
*Topic: Concept 8.5*
*Skill: Knowledge*

69) The regulation of enzyme function is an important aspect of cell metabolism. Which of the following is *least* likely to be a mechanism for enzyme regulation?

   A) allosteric regulation

   B) cooperativity

   C) feedback inhibition

   D) removing cofactors

   E) reversible inhibition

Answer: D
*Topic: Concept 8.5*
*Skill: Comprehension*

70) Which of the following statements is *true* regarding enzyme cooperativity?

 A) A multi-enzyme complex contains all the enzymes of a metabolic pathway.

 B) A product of a pathway serves as a competitive inhibitor of an early enzyme in the pathway.

 C) A substrate molecule bound to an active site affects the active site of several subunits.

 D) Several substrate molecules can be catalyzed by the same enzyme.

 E) A substrate binds to an active site and inhibits cooperation between enzymes in a pathway.

Answer: C
*Topic: Concept 8.5*
*Skill: Knowledge*

71) How does a non-competitive inhibitor decrease the rate of an enzyme reaction?

 A) by binding at the active site of the enzyme

 B) by changing the structure of the enzyme

 C) by changing the free energy change of the reaction

 D) by acting as a coenzyme for the reaction

 E) by decreasing the activation energy of the reaction

Answer: B
*Topic: Concept 8.5*
*Skill: Knowledge*

*Use Figure 8.3 to answer the following questions.*

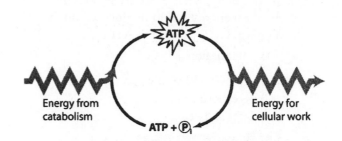

**Figure 8.3**

72) Which of the following statements correctly indicate(s) the role of ATP or ADP as an allosteric regulator? Assume that the supply of energy for cellular processes is adjusted to meet cellular demand for energy.

 A) ATP is an allosteric inhibitor of catabolic pathways.

 B) ADP is an allosteric activator of catabolic pathways.

 C) ATP is an allosteric activator of anabolic pathways.

 D) A and B only

 E) A, B, and C

Answer: E
*Topic: Concept 8.5*
*Skill: Application*

73) An increase in the level of cellular ATP is likely to occur under which of the following conditions?

 A) increased activity of catabolic pathways

 B) decreased activity of anabolic pathways

 C) allosteric inhibition of anabolic pathways

 D) A and B only

 E) A, B, and C

Answer: E
*Topic: Concept 8.5*
*Skill: Comprehension*

# Media Activity Questions

1) In your body, what process converts the chemical energy found in glucose into the chemical energy found in ATP?

   A) potentiation

   B) cellular respiration

   C) digestion

   D) anabolism

   E) redox

   Answer: B
   *Topic: Web/CD Activity: Energy Transformations*

2) What type of reaction breaks the bonds that join the phosphate groups in an ATP molecule?

   A) anabolism

   B) hydrolysis

   C) dehydration decomposition

   D) entropic

   E) dehydration synthesis

   Answer: B
   *Topic: Web/CD Activity: The Structure of ATP*

3) In the reaction A → B + C + heat,

   A) there is a net input of energy.

   B) the potential energy of the products is greater than that of the reactant.

   C) the potential energy of the products is the same as that of the reactant.

   D) the potential energy of the products is less than that of the reactant.

   E) entropy has decreased.

   Answer: D
   *Topic: Activity: Chemical Reactions and ATP*

4) What is the fate of the phosphate group that is removed when ATP is converted to ADP?

   A) It is acquired by a reactant in an endergonic reaction.

   B) It is used to convert an ATP into an AQP.

   C) It is acquired by a reactant in a spontaneous reaction.

   D) It is acquired by a reactant in an exergonic reaction.

   E) It is broken down into one phosphorus and four oxygen atoms.

   Answer: A
   *Topic: Activity: Chemical Reactions and ATP*

5) What name is given to the reactants in an enzymatically catalyzed reaction?

   A) $E_A$

   B) products

   C) active sites

   D) reactors

   E) substrate

   Answer: E
   *Topic: Web/CD Activity: How Enzymes Work*

# Self-Quiz Questions

1) Choose the pair of terms that correctly completes this sentence: Catabolism is to anabolism as _____ is to _____.

   A) exergonic; spontaneous

   B) exergonic; endergonic

   C) free energy; entropy

   D) work; energy

   E) entropy; enthalpy

   Answer: B

2) Most cells cannot harness heat to perform work because

   A) heat is not a form of energy.

   B) cells do not have much heat; they are relatively cool.

   C) temperature is usually uniform throughout a cell.

   D) heat can never be used to do work.

   E) heat denatures enzymes.

   Answer: C

3) According to the first law of thermodynamics,

   A) matter can be neither created nor destroyed.

   B) energy is conserved in all processes.

   C) all processes increase the order of the universe.

   D) systems rich in energy are intrinsically stable.

   E) the universe constantly loses energy because of friction.

   Answer: B

4) Which of the following metabolic processes can occur without a net influx of energy from some other process?

   A) $ADP + P_i \rightarrow ATP + H_2O$

   B) $C_6H_{12}O_6 + 6\,O_2 \rightarrow 6\,CO_2 + 6\,H_2O$

   C) $6\,CO_2 + 6\,H_2O \rightarrow C_6H_{12}O_6 + 6\,O_2$

   D) amino acids $\rightarrow$ protein

   E) glucose + fructose $\rightarrow$ sucrose

   Answer: B

5) If an enzyme has been inhibited noncompetitively,

   A) the $\Delta G$ for the reaction it catalyzes will always be negative.

   B) the active site will be occupied by the inhibitor molecule.

   C) raising substrate concentration will increase the inhibition.

   D) more energy will be necessary to initiate the reaction.

   E) the inhibitor molecule may be chemically unrelated to the substrate.

   Answer: E

6) If an enzyme solution is saturated with substrate, the most effective way to obtain an even faster yield of products is to

   A) add more of the enzyme.

   B) heat the solution to 90°C.

   C) add more substrate.

   D) add an allosteric inhibitor.

   E) add a noncompetitive inhibitor.

   Answer: A

7) If an enzyme is added to a solution where its substrates and products are in equilibrium, what would occur?

A) Additional product would be formed.

B) Additional substrate would be formed.

C) The reaction would change from endergonic to exergonic.

D) The free energy of the system would change.

E) Nothing; the reaction would stay at equilibrium.

Answer: E

8) Some bacteria are metabolically active in hot springs because

A) they are able to maintain a cooler internal temperature.

B) high temperatures make catalysis unnecessary.

C) their enzymes have high optimal temperatures.

D) their enzymes are insensitive to temperature.

E) they use molecules other than proteins as their main catalysts.

Answer: C

9) Which of the following characteristics is not associated with allosteric regulation of an enzyme's activity?

A) A mimic of the substrate competes for the active site.

B) A naturally occurring molecule stabilizes a catalytically active conformation.

C) Regulatory molecules bind to a site remote from the active site.

D) Inhibitor and activator may compete with one another.

E) The enzyme usually has a quaternary structure.

Answer: A

10) In the following branched metabolic pathway, a dotted arrow with a minus sign symbolizes inhibition of a metabolic step by an end product:

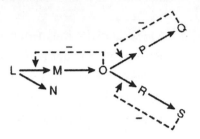

Which reaction would prevail if both Q and S were present in the cell in high concentrations?

A) L → M

B) M → O

C) L → N

D) O → P

E) R → S

Answer: C

# Chapter 9  Cellular Respiration: Harvesting Chemical Energy

1) What is the term for metabolic pathways that release stored energy by breaking down complex molecules?
   A) anabolic pathways
   B) catabolic pathways
   C) fermentation pathways
   D) thermodynamic pathways
   E) bioenergetic pathways

Answer: B
*Topic: Concept 9.1*
*Skill: Knowledge*

2) What is the term used for the metabolic pathway in which glucose ($C_6O_{12}H_6$) is degraded to carbon dioxide ($CO_2$) and water?
   A) cellular respiration
   B) glycolysis
   C) fermentation
   D) citric acid cycle
   E) oxidative phosphorylation

Answer: A
*Topic: Concept 9.1*
*Skill: Knowledge*

3) Which of the following statements concerning the metabolic degradation of glucose ($C_6H_{12}O_6$) to carbon dioxide ($CO_2$) and water is (are) *true*?
   A) The breakdown of glucose to carbon dioxide and water is exergonic.
   B) The breakdown of glucose to carbon dioxide and water has a free energy change of –686 kcal/mol.
   C) The breakdown of glucose to carbon dioxide and water involves oxidation–reduction or redox reactions.
   D) Only A and B are correct.
   E) A, B, and C are correct.

Answer: E
*Topic: Concept 9.1*
*Skill: Comprehension*

4) Which of the following statements is (are) correct about an oxidation–reduction (or redox) reaction?
   A) The molecule that is reduced gains electrons.
   B) The molecule that is oxidized loses electrons.
   C) The molecule that is reduced loses electrons.
   D) The molecule that is oxidized gains electrons.
   E) Both A and B are correct.

Answer: E
*Topic: Concept 9.1*
*Skill: Knowledge*

5) Which statement is *not* correct with regard to redox (oxidation–reduction) reactions?

   A) A molecule is reduced if it loses electrons.

   B) A molecule is oxidized if it loses electrons.

   C) An electron donor is called a reducing agent.

   D) An electron acceptor is called an oxidizing agent.

   E) Oxidation and reduction always go together.

Answer: A
*Topic: Concept 9.1*
*Skill: Knowledge*

6) The molecule that functions as the reducing agent (electron donor) in a redox or oxidation-reduction reaction

   A) gains electrons and gains energy.

   B) loses electrons and loses energy.

   C) gains electrons and loses energy.

   D) loses electrons and gains energy.

   E) neither gains nor loses electrons, but gains or loses energy.

Answer: B
*Topic: Concept 9.1*
*Skill: Comprehension*

7) When electrons move closer to a more electronegative atom, what happens?

   A) Energy is released.

   B) Energy is consumed.

   C) The more electronegative atom is reduced.

   D) The more electronegative atom is oxidized.

   E) A and C are correct.

Answer: E
*Topic: Concept 9.1*
*Skill: Comprehension*

8) Why does the oxidation of organic compounds by molecular oxygen to produce $CO_2$ and water release free energy?

   A) The covalent bonds in organic molecules are higher energy bonds than those in water and carbon dioxide.

   B) Electrons are being moved from atoms that have a lower affinity for electrons (such as C) to atoms with a higher affinity for electrons (such as O).

   C) The oxidation of organic compounds can be used to make ATP.

   D) The electrons have a higher potential energy when associated with water and $CO_2$ than they do in organic compounds.

   E) The covalent bond in $O_2$ is unstable and easily broken by electrons from organic molecules.

Answer: B
*Topic: Concept 9.1*
*Skill: Comprehension*

9) Which of the following statements describes the results of this reaction?

$$C_6H_{12}O_6 + 6\,O_2 \rightarrow 6\,CO_2 + 6\,H_2O + Energy$$

   A) $C_6H_{12}O_6$ is oxidized and $O_2$ is reduced.

   B) $O_2$ is oxidized and $H_2O$ is reduced.

   C) $CO_2$ is reduced and $O_2$ is oxidized.

   D) $C_6H_{12}O_6$ is reduced and $CO_2$ is oxidized.

   E) $O_2$ is reduced and $CO_2$ is oxidized.

Answer: A
*Topic: Concept 9.1*
*Skill: Comprehension*

10) When a glucose molecule loses a hydrogen atom (not a hydrogen ion) as the result of an oxidation–reduction reaction, the molecule becomes

A) dehydrogenated.

B) hydrogenated.

C) oxidized.

D) reduced.

E) an oxidizing agent.

Answer: C
*Topic: Concept 9.1*
*Skill: Comprehension*

11) When a molecule of $NAD^+$ (nicotinamide adenine dinucleotide) gains a hydrogen atom (not a hydrogen ion) the molecule becomes

A) hydrogenated.

B) oxidized.

C) reduced.

D) redoxed.

E) a reducing agent.

Answer: C
*Topic: Concept 9.1*
*Skill: Comprehension*

12) Which of the following statements about $NAD^+$ is *false*?

A) $NAD^+$ is reduced to NADH during both glycolysis and the citric acid cycle.

B) $NAD^+$ has more chemical energy than NADH.

C) $NAD^+$ is reduced by the action of dehydrogenases.

D) $NAD^+$ can receive electrons for use in oxidative phosphorylation.

E) In the absence of $NAD^+$, glycolysis cannot function.

Answer: B
*Topic: Concept 9.1*
*Skill: Comprehension*

13) In order for $NAD^+$ to remove electrons from glucose or other organic molecules, which of the following must be true?

A) The organic molecule or glucose must be negatively charged in order to reduce the positively charged $NAD^+$.

B) Oxygen must be present to oxidize the NADH produced back to $NAD^+$.

C) The free energy liberated when electrons are removed from the organic molecules must be greater than the energy required to give the electrons to $NAD^+$.

D) A and B are both correct.

E) A, B, and C are all correct.

Answer: C
*Topic: Concept 9.1*
*Skill: Comprehension*

14) Where does glycolysis takes place?

A) mitochondrial matrix

B) mitochondrial outer membrane

C) mitochondrial inner membrane

D) mitochondrial intermembrane space

E) cytosol

Answer: E
*Topic: Concept 9.1*
*Skill: Knowledge*

15) The ATP made during glycolysis is generated by

A) substrate–level phosphorylation.

B) electron transport.

C) photophosphorylation.

D) chemiosmosis.

E) oxidation of NADH to $NAD^+$.

Answer: A
*Topic: Concept 9.1*
*Skill: Knowledge*

16) The oxygen consumed during cellular respiration is involved directly in which process or event?

   A) glycolysis

   B) accepting electrons at the end of the electron transport chain

   C) the citric acid cycle

   D) the oxidation of pyruvate to acetyl CoA

   E) the phosphorylation of ADP to form ATP

Answer: B
*Topic: Concept 9.1*
*Skill: Knowledge*

17) Which process in eukaryotic cells will proceed normally whether oxygen ($O_2$) is present or absent?

   A) electron transport

   B) glycolysis

   C) the citric acid cycle

   D) oxidative phosphorylation

   E) chemiosmosis

Answer: B
*Topic: Concept 9.1*
*Skill: Knowledge*

18) Which of the following statements about glycolysis *false*?

   A) Glycolysis has steps involving oxidation–reduction reactions.

   B) The enzymes of glycolysis are located in the cytosol of the cell.

   C) Glycolysis can operate in the complete absence of $O_2$.

   D) The end products of glycolysis are $CO_2$ and $H_2O$.

   E) Glycolysis makes ATP exclusively through substrate–level phosphorylation.

Answer: D
*Topic: Concepts 9.1, 9.2*
*Skill: Knowledge*

*Refer to Figure 9.1 to answer the following questions.*

Figure 9.1 illustrates some of the steps (reactions) of glycolysis in their proper sequence. Each step is lettered. Use these letters to answer the questions.

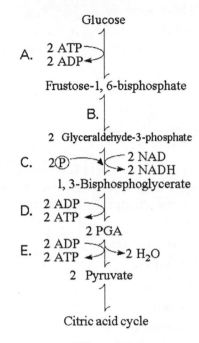

**Figure 9.1**

19) Which step shows a split of one molecule into two smaller molecules?

Answer: B
*Topic: Concept 9.2*
*Skill: Comprehension*

20) In which step is an inorganic phosphate added to the reactant?

Answer: C
*Topic: Concept 9.2*
*Skill: Comprehension*

21) In which reaction does an intermediate pathway become oxidized?

Answer: C
*Topic: Concept 9.2*
*Skill: Comprehension*

22) Which step involves an endergonic reaction?

Answer: A
*Topic: Concept 9.2*
*Skill: Comprehension*

23) Which step consists of a phosphorylation reaction in which ATP is the phosphate source?

Answer: A
*Topic: Concept 9.2*
*Skill: Comprehension*

24) Substrate–level phosphorylation accounts for approximately what percentage of the ATP formed during glycolysis?
   A) 0%
   B) 2%
   C) 10%
   D) 38%
   E) 100%

Answer: E
*Topic: Concept 9.2*
*Skill: Application*

25) During glycolysis, when glucose is catabolized to pyruvate, most of the energy of glucose is
   A) transferred to ADP, forming ATP.
   B) transferred directly to ATP.
   C) retained in the pyruvate.
   D) stored in the NADH produced.
   E) used to phosphorylate fructose to form fructose–6–phosphate.

Answer: C
*Topic: Concept 9.2*
*Skill: Comprehension*

26) In addition to ATP, what are the end products of glycolysis?
   A) $CO_2$ and $H_2O$
   B) $CO_2$ and pyruvate
   C) NADH and pyruvate
   D) $CO_2$ and NADH
   E) $H_2O$, $FADH_2$, and citrate

Answer: C
*Topic: Concept 9.2*
*Skill: Knowledge*

27) The free energy for the oxidation of glucose to $CO_2$ and water is –686 kcal/mole and the free energy for the reduction of $NAD^+$ to NADH is +53 kcal/mole. Why are only two molecules of NADH formed during glycolysis when it appears that as many as a dozen could be formed?
   A) Most of the free energy available from the oxidation of glucose is used in the production of ATP in glycolysis.
   B) Glycolysis is a very inefficient reaction, with much of the energy of glucose released as heat.
   C) Most of the free energy available from the oxidation of glucose remains in pyruvate, one of the products of glycolysis.
   D) There is no $CO_2$ or water produced as products of glycolysis.
   E) Glycolysis consists of many enzymatic reactions, each of which extracts some energy from the glucose molecule.

Answer: C
*Topic: Concept 9.2*
*Skill: Comprehension*

28) Starting with one molecule of glucose, the "net" products of glycolysis are

 A) 2 $NAD^+$, 2 $H^+$, 2 pyruvate, 2 ATP, and 2 $H_2O$.

 B) 2 NADH, 2 $H^+$, 2 pyruvate, 2 ATP, and 2 $H_2O$.

 C) 2 $FADH_2$, 2 pyruvate, 4 ATP, and 2 $H_2O$.

 D) 6 $CO_2$, 6 $H_2O$, 2 ATP, and 2 pyruvate.

 E) 6 $CO_2$, 6 $H_2O$, 36 ATP, and 2 citrate.

Answer: B
*Topic: Concept 9.2*
*Skill: Comprehension*

29) In glycolysis, for each molecule of glucose oxidized to pyruvate

 A) 2 molecules of ATP are used and 2 molecules of ATP are produced.

 B) 2 molecules of ATP are used and 4 molecules of ATP are produced.

 C) 4 molecules of ATP are used and 2 molecules of ATP are produced.

 D) 2 molecules of ATP are used and 6 molecules of ATP are produced.

 E) 6 molecules of ATP are used and 6 molecules of ATP are produced.

Answer: B
*Topic: Concept 9.2*
*Skill: Comprehension*

30) A molecule that is phosphorylated

 A) has an increased chemical reactivity; it is primed to do cellular work.

 B) has a decreased chemical reactivity; it is less likely to provide energy for cellular work.

 C) has been oxidized as a result of a redox reaction involving the gain of an inorganic phosphate.

 D) has been reduced as a result of a redox reaction involving the loss of an inorganic phosphate.

 E) has less energy than before its phosphorylation and therefore less energy for cellular work.

Answer: A
*Topic: Concept 9.2*
*Skill: Comprehension*

31) Which kind of metabolic poison would most directly interfere with glycolysis?

 A) An agent that reacts with oxygen and depletes its concentration in the cell

 B) An agent that binds to pyruvate and inactivates it

 C) An agent that closely mimics the structure of glucose but is not metabolized

 D) An agent that reacts with NADH and oxidizes it to $NAD^+$

 E) An agent that blocks the passage of electrons along the electron transport chain

Answer: C
*Topic: Concept 9.2*
*Skill: Application*

32) In the presence of oxygen, the three-carbon compound pyruvate can be catabolized in the citric acid cycle. First, however, the pyruvate 1) loses a carbon, which is given off as a molecule of $CO_2$, 2) is oxidized to form a two-carbon compound called acetate, and 3) is bonded to coenzyme A. These three steps result in the formation of

A) acetyl CoA, $O_2$, and ATP.

B) acetyl CoA, $FADH_2$, and $CO_2$.

C) acetyl CoA, FAD, $H_2$, and $CO_2$.

D) acetyl CoA, NADH, $H^+$, and $CO_2$.

E) acetyl CoA, $NAD^+$, ATP, and $CO_2$.

Answer: D
*Topic: Concept 9.3*
*Skill: Application*

33) Which of the following intermediary metabolites enters the citric acid cycle and is formed, in part, by the removal of a carbon ($CO_2$) from one molecule of pyruvate?

A) lactate

B) glyceraldehydes-3-phosphate

C) oxaloacetate

D) acetyl CoA

E) citrate

Answer: D
*Topic: Concept 9.3*
*Skill: Knowledge*

34) During cellular respiration, acetyl CoA accumulates in which location?

A) cytosol

B) mitochondrial outer membrane

C) mitochondrial inner membrane

D) mitochondrial intermembrane space

E) mitochondrial matrix

Answer: E
*Topic: Concept 9.3*
*Skill: Knowledge*

35) How many carbon atoms are fed into the citric acid cycle as a result of the oxidation of one molecule of pyruvate?

A) 2

B) 4

C) 6

D) 8

E) 10

Answer: A
*Topic: Concept 9.3*
*Skill: Comprehension*

36) All of the following are functions of the citric acid cycle *except*

A) production of ATP.

B) production of NADH.

C) production of $FADH_2$.

D) release of carbon dioxide.

E) adding electrons and protons to oxygen, forming water.

Answer: E
*Topic: Concept 9.3*
*Skill: Application*

*Refer to Figure 9.2, showing the citric acid cycle, as a guide to answer the following questions.*

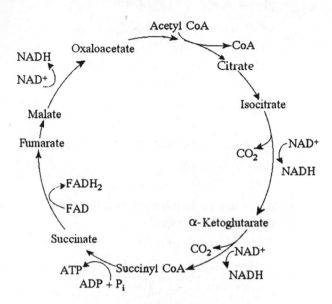

**Figure 9.2**

37) Starting with one molecule of isocitrate and ending with fumarate, what is the maximum number of ATP molecules that could be made through substrate-level phosphorylation?

   A) 1
   B) 2
   C) 11
   D) 12
   E) 24

   Answer: A
   *Topic: Concept 9.3*
   *Skill: Comprehension*

38) Carbon skeletons for amino acid biosynthesis are supplied by intermediates of the citric acid cycle. Which intermediate would supply the carbon skeleton for synthesis of a five-carbon amino acid?

   A) succinate
   B) malate
   C) citrate
   D) α-ketoglutarate
   E) isocitrate

   Answer: D
   *Topic: Concept 9.3*
   *Skill: Application*

39) Starting with one molecule of citrate and ending with oxaloacetate, how many ATP molecules can be formed from oxidative phosphorylation (chemiosmosis)?

   A) 1
   B) 3
   C) 4
   D) 11
   E) 12

   Answer: D
   *Topic: Concepts 9.3, 9.4*
   *Skill: Comprehension*

40) How many ATP molecules could be made through substrate-level phosphorylation plus oxidative phosphorylation (chemiosmosis) if you started with three molecules of succinyl CoA and ended with oxaloacetate?

   A) 6
   B) 12
   C) 18
   D) 24
   E) 36

   Answer: C
   *Topic: Concepts 9.3, 9.4*
   *Skill: Application*

41) How many molecules of carbon dioxide ($CO_2$) would be produced by five turns of the citric acid cycle?

A) 2

B) 5

C) 10

D) 12

E) 60

Answer: C
*Topic: Concept 9.3*
*Skill: Application*

42) How many reduced dinucleotides would be produced with four turns of the citric acid cycle?

A) 1 $FADH_2$ and 4 NADH

B) 2 $FADH_2$ and 8 NADH

C) 4 $FADH_2$ and 12 NADH

D) 1 FAD and 4 $NAD^+$

E) 4 $FAD^+$ and 12 $NAD^+$

Answer: C
*Topic: Concept 9.3*
*Skill: Comprehension*

43) Starting with citrate, how many of the following would be produced with three turns of the citric acid cycle?

A) 1 ATP, 2 $CO_2$, 3 NADH, and 1 $FADH_2$

B) 2 ATP, 2 $CO_2$, 1 NADH, and 3 $FADH_2$

C) 3 ATP, 3 $CO_2$, 3 NADH, and 3 $FADH_2$

D) 3 ATP, 6 $CO_2$, 9 NADH, and 3 $FADH_2$

E) 38 ATP, 6 $CO_2$, 3 NADH, and 12 $FADH_2$

Answer: D
*Topic: Concept 9.3*
*Skill: Comprehension*

44) Carbon dioxide ($CO_2$) is released during which of the following stages of cellular respiration?

A) glycolysis and the oxidation of pyruvate to acetyl CoA

B) oxidation of pyruvate to acetyl CoA and the citric acid cycle

C) the citric acid cycle and oxidative phosphorylation

D) oxidative phosphorylation and fermentation

E) fermentation and glycolysis

Answer: B
*Topic: Concept 9.3*
*Skill: Knowledge*

45) For each molecule of glucose that is metabolized by glycolysis and the citric acid cycle, what is the total number of NADH + $FADH_2$ molecules produced?

A) 4

B) 5

C) 6

D) 10

E) 12

Answer: E
*Topic: Concept 9.3*
*Skill: Comprehension*

46) A young relative of yours has never had much energy. He goes to a doctor for help and is sent to the hospital for some tests. There they discover his mitochondria can use only fatty acids and amino acids for respiration, and his cells produce more lactate than normal. Of the following, which is the best explanation of his condition?

A) His mitochondria lack the transport protein that moves pyruvate across the outer mitochondrial membrane.

B) His cells cannot move NADH from glycolysis into the mitochondria.

C) His cells contain something that inhibits oxygen use in his mitochondria.

D) His cells lack the enzyme in glycolysis that forms pyruvate.

E) His cells have a defective electron transport chain, so glucose goes to lactate instead of to acetyl CoA.

Answer: A
*Topic: Concept 9.3*
*Skill: Application*

47) Cellular respiration harvests the most chemical energy from which of the following?

A) substrate–level phosphorylation

B) chemiosmotic phosphorylation

C) converting oxygen to ATP

D) transferring electrons from organic molecules to pyruvate

E) generating carbon dioxide and oxygen in the electron transport chain

Answer: B
*Topic: Concept 9.3*
*Skill: Knowledge*

48) During aerobic respiration, electrons travel downhill in which sequence?

A) food → citric acid cycle → ATP → NAD+

B) food → NADH → electron transport chain → oxygen

C) glucose → pyruvate → ATP→ oxygen

D) glucose → ATP → electron transport chain → NADH

E) food → glycolysis → citric acid cycle – NADH → ATP

Answer: B
*Topic: Concept 9.3*
*Skill: Application*

49) Where do the catabolic products of fatty acid breakdown enter into the citric acid cycle?

A) pyruvate

B) malate or fumarate

C) acetyl CoA

D) α–ketoglutarate

E) succinyl CoA

Answer: C
*Topic: Concept 9.3*
*Skill: Comprehension*

50) Where are the proteins of the electron transport chain located?

A) cytosol

B) mitochondrial outer membrane

C) mitochondrial inner membrane

D) mitochondrial intermembrane space

E) mitochondrial matrix

Answer: C
*Topic: Concept 9.4*
*Skill: Knowledge*

51) Which of the following describes the sequence of electron carriers in the electron transport chain, starting with the least electronegative?

A) ubiquinone (Q), cytochromes (Cyt), FMN, Fe•S

B) cytochromes (Cyt), FMN, ubiquinone, Fe•S

C) Fe•S, FMN, cytochromes (Cyt), ubiquinone

D) FMN, Fe•S, ubiquinone, cytochromes (Cyt)

E) cytochromes (Cyt), Fe•S, ubiquinone, FMN

Answer: D
*Topic: Concept 9.4*
*Skill: Knowledge*

52) During aerobic respiration, which of the following directly donates electrons to the electron transport chain at the lowest energy level?

A) $NAD^+$

B) NADH

C) ATP

D) $ADP + P_i$

E) $FADH_2$

Answer: E
*Topic: Concept 9.4*
*Skill: Knowledge*

53) The primary role of oxygen in cellular respiration is to

A) yield energy in the form of ATP as it is passed down the respiratory chain.

B) act as an acceptor for electrons and hydrogen, forming water.

C) combine with carbon, forming $CO_2$.

D) combine with lactate, forming pyruvate.

E) catalyze the reactions of glycolysis.

Answer: B
*Topic: Concept 9.4*
*Skill: Knowledge*

54) Inside an active mitochondrion, most electrons follow which pathway?

A) glycolysis → NADH → oxidative phosphorylation → ATP → oxygen

B) citric acid cycle → $FADH_2$ → electron transport chain → ATP

C) electron transport chain → citric acid cycle → ATP → oxygen

D) pyruvate → citric acid cycle → ATP → NADH → oxygen

E) citric acid cycle → NADH → electron transport chain → oxygen

Answer: E
*Topic: Concept 9.4*
*Skill: Comprehension*

55) During oxidative phosphorylation, $H_2O$ is formed. Where does the oxygen for the synthesis of the water come from?

A) carbon dioxide ($CO_2$)

B) glucose ($C_6H_{12}O_6$)

C) molecular oxygen ($O_2$)

D) pyruvate ($C_3H_3O_3-$)

E) lactate ($C_3H_5O_3-$)

Answer: C
*Topic: Concept 9.4*
*Skill: Knowledge*

56) Which metabolic process is most closely associated with intracellular membranes?

A) substrate–level phosphorylation

B) oxidative phosphorylation

C) glycolysis

D) the citric acid cycle

E) alcohol fermentation

Answer: B
*Topic: Concept 9.4*
*Skill: Comprehension*

57) In chemiosmotic phosphorylation, what is the most direct source of energy that is used to convert ADP + $P_i$ to ATP?

A) energy released as electrons flow through the electron transport system

B) energy released from substrate-level phosphorylation

C) energy released from ATP synthase pumping hydrogen ions against their concentration gradient

D) energy released from movement of protons through ATP synthase

E) No external source of energy is required because the reaction is exergonic.

Answer: D
*Topic: Concept 9.4*
*Skill: Comprehension*

58) Energy released by the electron transport chain is used to pump $H^+$ ions into which location?

A) cytosol

B) mitochondrial outer membrane

C) mitochondrial inner membrane

D) mitochondrial intermembrane space

E) mitochondrial matrix

Answer: D
*Topic: Concept 9.4*
*Skill: Knowledge*

59) During aerobic cellular respiration, a proton gradient in mitochondria is generated by _____ and used primarily for _____.

A) the electron transport chain; ATP synthesis

B) the electron transport chain; substrate-level phosphorylation

C) glycolysis; production of $H_2O$

D) fermentation; $NAD^+$ reduction

E) diffusion of protons; ATP synthesis

Answer: A
*Topic: Concept 9.4*
*Skill: Comprehension*

60) The direct energy source that drives ATP synthesis during respiratory oxidative phosphorylation is

A) oxidation of glucose to $CO_2$ and water.

B) the thermodynamically favorable flow of electrons from NADH to the mitochondrial electron transport carriers.

C) the final transfer of electrons to oxygen.

D) the difference in $H^+$ concentrations on opposite sides of the inner mitochondrial membrane.

E) the thermodynamically favorable transfer of phosphate from glycolysis and the citric acid cycle intermediate molecules of ADP.

Answer: D
*Topic: Concept 9.4*
*Skill: Comprehension*

61) A major function of the mitochondrial inner membrane is the conversion of energy from electrons to the stored energy of the phosphate bond in ATP. To accomplish this function, the inner mitochondrial membrane must have all of the following features *except*

A) carrier proteins to accept electrons from NADH.

B) integral, transverse ATP synthase.

C) proton pumps embedded in the membrane.

D) the electron transport chain of proteins.

E) high permeability to protons.

Answer: A
*Topic: Concept 9.4*
*Skill: Knowledge*

62) When hydrogen ions are pumped from the mitochondrial matrix across the inner membrane and into the intermembrane space, the result is the

A) formation of ATP.

B) reduction of $NAD^+$.

C) restoration of the $Na^+/K^+$ balance across the membrane.

D) creation of a proton gradient.

E) lowering of pH in the mitochondrial matrix.

Answer: D
*Topic: Concept 9.4*
*Skill: Knowledge*

63) Where is ATP synthase located in the mitochondrion?

A) cytosol

B) electron transport chain

C) outer membrane

D) inner membrane

E) mitochondrial matrix

Answer: D
*Topic: Concept 9.4*
*Skill: Knowledge*

64) It is possible to prepare vesicles from portions of the inner membrane of the mitochondrial components. Which one of the following processes could still be carried on by this isolated inner membrane?

A) the citric acid cycle

B) oxidative phosphorylation

C) glycolysis and fermentation

D) reduction of $NAD^+$

E) both the citric acid cycle and oxidative phosphorylation

Answer: B
*Topic: Concept 9.4*
*Skill: Comprehension*

65) The primary function of the mitochondrion is the production of ATP. To carry out this function, the mitochondrion must have all of the following *except*

A) the membrane–bound electron transport chain carrier molecules.

B) proton pumps embedded in the inner mitochondrial membrane.

C) enzymes for glycolysis.

D) enzymes for the citric acid cycle.

E) mitochondrial ATP synthase.

Answer: C
*Topic: Concept 9.4*
*Skill: Knowledge*

66) Which process could be compared to how rushing steam turns a water wheel?

A) the citric acid cycle

B) ATP synthase activity

C) formation of NADH in glycolysis

D) oxidative phosphorylation

E) the electron transport system

Answer: B
*Topic: Concept 9.4*
*Skill: Application*

67) How many molecules of carbon dioxide ($CO_2$) would be released from the complete aerobic respiration of a molecule of sucrose ($C_{12}H_{22}O_{11}$), a disaccharide?

A) 2

B) 3

C) 6

D) 12

E) 38

Answer: D
*Topic: Concepts 9.3, 9.4*
*Skill: Application*

68) Each time a molecule of glucose ($C_6H_{12}O_6$) is completely oxidized via aerobic respiration, how many oxygen molecules ($O_2$) are required?

A) 1

B) 2

C) 6

D) 12

E) 38

Answer: C
*Topic: Concept 9.4*
*Skill: Knowledge*

69) Which of the following produces the most ATP when glucose ($C_6H_{12}O_6$) is completely oxidized to carbon dioxide ($CO_2$) and water?

A) glycolysis

B) fermentation

C) oxidation of pyruvate to acetyl CoA

D) citric acid cycle

E) oxidative phosphorylation (chemiosmosis)

Answer: E
*Topic: Concept 9.4*
*Skill: Knowledge*

70) Approximately how many molecules of ATP are produced from the complete oxidation of two molecules of glucose ($C_6H_{12}O_6$) in cellular respiration?

A) 2

B) 4

C) 15

D) 38

E) 76

Answer: E
*Topic: Concept 9.4*
*Skill: Comprehension*

71) Assume a mitochondrion contains 58 NADH and 19 $FADH_2$. If each of the 77 dinucleotides were used, approximately how many ATP molecules could be generated as a result of oxidative phosphorylation (chemiosmosis)?

A) 36

B) 77

C) 173

D) 212

E) 1102

Answer: D
*Topic: Concept 9.4*
*Skill: Application*

72) Approximately what percentage of the energy of glucose ($C_6H_{12}O_6$) is transferred to storage in ATP as a result of the complete oxidation of glucose to $CO_2$ and water in cellular respiration?

A) 2%

B) 4%

C) 10%

D) 25%

E) 40%

Answer: E
*Topic: Concept 9.4*
*Skill: Knowledge*

73) Recall that the complete oxidation of a mole of glucose releases 686 kcal of energy ($\Delta G = -686$ kcal/mol). The phosphorylation of ADP to form ATP stores approximately 7.3 kcal per mole of ATP. What is the approximate efficiency of cellular respiration for a "mutant" organism that produces only 29 moles of ATP for every mole of glucose oxidized, rather than the usual 36–38 moles of ATP?

A) 0.4%

B) 25%

C) 30%

D) 40%

E) 60%

Answer: C
*Topic: Concept 9.4*
*Skill: Application*

74) When glucose ($C_6H_{12}O_6$) is oxidized to $CO_2$ and water in cellular respiration, approximately 40% of the energy content of glucose is transferred to

A) the citric acid cycle.

B) glycolysis.

C) ATP (adenosine triphosphate).

D) heat.

E) oxygen ($O_2$).

Answer: C
*Topic: Concept 9.4*
*Skill: Knowledge*

75) Which of the following normally occurs whether or not oxygen ($O_2$) is present?

A) glycolysis

B) fermentation

C) oxidation of pyruvate to acetyl CoA

D) citric acid cycle

E) oxidative phosphorylation (chemiosmosis)

Answer: A
*Topic: Concepts 9.2, 9.5*
*Skill: Knowledge*

76) Which of the following occurs in the cytosol of the cell?

A) glycolysis and fermentation

B) fermentation and chemiosmosis

C) oxidation of pyruvate to acetyl CoA

D) citric acid cycle

E) oxidative phosphorylation

Answer: A
*Topic: Concepts 9.2, 9.5*
*Skill: Knowledge*

77) Fermentation takes place in the

A) cytosol.

B) mitochondrial outer membrane.

C) mitochondrial inner membrane.

D) mitochondrial intermembrane space.

E) mitochondrial matrix.

Answer: C
*Topic: Concept 9.5*
*Skill: Knowledge*

78) Which metabolic pathway is common to both cellular respiration and fermentation?

A) the oxidation of pyruvate to acetyl CoA

B) the citric acid cycle

C) oxidative phosphorylation

D) glycolysis

E) chemiosmosis

Answer: D
*Topic: Concept 9.5*
*Skill: Knowledge*

79) The ATP made during fermentation is generated by which of the following?

A) the electron transport chain

B) substrate–level phosphorylation

C) chemiosmosis

D) oxidative phosphorylation

E) aerobic respiration

Answer: B
*Topic: Concept 9.5*
*Skill: Knowledge*

80) Muscle cells in oxygen deprivation convert pyruvate to _____, and in this step gain _____.

A) lactate; ATP

B) alcohol; $CO_2$

C) alcohol; ATP

D) ATP; $NADH_2$

E) lactate; $NAD^+$

Answer: E
*Topic: Concept 9.5*
*Skill: Comprehension*

81) In the absence of oxygen, yeast cells can obtain energy by fermentation, resulting in the production of

A) ATP, $CO_2$, and ethanol (ethyl alcohol).

B) ATP, $CO_2$, and lactate.

C) ATP, NADH, and pyruvate.

D) ATP, pyruvate, and oxygen.

E) ATP, pyruvate, and acetyl CoA.

Answer: A
*Topic: Concept 9.5*
*Skill: Comprehension*

82) In alcohol fermentation, $NAD^+$ is regenerated from NADH during the

A) reduction of acetaldehyde to ethanol (ethyl alcohol).

B) oxidation of pyruvate to acetyl CoA.

C) reduction of pyruvate to form lactate.

D) oxidation of $NAD^+$ in the citric acid cycle.

E) phosphorylation of ADP to form ATP.

Answer: A
*Topic: Concept 9.5*
*Skill: Knowledge*

83) The function of both alcohol fermentation and lactic acid fermentation is to

A) reduce $NAD^+$ to NADH.

B) reduce $FAD^+$ to $FADH_2$.

C) oxidize NADH to $NAD^+$.

D) reduce $FADH_2$ to $FAD^+$.

E) none of the above

Answer: C
*Topic: Concept 9.5*
*Skill: Application*

84) Which of the following is *not* true concerning the cellular compartmentation of the steps of respiration or fermentation?

A) Acetyl CoA is produced only in the mitochondria.

B) Lactate is produced only in the cytosol.

C) NADH is produced only in the mitochondria.

D) $FADH_2$ is produced only in the mitochondria.

E) ATP is produced in the cytosol and the mitochondria.

Answer: C
*Topic: Concept 9.5*
*Skill: Application*

85) An organism is discovered that consumes a considerable amount of sugar, yet does not gain much weight when denied air. Curiously, the consumption of sugar increases as air is removed from the organism's environment, but the organism seems to thrive even in the absence of air. When returned to normal air, the organism does fine. Which of the following best describes the organism?

A) It must use a molecule other than oxygen to accept electrons from the electron transport chain.

B) It is a normal eukaryotic organism.

C) The organism obviously lacks the citric acid cycle and electron transport chain.

D) It is an anaerobic organism.

E) It is a facultative anaerobe.

Answer: E
*Topic: Concept 9.5*
*Skill: Application*

86) Glycolysis is thought to be one of the most ancient of metabolic processes. Which statement supports this idea?

A) Glycolysis is the most widespread metabolic pathway.

B) Glycolysis neither uses nor needs $O_2$.

C) Glycolysis is found in all eukaryotic cells.

D) The enzymes of glycolysis are found in the cytosol rather than in a membrane-enclosed organelle.

E) Ancient prokaryotic cells, the most primitive of cells, made extensive use of glycolysis long before oxygen was present in Earth's atmosphere.

Answer: A
*Topic: Concept 9.5*
*Skill: Comprehension*

87) Why is glycolysis considered to be one of the first metabolic pathways to have evolved?

A) It produces much less ATP than does oxidative phosphorylation.

B) It is found in the cytosol, does not involve oxygen, and is present in most organisms.

C) It is found in prokaryotic cells but not in eukaryotic cells.

D) It relies on chemiosmosis which is a metabolic mechanism present only in the first cells—prokaryotic cells.

E) It requires the presence of membrane-enclosed cell organelles found only in eukaryotic cells.

Answer: B
*Topic: Concept 9.5*
*Skill: Knowledge*

88) Molecules that can potentially be converted to intermediates of glycolysis and/or the citric acid cycle include

A) amino acids and proteins.

B) glycerol and fatty acids.

C) glucose and sucrose.

D) starch and glycogen.

E) all of the above

Answer: E
*Topic: Concept 9.6*
*Skill: Knowledge*

89) Which of the following organic molecules *cannot* be converted to an intermediate of glycolysis?

A) fatty acids

B) amino acids

C) glucose and sucrose

D) glycerol

E) starch and glycogen

Answer: A
*Topic: Concept 9.6*
*Skill: Comprehension*

90) Which of the following is *not* a true statement?

A) Glycerol can be converted to glyceraldehyde-3-phosphate, an intermediate of glycolysis.

B) Beta oxidation breaks fatty acids down to two-carbon fragments that can enter the citric acid cycle as acetyl CoA.

C) A gram of glucose oxidized by cellular respiration produces more than twice as much ATP as a gram of fat oxidized by cellular respiration.

D) Proteins can be used as a fuel for cellular respiration, but their constituent amino acids must first be converted to intermediates of glycolysis or the citric acid cycle.

E) Polysaccharides such as glycogen and starch are hydrolyzed to their constituent monosaccharides before they are used as fuel molecules for respiration.

Answer: C
*Topic: Concept 9.6*
*Skill: Knowledge*

91) You have a friend who lost 7 kg (about 15 pounds) of fat on a "low carb" diet. How did the fat leave her body?

A) It was released as $CO_2$ and $H_2O$.

B) Chemical energy was converted to heat and then released.

C) It was converted to ATP, which weighs much less than fat.

D) It was broken down to amino acids and eliminated from the body.

E) It was converted to urine and eliminated from the body.

Answer: A
*Topic: Concept 9.6*
*Skill: Application*

92) Phosphofructokinase is an important control enzyme in the regulation of cellular respiration. Which of the following statements concerning phosphofructokinase is *not* true?

A) It is activated by AMP (derived from ADP).

B) It is inhibited by ATP.

C) It is activated by citrate, an intermediate of the citric acid cycle.

D) It specifically catalyzes the conversion of fructose-6-phosphate to fructose-1,6-bisphosphate, an early step of glycolysis.

E) It is an allosteric enzyme.

Answer: A
*Topic: Concept 9.6*
*Skill: Knowledge*

93) Phosphofructokinase is an allosteric enzyme that catalyzes the conversion of fructose-6-phosphate to fructose-1,6-bisphosphate, an early step of glycolysis. In the presence of oxygen, an increase in the amount ATP in a cell would be expected to

A) inhibit the enzyme and thus slow the rates of glycolysis and the citric acid cycle.

B) activate the enzyme and thus slow the rates of glycolysis and the citric acid cycle.

C) inhibit the enzyme and thus increase the rates of glycolysis and the citric acid cycle.

D) activate the enzyme and increase the rates of glycolysis and the citric acid cycle.

E) inhibit the enzyme and thus increase the rate of glycolysis and the concentration of citrate.

Answer: A
*Topic: Concept 9.6*
*Skill: Comprehension*

# Media Activity Questions

1) How many ATP molecules are produced by glycolysis?

   A) 1

   B) 2

   C) 3

   D) 4

   E) 5

   Answer: D
   *Topic: Web/CD Activity: Glycolysis*

2) Glycolysis is an _____ reaction.

   A) exergonic

   B) endothermic

   C) unregulated

   D) endergonic

   E) abnormal

   Answer: A
   *Topic: Web/CD Activity: Glycolysis*

3) Pyruvate is formed

   A) on the inner mitochondrial membrane.

   B) in the mitochondrial matrix.

   C) on the outer mitochondrial membrane.

   D) in the nucleus.

   E) in the cytosol.

   Answer: E
   *Topic: Web/CD Activity: The Citric Acid Cycle*

4) Most of the energy that enters electron transport enters as

   A) ATP.

   B) acetyl CoA.

   C) glucose.

   D) $CO_2$.

   E) $FADH_2$ and NADH.

   Answer: E
   *Topic: Web/CD Activity: Electron Transport*

5) In fermentation, _____ is _____.

   A) NADH; reduced

   B) $NAD^+$; oxidized

   C) NADH; oxidized

   D) pyruvate; oxidized

   E) ethanol; oxidized

   Answer: C
   *Topic: Web/CD Activity: Fermentation*

# Self–Quiz Questions

1) What is the reducing agent in the following reaction?

   Pyruvate + NADH + H$^+$ → Lactate + NAD$^+$

   A) oxygen

   B) NADH

   C) NAD$^+$

   D) lactate

   E) pyruvate

   Answer: B

2) The immediate energy source that drives ATP synthesis by ATP synthase during oxidative phosphorylation is

   A) the oxidation of glucose and other organic compounds.

   B) the flow of electrons down the electron transport chain.

   C) the affinity of oxygen for electrons.

   D) the H$^+$ concentration gradient across the inner mitochondrial membrane.

   E) the transfer of phosphate to ADP.

   Answer: D

3) Which metabolic pathway is common to both fermentation and cellular respiration?

   A) the citric acid cycle

   B) the electron transport chain

   C) glycolysis

   D) synthesis of acetyl CoA from pyruvate

   E) reduction of pyruvate to lactate

   Answer: C

4) In mitochondria, exergonic redox reactions

   A) are the source of energy driving prokaryotic ATP synthesis.

   B) are directly coupled to substrate–level phosphorylation.

   C) provide the energy to establish the proton gradient.

   D) reduce carbon atoms to carbon dioxide.

   E) are coupled via phosphorylated intermediates to endergonic processes.

   Answer: C

5) The final electron acceptor of the electron transport chain that functions in oxidative phosphorylation is

   A) oxygen.

   B) water.

   C) NAD$^+$.

   D) pyruvate.

   E) ADP.

   Answer: A

6) When electrons flow along the electron transport chains of mitochondria, which of the following changes occurs?

   A) The pH of the matrix increases.

   B) ATP synthase pumps protons by active transport.

   C) The electrons gain free energy.

   D) The cytochromes phosphorylate ADP to form ATP.

   E) NAD$^+$ is oxidized.

   Answer: A

7) In the presence of a metabolic poison that specifically and completely inhibits all function of mitochondrial ATP synthase, which of the following would you expect?

A) a decrease in the pH difference across the inner mitochondrial membrane

B) an increase in the pH difference across the inner mitochondrial membrane

C) increased synthesis of ATP

D) increased oxygen consumption

E) an accumulation of $NAD^+$

Answer: B

8) Cells do not catabolize carbon dioxide because

A) its double bonds are too stable to be broken.

B) $CO_2$ has fewer bonding electrons than other organic compounds.

C) $CO_2$ is already completely reduced.

D) $CO_2$ is already completely oxidized.

E) the molecule has too few atoms.

Answer: D

9) Which of the following is a true distinction between fermentation and cellular respiration?

A) Only respiration oxidizes glucose.

B) NADH is oxidized by the electron transport chain in respiration only.

C) Fermentation, but not respiration, is an example of a catabolic pathway.

D) Substrate-level phosphorylation is unique to fermentation.

E) $NAD^+$ functions as an oxidizing agent only in respiration.

Answer: B

10) Most $CO_2$ from catabolism is released during

A) glycolysis.

B) the citric acid cycle.

C) lactate fermentation.

D) electron transport.

E) oxidative phosphorylation.

Answer: B

# Chapter 10  Photosynthesis

1) Organisms that can exist with light as an energy source and an inorganic form of carbon and other raw materials

   A) are called photoautotrophs.

   B) do not exist in nature.

   C) are called heterotrophs.

   D) are best classified as decomposers.

   E) both C and D

   Answer: A
   *Topic: Overview*
   *Skill: Knowledge*

2) Which type of organism obtains energy by metabolizing molecules produced by other organisms?

   A) autotrophs

   B) heterotrophs

   C) decomposers

   D) B and C

   E) A, B, and C

   Answer: D
   *Topic: Concept 10.1*
   *Skill: Knowledge*

3) The early suggestion that the oxygen ($O_2$) liberated from plants during photosynthesis comes from water was

   A) first proposed by C.B. van Niel of Stanford University.

   B) confirmed by experiments using oxygen–18 ($^{18}O$).

   C) made following the discovery of photorespiration because of rubisco's sensitivity to oxygen.

   D) A and B

   E) A, B, and C

   Answer: D
   *Topic: Concept 10.1*
   *Skill: Application*

4) If photosynthesizing green algae are provided with $CO_2$ synthesized with heavy oxygen ($^{18}O$), later analysis will show that all but one of the following compounds produced by the algae contain the $^{18}O$ label. That one exception is

   A) PGA.

   B) PGAL.

   C) glucose.

   D) RuBP.

   E) $O_2$.

   Answer: E
   *Topic: Concept 10.1*
   *Skill: Comprehension*

5) Which of the following are products of the light reactions of photosynthesis that are utilized in the Calvin cycle?

   A) $CO_2$ and glucose

   B) $H_2O$ and $O_2$

   C) ADP, $P_i$, and $NADP^+$

   D) electrons and $H^+$

   E) ATP and NADPH

   Answer: E
   *Topic: Concept 10.1*
   *Skill: Comprehension*

6) What is the primary function of the light reactions of photosynthesis?

A) to produce energy–rich glucose from carbon dioxide and water

B) to produce ATP and NADPH

C) to produce NADPH used in respiration

D) to convert light energy to the chemical energy of PGAL

E) to use ATP to make glucose

Answer: B
*Topic: Concept 10.1*
*Skill: Comprehension*

7) What are the products of the light reactions that are subsequently used by the Calvin cycle?

A) oxygen and carbon dioxide

B) carbon dioxide and RuBP

C) water and carbon

D) electrons and photons

E) ATP and NADPH

Answer: E
*Topic: Concept 10.1*
*Skill: Knowledge*

8) Where does the Calvin cycle take place?

A) stroma of the chloroplast

B) thylakoid membrane

C) cytoplasm surrounding the chloroplast

D) chlorophyll molecule

E) outer membrane of the chloroplast

Answer: A
*Topic: Concept 10.1*
*Skill: Knowledge*

9) A plant has a unique photosynthetic pigment. The leaves of this plant appear to be reddish yellow. What wavelengths of visible light are *not* being absorbed by this pigment?

A) red and yellow

B) blue and violet

C) green and yellow

D) blue, green, and red

E) green, blue, and violet

Answer: A
*Topic: Concept 10.2*
*Skill: Comprehension*

10) During photosynthesis, visible light has enough energy to

A) force electrons closer to the nucleus.

B) excite electrons.

C) split a water molecule into hydrogen and oxygen.

D) B and C only.

E) A, B, and C.

Answer: B
*Topic: Concept 10.2*
*Skill: Knowledge*

*Use the following information to answer the questions below.*

Theodor W. Engelmann illuminated a filament of algae with light that passed through a prism, thus exposing different segments of algae to different wavelengths of light. He added aerobic bacteria and then noted in which areas the bacteria congregated. He noted that the largest groups were found in the areas illuminated by the red and blue light.

11) What did Engelmann conclude about the congregation of bacteria in the red and blue areas?

   A) Bacteria released excess carbon dioxide in these areas.

   B) Bacteria congregated in these areas due to an increase in the temperature of the red and blue light.

   C) Bacteria congregated in these areas because these areas had the most oxygen being released.

   D) Bacteria are attracted to red and blue light and thus these wavelengths are more reactive than other wavelengths.

   E) Bacteria congregated in these areas due to an increase in the temperature caused by an increase in photosynthesis.

Answer: C
*Topic: Concept 10.2*
*Skill: Knowledge*

12) An outcome of this experiment was to help determine

   A) the relationship between heterotrophic and autotrophic organisms.

   B) the relationship between wavelengths of light and the rate of aerobic respiration.

   C) the relationship between wavelengths of light and the amount of heat released.

   D) the relationship between wavelengths of light and the oxygen released during photosynthesis.

   E) the relationship between the concentration of carbon dioxide and the rate of photosynthesis.

Answer: D
*Topic: Concept 10.2*
*Skill: Knowledge*

13) If you ran the same experiment without passing light through a prism, what would you predict?

   A) There would be no difference in results.

   B) The bacteria would be relatively evenly distributed along the algal filaments.

   C) The number of bacteria present would decrease due to an increase in the carbon dioxide concentration.

   D) The number of bacteria present would increase due to an increase in the carbon dioxide concentration.

   E) The number of bacteria would decrease due to a decrease in the temperature of the water.

Answer: B
*Topic: Concept 10.2*
*Skill: Application*

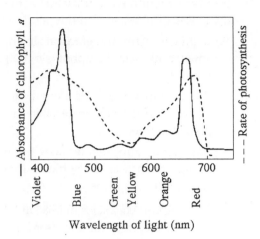

**Figure 10.1**

14) Figure 10.1 shows the absorption spectrum for chlorophyll *a* and the action spectrum for photosynthesis. Why are they different?

   A) Green and yellow wavelengths inhibit the absorption of red and blue wavelengths.

   B) Bright sunlight destroys photosynthetic pigments.

   C) Oxygen given off during photosynthesis interferes with the absorption of light.

   D) Other pigments absorb light in addition to chlorophyll *a*.

   E) Aerobic bacteria take up oxygen which changes the measurement of the rate of photosynthesis.

Answer: D
*Topic: Concept 10.2*
*Skill: Comprehension*

15) What wavelength of light is *most* effective in driving photosynthesis?

   A) 420 mm

   B) 475 mm

   C) 575 mm

   D) 625 mm

   E) 730 mm

Answer: A
*Topic: Concept 10.2*
*Skill: Knowledge*

16) In the thylakoid membranes, what is the main role of the antenna pigment molecules?

   A) split water and release oxygen to the reaction–center chlorophyll

   B) harvest photons and transfer light energy to the reaction–center chlorophyll

   C) synthesize ATP from ADP and $P_i$

   D) transfer electrons to ferredoxin and then NADPH

   E) concentrate photons within the stroma

Answer: B
*Topic: Concept 10.2*
*Skill: Knowledge*

17) The reaction–center chlorophyll of photosystem I is known as P700 because

   A) there are 700 chlorophyll molecules in the center.

   B) this pigment is best at absorbing light with a wavelength of 700 nm.

   C) there are 700 photosystem I components to each chloroplast.

   D) it absorbs 700 photons per microsecond.

   E) the plastoquinone reflects light with a wavelength of 700 nm.

Answer: B
*Topic: Concept 10.2*
*Skill: Application*

18) All of the events listed below occur in the light reactions of photosynthesis *except*

   A) oxygen is produced.

   B) $NADP^+$ is reduced to NADPH.

   C) carbon dioxide is incorporated into PGA.

   D) ADP is phosphorylated to yield ATP.

   E) light is absorbed and funneled to reaction–center chlorophyll *a*.

Answer: C
*Topic: Concept 10.2*
*Skill: Knowledge*

19) Which of the following statements about the light reactions of photosynthesis are true?

   A) The splitting of water molecules provides a source of electrons.

   B) Chlorophyll (and other pigments) absorb light energy, which excites electrons.

   C) ATP is generated by photophosphorylation.

   D) Only A and C are true.

   E) A, B, and C are true.

Answer: E
*Topic: Concept 10.2*
*Skill: Comprehension*

20) Which statement regarding events in the functioning of photosystem II is *false*?

   A) Light energy excites electrons in an antenna pigment in a photosynthetic unit.

   B) The excitation is passed along to a molecule of P680 chlorophyll in the photosynthetic unit.

   C) The P680 chlorophyll donates a pair of protons to NADPH, which is thus converted to $NADP^+$.

   D) The electron vacancies in P680 are filled by electrons derived from water.

   E) The splitting of water yields molecular oxygen as a by–product.

Answer: C
*Topic: Concept 10.2*
*Skill: Comprehension*

21) All of the following are directly associated with photosystem II *except*

   A) extraction of hydrogen electrons from the splitting of water.

   B) release of oxygen.

   C) harvesting of light energy by chlorophyll.

   D) $NADP^+$ reductase.

   E) P680 reaction–center chlorophyll.

Answer: D
*Topic: Concept 10.2*
*Skill: Application*

22) All of the following are directly associated with photosystem I *except*

    A) harvesting of light energy by chlorophyll.

    B) receiving electrons from plastocyanin.

    C) P700 reaction–center chlorophyll.

    D) extraction of hydrogen electrons from the splitting of water.

    E) passing electrons to ferredoxin.

Answer: D
*Topic: Concept 10.2*
*Skill: Comprehension*

23) Some photosynthetic organisms contain chloroplasts that lack photosystem II, yet are able to survive. The best way to detect the lack of photosystem II in these organisms would be

    A) to determine if they have thylakoids in the chloroplasts.

    B) to test for liberation of $O_2$ in the light.

    C) to test for $CO_2$ fixation in the dark.

    D) to do experiments to generate an action spectrum.

    E) to test for production of either sucrose or starch.

Answer: B
*Topic: Concept 10.2*
*Skill: Application*

24) What are the products of noncyclic photophosphorylation?

    A) heat and fluorescence

    B) ATP and P700

    C) ATP and NADPH

    D) ADP and NADP

    E) P700 and P680

Answer: C
*Topic: Concept 10.2*
*Skill: Knowledge*

25) What does cyclic electron flow in the chloroplast produce?

    A) ATP

    B) NADPH

    C) glucose

    D) A and B

    E) A, B, and C

Answer: A
*Topic: Concept 10.2*
*Skill: Knowledge*

26) As a research scientist, you measure the amount of ATP and NADPH consumed by the Calvin cycle in 1 hour. You find 30,000 molecules of ATP consumed, but only 20,000 molecules of NADPH. Where did the extra ATP molecules come from?

    A) photosystem II

    B) photosystem I

    C) cyclic electron flow

    D) noncyclic electron flow

    E) chlorophyll

Answer: C
*Topic: Concept 10.2*
*Skill: Comprehension*

27) Assume a thylakoid is somehow punctured so that the interior of the thylakoid is no longer separated from the stroma. This damage will have the most direct effect on which of the following processes?

    A) the splitting of water

    B) the absorption of light energy by chlorophyll

    C) the flow of electrons from photosystem II to photosystem I

    D) the synthesis of ATP

    E) the reduction of $NADP^+$

Answer: D
*Topic: Concept 10.2*
*Skill: Application*

28) What does the chemiosmotic process in chloroplasts involve?

  A) establishment of a proton gradient

  B) diffusion of electrons through the thylakoid membrane

  C) reduction of water to produce ATP energy

  D) movement of water by osmosis into the thylakoid space from the stroma

  E) formation of glucose, using carbon dioxide, NADPH, and ATP

Answer: A
*Topic: Concept 10.2*
*Skill: Knowledge*

29) Suppose the interior of the thylakoids of isolated chloroplasts were made acidic and then transferred in the dark to a pH–8 solution. What would be likely to happen?

  A) The isolated chloroplasts will make ATP.

  B) The Calvin cycle will be activated.

  C) Cyclic photophosphorylation will occur.

  D) Only A and B will occur.

  E) A, B, and C will occur.

Answer: A
*Topic: Concept 10.2*
*Skill: Comprehension*

30) In a plant cell, where are the ATP synthase complexes located?

  A) thylakoid membrane

  B) plasma membrane

  C) inner mitochondrial membrane

  D) A and C

  E) A, B, and C

Answer: D
*Topic: Concept 10.2*
*Skill: Comprehension*

31) In mitochondria, chemiosmosis translocates protons from the matrix into the intermembrane space, whereas in chloroplasts, chemiosmosis translocates protons from

  A) the stroma to the photosystem II.

  B) the matrix to the stroma.

  C) the stroma to the thylakoid space.

  D) the intermembrane space to the matrix.

  E) ATP synthase to $NADP^+$ reductase.

Answer: C
*Topic: Concept 10.2*
*Skill: Comprehension* ·

32) Which of the following statements *best* describes the relationship between photosynthesis and respiration?

  A) Respiration is the reversal of the biochemical pathways of photosynthesis.

  B) Photosynthesis stores energy in complex organic molecules, while respiration releases it.

  C) Photosynthesis occurs only in plants and respiration occurs only in animals.

  D) ATP molecules are produced in photosynthesis and used up in respiration.

  E) Respiration is anabolic and photosynthesis is catabolic.

Answer: B
*Topic: Concept 10.2*
*Skill: Comprehension*

33) Where is the electron transport chain found in plant cells?

   A) thylakoid membranes of chloroplasts

   B) stroma of chloroplasts

   C) inner membrane of mitochondria

   D) matrix of mitochondria

   E) cytoplasm

   Answer: A
   *Topic: Concept 10.2*
   *Skill: Knowledge*

34) Of the following, what do both mitochondria and chloroplasts have in common?

   A) thylakoid membranes

   B) chemiosmosis

   C) ATP synthase

   D) B and C only

   E) A, B, and C

   Answer: D
   *Topic: Concept 10.2*
   *Skill: Knowledge*

*Refer to the choices to answer the following questions. Each choice may be used once, more than once, or not at all. Indicate whether the following events occur during*

   A. photosynthesis
   B. respiration
   C. both photosynthesis and respiration
   D. neither photosynthesis nor respiration

35) synthesis of ATP by the chemiosmotic mechanism

   Answer: C
   *Topic: Concept 10.2*
   *Skill: Comprehension*

36) reduction of oxygen which forms water

   Answer: B
   *Topic: Concept 10.2*
   *Skill: Comprehension*

37) reduction of NADP$^+$

   Answer: A
   *Topic: Concept 10.2*
   *Skill: Knowledge*

38) the splitting of carbon dioxide to form oxygen gas and carbon compounds

   Answer: C
   *Topic: Concept 10.2*
   *Skill: Knowledge*

39) generation of proton gradients across membranes

   Answer: C
   *Topic: Concept 10.2*
   *Skill: Comprehension*

40) Which of the following statements best represents the relationships between the light reactions and the Calvin cycle?

   A) The light reactions provide ATP and NADPH to the Calvin cycle, and the cycle returns ADP, $P_i$, and NADP$^+$ to the light reactions.

   B) The light reactions provide ATP and NADPH to the carbon fixation step of the Calvin cycle, and the cycle provides water and electrons to the light reactions.

   C) The light reactions supply the Calvin cycle with $CO_2$ to produce sugars, and the Calvin cycle supplies the light reactions with sugars to produce ATP.

   D) The light reactions provide the Calvin cycle with oxygen for electron flow, and the Calvin cycle provides the light reactions with water to split.

   E) There is no relationship between the light reactions and the Calvin cycle.

   Answer: A
   *Topic: Concept 10.3*
   *Skill: Comprehension*

41) Where do the enzymatic reactions of the Calvin cycle take place?

A) stroma of the chloroplast

B) thylakoid membranes

C) outer membrane of the chloroplast

D) electron transport chain

E) thylakoid space

Answer: A
*Topic: Concept 10.3*
*Skill: Knowledge*

42) What is the primary function of the Calvin cycle?

A) use ATP to release carbon dioxide

B) use NADPH to release carbon dioxide

C) split water and release oxygen

D) transport RuBP out of the chloroplast

E) synthesize simple sugars from carbon dioxide

Answer: E
*Topic: Concept 10.3*
*Skill: Comprehension*

43) Which of the following is (are) required in the Calvin cycle?

A) $CO_2$

B) ATP

C) RuBP

D) A and B only

E) A, B, and C

Answer: E
*Topic: Concept 10.3*
*Skill: Knowledge*

44) Which statement is *false*?

A) Thylakoid membranes contain the photosynthetic pigments.

B) The $O_2$ released during photosynthesis comes from water.

C) RuBP is produced during cyclic electron flow in the light reactions of photosynthesis.

D) The light reactions of photosynthesis provide the energy for the Calvin cycle.

E) When chlorophyll is reduced, it gains electrons.

Answer: C
*Topic: Concept 10.3*
*Skill: Comprehension*

45) One carbon dioxide molecule reacts in each "turn" of the Calvin cycle. How many turns of the cycle are required for the synthesis of one glucose molecule?

A) 1

B) 2

C) 3

D) 6

E) 12

Answer: D
*Topic: Concept 10.3*
*Skill: Knowledge*

46) All of the following statements are correct regarding the Calvin cycle *except:*

A) The energy source utilized is the ATP and NADPH obtained through the light reaction.

B) These reactions begin soon after sundown and end before sunrise.

C) The 5-carbon sugar RuBP is constantly being regenerated.

D) One of the end products is glyceraldehyde phosphate.

E) Rubisco attaches carbon dioxide to ribulose bisphosphate.

Answer: B
*Topic: Concept 10.3*
*Skill: Comprehension*

*For the following questions, compare the light reactions with the Calvin cycle of photosynthesis in plants.*
*Use the following key:*

A. light reactions alone
B. the Calvin cycle alone
C. both the light reactions and the Calvin cycle
D. neither the light reactions nor the Calvin cycle
E. occurs in the chloroplast but is not part of photosynthesis

47) produces molecular oxygen ($O_2$)

Answer: A
*Topic: Concept 10.2*
*Skill: Knowledge*

48) requires ATP

Answer: B
*Topic: Concept 10.3*
*Skill: Knowledge*

49) produces NADH

Answer: D
*Topic: Concept 10.3*
*Skill: Knowledge*

50) produces NADPH

Answer: A
*Topic: Concept 10.2*
*Skill: Knowledge*

51) produces three-carbon sugars

Answer: B
*Topic: Concept 10.3*
*Skill: Knowledge*

52) inactive in the dark

Answer: C
*Topic: Concept 10.3*
*Skill: Knowledge*

53) requires $CO_2$

Answer: B
*Topic: Concept 10.3*
*Skill: Knowledge*

54) requires glucose

Answer: D
*Topic: Concept 10.3*
*Skill: Knowledge*

55) Which of the following is (are) true of the enzyme ribulose bisphosphate carboxylase?

A) It participates in the Calvin cycle.

·B) It catalyzes a phosphorylation reaction.

C) It has an affinity for both $O_2$ and $CO_2$.

D) A and C are true.

E) A, B, and C are true.

Answer: D
*Topic: Concept 10.4*
*Skill: Comprehension*

56) What are the substrates (normal reactants) for the enzyme RuBP carboxylase?

   A) $CO_2$ and $O_2$

   B) $CO_2$ and glucose

   C) ATP and NADPH

   D) triose–P, glucose, and $CO_2$

   E) $CO_2$ and ATP

Answer: A
*Topic: Concept 10.4*
*Skill: Application*

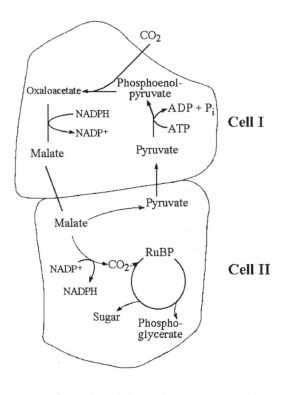

**Figure 10.2**

57) Which of the following statements is *true* concerning Figure 10.2?

   A) It represents cell processes involved in $C_4$ photosynthesis.

   B) It represents the type of cell structures found in CAM plants.

   C) It represents an adaptation that minimizes photorespiration.

   D) A and C are true.

   E) A, B, and C are true.

Answer: D
*Topic: Concept 10.4*
*Skill: Knowledge*

58) Referring to Figure 10.2, oxygen would inhibit the $CO_2$ fixation reactions in

   A) cell I only.

   B) cell II only.

   C) neither cell I nor cell II.

   D) both cell I and cell II.

   E) cell I during the night and cell II during the day.

Answer: B
*Topic: Concept 10.4*
*Skill: Comprehension*

59) In which cell would you expect photorespiration?

   A) Cell I

   B) Cell II

   C) Cell I at night

   D) Cell II at night

   E) neither Cell I nor Cell II

Answer: B
*Topic: Concept 10.4*
*Skill: Comprehension*

60) In an experiment studying photosynthesis performed during the day, you provide a plant with radioactive carbon ($^{14}C$) dioxide as a metabolic tracer. The $^{14}C$ is incorporated first into oxaloacetate. The plant is best characterized as a

   A) $C_4$ plant.

   B) $C_3$ plant.

   C) CAM plant.

   D) heterotroph.

   E) chemoautotroph.

Answer: A
*Topic: Concept 10.4*
*Skill: Application*

61) Why are $C_4$ plants able to photosynthesize with no apparent photorespiration?

A) They do not participate in the Calvin cycle.

B) They use PEP carboxylase to initially fix $CO_2$.

C) They are adapted to cold, wet climates.

D) They conserve water more efficiently.

E) They exclude oxygen from their tissues.

Answer: B
*Topic: Concept 10.4*
*Skill: Comprehension*

62) CAM plants keep stomata closed in daytime, thus reducing loss of water. They can do this because they

A) fix $CO_2$ into organic acids during the night.

B) fix $CO_2$ into sugars in the bundle-sheath cells.

C) fix $CO_2$ into pyruvate in the mesophyll cells.

D) use the enzyme phosphofructokinase, which outcompetes rubisco for $CO_2$.

E) use photosystems I and II at night.

Answer: A
*Topic: Concept 10.4*
*Skill: Knowledge*

63) In $C_4$ photosynthesis, carbon fixation takes place in the _____ cells, and then is transferred as malic or aspartic acid to _____ cells, where carbon dioxide is released for entry into the Calvin cycle.

A) mesophyll; bundle-sheath

B) stomatal; mesophyll

C) bundle-sheath; epidermal

D) epidermal; mesophyll

E) stomatal; epidermal

Answer: A
*Topic: Concept 10.4*
*Skill: Knowledge*

64) Photorespiration lowers the efficiency of photosynthesis by preventing the formation of

A) carbon dioxide molecules.

B) 3-phosphoglycerate molecules.

C) ATP molecules.

D) ribulose bisphosphate molecules.

E) RuBP carboxylase molecules.

Answer: B
*Topic: Concept 10.4*
*Skill: Knowledge*

65) Plants that fix $CO_2$ into organic acids at night when the stomata are open and carry out the Calvin cycle during the day when the stomata are closed are called

A) $C_3$ plants.

B) $C_4$ plants.

C) CAM plants.

D) B and C only.

E) A, B, and C

Answer: C
*Topic: Concept 10.4*
*Skill: Knowledge*

# Media Activity Questions

1) Carbon fixation involves the addition of carbon dioxide to

   A) rubisco.

   B) RuBP.

   C) G3P.

   D) 3–PGA.

   E) NADPH.

   Answer: B
   *Topic: Web/CD Activity: The Calvin Cycle*

2) After 3–PGA is phosphorylated, it is reduced by

   A) $NADP^+$.

   B) ADP.

   C) $CO_2$.

   D) NADPH.

   E) ATP.

   Answer: D
   *Topic: Web/CD Activity: The Calvin Cycle*

3) How many carbon dioxide molecules must be added to RuBP to make a single molecule of glucose?

   A) 2

   B) 4

   C) 6

   D) 8

   E) 10

   Answer: C
   *Topic: Web/CD Activity: The Calvin Cycle*

4) In $C_3$ plants the conservation of water promotes

   A) photorespiration.

   B) the light reactions.

   C) a shift to $C_4$ photosynthesis.

   D) the opening of stomata.

   E) photosynthesis.

   Answer: A
   *Topic: Activity: Photosynthesis in Dry Climates*

5) $C_4$ plants differ from $C_3$ and CAM plants in that $C_4$ plants

   A) open their stomata only at night.

   B) are better adapted to wet conditions.

   C) transfer fixed carbon dioxide to cells in which the Calvin cycle occurs.

   D) use malic acid to transfer carbon dioxide to the Calvin cycle.

   E) use PEP carboxylase to fix carbon dioxide.

   Answer: C
   *Topic: Activity: Photosynthesis in Dry Climates*

# Self-Quiz Questions

1) The light reactions of photosynthesis supply the Calvin cycle with
   A) light energy.
   B) $CO_2$ and ATP.
   C) $H_2O$ and NADPH.
   D) ATP and NADPH.
   E) sugar and $O_2$.

   Answer: D

2) Which of the following sequences correctly represents the flow of electrons during photosynthesis?
   A) NADPH → $O_2$ → $CO_2$
   B) $H_2O$ → NADPH → Calvin cycle
   C) NADPH → chlorophyll → Calvin cycle
   D) $H_2O$ → photosystem I → photosystem II
   E) NADPH → electron transport chain → $O_2$

   Answer: B

3) Which of the following conclusions does *not* follow from studying the absorption spectrum for chlorophyll *a* and the action spectrum for photosynthesis?
   A) Not all wavelengths are equally effective for photosynthesis.
   B) There must be accessory pigments that broaden the spectrum of light that contributes to photosynthesis.
   C) The red and blue areas of the spectrum are most effective in driving photosynthesis.
   D) Chlorophyll owes its color to the absorption of green light.
   E) Chlorophyll *a* has two absorption peaks.

   Answer: D

4) Cooperation of the *two* photosystems is required for
   A) ATP synthesis.
   B) reduction of $NADP^+$.
   C) cyclic photophosphorylation.
   D) oxidation of the reaction center of photosystem I.
   E) generation of a proton–motive force.

   Answer: B

5) In *mechanism*, photophosphorylation is most similar to
   A) substrate-level phosphorylation in glycolysis.
   B) oxidative phosphorylation in cellular respiration.
   C) the Calvin cycle.
   D) carbon fixation.
   E) reduction of $NADP^+$.

   Answer: B

6) In what respect are the photosynthetic adaptations of $C_4$ plants and CAM plants similar?
   A) In both cases, only photosystem I is used.
   B) Both types of plants make sugar without the Calvin cycle.
   C) In both cases, an enzyme other than rubisco carries out the first step in carbon fixation.
   D) Both types of plants make most of their sugar in the dark.
   E) Neither $C_4$ plants nor CAM plants have thylakoids.

   Answer: C

7) Which of the following processes is most directly driven by light energy?

A) creation of a pH gradient by pumping protons across the thylakoid membrane

B) carbon fixation in the stroma

C) reduction of NADP$^+$ molecules

D) removal of electrons from chlorophyll molecules

E) ATP synthesis

Answer: D

8) Which of the following statements is a correct distinction between cyclic and noncyclic electron flow?

A) Only noncyclic electron flow produces ATP.

B) In addition to ATP, cyclic electron flow also produces $O_2$ and NADPH.

C) Only cyclic electron flow utilizes light at 700 nm.

D) Chemiosmosis is unique to noncyclic electron flow.

E) Only cyclic electron flow can operate in the absence of photosystem II.

Answer: E

9) Which of the following statements is a correct distinction between autotrophs and heterotrophs?

A) Only heterotrophs require chemical compounds from the environment.

B) Cellular respiration is unique to heterotrophs.

C) Only heterotrophs have mitochondria.

D) Autotrophs, but not heterotrophs, can nourish themselves beginning with $CO_2$ and other nutrients that are inorganic.

E) Only heterotrophs require oxygen.

Answer: D

10) Which of the following does *not* occur during the Calvin cycle?

A) carbon fixation

B) oxidation of NADPH

C) release of oxygen

D) regeneration of the $CO_2$ acceptor

E) consumption of ATP

Answer: C

# Chapter 11  Cell Communication

1) In yeast (*Saccharomyces cerevisiae*), the two sexes are called

A) S plus and S minus.

B) **a** and α.

C) **a** and b.

D) b and β.

E) male and female.

Answer: B
*Topic: Concept 11.1*
*Skill: Knowledge*

2) In the yeast signal transduction pathway, after both types of mating cells have released the mating factors and the factors have bound to specific receptors on the correct cells,

A) binding induces changes in the cells that lead to cell fusion.

B) the cells then produce the **a** factor and the α factor.

C) one cell nucleus binds the mating factors and produces a new nucleus in the opposite cell.

D) the cell membranes fall apart, releasing the mating factors that lead to new yeast cells.

E) a growth factor is secreted that stimulates mitosis in both cells.

Answer: A
*Topic: Concept 11.1*
*Skill: Comprehension*

3) Which of the following is *true* of the mating signal transduction pathway in yeast?

A) The pathway carries an electrical signal between mating cell types.

B) Mating type **a** secretes a signal called **a** factor.

C) The molecular details of the pathway in yeast and in animals are very different.

D) Scientists think the pathway evolved long after multicellular creatures appeared on Earth.

E) The signal reception, transduction, and response occur in the nucleus.

Answer: B
*Topic: Concept 11.1*
*Skill: Knowledge*

4) What could happen to the target cells in an animal that lack receptors for local regulators?

A) They could compensate by receiving nutrients via an **a** factor.

B) They could develop normally in response to neurotransmitters instead.

C) They could divide but never reach full size.

D) They would not be able to multiply in response to growth factors from nearby cells.

E) Hormones would not be able to interact with target cells.

Answer: D
*Topic: Concept 11.1*
*Skill: Comprehension*

5) Paracrine signaling
   A) involves secreting cells acting on nearby target cells by discharging a local regulator into the extracellular fluid.
   B) requires nerve cells to release a neurotransmitter into the synapse.
   C) occurs only in paracrine yeast cells.
   D) has been found in plants but not animals.
   E) involves mating factors attaching to target cells and causing production of new paracrine cells.

Answer: A
*Topic: Concept 11.1*
*Skill: Knowledge*

6) Which of the following is *true* of synaptic signaling and hormonal signaling?
   A) Hormonal signaling occurs in animals only.
   B) Hormonal signaling is important between cells that are at greater distances apart than in synaptic signaling.
   C) Both act on target cells by a G–protein–signaling pathway.
   D) Only A and B are true.
   E) A , B, and C are true.

Answer: B
*Topic: Concept 11.1*
*Skill: Comprehension*

7) The old saying "one rotten apple spoils the whole barrel" is due to chemical signaling in plants via
   A) an increased uptake of carbon dioxide during respiration in target cells.
   B) a local regulator for apple development.
   C) release of ethylene gas, a plant hormone for ripening.
   D) an **a**/α cell signal system in the rotten apple.
   E) a signal transduction pathway involving glycogen phosphorylase.

Answer: C
*Topic: Concept 11.1*
*Skill: Comprehension*

8) From the perspective of the cell receiving the message, the three stages of cell signaling are
   A) the paracrine, local, and synaptic stages.
   B) signal reception, signal transduction, and cellular response.
   C) signal reception, nucleus disintegration, and new cell generation.
   D) the alpha, beta, and gamma stages.
   E) signal reception, cellular response, and cell division.

Answer: B
*Topic: Concept 11.1*
*Skill: Knowledge*

9) The process of transduction usually begins

A) when the chemical signal is released from the alpha cell.

B) when the signal molecule changes the receptor protein in some way.

C) after the target cell divides.

D) after the third stage of cell signaling is completed.

E) when the hormone is released from the gland into the blood.

Answer: B
*Topic: Concept 11.1*
*Skill: Knowledge*

10) When a cell releases a signal molecule into the environment and a number of cells in the immediate vicinity respond, this type of signaling is

A) typical of hormones.

B) autocrine signaling.

C) paracrine signaling.

D) endocrine signaling.

E) synaptic signaling.

Answer: C
*Topic: Concept 11.1*
*Skill: Knowledge*

11) The signal transduction pathway in animal cells that use epinephrine

A) activates the breakdown of glycogen in liver and skeletal muscle cells.

B) is a classic example of synaptic signaling.

C) operates independently of hormone receptors on target cells.

D) A and B only

E) A, B, and C

Answer: A
*Topic: Concept 11.1*
*Skill: Knowledge*

12) A small molecule that specifically binds to another molecule, usually a larger one

A) is called a signal transducer.

B) is called a ligand.

C) is called a polymer.

D) seldom is involved in hormonal signaling.

E) usually terminates a signal reception.

Answer: B
*Topic: Concept 11.2*
*Skill: Knowledge*

13) Which of the following is (are) true of ligand–gated ion channels?

A) They are important in the nervous system.

B) They lead to changes in sodium and calcium concentrations in cells.

C) They open or close in response to a chemical signal.

D) Only A and B are true.

E) A, B, and C are true.

Answer: E
*Topic: Concept 11.2*
*Skill: Knowledge*

14) Of the following, a receptor protein in a membrane that recognizes a chemical signal is most similar to

A) the active site of an enzyme in the cytoplasm that binds to a specific substrate.

B) RNA specifying the amino acids in a polypeptide.

C) a particular metabolic pathway operating within a specific organelle.

D) an enzyme with an optimum pH and temperature for activity.

E) genes making up a chromosome.

Answer: A
*Topic: Concept 11.2*
*Skill: Comprehension*

15) Most signal molecules

   A) bind to specific sites on receptor proteins in a membrane.

   B) are water-soluble.

   C) are able to pass through the plasma membrane by active transport.

   D) A and B only

   E) A, B, and C

   Answer: D
   *Topic: Concept 11.2*
   *Skill: Comprehension*

16) Which of the following signal systems use(s) G-protein-linked receptors?

   A) yeast mating factors

   B) epinephrine

   C) neurotransmitters

   D) A and C only

   E) A, B, and C

   Answer: E
   *Topic: Concept 11.2*
   *Skill: Comprehension*

17) What would be *true* for the signaling system in an animal cell that lacks the ability to produce GTP?

   A) It would not be able to activate and inactivate the G protein on the cytoplasmic side of the plasma membrane.

   B) It could activate only the epinephrine system.

   C) It would be able to carry out reception and transduction, but would not be able to respond to a signal.

   D) Only A and C are true.

   E) A, B, and C are true.

   Answer: A
   *Topic: Concept 11.2*
   *Skill: Comprehension*

18) G proteins and G-protein-linked receptors

   A) are found only in animal cells.

   B) are found only in bacterial cells.

   C) are thought to have evolved very early, because of their similar structure and function in a wide variety of modern organisms whose common ancestors diverged billions of years ago.

   D) probably evolved from an adaptation of the citric acid cycle.

   E) are not widespread in nature and were unimportant in the evolution of eukaryotes.

   Answer: C
   *Topic: Concept 11.2*
   *Skill: Knowledge*

19) The ability of a single ligand bound to a receptor protein to trigger several pathways is

   A) characteristic of the synaptic signal system.

   B) unique to the yeast mating system.

   C) rare in animals, but common in bacteria.

   D) a key difference between the tyrosine-kinase and G-protein-linked receptor systems.

   E) common to all plasma membrane receptor proteins.

   Answer: D
   *Topic: Concept 11.2*
   *Skill: Knowledge*

20) Membrane receptors that attach phosphates to specific animo acids in proteins are

A) not found in humans.

B) called receptor tyrosine-kinases.

C) a class of GTP G-protein signal receptors.

D) associated with several bacterial diseases in humans.

E) important in yeast mating factors that contain amino acids.

Answer: B
*Topic: Concept 11.2*
*Skill: Knowledge*

21) Up to 60% of all medicines used today exert their effects by influencing what structures in the cell membrane?

A) tyrosine-kinases receptors

B) ligand-gated ion channel receptors

C) growth factors

D) G proteins

E) cholesterol

Answer: D
*Topic: Concept 11.2*
*Skill: Knowledge*

22) Which of the following are chemical messengers that pass through the plasma membrane of cells and have receptor molecules in the cytoplasm?

A) insulin

B) nitric oxide

C) testosterone

D) B and C only

E) A, B, and C

Answer: D
*Topic: Concept 11.2*
*Skill: Knowledge*

23) Testosterone functions inside a cell by

A) acting as a signal receptor that activates ion-channel proteins.

B) binding with a receptor protein that enters the nucleus and activates specific genes.

C) acting as a steroid signal receptor that activates ion-channel proteins.

D) becoming a second messenger that inhibits adenylyl cyclase.

E) coordinating a phosphorylation cascade that increases glycogen metabolism.

Answer: B
*Topic: Concept 11.2*
*Skill: Comprehension*

24) Which is true of transcription factors?

A) They regulate the synthesis of DNA in response to a signal.

B) Some transcribe ATP into cAMP.

C) They initiate the epinephrine response in animal cells.

D) They control which genes are turned on to form mRNA.

E) They are needed to regulate the synthesis of protein in the cytoplasm.

Answer: D
*Topic: Concept 11.2*
*Skill: Knowledge*

25) Chemical signal pathways

    A) operate in animals, but not in plants.

    B) are absent in bacteria, but are plentiful in yeast.

    C) involve the release of hormones into the blood.

    D) often involve the binding of signal molecules to a protein on the surface of a target cell.

    E) use hydrophilic molecules to activate enzymes.

Answer: D
*Topic: Concept 11.2*
*Skill: Knowledge*

26) The receptors for a group of signaling molecules known as growth factors are often

    A) ligand–gated ion channels.

    B) G–protein–linked receptors.

    C) cyclic AMP.

    D) receptor tyrosine kinases.

    E) neurotransmitters.

Answer: D
*Topic: Concept 11.3*
*Skill: Knowledge*

27) In general, a signal transmitted via phosphorylation of a series of proteins

    A) brings a conformational change to each protein.

    B) requires binding of a hormone to a cytosol receptor.

    C) cannot occur in yeasts because they lack protein phosphatases.

    D) requires phosphorylase activity.

    E) allows target cells to change their shape and therefore their activity.

Answer: A
*Topic: Concept 11.3*
*Skill: Comprehension*

28) Which of the following is (are) *true* regarding the activity of a protein regulated by phosphorylation?

    A) It depends mostly on the concentration of inorganic phosphate inside the cell.

    B) It depends on the balance in the cell between active kinase and active phosphatase molecules.

    C) It is dependent on the site of attachment of the protein to the plasma membrane.

    D) Only A and B are true.

    E) A, B, and C are true.

Answer: B
*Topic: Concept 11.3*
*Skill: Comprehension*

29) Which of the following is a widely used second messenger in signal transduction pathways?

    A) calcium ions

    B) cyclic AMP

    C) inositol trisphosphate

    D) A and B only

    E) A, B, and C

Answer: E
*Topic: Concept 11.3*
*Skill: Knowledge*

30) Sutherland discovered that epinephrine

    A) signals bypass the plasma membrane of cells.

    B) lowers blood glucose by binding to liver cells.

    C) interacts with insulin inside muscle cells.

    D) interacts directly with glycogen phosphorylase.

    E) elevates the cytosolic concentration of cyclic AMP.

Answer: E
*Topic: Concept 11.3*
*Skill: Knowledge*

31) A plant deficient in calcium could experience several problems, including

A) poor response to signals of stress, drought, or cold.

B) decreased response to epinephrine.

C) overactive cyclic AMP responses.

D) B and C only

E) A, B, and C

Answer: A
*Topic: Concept 11.3*
*Skill: Comprehension*

32) An animal deficient in adenylyl cyclase

A) would not respond properly to epinephrine.

B) could not convert GTP to ATP.

C) would lack plasma membrane bound receptors.

D) A and B only

E) A, B, and C

Answer: A
*Topic: Concept 11.3*
*Skill: Comprehension*

33) Which of the following is *not* considered a second messenger?

A) cAMP

B) GTP

C) calcium ions

D) diacylglycerol (DAG)

E) inositol trisphosphate (IP3)

Answer: B
*Topic: Concept 11.3*
*Skill: Knowledge*

34) Which of the following is the best explanation for the inability of an animal cell to reduce the $Ca^{2+}$ concentration in its cytosol compared with the extracellular fluid?

A) blockage of the synaptic signal

B) loss of transcription factors

C) insufficient ATP levels in the cytoplasm

D) low oxygen concentration around the cell

E) low levels of protein kinase in the cell

Answer: C
*Topic: Concept 11.3*
*Skill: Comprehension*

35) The general name for an enzyme that transfers phosphate groups from ATP to a protein is

A) phosphorylase.

B) phosphatase.

C) protein kinase.

D) ATPase.

E) protease.

Answer: C
*Topic: Concept 11.3*
*Skill: Knowledge*

36) Which of the following is *not* true of cell communication systems?

A) Cell signaling was an early event in the evolution of life.

B) Communicating cells may be far apart or close together.

C) Most signal receptors are bound to the outer membrane of the nuclear envelope.

D) Protein phosphorylation is a major mechanism of signal transduction.

E) In response to a signal, the cell may alter activities by changes in cytosol activity or in transcription of RNA.

Answer: C
*Topic: Concept 11.3*
*Skill: Comprehension*

37) The toxin of *Vibrio cholerae* causes profuse diarrhea because it

A) modifies a G protein involved in regulating salt and water secretion.

B) decreases the cytosolic concentration of calcium ions, making the cells hypotonic to the intestinal cells.

C) binds with adenylyl cyclase and triggers the formation of cAMP.

D) signals inositol trisphosphate to become a second messenger for the release of calcium.

E) modifies calmodulin and activates a cascade of protein kinases.

Answer: A
*Topic: Concept 11.3*
*Skill: Knowledge*

38) Which of the following is *not* part of the phosphorylation cascade model?

A) A signal molecule binds to a membrane receptor protein.

B) Protein kinase is activated.

C) GTP donates a phosphate group to an inactive protein kinase.

D) A specific protein is activated via phosphorylation.

E) A cellular response is initiated.

Answer: C
*Topic: Concept 11.3*
*Skill: Knowledge*

39) In a typical cell, calcium ions are

A) far more abundant in the blood and other extracellular fluid than in the cytoplasm.

B) rapidly released from the endoplasmic reticulum in response to G–protein–mediated signals.

C) often concentrated within the endoplasmic reticulum.

D) A and B only

E) A, B, and C

Answer: E
*Topic: Concept 11.3*
*Skill: Knowledge*

40) Which of the following would be inhibited by a drug that specifically blocks the addition of phosphate groups to proteins?

A) G–protein–linked receptor signaling

B) ligand–gated ion channel signaling

C) adenylyl cyclase activity

D) phosphatase activity

E) receptor tyrosine kinase activity

Answer: E
*Topic: Concept 11.3*
*Skill: Application*

41) Which of the following most likely would be an immediate result of growth factor binding to its receptor?

    A) protein kinase activity

    B) adenylyl cyclase activity

    C) GTPase activity

    D) protein phosphatase activity

    E) phosphorylase activity

Answer: A
*Topic: Concept 11.3*
*Skill: Comprehension*

42) An inhibitor of phosphodiesterase activity would have which of the following effects?

    A) block the response of epinephrine

    B) decrease the amount of cAMP in the cytoplasm

    C) block the activation of G proteins in response to epinephrine binding to its receptor

    D) prolong the effect of epinephrine by maintaining elevated cAMP levels in the cytoplasm

    E) block the activation of protein kinase A

Answer: D
*Topic: Concept 11.3*
*Skill: Application*

43) Adenylyl cyclase has the opposite effect of which of the following?

    A) protein kinase

    B) protein phosphatase

    C) phosphodiesterase

    D) phosphorylase

    E) GTPase

Answer: C
*Topic: Concept 11.3*
*Skill: Knowledge*

44) Caffeine is an inhibitor of phosphodiesterase. Therefore, the cells of a person who has recently consumed coffee would have increased levels of

    A) phosphorylated proteins.

    B) GTP.

    C) cAMP.

    D) adenylyl cyclase.

    E) activated G proteins.

Answer: C
*Topic: Concept 11.3*
*Skill: Application*

45) If a pharmaceutical company wished to design a drug to maintain low blood sugar levels, one approach might be to

    A) design a compound that blocks epinephrine receptor activation.

    B) design a compound that inhibits cAMP production in liver cells.

    C) design a compound to block G-protein activity in liver cells.

    D) design a compound that inhibits phosphorylase activity.

    E) All of the above are possible approaches.

Answer: E
*Topic: Concept 11.3*
*Skill: Application*

46) If a pharmaceutical company wished to design a drug to maintain low blood sugar levels, one approach might be to

A) design a compound that mimics epinephrine and can bind to the epinephrine receptor.

B) design a compound that stimulates cAMP production in liver cells.

C) design a compound to stimulate G protein activity in liver cells.

D) design a compound that increases phosphodiesterase activity.

E) All of the above are possible approaches.

Answer: D
*Topic: Concept 11.3*
*Skill: Application*

47) An inhibitor of which of the following could be used to block the release of calcium from the endoplasmic reticulum?

A) tyrosine kinases

B) serine/threonine kinases

C) phosphodiesterase

D) phospholipase C

E) adenylyl cyclase

Answer: D
*Topic: Concept 11.3*
*Skill: Application*

48) Which of the following statements is *incorrect*?

A) When signal molecules bind to receptor tyrosine kinases, the receptors phosphorylate themselves.

B) In response to some G–protein–mediated signals, a special type of lipid molecule associated with the plasma membrane is cleaved to form $IP_3$ and calcium.

C) In most cases, signal molecules interact with the cell at the plasma membrane and never actually enter the cell.

D) Toxins such as those that cause botulism and cholera interfere with the ability of activated G proteins to hydrolyze GTP to GDP, resulting in adenylyl cyclase activity in the absence of an appropriate signal molecule.

E) Protein kinase A activation is one possible result of signal molecules binding to G–protein–linked receptors.

Answer: B
*Topic: Concept 11.3*
*Skill: Comprehension*

49) Which of the following is an *incorrect* association?

A) kinase activity and the addition of a phosphate group

B) phosphodiesterase activity and the removal of phosphate groups

C) GTPase activity and hydrolysis of GTP to GDP

D) phosphorylase activity and the catabolism of glycogen

E) adenylyl cyclase activity and the conversion of AMP to cAMP

Answer: B
*Topic: Concept 11.3*
*Skill: Application*

50) A drug designed to inhibit the response of cells to testosterone would almost certainly result in which of the following?

    A) lower cytoplasmic levels of cAMP

    B) an increase in receptor tyrosine kinase activity

    C) a decrease in transcriptional activity of certain genes

    D) an increase in cytosolic calcium concentration

    E) a decrease in G-protein activity

Answer: C
*Topic: Concept 11.4*
*Skill: Application*

51) The response of a particular cell to a signal depends on

    A) its particular collection of signal receptor proteins.

    B) its relay proteins.

    C) the proteins needed to carry out the response.

    D) A and B only

    E) A, B, and C

Answer: E
*Topic: Concept 11.4*
*Skill: Knowledge*

52) Which example below is a protein that can hold several other relay proteins as it binds to an activated membrane receptor?

    A) active transcription factor

    B) third messenger

    C) ligand

    D) scaffolding protein

    E) protein kinase

Answer: D
*Topic: Concept 11.4*
*Skill: Knowledge*

# Media Activity Questions

1) A(n) _____ is an example of a signal molecule that can bind to an intracellular receptor and thereby cause a gene to be turned on or off.

   A) ion

   B) protein

   C) carbohydrate

   D) nucleic acid

   E) steroid

   Answer: E
   *Topic: Web/CD Activity: Reception*

2) Thyroid hormones bind to _____ receptors.

   A) receptor tyrosine kinases

   B) plasma membrane ion–channel

   C) steroid

   D) intracellular

   E) G–protein–linked

   Answer: D
   *Topic: Web/CD Activity: Reception*

3) _____ catalyzes the production of _____, which then opens an ion channel that releases _____ into the cell's cytoplasm.

   A) Adenylyl cyclase; cyclic AMP; $Ca^{2+}$

   B) Adenylyl cyclase; $IP_3$; $Ca^{2+}$

   C) Protein kinase; $PIP_2$; $Na^+$

   D) Phospholipase C; cyclic AMP; $Ca^{2+}$

   E) Phospholipase C; $IP_3$; $Ca^{2+}$

   Answer: E
   *Topic: Activity: Signal Transduction Pathways*

4) The cleavage of glycogen by glycogen phosphorylase releases _____.

   A) glucose-1-phosphate

   B) cellulose

   C) galactose-1-phosphate

   D) fructose-1-phosphate

   E) nothing; glycogen phosphorylase cannot cleave glycogen

   Answer: A
   *Topic: Web/CD Activity: Cellular Responses*

5) Which of these is *not* correct?

   A) Phospholipase C catalyzes the formation of $IP_3$.

   B) Receptor tyrosine kinases consist of two polypeptides that join when activated by a signal molecule.

   C) Ion channels are found on both the plasma membrane and the endoplasmic reticulum.

   D) Cyclic AMP binds to calmodulin.

   E) Kinases are enzymes that phosphorylate other molecules.

   Answer: D
   *Topic: Web/CD Activity: Cellular Responses*

# Self-Quiz Questions

1) Phosphorylation cascades involving a series of protein kinases are useful for cellular signal transduction because
   A) they are species specific.
   B) they always lead to the same cellular response.
   C) they amplify the original signal manyfold.
   D) they counter the harmful effects of phosphatases.
   E) the number of molecules used is small and fixed.

   Answer: C

2) Binding of a signal molecule to which type of receptor leads directly to a change in the distribution of anions and/or cations on opposite sides of the membrane?
   A) receptor tyrosine kinase
   B) G-protein-linked receptor
   C) phosphorylated receptor tyrosine kinase dimer
   D) ligand-gated ion channel
   E) intracellular receptor

   Answer: D

3) The activation of receptor tyrosine kinases is always characterized by
   A) dimerization and phosphorylation.
   B) IP3 binding.
   C) a phosphorylation cascade.
   D) GTP hydrolysis.
   E) channel protein conformational change.

   Answer: A

4) Which of the following provides the best evidence that cell-signaling pathways evolved early in the history of life?
   A) They are seen in "primitive" cells such as yeast.
   B) Yeast cells signal each other for mating.
   C) Signal transduction molecules found in distantly related organisms are similar.
   D) Signals can be sent long distances by cells.
   E) Most signals are received by cell surface receptors.

   Answer: C

5) Which observation suggested to Sutherland the involvement of a second messenger in epinephrine's effect on liver cells?
   A) Enzymatic activity was proportional to the amount of calcium added to a cell-free extract.
   B) Receptor studies indicated that epinephrine was a ligand.
   C) Glycogen breakdown was observed only when epinephrine was administered to intact cells.
   D) Glycogen breakdown was observed when epinephrine and glycogen phosphorylase were combined.
   E) Epinephrine was known to have different effects on different types of cells.

   Answer: C

6) Protein phosphorylation is commonly involved with all of the following *except*

A) regulation of transcription by extracellular signal molecules.

B) enzyme activation.

C) activation of G-protein-linked receptors.

D) activation of receptor tyrosine kinases.

E) activation of protein kinase molecules.

Answer: C

7) Amplification of a chemical signal occurs when

A) a receptor in the plasma membrane activates several G-protein molecules while a signal molecule is bound to it.

B) a cAMP molecule activates one protein kinase molecule before being converted to AMP.

C) phosphorylase and phosphatase activities are balanced.

D) receptor tyrosine kinases dimerize upon ligand binding.

E) Both A and D occur.

Answer: A

8) Lipid-soluble signal molecules, such as testosterone, cross the membranes of all cells but affect only target cells because

A) only target cells retain the appropriate DNA segments.

B) intracellular receptors are present only in target cells.

C) most cells lack the Y chromosome required.

D) only target cells possess the cytosolic enzymes that transduce the testosterone.

E) only in target cells is testosterone able to initiate the phosphorylation cascade leading to activated transcription factor.

Answer: B

9) Signal transduction pathways benefit cells for all of the following reasons *except*

A) they help cells respond to signal molecules that are too large or too polar to cross the plasma membrane.

B) they enable different cells to respond appropriately to the same signal.

C) they help cells use up phosphate generated by ATP breakdown.

D) they can amplify a signal.

E) variations in the signal transduction pathways can enhance response specificity.

Answer: C

10) Consider this pathway: epinephrine → G-protein-linked receptor → G protein → adenylyl cyclase → cAMP. Identify the second messenger.

A) cAMP

B) G protein

C) GTP

D) adenylyl cyclase

E) G-protein-linked receptor

Answer: A

# Chapter 12 The Cell Cycle

1) The centromere is a region in which
   A) chromatids are attached to one another.
   B) metaphase chromosomes become aligned.
   C) chromosomes are grouped during telophase.
   D) the nucleus is located prior to mitosis.
   E) new spindle microtubules form.

   Answer: A
   *Topic: Concept 12.1*
   *Skill: Knowledge*

2) What is a chromatid?
   A) a chromosome in $G_1$ of the cell cycle
   B) a replicated chromosome
   C) a chromosome found outside the nucleus
   D) a special region that holds two centromeres together
   E) another name for the chromosomes found in genetics

   Answer: B
   *Topic: Concept 12.1*
   *Skill: Knowledge*

3) What is the name for the special region on a duplicated chromosome that holds the sister chromatids together?
   A) centrosome
   B) centromere
   C) kinetochore
   D) desmosome
   E) microtubule organizer region

   Answer: B
   *Topic: Concept 12.1*
   *Skill: Knowledge*

4) Starting with a fertilized egg (zygote), a series of five cell divisions would produce an early embryo with how many cells?
   A) 4
   B) 8
   C) 16
   D) 32
   E) 64

   Answer: D
   *Topic: Concept 12.1*
   *Skill: Knowledge*

5) If there are 20 chromatids in a cell, how many centromeres are there?
   A) 10
   B) 20
   C) 30
   D) 40
   E) 80

   Answer: A
   *Topic: Concept 12.1*
   *Skill: Application*

6) Which of the following statements is *not* true?
   A) Mitosis produces new nuclei with exactly the same chromosomal endowment as the parent nucleus.
   B) Mitosis may occur without cytokinesis.
   C) Mitosis and cytokinesis are required for asexual reproduction.
   D) All cells come from a preexisting cell.
   E) The mitotic spindles in prokaryotic cells are composed of microtubules.

   Answer: E
   *Topic: Concept 12.2*
   *Skill: Knowledge*

*Use the following information to answer the questions below.*

The lettered circle in Figure 12.1 shows a diploid nucleus with four chromosomes. There are two pairs of homologous chromosomes, one long and the other short. One haploid set is symbolized as black and the other haploid set is gray. The chromosomes in the unlettered circle have not yet replicated. Choose the correct chromosomal conditions for the following stages.

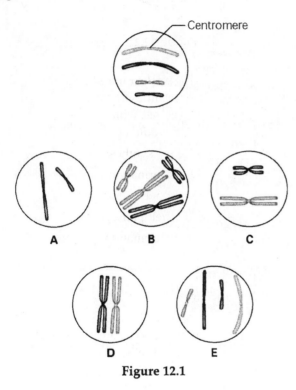

**Figure 12.1**

7) at prometaphase of mitosis

Answer: B
*Topic: Concept 12.2*
*Skill: Comprehension*

8) one daughter nucleus at telophase of mitosis

Answer: E
*Topic: Concept 12.2*
*Skill: Knowledge*

*The questions below refer to the following terms. Each term may be used once, more than once, or not at all.*

A. telophase
B. anaphase
C. prometaphase
D. metaphase
E. prophase

9) Two centrosomes are arranged at opposite poles of the cell.

Answer: C
*Topic: Concept 12.2*
*Skill: Knowledge*

10) Centrioles begin to move apart in animal cells.

Answer: E
*Topic: Concept 12.2*
*Skill: Knowledge*

11) This is the longest of the mitotic stages.

Answer: D
*Topic: Concept 12.2*
*Skill: Knowledge*

12) Centromeres uncouple, sister chromatids are separated, and the two new chromosomes move to opposite poles of the cell.

Answer: B
*Topic: Concept 12.2*
*Skill: Knowledge*

13) If cells in the process of dividing are subjected to colchicine, a drug that interferes with the functioning of the spindle apparatus, at which stage will mitosis be arrested?

    A) anaphase

    B) prophase

    C) telophase

    D) metaphase

    E) interphase

Answer: D
*Topic: Concept 12.2*
*Skill: Application*

14) A cell containing 92 chromatids at metaphase of mitosis would, at its completion, produce two nuclei containing how many chromosomes?

    A) 12

    B) 16

    C) 23

    D) 46

    E) 92

Answer: D
*Topic: Concept 12.2*
*Skill: Comprehension*

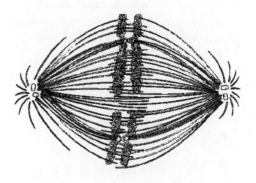

**Figure 12.2**

15) If the cell whose nuclear material is shown in Figure 12.2 continues toward completion of mitosis, which of the following events would occur next?

    A) cell membrane synthesis

    B) spindle fiber formation

    C) nuclear envelope breakdown

    D) formation of telophase nuclei

    E) synthesis of chromatids

Answer: D
*Topic: Concept 12.2*
*Skill: Knowledge*

16) All of the following occur during prophase of mitosis in animal cells *except*

    A) the centrioles move toward opposite poles.

    B) the nucleolus can no longer be seen.

    C) the nuclear envelope disappears.

    D) chromosomes are duplicated.

    E) the spindle is organized.

Answer: D
*Topic: Concept 12.2*
*Skill: Comprehension*

17) If there are 20 centromeres in a cell at anaphase, how many chromosomes are there in each daughter cell following cytokinesis?

A) 10

B) 20

C) 30

D) 40

E) 80

Answer: B
*Topic: Concept 12.2*
*Skill: Application*

18) If there are 20 chromatids in a cell at metaphase, how many chromosomes are there in each daughter cell following cytokinesis?

A) 10

B) 20

C) 30

D) 40

E) 80

Answer: A
*Topic: Concepts 12.1, 12.2*
*Skill: Application*

*Use the data in Table 12.1 to answer the following questions.*

The data were obtained from a study of the length of time spent in each phase of the cell cycle by cells of three eukaryotic organisms designated beta, delta, and gamma.

**Table 12.1: Minutes Spent in Cell Cycle Phases**

| Cell Type | $G_1$ | S | $G_2$ | M |
|---|---|---|---|---|
| Beta | 18 | 24 | 12 | 16 |
| Delta | 100 | 0 | 0 | 0 |
| Gamma | 18 | 48 | 14 | 20 |

19) Of the following, the best conclusion concerning the difference between the S phases for beta and gamma is that

A) gamma contains more DNA than beta.

B) beta and gamma contain the same amount of DNA.

C) beta contains more RNA than gamma.

D) gamma contains 48 times more DNA and RNA than beta.

E) beta is a plant cell and gamma is an animal cell.

Answer: A
*Topic: Concept 12.2*
*Skill: Application*

20) The best conclusion concerning delta is that the cells

A) contain no DNA.

B) contain no RNA.

C) contain only one chromosome that is very short.

D) are actually in the $G_0$ phase.

E) divide in the $G_1$ phase.

Answer: D
*Topic: Concept 12.2*
*Skill: Application*

21) How is the S phase of the cell cycle measured?

A) counting the number of cells produced per hour

B) determining the length of time during which DNA synthesis occurred in the cells

C) comparing the synthesis versus the breakdown of S protein

D) determining when the S chromosome is synthesized

E) stopping $G_1$ and measuring the number of picograms of DNA per cell

Answer: B
*Topic: Concept 12.2*
*Skill: Application*

22) Where do the microtubules of the spindle originate during mitosis in both plant and animal cells?

A) centromere

B) centrosome

C) centriole

D) chromatid

E) kinetochore

Answer: B
*Topic: Concept 12.2*
*Skill: Knowledge*

23) All of the following occur during mitosis *except* the

A) condensing of chromosomes.

B) uncoupling of chromatids at the centromere.

C) formation of a spindle.

D) synthesis of DNA.

E) disappearance of the nucleolus.

Answer: D
*Topic: Concept 12.2*
*Skill: Knowledge*

24) If a cell has 8 chromosomes at metaphase of mitosis, how many chromosomes will it have during anaphase?

A) 1

B) 2

C) 4

D) 8

E) 16

Answer: E
*Topic: Concept 12.2*
*Skill: Comprehension*

25) Cytokinesis usually, but not always, follows mitosis. If a cell completed mitosis but not cytokinesis, the result would be a cell with

A) a single large nucleus.

B) high concentrations of actin and myosin.

C) two abnormally small nuclei.

D) two nuclei.

E) two nuclei but with half the amount of DNA.

Answer: D
*Topic: Concept 12.2*
*Skill: Knowledge*

26) Regarding mitosis and cytokinesis, one difference between higher plants and animals is that in plants

A) the spindles contain microfibrils in addition to microtubules, whereas animal spindles do not contain microfibrils.

B) sister chromatids are identical, but they differ from one another in animals.

C) a cell plate begins to form at telophase, whereas animals a cleavage furrow is initiated at that stage.

D) chromosomes become attached to the spindle at prophase, whereas in animals chromosomes do not become attached until anaphase.

E) spindle poles contain centrioles, whereas spindle poles in animals do not.

Answer: C
Topic: Concept 12.2
Skill: Knowledge

27) How do the daughter cells at the end of mitosis and cytokinesis compare with their parent cell when it was in $G_1$ of the cell cycle?

A) The daughter cells have half the amount of cytoplasm and half the amount of DNA.

B) The daughter cells have half the number of chromosomes and half the amount of DNA.

C) The daughter cells have the same number of chromosomes and half the amount of DNA.

D) The daughter cells have the same number of chromosomes and the same amount of DNA.

E) The daughter cells have the same number of chromosomes and twice the amount of DNA.

Answer: D
Topic: Concepts 12.1, 12.2
Skill: Comprehension

28) The formation of a cell plate is beginning across the middle of a cell and nuclei are re-forming at opposite ends of the cell. What kind of cell is this?

A) an animal cell in metaphase

B) an animal cell in telophase

C) an animal cell undergoing cytokinesis

D) a plant cell in metaphase

E) a plant cell undergoing cytokinesis

Answer: E
Topic: Concept 12.2
Skill: Knowledge

29) Taxol is an anticancer drug extracted from the Pacific yew tree. In animal cells, taxol disrupts microtubule formation by binding to microtubules and accelerating their assembly from the protein precursor, tubulin. Surprisingly, this stops mitosis. Specifically, taxol must affect

   A) the fibers of the mitotic spindle.

   B) anaphase.

   C) formation of the centrioles.

   D) chromatid assembly.

   E) S phase of the cell cycle.

Answer: A
*Topic: Concept 12.2*
*Skill: Application*

30) Which of the following are primarily responsible for cytokinesis in plant cells?

   A) kinetochores

   B) Golgi-derived vesicles

   C) actin and myosin

   D) centrioles and basal bodies

   E) cyclin-dependent kinases

Answer: B
*Topic: Concept 12.2*
*Skill: Knowledge*

31) Which of the following organisms does *not* reproduce cells by mitosis and cytokinesis?

   A) cow

   B) bacterium

   C) mushroom

   D) cockroach

   E) banana tree

Answer: B
*Topic: Concept 12.2*
*Skill: Knowledge*

32) Chromosomes first become visible during _____ of mitosis.

   A) prometaphase

   B) telophase

   C) prophase

   D) metaphase

   E) anaphase

Answer: C
*Topic: Concept 12.2*
*Skill: Knowledge*

33) The correct sequence of steps in the M phase of the cell cycle is

   A) prophase, prometaphase, metaphase, anaphase, telophase.

   B) prophase, metaphase, prometaphase, anaphase, telophase.

   C) prophase, prometaphase, metaphase, anaphase, telophase, cytokinesis.

   D) prophase, metaphase, anaphase, telophase, cytokinesis.

   E) cytokinesis, telophase, prophase, prometaphase, metaphase, anaphase.

Answer: C
*Topic: Concept 12.2*
*Skill: Knowledge*

34) During which phases of mitosis are chromosomes composed of two chromatids?

   A) from interphase through anaphase

   B) from $G_1$ of interphase through metaphase

   C) from metaphase through telophase

   D) from anaphase through telophase

   E) from $G_2$ of interphase through metaphase

Answer: E
*Topic: Concept 12.2*
*Skill: Comprehension*

35) Which of the following is *false* regarding the bacterial chromosome?

A) It consists of a single, circular DNA molecule.

B) DNA replication begins at the origin of replication.

C) Its centromeres uncouple during metaphase of mitosis.

D) It is highly folded within the cell.

E) It has genes that control binary fission.

Answer: C
*Topic: Concept 12.2*
*Skill: Knowledge*

36) In which group of eukaryotic organisms does the nuclear envelope remain intact during mitosis?

A) seedless plants

B) dinoflagellates

C) diatoms

D) B and C only

E) A, B, and C

Answer: D
*Topic: Concept 12.2*
*Skill: Knowledge*

37) Movement of the chromosomes during anaphase would be *most* affected by a drug that

A) reduces cyclin concentrations.

B) increases cyclin concentrations.

C) prevents elongation of microtubules.

D) prevents shortening of microtubules.

E) prevents attachment of the microtubules to the kinetochore.

Answer: D
*Topic: Concept 12.2*
*Skill: Application*

38) Measurements of the amount of DNA per nucleus were taken on a large number of cells from a growing fungus. The measured DNA levels ranged from 3 to 6 picograms per nucleus. In which stage of the cell cycle was the nucleus with 6 picograms of DNA?

A) $G_0$

B) $G_1$

C) S

D) $G_2$

E) M

Answer: D
*Topic: Concept 12.2*
*Skill: Application*

39) A group of cells is assayed for DNA content immediately following mitosis and is found to have an average of 8 picograms of DNA per nucleus. Those cells would have _____ picograms at the end of the S phase and _____ picograms at the end of $G_2$.

A) 8; 8

B) 8; 16

C) 16; 8

D) 16; 16

E) 12; 16

Answer: D
*Topic: Concept 12.2*
*Skill: Application*

40) The somatic cells derived from a single-celled zygote divide by which process?

A) meiosis

B) mitosis

C) replication

D) cytokinesis alone

E) binary fission

Answer: B
*Topic: Concept 12.2*
*Skill: Knowledge*

41) Cytoskeletal elements play important roles in cell division. The mitotic spindle apparatus is made of _____ and pulls sister chromatids apart, whereas the contractile ring is made of _____ and required for the separation of daughter cells at the end of the mitotic phase of the cell cycle.

A) intermediate filaments; actin microfilaments

B) microtubules; actin microfilaments

C) microtubules; contractile filaments

D) intermediate filaments; contractile filaments

E) actin microfilaments; myosin

Answer: B
*Topic: Concept 12.2*
*Skill: Knowledge*

42) Imagine looking through a microscope at a squashed onion root tip. The chromosomes of many of the cells are plainly visible. In some cells, replicated chromosomes are aligned along the center (equator) of the cell. These particular cells are in which stage of mitosis?

A) telophase

B) prophase

C) anaphase

D) metaphase

E) prometaphase

Answer: D
*Topic: Concept 12.2*
*Skill: Application*

43) If mammalian cells receive a go-ahead signal at the $G_1$ checkpoint, they will

A) move directly into telophase.

B) complete the cycle and divide.

C) exit the cycle and switch to a nondividing state.

D) show a drop in MPF concentration.

E) complete cytokinesis and form new cell walls.

Answer: B
*Topic: Concept 12.3*
*Skill: Knowledge*

44) Cells that are in a nondividing state are in which phase?

A) $G_0$

B) $G_2$

C) $G_1$

D) S

E) M

Answer: A
*Topic: Concept 12.3*
*Skill: Knowledge*

45) What causes the decrease in the amount of cyclin at a specific point in the cell cycle?

A) an increase in production once the restriction point is passed

B) the cascade of increased production once its protein is phosphorylated by Cdk

C) the changing ratio of cytoplasm to genome

D) its destruction by a process initiated by the activity of MPF complexes

E) the binding of PDGF to receptors on the cell surface

Answer: D
*Topic: Concept 12.3*
*Skill: Knowledge*

*The following questions consist of five phrases or sentences related to the control of cell division. For each one, select the term below that is most closely related to it. Each term may be used once, more than once, or not at all.*

    A. PDGF
    B. MPF
    C. protein kinase
    D. cyclin
    E. Cdk

46) released by platelets in the vicinity of an injury

Answer: A
*Topic: Concept 12.3*
*Skill: Knowledge*

47) a general term for enzymes that activate or inactivate other proteins by phosphorylating them

Answer: C
*Topic: Concept 12.3*
*Skill: Knowledge*

48) Fibroblasts have receptors for this substance on their plasma membranes.

Answer: A
*Topic: Concept 12.3*
*Skill: Knowledge*

49) a protein synthesized at specific times during the cell cycle that associates with a kinase to form a catalytically active complex

Answer: D
*Topic: Concept 12.3*
*Skill: Knowledge*

50) a protein maintained at constant levels throughout the cell cycle that requires cyclin to become catalytically active

Answer: E
*Topic: Concept 12.3*
*Skill: Knowledge*

51) triggers the cell's passage past the $G_2$ checkpoint into mitosis

Answer: B
*Topic: Concept 12.3*
*Skill: Knowledge*

*The questions below consist of five phrases or sentences concerned with the cell cycle. For each one, select the answer below that is most closely related to it. Each answer may be used once, more than once, or not at all.*

    A. $G_0$
    B. $G_1$
    C. S
    D. $G_2$
    E. M

52) The "restriction point" occurs here.

Answer: B
*Topic: Concept 12.3*
*Skill: Knowledge*

53) Nerve and muscle cells are in this phase.

Answer: A
*Topic: Concept 12.3*
*Skill: Knowledge*

54) the shortest part of the cell cycle

Answer: E
*Topic: Concept 12.2*
*Skill: Knowledge*

55) DNA is replicated at this time of the cell cycle.

Answer: C
*Topic: Concept 12.2*
*Skill: Knowledge*

56) The cyclin component of MPF is destroyed toward the end of this phase.

Answer: E
*Topic: Concept 12.3*
*Skill: Knowledge*

*The following questions are based on Figure 12.3.*

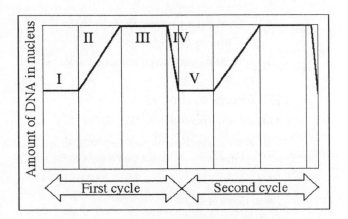

**Figure 12.3**

57) In the figure above, mitosis is represented by which number?

A) I

B) II

C) III

D) IV

E) V

Answer: D
*Topic: Concept 12.2*
*Skill: Comprehension*

58) MPF reaches its threshold concentration at the end of this stage.

A) I

B) II

C) III

D) IV

E) V

Answer: C
*Topic: Concept 12.3*
*Skill: Comprehension*

59) $G_1$ is represented by which number(s)?

A) I and V

B) II and IV

C) III

D) IV

E) V

Answer: A
*Topic: Concept 12.2*
*Skill: Comprehension*

60) Which number represents DNA synthesis?

A) I

B) II

C) III

D) IV

E) V

Answer: B
*Topic: Concept 12.2*
*Skill: Comprehension*

61) Which number represents the point in the cell cycle during which the chromosomes are replicated?

A) I

B) II

C) III

D) IV

E) V

Answer: B
*Topic: Concept 12.2*
*Skill: Comprehension*

62) What is the name of enzymes that control the activities of other proteins by phosphorylating them?
   A) ATPases
   B) kinases
   C) cyclins
   D) chromatin
   E) protein kinases

Answer: B
*Topic: Concept 12.3*
*Skill: Knowledge*

63) An enzyme that attaches a phosphate group to another molecule is called a
   A) phosphatase.
   B) phosphorylase.
   C) kinase.
   D) cyclase.
   E) ATPase.

Answer: C
*Topic: Concept 12.3*
*Skill: Knowledge*

64) Proteins that are involved in the regulation of the cell cycle, and that show fluctuations in concentration during the cell cycle, are called
   A) ATPases.
   B) kinetochores.
   C) centrioles.
   D) proton pumps.
   E) cyclins.

Answer: E
*Topic: Concept 12.3*
*Skill: Knowledge*

65) The MPF protein complex turns itself off by
   A) activating a process that destroys cyclin.
   B) activating an enzyme that stimulates cyclin.
   C) binding to chromatin.
   D) exiting the cell.
   E) activating the anaphase–promoting complex.

Answer: A
*Topic: Concept 12.3*
*Skill: Knowledge*

66) A mutation results in a cell that no longer produces a normal protein kinase for the M phase checkpoint. Which of the following would likely be the immediate result of this mutation?
   A) The cell would prematurely enter anaphase.
   B) The cell would never leave metaphase.
   C) The cell would never enter metaphase.
   D) The cell would never enter prophase.
   E) The cell would undergo normal mitosis, but fail to enter the next $G_1$ phase.

Answer: E
*Topic: Concept 12.3*
*Skill: Comprehension*

67) Density-dependent inhibition is explained by which of the following?

A) As cells become more numerous, they begin to squeeze against each other, restricting their size and ability to produce control factors.

B) As cells become more numerous, the amount of required growth factors and nutrients per cell becomes insufficient to allow for cell growth.

C) As cells become more numerous, the protein kinases they produce begin to compete with each other, such that the proteins produced by one cell essentially cancel those produced by its neighbor.

D) As cells become more numerous, more and more of them enter the S phase of the cell cycle.

E) As cells become more numerous, the level of waste products increases, eventually slowing down metabolism.

Answer: B
*Topic: Concept 12.3*
*Skill: Knowledge*

68) Which of the following is *true* concerning cancer cells?

A) They do not exhibit density-dependent inhibition when growing in culture.

B) When they stop dividing, they do so at random points in the cell cycle.

C) They are not subject to cell cycle controls.

D) B and C only

E) A, B, and C

Answer: E
*Topic: Concept 12.3*
*Skill: Knowledge*

69) Which of the following is (are) true concerning cyclin-dependent kinase (Cdk)?

A) Cdk is inactive, or "turned off," in the presence of cyclin.

B) Cdk is present throughout the cell cycle.

C) Cdk is an enzyme that attaches phosphate groups to other proteins.

D) Both A and B are true.

E) Both B and C are true.

Answer: E
*Topic: Concept 12.3*
*Skill: Comprehension*

70) A particular cyclin called cyclin E forms a complex with a cyclin-dependent kinase called Cdk 2. This complex is important for the progression of the cell from $G_1$ into the S phase of the cell cycle. Which of the following statements is *correct*?

A) The amount of cyclin E is greatest during the S phase.

B) The amount of Cdk 2 is greater during $G_1$ compared to the S phase.

C) The amount of cyclin E is highest during $G_1$.

D) The amount of Cdk 2 is greatest during $G_1$.

E) The activity of the cyclin E/Cdk 2 complex is highest during $G_2$.

Answer: C
*Topic: Concept 12.3*
*Skill: Comprehension*

# Media Activity Questions

1) Nucleoli are present during

    A) interphase.

    B) prophase.

    C) prometaphase.

    D) metaphase.

    E) anaphase.

Answer: A
*Topic: Web/CD Activity: Mitosis and Cytokinesis*

2) Chromosomes become visible during

    A) metaphase.

    B) prophase.

    C) interphase.

    D) prometaphase.

    E) anaphase.

Answer: B
*Topic: Web/CD Activity: Mitosis and Cytokinesis*

3) Spindle fibers attach to kinetochores during

    A) metaphase.

    B) prometaphase.

    C) interphase.

    D) anaphase.

    E) telophase.

Answer: B
*Topic: Web/CD Activity: Mitosis and Cytokinesis*

4) During prophase a homologous pair of chromosomes consists of

    A) four chromosomes and two chromatids.

    B) two chromosomes and two chromatids.

    C) two chromosomes and four chromatids.

    D) one chromosome and two chromatids.

    E) one chromosome and four chromatids.

Answer: C
*Topic: Web/CD Activity: Mitosis and Cytokinesis*

5) Which of these is *not* a carcinogen?

    A) testosterone

    B) cigarette smoke

    C) UV light

    D) fat

    E) All of the above are carcinogens.

Answer: E
*Topic: Web/CD Activity: Causes of Cancer*

# Self–Quiz Questions

1) Increases in the enzymatic activity of some protein kinases important for the regulation of the cell cycle are due to

A) kinase synthesis by ribosomes.

B) activation of inactive kinases by binding to cyclins.

C) conversion of inactive cyclins to active kinases by means of phosphorylation.

D) cleavage of the inactive kinase molecules by cytoplasmic proteases.

E) a decline in external growth factors to a concentration below the inhibitory threshold.

Answer: B

2) Through a microscope, you can see a cell plate beginning to develop across the middle of the cell and nuclei re-forming on either side of the cell plate. The cell is most likely

A) an animal cell in the process of cytokinesis.

B) a plant cell in the process of cytokinesis.

C) an animal cell in the S phase of the cell cycle.

D) a bacterial cell dividing.

E) a plant cell in metaphase.

Answer: B

3) Vinblastine is a standard chemotherapeutic drug used to treat cancer. Because it interferes with the assembly of microtubules, its effectiveness must be related to

A) disruption of mitotic spindle formation.

B) inhibition of regulatory protein phosphorylation.

C) suppression of cyclin production.

D) myosin denaturation and inhibition of cleavage furrow formation.

E) inhibition of DNA synthesis.

Answer: A

4) A particular cell has half as much DNA as some of the other cells in a mitotically active tissue. The cell in question is most likely in

A) $G_1$.

B) $G_2$.

C) prophase.

D) metaphase.

E) anaphase.

Answer: A

5) One difference between a cancer cell and a normal cell is that

A) the cancer cell is unable to synthesize DNA.

B) the cell cycle of the cancer cell is arrested at the S phase.

C) cancer cells continue to divide even when they are tightly packed together.

D) cancer cells cannot function properly because they suffer from density-dependent inhibition.

E) cancer cells are always in the M phase of the cell cycle.

Answer: C

6) The decline of MPF activity at the end of mitosis is caused by
   A) the destruction of the protein kinase (Cdk).
   B) decreased synthesis of cyclin.
   C) the degradation of cyclin.
   D) synthesis of DNA.
   E) an increase in the cell's volume-to-genome ratio.

   Answer: C

7) A red blood cell (RBC) has a 120-day life span. If an average adult has 5 L of blood, and each microliter (μL) contains 5 million RBCs, how many new cells must be produced each *second* to replace the entire RBC population? (1 μL = $10^{-6}$ L)
   A) 30,000
   B) 2,400
   C) 2,400,000
   D) 18,000
   E) 30,000,000

   Answer: C

8) The drug cytochalasin B blocks the function of actin. Which of the following aspects of the cell cycle would be most disrupted by cytochalasin B?
   A) spindle formation
   B) spindle attachment to kinetochores
   C) DNA synthesis
   D) cell elongation during anaphase
   E) cleavage furrow formation

   Answer: E

9) In some organisms, mitosis occurs without cytokinesis occurring. This will result in
   A) cells with more than one nucleus.
   B) cells that are unusually small.
   C) cells lacking nuclei.
   D) destruction of chromosomes.
   E) cell cycles lacking an S phase.

   Answer: A

10) Which of the following does *not* occur during mitosis?
   A) condensation of the chromosomes
   B) replication of the DNA
   C) separation of sister chromatids
   D) spindle formation
   E) separation of the centrosomes

   Answer: B

# Chapter 13 Meiosis and Sexual Life Cycles

1) What is a genome?
   A) the complete complement of an organism's genes
   B) a specific sequence of polypeptides within each cell
   C) a specialized polymer of four different kinds of monomers
   D) a specific segment of DNA that is found within a prokaryotic chromosome
   E) an ordered display of chromosomes arranged from largest to smallest

Answer: A
*Topic: Concept 13.1*
*Skill: Knowledge*

2) Which of the following statements about genes is *incorrect*?
   A) Genes correspond to segments of DNA.
   B) Many genes contain the information needed for cells to synthesize enzymes and other proteins.
   C) During fertilization, both the sperm and the ovum contribute genes to the resulting fertilized egg.
   D) Under normal circumstances, each chromosome contains precisely one gene.
   E) Genetic differences can result from changes in the DNA called mutations.

Answer: D
*Topic: Concept 13.1*
*Skill: Comprehension*

3) Asexual reproduction and sexual reproduction are different in that
   A) individuals reproducing asexually transmit 100% of their genes to their progeny, whereas individuals reproducing sexually only transmit 50%.
   B) asexual reproduction produces offspring that are genetically identical to the parents, whereas sexual reproduction gives rise to genetically distinct offspring.
   C) asexual reproduction involves a single parent, whereas sexual reproduction involves two.
   D) asexual reproduction only requires mitosis, whereas sexual reproduction always involves meiosis.
   E) all of the above

Answer: E
*Topic: Concept 13.1*
*Skill: Comprehension*

4) How do the two members of a pair of homologous chromosomes differ from each other?
   A) their length
   B) the identity and relative position of the genes present on each of the chromosomes
   C) their staining patterns
   D) the position of the centromere within each of the chromosomes
   E) the precise sequence of the DNA within each of the chromosomes

Answer: E
*Topic: Concept 13.2*
*Skill: Comprehension*

5) What is a karyotype?

    A) the set of unique physical characteristics that define an individual

    B) the collection of all the mutations present within a genome

    C) a unique combination of chromosomes found in a gamete

    D) a system of classifying cell nuclei

    E) a display of every pair of homologous chromosomes within a cell, organized according to size and shape

Answer: E
*Topic: Concept 13.2*
*Skill: Knowledge*

6) By examining a karyotype, it is possible to determine

    A) which of two related plant forms is a gametophyte, and which is a sporophyte.

    B) the sex of an animal.

    C) the age of a fungus.

    D) A and B only

    E) A, B, and C

Answer: D
*Topic: Concept 13.2*
*Skill: Comprehension*

7) At which stage of mitosis are chromosomes photographed in the preparation of a karyotype?

    A) prophase

    B) metaphase

    C) anaphase

    D) telophase

    E) interphase

Answer: B
*Topic: Concept 13.2*
*Skill: Knowledge*

8) The human X and Y chromosomes are

    A) both present in every somatic cell of males and females alike.

    B) of approximately equal size.

    C) almost entirely homologous, despite their different names.

    D) called "sex chromosomes" because they determine an individual's sex.

    E) all of the above

Answer: D
*Topic: Concept 13.2*
*Skill: Comprehension*

9) If the liver cells of an animal have 24 chromosomes, how many chromosomes do its sperm cells have?

    A) 6

    B) 12

    C) 24

    D) 48

    E) 64

Answer: B
*Topic: Concept 13.2*
*Skill: Comprehension*

10) Which of the following is *true* of a species that has a chromosome number of $2n = 16$?

    A) The species is diploid with 32 chromosomes.

    B) The species has 16 sets of chromosomes.

    C) There are 8 homologous pairs.

    D) During the S phase of the cell cycle there will be 32 separate chromosomes.

    E) A gamete from this species has 4 chromosomes.

Answer: C
*Topic: Concept 13.2*
*Skill: Comprehension*

11) Which of the following is the term for a human cell that contains 22 pairs of autosomes and two X chromosomes?

A) an unfertilized egg cell

B) a sperm cell

C) a male somatic cell

D) a female somatic cell

E) both A and D

Answer: D
*Topic: Concept 13.2*
*Skill: Knowledge*

12) Eukaryotic sexual life cycles show tremendous variation. Of the following elements, which do *all* sexual life cycles have in common?

    I.   alternation of generations
    II.  meiosis
    III. fertilization
    IV. gametes
    V.  spores

A) I, IV, and V

B) I, II, and IV

C) II, III, and IV

D) II, IV, and V

E) all of the above

Answer: C
*Topic: Concept 13.2*
*Skill: Comprehension*

13) Which of these statements is *false*?

A) In humans, each of the 22 maternal autosomes has a homologous paternal chromosome.

B) In humans, the 23rd pair, the sex chromosomes, determines whether the person is female (XX) or male (XY).

C) Single, haploid (*n*) sets of chromosomes in ovum and sperm unite during fertilization, forming a diploid (2*n*), single-celled zygote.

D) At sexual maturity, ovaries and testes produce diploid gametes by meiosis.

E) Sexual life cycles differ with respect to the relative timing of meiosis and fertilization.

Answer: D
*Topic: Concept 13.2*
*Skill: Knowledge*

14) In animals, meiosis results in gametes, and fertilization results in

A) spores.

B) gametophytes.

C) zygotes.

D) sporophytes.

E) clones.

Answer: C
*Topic: Concept 13.2*
*Skill: Knowledge*

15) Referring to a plant sexual life cycle, which of the following terms describes the process that leads *directly* to the formation of gametes?

A) sporophyte meiosis

B) gametophyte mitosis

C) gametophyte meiosis

D) sporophyte mitosis

E) alternation of generations

Answer: B
*Topic: Concept 13.2*
*Skill: Knowledge*

16) Which of the following is an example of alternation of generations?

    A) A grandparent and grandchild each have dark hair, but the parent has blond hair.

    B) A diploid plant (sporophyte) produces, by meiosis, a spore that gives rise to a multicellular, haploid pollen grain (gametophyte).

    C) A diploid animal produces gametes by meiosis, and the gametes undergo fertilization to produce a diploid zygote.

    D) A haploid mushroom produces gametes by mitosis, and the gametes undergo fertilization, which is immediately followed by meiosis.

    E) A diploid cell divides by mitosis to produce two diploid daughter cells, which then fuse to produce a tetraploid cell.

Answer: B
*Topic: Concept 13.2*
*Skill: Application*

*Refer to the life cycles illustrated in Figure 13.1 to answer the following questions.*

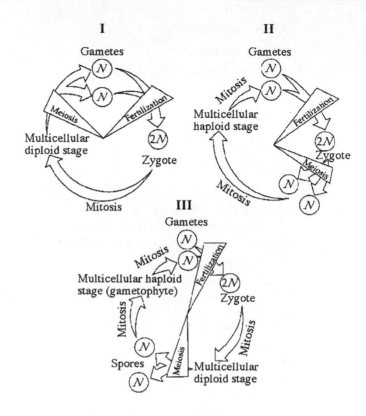

**Figure 13.1**

17) Which of the life cycles is typical for animals?

    A) I only

    B) II only

    C) III only

    D) I and II

    E) I and III

Answer: A
*Topic: Concept 13.2*
*Skill: Comprehension*

18) Which of the life cycles is typical for plants and some algae?

  A) I only

  B) II only

  C) III only

  D) I and II

  E) I and III

Answer: C
*Topic: Concept 13.2*
*Skill: Comprehension*

19) Which of the life cycles is typical for most fungi and some protists?

  A) I only

  B) II only

  C) III only

  D) I and II

  E) I and III

Answer: B
*Topic: Concept 13.2*
*Skill: Comprehension*

20) Which of the following is missing from the life cycle progression shown below?
sporophyte-*meiosis*-spore-_____-gametophyte-*mitosis*-gametes-*fertilization*-zygote

  A) meiosis

  B) mitosis

  C) synapsis

  D) karyotype

  E) fertilization

Answer: B
*Topic: Concept 13.2*
*Skill: Knowledge*

21) In animals, somatic cells are produced by mitosis and _____ are produced by meiosis.

  A) gametes

  B) clones

  C) zygotes

  D) spores

  E) diploid cells

Answer: A
*Topic: Concept 13.2*
*Skill: Knowledge*

22) All of the following are functions of meiosis in plants *except*

  A) production of spores.

  B) reduction of chromosome number by half.

  C) independent assortment of chromosomes.

  D) crossing over and recombination of homologous chromosomes.

  E) production of identical daughter cells.

Answer: E
*Topic: Concepts 13.2–13.3*
*Skill: Comprehension*

23) After telophase I of meiosis, the chromosomal makeup of each daughter cell is

  A) diploid, and the chromosomes are composed of a single chromatid.

  B) diploid, and the chromosomes are composed of two chromatids.

  C) haploid, and the chromosomes are composed of a single chromatid.

  D) haploid, and the chromosomes are composed of two chromatids.

  E) tetraploid, and the chromosomes are composed of two chromatids.

Answer: D
*Topic: Concept 13.3*
*Skill: Knowledge*

24) How do cells at the completion of meiosis compare with cells that have replicated their DNA and are just about to begin meiosis?
    A) They have twice the amount of cytoplasm and half the amount of DNA.
    B) They have half the number of chromosomes and half the amount of DNA.
    C) They have the same number of chromosomes and half the amount of DNA.
    D) They have half the number of chromosomes and one-fourth the amount of DNA.
    E) They have half the amount of cytoplasm and twice the amount of DNA.

Answer: D
*Topic: Concept 13.3*
*Skill: Comprehension*

25) When does the synaptonemal complex disappear?
    A) late prophase of meiosis I
    B) during fertilization or fusion of gametes
    C) early anaphase of meiosis I
    D) mid-prophase of meiosis II
    E) late metaphase of meiosis II

Answer: A
*Topic: Concept 13.3*
*Skill: Knowledge*

26) Which of the following terms belongs with the words synapsis, tetrads, and chiasmata?
    A) haploid
    B) crossing over
    C) autosomes
    D) prophase II
    E) fertilization

Answer: B
*Topic: Concept 13.3*
*Skill: Knowledge*

*For the following questions, match the key event of meiosis with the stages listed below.*

| I. | prophase I | V. | prophase II |
| II. | metaphase I | VI. | metaphase II |
| III. | anaphase I | VII. | anaphase II |
| IV. | telophase I | VIII. | telophase II |

27) Tetrads of chromosomes are aligned at the center of the cell; independent assortment soon follows.
    A) I
    B) II
    C) IV
    D) VII
    E) VIII

Answer: B
*Topic: Concept 13.3*
*Skill: Knowledge*

28) Synapsis of homologous pairs occurs; crossing over may occur.
    A) I
    B) II
    C) IV
    D) VI
    E) VII

Answer: A
*Topic: Concept 13.3*
*Skill: Knowledge*

29) Centromeres of sister chromatids uncouple and chromatids separate.

A) II

B) III

C) IV

D) V

E) VII

Answer: E
*Topic: Concept 13.3*
*Skill: Knowledge*

30) Which of the following happens at the conclusion of meiosis I?

A) Homologous chromosomes are separated.

B) The chromosome number is conserved.

C) Sister chromatids are separated.

D) Four daughter cells are formed.

E) The sperm cells elongate to form a head and a tail end.

Answer: A
*Topic: Concept 13.3*
*Skill: Knowledge*

31) Which of the following is *true* of the process of meiosis?

A) Two diploid cells result.

B) Four diploid cells result.

C) Four haploid cells result.

D) Four autosomes result.

E) Four chiasmata result.

Answer: C
*Topic: Concept 13.3*
*Skill: Knowledge*

32) Crossing over occurs during which phase of meiosis?

A) prophase I

B) anaphase I

C) telophase I

D) prophase II

E) metaphase II

Answer: A
*Topic: Concept 13.3*
*Skill: Knowledge*

*Refer to the drawings in Figure 13.2 of a single pair of homologous chromosomes as they might appear during various stages of either mitosis or meiosis, and answer the following questions.*

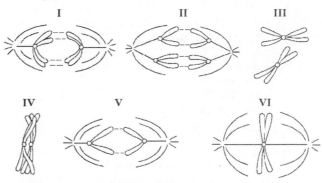

**Figure 13.2**

33) Which diagram represents prophase I of meiosis?

A) I

B) II

C) III

D) IV

E) V

Answer: D
*Topic: Concept 13.3*
*Skill: Comprehension*

34) Which drawing represents anaphase of mitosis?

A) II

B) III

C) IV

D) V

E) VI

Answer: A
*Topic: Concept 13.3*
*Skill: Comprehension*

35) Which drawing represents metaphase II of meiosis?

A) I

B) II

C) IV

D) V

E) VI

Answer: E
*Topic: Concept 13.3*
*Skill: Comprehension*

36) Which drawing represents a stage of meiosis in which independent assortment might occur if there were more than one pair of chromosomes represented?

A) I

B) II

C) IV

D) V

E) VI

Answer: A
*Topic: Concept 13.3*
*Skill: Application*

*Use the following key to answer the following questions. Each answer may be used once, more than once, or not at all.*

A.  The statement is true for mitosis only.
B.  The statement is true for meiosis I only.
C.  The statement is true for meiosis II only.
D.  The statement is true for mitosis and meiosis I.
E.  The statement is true for mitosis and meiosis II.

37) A cell divides to produce two daughter cells that are genetically identical.

Answer: A
*Topic: Concept 13.3*
*Skill: Comprehension*

38) Homologous chromosomes synapse and crossing over occurs.

Answer: B
*Topic: Concept 13.3*
*Skill: Comprehension*

39) Centromeres uncouple and chromatids are separated from each other.

Answer: E
*Topic: Concept 13.3*
*Skill: Comprehension*

40) Independent assortment of chromosomes occurs.

Answer: B
*Topic: Concept 13.3*
*Skill: Comprehension*

41) The process is preceded by replication of the DNA.

Answer: D
*Topic: Concept 13.3*
*Skill: Comprehension*

42) You have in your possession a microscope slide with meiotic cells on it and a light microscope. What would you look for if you wanted to identify metaphase I cells on the slide?

   A) a visible nuclear envelope

   B) separated sister chromatids at each pole of the cell

   C) tetrads lined up at the center of the cell

   D) a synaptonemal complex

   E) a cleavage furrow

Answer: C
*Topic: Concept 13.3*
*Skill: Application*

You isolate DNA from three different cell types of an organism, determine the relative DNA content for each type, and plot the results on the graph shown in Figure 13.3. Refer to the graph to answer the following questions.

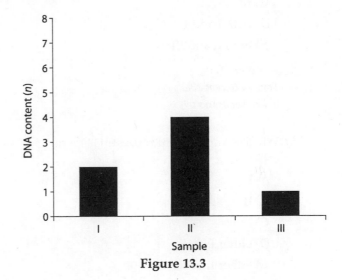

**Figure 13.3**

43) If the cells were from a plant, which sample might represent a gametophyte cell?

   A) I

   B) II

   C) III

   D) either I or II

   E) either II or III

Answer: C
*Topic: Concept 13.3*
*Skill: Application*

44) Which sample of DNA might be from a nerve cell arrested in $G_0$ of the cell cycle?

   A) I

   B) II

   C) III

   D) either I or II

   E) either II or III

Answer: A
*Topic: Concept 13.3*
*Skill: Application*

45) Which sample might represent an animal cell in G$_2$ phase of the cell cycle?

    A) I

    B) II

    C) III

    D) both I and II

    E) both II and III

Answer: B
*Topic: Concept 13.3*
*Skill: Application*

46) Which sample might represent a sperm cell?

    A) I

    B) II

    C) III

    D) either I or II

    E) either II or III

Answer: C
*Topic: Concept 13.3*
*Skill: Application*

47) During meiosis, cells go from what number to what number?

    A) I to II to I to III

    B) I to II to III

    C) II to I

    D) III to I

    E) always remain at I

Answer: A
*Topic: Concept 13.3*
*Skill: Application*

48) During mitosis, diploid cells go from what number to what number?

    A) I to III

    B) I to II

    C) II to III

    D) II to I

    E) always remain at II

Answer: D
*Topic: Concept 13.3*
*Skill: Application*

*The following questions refer to the essential steps in meiosis described below.*

1.  formation of four new nuclei, each with half the chromosomes present in the parental nucleus
2.  alignment of tetrads at the metaphase plate
3.  separation of sister chromatids
4.  separation of the homologues; no uncoupling of the centromere
5.  synapsis; chromosomes moving to the middle of the cell in pairs

49) From the descriptions above, which of the following is the order that most logically illustrates a sequence of meiosis?

    A) 1, 2, 3, 4, 5

    B) 5, 4, 2, 1, 3

    C) 5, 3, 2, 4, 1

    D) 4, 5, 2, 1, 3

    E) 5, 2, 4, 3, 1

Answer: E
*Topic: Concept 13.3*
*Skill: Knowledge*

50) Which of the steps take place in both mitosis and meiosis?

  A) 2

  B) 3

  C) 5

  D) 2 and 3 only

  E) 2, 3, and 5

Answer: B
*Topic: Concept 13.3*
*Skill: Knowledge*

51) When comparing prophase I of meiosis with prophase of mitosis, which of the following occurs only in meiosis?

  A) The chromosomes condense.

  B) Tetrads form.

  C) The nuclear envelope disassembles.

  D) A spindle forms.

  E) Each chromosome is composed of two chromatids.

Answer: B
*Topic: Concept 13.3*
*Skill: Knowledge*

52) Which of the following occurs in meiosis but not in mitosis?

  A) chromosome replication

  B) synapsis

  C) production of daughter cells

  D) alignment of tetrads at metaphase plate

  E) both B and D

Answer: E
*Topic: Concept 13.3*
*Skill: Comprehension*

53) How does the sexual life cycle increase the genetic variation in a species?

  A) by allowing independent assortment of chromosomes

  B) by allowing random fertilization

  C) by allowing crossing over

  D) A and B only

  E) A, B, and C

Answer: E
*Topic: Concept 13.4*
*Skill: Comprehension*

54) For a species with a haploid number of 23 chromosomes, how many different combinations of maternal and paternal chromosomes are possible for the gametes?

  A) 23

  B) 46

  C) 460

  D) 920

  E) about 8 million

Answer: E
*Topic: Concept 13.4*
*Skill: Comprehension*

55) For a species with a diploid number of 10 chromosomes, how many different combinations of maternal and paternal chromosomes are possible for the gametes?

  A) 5

  B) 25

  C) 32

  D) 100

  E) about 10,000

Answer: C
*Topic: Concept 13.4*
*Skill: Comprehension*

56) Independent assortment of chromosomes is a result of

A) the random and independent way in which each pair of homologous chromosomes lines up at the metaphase plate during meiosis I.

B) the random nature of the fertilization of ova by sperm.

C) the random distribution of the sister chromatids to the two daughter cells during anaphase II.

D) the relatively small degree of homology shared by the X and Y chromosomes.

E) all of the above

Answer: A
*Topic: Concept 13.4*
*Skill: Comprehension*

57) When pairs of homologous chromosomes separate during anaphase I,

A) the maternal chromosomes all move to one daughter cell, and the paternal chromosomes all move to the other daughter cell.

B) the sister chromatids remain linked to one another.

C) most of the recombination has already occurred, with the remainder taking place during prophase II.

D) the synaptonemal complex is visible under the light microscope.

Answer: B
*Topic: Concepts 13.3–13.4*
*Skill: Comprehension*

58) Which of the following statements about crossing over is *incorrect*?

A) Crossing over combines sections of the maternal and paternal chromosomes.

B) Crossing over plays a role in both sexual and asexual reproduction.

C) There are on average one to three crossover events per chromosome.

D) Crossing over increases the extent of genetic variation beyond what is possible through independent assortment alone.

E) Crossing over results in recombinant chromosomes.

Answer: B
*Topic: Concepts 13.2–13.4*
*Skill: Knowledge*

# Media Activity Questions

1) What name is given to the process that restores the diploid number of chromosomes?

   A) fertilization

   B) asexual reproduction

   C) meiosis

   D) mitosis

   E) the cell cycle

   Answer: A
   *Topic: Web/CD Activity: Asexual/Sexual Life Cycles*

2) At the end of _____ and cytokinesis, haploid cells contain chromosomes that each consist of two sister chromatids.

   A) metaphase II

   B) telophase I

   C) telophase

   D) telophase II

   E) interphase

   Answer: B
   *Topic: Web/CD Activity: Meiosis Animation*

3) Synapsis occurs during

   A) prophase I.

   B) telophase I and cytokinesis.

   C) prophase II.

   D) metaphase II.

   E) anaphase II.

   Answer: A
   *Topic: Web/CD Activity: Meiosis Animation*

4) Homologous chromosomes migrate to opposite poles during

   A) telophase II and cytokinesis.

   B) prophase II.

   C) anaphase I.

   D) metaphase I.

   E) metaphase II.

   Answer: C
   *Topic: Web/CD Activity: Meiosis Animation*

5) In a cell in which $2n = 6$, the independent assortment of chromosomes during meiosis can by itself give rise to _____ genetically different gametes.

   A) two

   B) four

   C) five

   D) six

   E) eight

   Answer: E
   *Topic: Web/CD Activity: Origins of Genetic Variation*

# Self-Quiz Questions

1) A human cell containing 22 autosomes and a Y chromosome is
   A) a somatic cell of a male.
   B) a zygote.
   C) a somatic cell of a female.
   D) a sperm cell.
   E) an ovum.

   Answer: D

2) Homologous chromosomes move to opposite poles of a dividing cell during
   A) mitosis.
   B) meiosis I.
   C) meiosis II.
   D) fertilization.
   E) binary fission.

   Answer: B

3) Meiosis II is similar to mitosis in that
   A) homologous chromosomes synapse.
   B) DNA replicates before the division.
   C) the daughter cells are diploid.
   D) sister chromatids separate during anaphase.
   E) the chromosome number is reduced.

   Answer: D

4) If the DNA content of a diploid cell in the $G_1$ phase of the cell cycle is $x$, then the DNA content of the same cell at metaphase of meiosis I would be
   A) $0.25x$
   B) $0.5x$
   C) $x$.
   D) $2x$.
   E) $4x$.

   Answer: D

5) If we continued to follow the cell lineage from question 4, then the DNA content at metaphase of meiosis II would be
   A) $0.25x$.
   B) $0.5x$.
   C) $x$.
   D) $2x$.
   E) $4x$.

   Answer: C

6) How many different combinations of maternal and paternal chromosomes can be packaged in gametes made by an organism with a diploid number of 8 ($2n = 8$)?
   A) 2
   B) 4
   C) 8
   D) 16
   E) 32

   Answer: D

7) The immediate product of meiosis in a plant is a
   A) spore.
   B) gamete.
   C) sporophyte.
   D) gametophyte.
   E) zygote.

   Answer: A

8) Multicellular haploid organisms
   A) are typically called sporophytes.
   B) produce new cells for growth by meiosis.
   C) produce gametes by mitosis.
   D) are found only in aquatic environments.
   E) are the direct result of fertilization.

   Answer: C

9) Crossing over usually contributes to genetic variation by exchanging chromosomal segments between

A) sister chromatids of a chromosome.

B) chromatids of nonhomologues.

C) nonsister chromatids of homologues.

D) nonhomologous loci of the genome.

E) autosomes and sex chromosomes.

Answer: C

10) In comparing the typical life cycles of plants and animals, a stage found in plants but not in animals is a

A) gamete.

B) zygote.

C) multicellular diploid.

D) multicellular haploid.

Answer: D

# Chapter 14  Mendel and the Gene Idea

1) Pea plants were particularly well suited for use in Mendel's breeding experiments for all of the following reasons *except* that

A) peas show easily observed variations in a number of characters, such as pea shape and flower color.

B) it is possible to completely control matings between different pea plants.

C) it is possible to obtain large numbers of progeny from any given cross.

D) peas have an unusually long generation time.

E) many of the observable characters that vary in pea plants are controlled by single genes.

Answer: D
*Topic: Concept 14.1*
*Skill: Comprehension*

2) A plant with purple flowers is allowed to self-pollinate. Generation after generation, it produces purple flowers. This is an example of

A) hybridization.

B) incomplete dominance.

C) true-breeding.

D) the law of segregation.

E) polygenetics.

Answer: C
*Topic: Concept 14.1*
*Skill: Knowledge*

3) Which of the following statements about Mendel's breeding experiments is *correct*?

A) None of the parental (P) plants were true-breeding.

B) All of the $F_2$ progeny showed a phenotype that was intermediate between the two parental (P) phenotypes.

C) Half of the $F_1$ progeny had the same phenotype as one of the parental (P) plants, and the other half had the same phenotype as the other parent.

D) All of the $F_1$ progeny resembled one of the parental (P) plants, but only some of the $F_2$ progeny did.

E) none of the above

Answer: D
*Topic: Concept 14.1*
*Skill: Comprehension*

4) What is the difference between a monohybrid cross and a dihybrid cross?

A) A monohybrid cross involves a single parent, whereas a dihybrid cross involves two parents.

B) A monohybrid cross produces a single progeny, whereas a dihybrid cross produces two progeny.

C) A monohybrid cross involves organisms that are heterozygous for a single character, whereas a dihybrid cross involves organisms that are heterozygous for two characters.

D) A monohybrid cross is performed only once, whereas a dihybrid cross is performed twice.

E) A monohybrid cross results in a 9:3:3:1 ratio whereas a dihybrid cross gives a 3:1 ratio.

Answer: C
*Topic: Concept 14.1*
*Skill: Knowledge*

5) A cross between homozygous purple-flowered and homozygous white-flowered pea plants results in offspring with purple flowers. This demonstrates

    A) the blending model of genetics.

    B) true-breeding.

    C) dominance.

    D) a dihybrid cross.

    E) the mistakes made by Mendel.

Answer: C
*Topic: Concept 14.1*
*Skill: Comprehension*

6) The $F_1$ offspring of Mendel's classic pea cross always looked like one of the two parental varieties because

    A) one allele was completely dominant over another.

    B) each allele affected phenotypic expression.

    C) the traits blended together during fertilization.

    D) no genes interacted to produce the parental phenotype.

    E) different genes interacted to produce the parental phenotype.

Answer: A
*Topic: Concept 14.1*
*Skill: Knowledge*

7) What was the most significant conclusion that Gregor Mendel drew from his experiments with pea plants?

    A) There is considerable genetic variation in garden peas.

    B) Traits are inherited in discrete units, and are not the results of "blending."

    C) Recessive genes occur more frequently in the $F_1$ than do dominant ones.

    D) Genes are composed of DNA.

    E) An organism that is homozygous for many recessive traits is at a disadvantage.

Answer: B
*Topic: Concept 14.1*
*Skill: Comprehension*

8) Which of the following is (are) true for alleles?

    A) They can be identical or different for any given gene in a somatic cell.

    B) They can be dominant or recessive.

    C) They can represent alternative forms of a gene.

    D) Only A and B are correct.

    E) A, B, and C are correct.

Answer: E
*Topic: Concept 14.1*
*Skill: Knowledge*

9) What is genetic cross between an individual showing a dominant phenotype (but of unknown genotype) and a homozygous recessive individual called?

    A) a self-cross

    B) a testcross

    C) a hybrid cross

    D) an $F_1$ cross

    E) a dihybrid cross

Answer: B
*Topic: Concept 14.1*
*Skill: Knowledge*

10) How many unique gametes could be produced through independent assortment by an individual with the genotype *AaBbCCDdEE*?

    A) 4

    B) 8

    C) 16

    D) 32

    E) 64

Answer: B
*Topic: Concept 14.1*
*Skill: Application*

11) Two plants are crossed, resulting in offspring with a 3:1 ratio for a particular trait. This suggests

    A) that the parents were true-breeding for contrasting traits.

    B) incomplete dominance.

    C) that a blending of traits has occurred.

    D) that the parents were both heterozygous.

    E) that each offspring has the same alleles.

Answer: D
*Topic: Concept 14.1*
*Skill: Knowledge*

12) Two characters that appear in a 9:3:3:1 ratio in the $F_2$ generation should have which of the following properties?

    A) Each of the characters is controlled by a single gene.

    B) The genes controlling the characters obey the law of independent assortment.

    C) Each of the genes controlling the characters has two alleles.

    D) Only A and C are correct.

    E) A, B, and C are correct.

Answer: E
*Topic: Concept 14.1*
*Skill: Comprehension*

13) A 9:3:3:1 phenotypic ratio is characteristic of which of the following?

    A) a monohybrid cross

    B) a dihybrid cross

    C) a trihybrid cross

    D) linked genes

    E) both A and D

Answer: B
*Topic: Concept 14.1*
*Skill: Knowledge*

14) A sexually reproducing animal has two unlinked genes, one for head shape (*H*) and one for tail length (*T*). Its genotype is *HhTt*. Which of the following genotypes is possible in a gamete from this organism?

    A) *HT*

    B) *Hh*

    C) *HhTt*

    D) *T*

    E) *tt*

Answer: A
*Topic: Concept 14.1*
*Skill: Comprehension*

15) It was important that Mendel examined not just the $F_1$ generation in his breeding experiments, but the $F_2$ generation as well, because

A) he obtained very few $F_1$ progeny, making statistical analysis difficult.

B) parental traits that were not observed in the $F_1$ reappeared in the $F_2$, suggesting that the traits did not truly disappear in the $F_1$.

C) analysis of the $F_1$ progeny would have allowed him to discover the law of segregation, but not the law of independent assortment.

D) the dominant phenotypes were visible in the $F_2$ generation, but not in the $F_1$.

E) all of the above

Answer: B
*Topic: Concept 14.1*
*Skill: Comprehension*

16) When crossing a homozygous recessive with a heterozygote, what is the chance of getting an offspring with the homozygous recessive phenotype?

A) 0%

B) 25%

C) 50%

D) 75%

E) 100%

Answer: C
*Topic: Concept 14.1*
*Skill: Application*

*Use the following diagram and description to answer the questions below.*

In a particular plant, leaf color is controlled by gene $D$. Plants with the dominant allele $D$ have dark green leaves, and plants with the homozygous recessive $dd$ genotype have light green leaves. A true–breeding dark–leaved plant is crossed with a light–leaved one, and the $F_1$ offspring is allowed to self–pollinate. The predicted outcome of this cross is diagrammed in the Punnett square shown below, where 1, 2, 3, and 4 represent the genotypes corresponding to each box within the square.

|     | $D$ | $d$ |
|-----|-----|-----|
| $D$ | 1   | 2   |
| $d$ | 3   | 4   |

17) Which of the boxes marked 1–4 correspond to plants with dark leaves?

A) 1 only

B) 1 and 2

C) 2 and 3

D) 4 only

E) 1, 2, and 3

Answer: E
*Topic: Concept 14.1*
*Skill: Application*

18) Which of the boxes correspond to plants with a heterozygous genotype?

A) 1

B) 1 and 2

C) 1, 2, and 3

D) 2 and 3

E) 2, 3, and 4

Answer: D
*Topic: Concept 14.1*
*Skill: Application*

19) Which of the plants will be true-breeding?

    A) 1 and 4

    B) 2 and 3

    C) 1-4

    D) 1 only

    E) none

Answer: A
*Topic: Concept 14.1*
*Skill: Application*

20) $P$ = purple, $pp$ = white. The offspring of a cross between two heterozygous purple-flowering plants ($Pp \times Pp$) results in

    A) all purple-flowered plants.

    B) purple-flowered plants and white-flowered plants.

    C) two types of white-flowered plants: $PP$ and $Pp$.

    D) all white-flowered plants.

    E) all pink-flowered plants.

Answer: B
*Topic: Concept 14.1*
*Skill: Comprehension*

21) Mendel accounted for the observation that traits which had disappeared in the $F_1$ generation reappeared in the $F_2$ generation by proposing that

    A) new mutations were frequently generated in the $F_2$ progeny, "reinventing" traits that had been lost in the $F_1$.

    B) the mechanism controlling the appearance of traits was different between the $F_1$ and the $F_2$ plants.

    C) traits can be dominant or recessive, and the recessive traits were obscured by the dominant ones in the $F_1$.

    D) the traits were lost in the $F_1$ due to blending of the parental traits.

    E) members of the $F_1$ generation had only one allele for each character, but members of the $F_2$ had two alleles for each character.

Answer: C
*Topic: Concept 14.1*
*Skill: Comprehension*

22) What are Punnett squares used for?

    A) predicting the result of genetic crosses between organisms of known genotypes

    B) determining the DNA sequence of a given gene

    C) identifying the gene locus where allelic variations are possible

    D) testing for the presence of the recessive allele

    E) more than one of the above

Answer: A
*Topic: Concept 14.1*
*Skill: Knowledge*

23) Which of the following is *false*, regarding the law of segregation?

   A) It states that each of two alleles for a given trait segregate into different gametes.

   B) It can be explained by the segregation of homologous chromosomes during meiosis.

   C) It can account for the 3:1 ratio seen in the $F_2$ generation of Mendel's crosses.

   D) It can be used to predict the likelihood of transmission of certain genetic diseases within families.

   E) It is a method that can be used to determine the number of chromosomes in a plant.

Answer: E
*Topic: Concept 14.1*
*Skill: Knowledge*

24) The fact that all seven of the pea plant traits studied by Mendel obeyed the principle of independent assortment means that

   A) none of the traits obeyed the law of segregation.

   B) the diploid number of chromosomes in the pea plants was 7.

   C) all of the genes controlling the traits were located on the same chromosome.

   D) all of the genes controlling the traits behaved as if they were on different chromosomes.

   E) the formation of gametes in plants occurs by mitosis only.

Answer: D
*Topic: Concept 14.1*
*Skill: Comprehension*

25) Black fur in mice (*B*) is dominant to brown fur (*b*). Short tails (*T*) are dominant to long tails (*t*). What fraction of the progeny of the cross *BbTt* × *BBtt* will have black fur and long tails?

   A) 1/16

   B) 3/16

   C) 3/8

   D) 1/2

   E) 9/16

Answer: D
*Topic: Concept 14.2*
*Skill: Application*

26) In certain plants, tall is dominant to short. If a heterozygous plant is crossed with a homozygous tall plant, what is the probability that the offspring will be short?

   A) 1/2

   B) 1/4

   C) 0

   D) 1

   E) 1/6

Answer: C
*Topic: Concept 14.2*
*Skill: Comprehension*

27) A couple has three children, all of whom have brown eyes and blond hair. Both parents are homozygous for brown eyes (*BB*), but one is a blond (*rr*) and the other is a redhead (*Rr*). What is the probability that their next child will be a brown-eyed redhead?

   A) 1/16

   B) 1/8

   C) 1/4

   D) 1/2

   E) 1

Answer: D
*Topic: Concept 14.2*
*Skill: Application*

28) Two true-breeding stocks of pea plants are crossed. One parent has red, axial flowers and the other has white, terminal flowers; all $F_1$ individuals have red, axial flowers. If 1,000 $F_2$ offspring resulted from the cross, approximately how many of them would you expect to have red, terminal flowers? (Assume independent assortment.)

A) 65

B) 190

C) 250

D) 565

E) 750

Answer: B
*Topic: Concept 14.2*
*Skill: Application*

29) In a cross *AaBbCc* × *AaBbCc*, what is the probability of producing the genotype *AABBCC*?

A) 1/4

B) 1/8

C) 1/16

D) 1/32

E) 1/64

Answer: E
*Topic: Concept 14.2*
*Skill: Application*

30) Given the parents *AABBCc* × *AabbCc*, assume simple dominance and independent assortment. What proportion of the progeny will be expected to phenotypically resemble the first parent?

A) 1/4

B) 1/8

C) 3/4

D) 3/8

E) 1

Answer: C
*Topic: Concept 14.2*
*Skill: Application*

31) A 1:2:1 phenotypic ratio in the $F_2$ generation of a monohybrid cross is a sign of

A) complete dominance.

B) multiple alleles.

C) incomplete dominance.

D) polygenic inheritance.

E) pleiotropy.

Answer: C
*Topic: Concept 14.3*
*Skill: Knowledge*

*Refer to the following result to answer the next several questions.*

A tall plant is crossed with a short plant, and the progeny are all intermediate in size between the two parental plants.

32) This could be an example of

A) incomplete dominance.

B) polygenic inheritance.

C) complete dominance.

D) A and B

E) B and C

Answer: D
*Topic: Concept 14.3*
*Skill: Comprehension*

33) If the intermediate $F_1$ progeny were allowed to self-pollinate, and the $F_2$ progeny were also intermediate in size, but following a normal distribution, this would suggest

A) incomplete dominance.

B) polygenic inheritance.

C) complete dominance.

D) a strong environmental influence.

E) codominance.

Answer: B
*Topic: Concept 14.3*
*Skill: Application*

34) If the intermediate $F_1$ progeny were allowed to self-pollinate, and 25% of the $F_2$ progeny were tall, 50% were intermediate in size, and 25% were short, this would suggest

    A) incomplete dominance.

    B) polygenic inheritance.

    C) complete dominance.

    D) pleiotropy.

    E) multifactorial inheritance.

Answer: A
*Topic: Concept 14.3*
*Skill: Application*

35) In snapdragons, heterozygotes have pink flowers, whereas homozygotes have red or white flowers. When plants with red flowers are crossed with plants with white flowers, what proportion of the offspring will have pink flowers?

    A) 0%

    B) 25%

    C) 50%

    D) 75%

    E) 100%

Answer: E
*Topic: Concept 14.3*
*Skill: Application*

36) Tallness ($T$) is dominant to dwarfness ($t$), while red ($R$) flower color is dominant to white ($r$). The heterozygous condition results in pink ($Rr$) flower color. A dwarf, red snapdragon is crossed with a plant homozygous for tallness and white flowers. What are the genotype and phenotype of the $F_1$ individuals?

    A) *ttRr*—dwarf and pink

    B) *ttrr*—dwarf and white

    C) *TtRr*—tall and red

    D) *TtRr*—tall and pink

    E) *TTRR*—tall and red

Answer: D
*Topic: Concept 14.3*
*Skill: Application*

37) Skin color in a fish is inherited via a single gene with four different alleles. How many different types of gametes would be possible in this system?

    A) 1

    B) 2

    C) 4

    D) 8

    E) 16

Answer: C
*Topic: Concept 14.3*
*Skill: Comprehension*

38) In cattle, roan coat color (mixed red and white hairs) occurs in the heterozygous (*Rr*) offspring of red (*RR*) and white (*rr*) homozygotes. Which of the following crosses would produce offspring in the ratio of 1 red:2 roan:1 white?

 A) red × white

 B) roan × roan

 C) white × roan

 D) red × roan

 E) The answer cannot be determined from the information provided.

Answer: B
*Topic: Concept 14.3*
*Skill: Application*

*Refer to the following to answer the questions below.*

Gene *S* controls the sharpness of spines in a type of cactus. Cactuses with the dominant allele, *S*, have sharp spines, whereas homozygous recessive *ss* cactuses have dull spines. At the same time, a second gene, *N*, determines whether cactuses have spines. Homozygous recessive *nn* cactuses have no spines at all.

39) The relationship between genes *S* and *N* is an example of

 A) incomplete dominance.

 B) epistasis.

 C) complete dominance.

 D) pleiotropy.

 E) codominance.

Answer: B
*Topic: Concept 14.3*
*Skill: Comprehension*

40) A cross between a true-breeding sharp-spined cactus and a spineless cactus would produce

 A) all sharp-spined progeny.

 B) 50% sharp-spined, 50% dull-spined progeny.

 C) 25% sharp-spined, 50% dull-spined, 25% spineless progeny

 D) all spineless progeny

 E) It is impossible to determine the phenotypes of the progeny.

Answer: A
*Topic: Concept 14.3*
*Skill: Application*

41) If doubly heterozygous *SsNn* cactuses were allowed to self-pollinate, the $F_2$ would segregate in which of the following ratios?

 A) 3 sharp-spined : 1 spineless

 B) 1 sharp-spined : 2 dull-spined : 1 spineless

 C) 1 sharp spined : 1 dull-spined : 1 spineless

 D) 1 sharp-spined : 1 dull-spined

 E) 9 sharp-spined : 3 dull-spined : 4 spineless

Answer: E
*Topic: Concept 14.3*
*Skill: Application*

*Use the information given here to answer the following questions.*

Feather color in budgies is determined by two different genes Y and B. YYBB, YyBB, or YYBb is green; yyBB or yyBb is blue; YYbb or Yybb is yellow; and yybb is white.

42) A blue budgie is crossed with a white budgie. Which of the following results is *not* possible?

A) green offspring

B) yellow offspring

C) blue offspring

D) A and B

E) A, B, and C

Answer: D
*Topic: Concept 14.3*
*Skill: Application*

43) Two blue budgies were crossed. Over the years, they produced 22 offspring, 5 of which were white. What are the most likely genotypes for the two blue budgies?

A) yyBB and yyBB

B) yyBB and yyBb

C) yyBb and yyBb

D) yyBB and yybb

E) yyBb and yybb

Answer: C
*Topic: Concept 14.3*
*Skill: Application*

44) Three babies were mixed up in a hospital. After consideration of the data below, which of the following represent the correct baby and parent combinations?

| Couple # | I | II | III |
|---|---|---|---|
| Blood groups | A and A | A and B | B and O |

| Baby # | 1 | 2 | 3 |
|---|---|---|---|
| Blood groups | B | O | AB |

A) I–3, II–1, III–2

B) I–1, II–3, III–2

C) I–2, II–3, III–1

D) I–2, II–1, III–3

E) I–3, II–2, III–1

Answer: C
*Topic: Concept 14.3*
*Skill: Application*

*Use the following information to answer the questions below.*

A woman who has blood type A, has a daughter who is type O positive and a son who is type B negative. Rh positive is a simple dominant trait over Rh negative.

45) Which of the following is a possible genotype for the son?

A) $I^B I^B$

B) $I^B I^A$

C) $ii$

D) $I^B i$

E) $I^A I^A$

Answer: D
*Topic: Concept 14.3*
*Skill: Application*

46) Which of the following is a possible genotype for the mother?

   A) $I^A I^A$

   B) $I^B I^B$

   C) $ii$

   D) $I^A i$

   E) $I^A I^B$

Answer: D
*Topic: Concept 14.3*
*Skill: Application*

47) Which of the following is a possible phenotype for the father?

   A) A

   B) O

   C) B

   D) AB

   E) impossible to determine

Answer: C
*Topic: Concept 14.3*
*Skill: Application*

48) Which of the following is the probable genotype for the mother?

   A) $I^A I^A RR$

   B) $I^A I^A Rr$

   C) $I^A irr$

   D) $I^A iRr$

   E) $I^A iRR$

Answer: D
*Topic: Concept 14.3, Concept 14.4*
*Skill: Application*

49) Which of the following is a possible phenotype of the father?

   A) A negative

   B) O negative

   C) B positive

   D) A positive

   E) O positive

Answer: C
*Topic: Concept 14.3, Concept 14.4*
*Skill: Application*

*The questions below refer to the following terms. Each term may be used once, more than once, or not at all.*

   A. incomplete dominance
   B. multiple alleles
   C. pleiotropy
   D. epistasis

50) the ability of a single gene to have multiple phenotypic effects

Answer: C
*Topic: Concept 14.3*
*Skill: Knowledge*

51) the ABO blood group system

Answer: B
*Topic: Concept 14.3*
*Skill: Knowledge*

52) the phenotype of the heterozygote differs from the phenotypes of both homozygotes

Answer: A
*Topic: Concept 14.3*
*Skill: Knowledge*

53) cystic fibrosis affects the lungs, the pancreas, the digestive system, and other organs, resulting in symptoms ranging from breathing difficulties to recurrent infections

Answer: C
*Topic: Concept 14.3*
*Skill: Knowledge*

54) Which of the following is an example of polygenic inheritance?

    A) pink flowers in snapdragons

    B) the ABO blood groups in humans

    C) Huntington's disease in humans

    D) white and purple flower color in peas

    E) skin pigmentation in humans

Answer: E
*Topic: Concept 14.3*
*Skill: Knowledge*

55) Hydrangea plants of the same genotype are planted in a large flower garden. Some of the plants produce blue flowers and others pink flowers. This can be best explained by

    A) environmental factors such as soil pH.

    B) the allele for blue hydrangea being completely dominant.

    C) the alleles being codominant.

    D) the fact that a mutation has occurred.

    E) acknowledging that multiple alleles are involved.

Answer: A
*Topic: Concept 14.3*
*Skill: Comprehension*

*Use the following information to answer the questions below.*

A woman and her spouse both show the normal phenotype for pigmentation, but both had one parent who was an albino. Albinism is an autosomal recessive trait.

56) What is the probability that their first child will be an albino?

    A) 0

    B) 1/4

    C) 1/2

    D) 3/4

    E) 1

Answer: B
*Topic: Concept 14.4*
*Skill: Application*

57) If their first two children have normal pigmentation, what is the probability that their third child will be an albino?

    A) 0

    B) 1/4

    C) 1/2

    D) 3/4

    E) 1

Answer: B
*Topic: Concept 14.4*
*Skill: Application*

58) Huntington's disease is caused by a dominant allele. If one of your parents has the disease, what is the probability that you, too, will have the disease?

    A) 1

    B) 3/4

    C) 1/2

    D) 1/4

    E) 0

Answer: C
*Topic: Concept 14.4*
*Skill: Knowledge*

59) A woman has six sons. The chance that her next child will be a daughter is

A) 1.

B) 0.

C) 1/2.

D) 1/6.

E) 5/6.

Answer: C
*Topic: Concept 14.4*
*Skill: Knowledge*

*The following questions refer to the pedigree chart in Figure 14.1 for a family, some of whose members exhibit the recessive trait, wooly hair. Affected individuals are indicated by an open square or circle.*

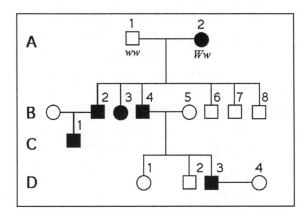

**Figure 14.1**

60) What is the genotype of individual B-5?

A) *WW*

B) *Ww*

C) *ww*

D) *WW* or *ww*

E) *ww* or *Ww*

Answer: C
*Topic: Concept 14.4*
*Skill: Application*

61) What is the likelihood that the progeny of D-3 and D-4 will have wooly hair?

A) *0%*

B) *25%*

C) *50%*

D) *75%*

E) *100%*

Answer: C
*Topic: Concept 14.4*
*Skill: Application*

62) What is the probability that individual C-1 is *Ww*?

A) 3/4

B) 1/4

C) 2/4

D) 2/3

E) 1

Answer: E
*Topic: Concept 14.4*
*Skill: Application*

63) People with sickle-cell trait

A) are heterozygous for the sickle-cell allele.

B) are usually healthy.

C) have increased resistance to malaria.

D) produce normal and abnormal hemoglobin.

E) all of the above

Answer: E
*Topic: Concept 14.4*
*Skill: Knowledge*

64) When a disease is said to have a multifactorial basis, it means that

A) many factors, both genetic and environmental, contribute to the disease.

B) it is caused by a gene with a large number of alleles.

C) it affects a large number of people.

D) it has many different symptoms.

E) it tends to skip a generation.

Answer: A
*Topic: Concept 14.4*
*Skill: Knowledge*

65) Which of the following terms is *least* related to the others?

A) pedigree

B) karyotype

C) amniocentesis

D) chorionic villus sampling

E) epistasis

Answer: E
*Topic: Concept 14.4*
*Skill: Knowledge*

*The questions below will use the following answers. Each answer may be used once, more than once, or not at all.*

A. Huntington's disease
B. Tay-Sachs disease
C. phenylketonuria
D. cystic fibrosis
E. sickle-cell disease

66) Substitution of the "wrong" amino acid in the hemoglobin protein results in this disorder.

Answer: E
*Topic: Concept 14.4*
*Skill: Knowledge*

67) Individuals with this disorder are unable to metabolize certain lipids, affecting proper brain development. Affected individuals die in early childhood.

Answer: B
*Topic: Concept 14.3*
*Skill: Knowledge*

68) This is caused by a dominant single gene defect and generally does not appear until the individual is 35–45 years of age.

Answer: A
*Topic: Concept 14.4*
*Skill: Knowledge*

69) Effects of this recessive disorder can be completely overcome by regulating the diet of the affected individual.

Answer: C
*Topic: Concept 14.4*
*Skill: Knowledge*

70) This results from a defect in membrane proteins that normally function in chloride ion transport.

Answer: D
*Topic: Concept 14.4*
*Skill: Knowledge*

71) Which of the following techniques involves the preparation of a karyotype?

A) amniocentesis

B) chorionic villus sampling

C) fetoscopy

D) A and B only

E) A, B, and C

Answer: D
*Topic: Concept 14.4*
*Skill: Knowledge*

# Media Activity Questions

1) All the offspring of a cross between a black-eyed MendAlien and an orange-eyed MendAlien have black eyes. This means that the allele for black eyes is _____ the allele for orange eyes.

A) codominant to

B) recessive to

C) more aggressive than

D) dominant to

E) better than

Answer: D
*Topic: Web/CD Activity: Monohybrid Crosses*

2) What is the expected phenotypic ratio of a cross between two orange-eyed MendAliens?

A) 3 black-eyed:1 orange-eyed

B) 0 black-eyed:1 orange-eyed

C) 1 black-eyed:3 orange-eyed

D) 1 black-eyed:0 orange-eyed

E) 1 black-eyed:1 orange-eyed

Answer: B
*Topic: Web/CD Activity: Monohybrid Crosses*

3) Andalusian chickens with the genotype $C^B C^B$ are black, those with the genotype $C^B C^W$ are gray. What is the relationship between the $C^B$ and the $C^W$ alleles?

A) $C^B$ is dominant to $C^W$.

B) $C^B$ is recessive to $C^W$.

C) $C^W$ is dominant to $C^B$.

D) The relationship is one of incomplete dominance.

E) $C^B$ and $C^W$ are codominant.

Answer: A
*Topic: Web/CD Activity: Incomplete Dominance*

4) Black eyes are dominant to orange eyes, and green skin is dominant to white skin. Sam, a MendAlien with black eyes and green skin, has a parent with orange eyes and white skin. Carole is MendAlien with orange eyes and white skin. If Sam and Carole were to mate, the predicted ratio of their offspring would be:

A) 1 black eyes, green skin : 1 black eyes, white skin : 1 orange eyes, green skin : 1 orange eyes, white skin

B) 3 black eyes, green skin : 3 black eyes, white skin : 9 orange eyes, green skin : 1 orange eyes, white skin

C) 1 black eyes, green skin : 3 black eyes, white skin : 3 orange eyes, green skin : 9 orange eyes, white skin

D) 9 black eyes, green skin : 3 black eyes, white skin : 3 orange eyes, green skin : 1 orange eyes, white skin

E) There is insufficient information to determine Sam's genotype.

Answer: A
*Topic: Web/CD Activity: Dihybrid Crosses*

5) All the offspring of a cross between a red-flowered plant and a white-flowered plant have pink flowers. This means that the allele for red flowers is _____ to the allele for white flowers.

A) dominant

B) codominant

C) pleiotropic

D) incompletely dominant

E) recessive

Answer: D
*Topic: Web/CD Activity: Incomplete Dominance*

# Self-Quiz Questions

1) In some plants, a true-breeding, red-flowered strain gives all pink flowers when crossed with a white-flowered strain: $RR$ (red) × $rr$ (white) → $Rr$ (pink). If flower position (axial or terminal) is inherited as it is in peas (see Table 14.1 in your text), what will be the ratios of genotypes and phenotypes of the $F_1$ generation resulting from the following cross: axial-red (true-breeding) × terminal-white? What will be the ratios in the $F_2$ generation?

   Answer: Parental cross is $AARR × aarr$. Genotype of $F_1$ is $AaRr$, phenotype is all axial-pink. Genotypes of $F_2$ are 4 $AaRr$ : 2 $AaRR$ : 1 $AARr$ : 2 $aaRr$ : 2 $Aarr$ : 1$AARR$ : 1 $aaRR$ : 1 $AArr$ : 1 $aarr$. Phenotypes of $F_2$ are 6 axial-pink : 3 axial-white : 2 terminal-pink : 1 terminal-white : 1 terminal red.

2) Flower position, stem length, and seed shape were three characters that Mendel studied. Each is controlled by an independently assorting gene and has dominant and recessive expression as follows:

   | Character | Dominant | Recessive |
   |---|---|---|
   | Flower position | Axial ($A$) | Terminal ($a$) |
   | Stem length | Tall ($L$) | Dwarf ($l$) |
   | Seed shape | Round ($R$) | Wrinkled ($r$) |

   If a plant that is heterozygous for all three characters is allowed to self-fertilize, what proportion of the offspring would you expect to be as follows? (*Note:* Use the rules of probability instead of a huge Punnett square.)
   A) homozygous for the three dominant traits
   B) homozygous for the three recessive traits
   C) heterozygous for all three characters
   D) homozygous for axial and tall, heterozygous for seed shape

   Answer: A) 1/64
   B) 1/64
   C) 1/8
   D) 1/32

3) A black guinea pig crossed with an albino guinea pig produces 12 black offspring. When the albino is crossed with a second black one, 7 blacks and 5 albinos are obtained. What is the best explanation for this genetic situation? Write genotypes for the parents, gametes, and offspring.

   Answer: Albino ($b$) is a recessive trait; black ($B$) is dominant. First cross: parents $BB × bb$; gametes $B$ and $b$; offspring all $Bb$ (black coat). Second cross: parents $bb × Bb$; gametes 1/2 $B$ and 1/2 $b$ (heterozygous parent) and $b$; offspring 1/2 $Bb$ and 1/2 $bb$.

4) In sesame plants, the one-pod condition ($P$) is dominant to the three-pod condition ($p$), and normal leaf ($L$) is dominant to wrinkled leaf ($l$). Pod type and leaf type are inherited independently. Determine the genotypes for the two parents for all possible matings producing the following offspring:
A) 318 one-pod, normal leaf : 98 one-pod, wrinkled leaf
B) 323 three-pod, normal leaf : 106 three-pod, wrinkled leaf
C) 401 one-pod, normal leaf
D) 150 one-pod, normal leaf : 147 one-pod, wrinkled leaf : 51 three-pod, normal leaf : 48 three-pod, wrinkled leaf
E) 223 one-pod, normal leaf : 72 one-pod, wrinkled leaf : 76 three-pod, normal leaf; 27 three-pod, wrinkled leaf

Answer: A) *PPLl* × *PPLl*, *PpLl*, or *ppLl*
B) *ppLl* × *ppLl*
C) *PPLL* × any of the 9 possible genotypes or *PPll* × *ppLL*
D) *PpLl* × *Ppll*
E) *PpLl* × *PpLl*

5) A man with type A blood marries a woman with type B blood. Their child has type O blood. What are the genotypes of these individuals? What other genotypes, and in what frequencies, would you expect in offspring from this marriage?

Answer: Man $I^Ai$; woman $I^Bi$; child $ii$. Other genotypes for children are $1/4\ I^AI^B$, $1/4\ I^Ai$, $1/4\ I^Bi$

6) Phenylketonuria (PKU) is an inherited disease caused by a recessive allele. If a woman and her husband, who are both carriers, have three children, what is the probability of each of the following?
A) All three children are of normal phenotype.
B) One or more of the three children have the disease.
C) All three children have the disease.
D) At least one child is phenotypically normal.
(*Note:* Remember that the probabilities of all possible outcomes always add up to 1.)

Answer: A) $3/4 \times 3/4 \times 3/4 = 27/64$
B) $1 - 27/64 = 37/64$
C) $1/4 \times 1/4 \times 1/4 = 1/64$
D) $1 - 1/64 = 63/64$

7) The genotype of $F_1$ individuals in a tetrahybrid cross is *AaBbCcDd*. Assuming independent assortment of these four genes, what are the probabilities that $F_2$ offspring will have the following genotypes?
A) *aabbccdd*
B) *AaBbCcDd*
C) *AABBCCDD*
D) *AaBBccDd*
E) *AaBBCCdd*

Answer: A) 1/256
B) 1/16
C) 1/256
D) 1/64
E) 1/128

8) What is the probability that each of the following pairs of parents will produce the indicated offspring? (Assume independent assortment of all gene pairs.)
A) *AABBCC* × *aabbcc* → *AaBbCc*
B) *AABbCc* × *AaBbCc* → *AAbbCC*
C) *AaBbCc* × *AaBbCc* → *AaBbCc*
D) *aaBbCC* × *AABbcc* → *AaBbCc*

Answer: A) 1
B) 1/32
C) 1/8
D) 1/2

9) Karen and Steve each have a sibling with sickle-cell disease. Neither Karen nor Steve nor any of their parents have the disease, and none of them have been tested to reveal sickle-cell trait. Based on this incomplete information, calculate the probability that if this couple has a child, the child will have sickle-cell disease.

Answer: 1/9

10) In 1981, a stray black cat with unusual rounded, curled-back ears was adopted by a family in California. Hundreds of descendants of the cat have since been born, and cat fanciers hope to develop the curl cat into a show breed. Suppose you owned the first curl cat and wanted to develop a true-breeding variety. How would you determine whether the curl allele is dominant or recessive? How would you obtain true-breeding curl cats? How could you be sure they are true-breeding?

Answer: Matings of the original mutant cat with true-breeding noncurl cats will produce both curl and noncurl $F_1$ offspring if the curl allele is dominant, but only noncurl offspring if the curl allele is recessive. You would obtain some true-breeding offspring homozygous for the curl allele from matings between the $F_1$ cats resulting from the original curl × noncurl crosses whether the curl trait is dominant or recessive. You know that cats are true-breeding when curl × curl matings produce only curl offspring. As it turns out, the allele that causes curled ears is dominant.

# Chapter 15 The Chromosomal Basis of Inheritance

1) Chromosomes and genes share all of the following characteristics *except* that
   A) they are both present in pairs in all diploid cells.
   B) they both undergo segregation during meiosis.
   C) their copy numbers in the cell decrease after meiosis, and increase during fertilization.
   D) they are both copied during the S phase of the cell cycle.
   E) they both pair up with their homologues during prophase of mitosis.

   Answer: E
   *Topic: Concept 15.1*
   *Skill: Knowledge*

2) The improvement of microscopy techniques in the late 1800s set the stage for the emergence of modern genetics because
   A) it revealed new and unanticipated features of Mendel's pea plant varieties.
   B) it allowed biologists to study meiosis and mitosis, revealing the parallels between the behaviors of genes and chromosomes.
   C) it allowed scientists to see the DNA present within chromosomes.
   D) it led to the discovery of mitochondria.
   E) All of the above are true.

   Answer: B
   *Topic: Concept 15.1*
   *Skill: Comprehension*

3) When Thomas Hunt Morgan crossed his red-eyed $F_1$ generation flies to each other, the $F_2$ generation included both red- and white-eyed flies. Remarkably, all the white-eyed flies were male. What was the explanation for this result?
   A) The involved gene was on the X chromosome.
   B) The involved gene was on the Y chromosome.
   C) The involved gene was on an autosome.
   D) Other male-specific factors influence eye color in flies.
   E) Other female-specific factors influence eye color in flies.

   Answer: A
   *Topic: Concept 15.1*
   *Skill: Knowledge*

4) Which of the following statements is (are) true?
   A) The closer two genes are on a chromosome, the higher the probability that a crossover will occur between them.
   B) The observed frequency of recombination of two genes that are far apart from each other has a maximum value of 50%.
   C) Two of the traits that Mendel studied—seed color and flower color—are linked on the same chromosome.
   D) Only B and C are correct.
   E) A, B, and C are correct.

   Answer: D
   *Topic: Concept 15.2*
   *Skill: Knowledge*

5) How would one explain a testcross involving F$_1$ dihybrid flies in which more parental–type offspring than recombinant–type offspring are produced?

A) The two genes are linked.

B) The two genes are unlinked.

C) Recombination did not occur in the cell during meiosis.

D) The testcross was improperly performed.

E) Both of the characters are controlled by more than one gene.

Answer: A
*Topic: Concept 15.2*
*Skill: Comprehension*

6) New combinations of linked genes are due to which of the following?

A) nondisjunction

B) crossing over

C) independent assortment

D) mixing of sperm and egg

E) both A and C

Answer: B
*Topic: Concept 15.2*
*Skill: Comprehension*

7) What does a frequency of recombination of 50% indicate?

A) The two genes likely are located on different chromosomes.

B) All of the offspring have combinations of traits that match one of the two parents.

C) The genes are located on sex chromosomes.

D) Abnormal meiosis has occurred.

E) Independent assortment is hindered.

Answer: A
*Topic: Concept 15.2*
*Skill: Comprehension*

*The following questions refer to the data below and to Figures 15.1 and 15.2.*

*CROSS I. Purebred lines of wild–type fruit flies (gray body and normal wings) are mated to flies with black bodies and vestigial wings.*

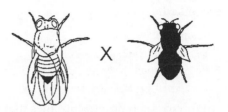

**Figure 15.1**

*F$_1$ offspring all have a normal phenotype.*

**Figure 15.2**

*CROSS II. F$_1$ flies are crossed with flies recessive for both traits (a testcross).*

| Resulting Offspring | Normal | Percentage |
|---|---|---|
| Gray body; normal wings | 575 | 25.1 |
| Black body; vestigial wings | 571 | 24.9 |
| Black body; normal wings | 577 | 25.2 |
| Gray body; vestigial wings | 568 | 24.8 |

KEY:
A. CROSS I results give evidence supporting the statement.
B. CROSS I results give evidence against the statement.
C. CROSS II results give evidence supporting the statement.
D. CROSS II results give evidence against the statement.
E. Neither CROSS I nor CROSS II results support the statement.

8) Vestigial wings are a recessive trait.

Answer: A
*Topic: Concept 15.2*
*Skill: Application*

9) The genes for body color and wing shape are linked.

Answer: D
*Topic: Concept 15.2*
*Skill: Application*

10) An $F_1$ cross should produce flies that will fall into a Mendelian 9:3:3:1 ratio.

Answer: C
*Topic: Concept 15.2*
*Skill: Application*

11) There are 25 centimorgans (map units) between the genes for body color and wing shape.

Answer: D
*Topic: Concept 15.2*
*Skill: Application*

12) A 0.1% frequency of recombination is observed

A) only in sex chromosomes.

B) only on genetic maps of viral chromosomes.

C) on unlinked chromosomes.

D) in any two genes on different chromosomes.

E) in genes located very close to one another on the same chromosome.

Answer: E
*Topic: Concept 15.2*
*Skill: Knowledge*

13) The following is a map of four genes on a chromosome:

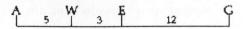

Between which two genes would you expect the highest frequency of recombination?

A) *A* and *W*

B) *W* and *E*

C) *E* and *G*

D) *A* and *E*

E) *A* and *G*

Answer: E
*Topic: Concept 15.2*
*Skill: Comprehension*

14) The reason that linked genes are inherited together is that

A) they are located on the same chromosome.

B) the number of genes in a cell is greater than the number of chromosomes.

C) chromosomes are unbreakable.

D) alleles are paired.

E) genes align that way during metaphase I.

Answer: A
*Topic: Concept 15.2*
*Skill: Knowledge*

15) What is the mechanism for the production of genetic recombinants?

A) X inactivation

B) methylation of cytosine

C) crossing over and independent assortment

D) nondisjunction

E) deletions and duplications during meiosis

Answer: C
*Topic: Concept 15.2*
*Skill: Knowledge*

16) There is good evidence for linkage when

A) two genes occur together in the same gamete.

B) a gene is associated with a specific phenotype.

C) two genes work together to control a specific characteristic.

D) genes do not segregate independently during meiosis.

E) two characteristics are caused by a single gene.

Answer: D
*Topic: Concept 15.2*
*Skill: Knowledge*

*Refer to Figure 15.3 to answer the following questions.*

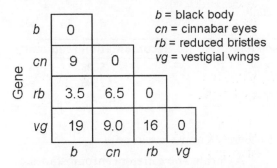

The numbers in the boxes are the recombination frequencies in between the genes (in percent).

**Figure 15.3**

17) In a series of mapping experiments, the recombination frequencies for four different linked genes of *Drosophila* were determined as shown in the figure. What is the order of these genes on a chromosome map?

A) *rb–cn–vg–b*

B) *vg–b–rb–cn*

C) *cn–rb–b–vg*

D) *b–rb–cn–vg*

E) *vg–cn–b–rb*

Answer: D
*Topic: Concept 15.2*
*Skill: Application*

18) Which of the following two genes are closest on a genetic map of *Drosophila*?

A) *b* and *vg*

B) *vg* and *cn*

C) *rb* and *cn*

D) *cn* and *b*

E) *b* and *rb*

Answer: E
*Topic: Concept 15.2*
*Skill: Application*

*X, Y, and Z are three genes in* Drosophila. *The recombination frequencies for two of the three genes are shown below.*

| Gene Pair | Recombination Frequency |
|-----------|------------------------|
| X–Y | 50% |
| X–Z | 25% |
| Y–Z | ? |

19) Genes X and Y could be

A) located on different chromosomes.

B) located very near to each other on the same chromosome.

C) located far from each other on the same chromosome.

D) both A and B

E) both A and C

Answer: E
*Topic: Concept 15.2*
*Skill: Application*

20) If the recombination frequency for Y and Z was found to be 50%, this would mean that

A) genes X and Y are on the same chromosome.

B) genes X and Y are on different chromosomes.

C) genes Y and Z are on different chromosomes.

D) both A and C.

E) both B and C

Answer: E
*Topic: Concept 15.2*
*Skill: Application*

21) Which of the following is true regarding linkage maps? They

A) always have a total of 100 map units.

B) can be used to pinpoint the precise physical position of a gene on a chromosome.

C) are a genetic map based on recombination frequencies.

D) require preparation of karyotypes.

E) reflect the frequency of crossing over between X and Y chromosomes.

Answer: C
*Topic: Concept 15.2*
*Skill: Knowledge*

22) The frequency of crossing over between any two linked genes is

A) higher if they are recessive.

B) different between males and females.

C) determined by their relative dominance.

D) the same as if they were not linked.

E) proportional to the distance between them.

Answer: E
*Topic: Concept 15.2*
*Skill: Knowledge*

23) Sturtevant provided genetic evidence for the existence of four pairs of chromosomes in *Drosophila* by showing that

A) there are four major functional classes of genes in *Drosophila*.

B) *Drosophila* genes cluster into four distinct groups of linked genes.

C) the overall number of genes in *Drosophila* is a multiple of four.

D) the entire *Drosophila* genome has approximately 400 map units.

E) *Drosophila* genes have, on average, four different alleles.

Answer: B
*Topic: Concept 15.2*
*Skill: Knowledge*

24) Map units on a linkage map cannot be relied upon to calculate physical distances on a chromosome because

A) the frequency of crossing over varies along the length of the chromosome.

B) the relationship between recombination frequency and map units is different in every individual.

C) physical distances between genes change during the course of the cell cycle.

D) the gene order on the chromosomes is slightly different in every individual.

E) all of the above

Answer: A
*Topic: Concept 15.2*
*Skill: Knowledge*

25) A map of a chromosome that includes the positions of genes relative to visible chromosomal features, such as stained bands, is called a

A) linkage map.

B) physical map.

C) recombination map.

D) cytogenetic map.

E) banded map.

Answer: D
*Topic: Concept 15.2*
*Skill: Knowledge*

26) Males are more often affected by sex-linked traits than females because

A) males are hemizygous for the X chromosome.

B) male hormones such as testosterone often exacerbate the effects of mutations on the X chromosome.

C) female hormones such as estrogen often compensate for the effects of mutations on the X.

D) X chromosomes in males generally have more mutations than X chromosomes in females.

E) mutations on the Y chromosome often exacerbate the effects of X-linked mutations.

Answer: A
*Topic: Concept 15.3*
*Skill: Comprehension*

*Use the list of chromosomal systems below to answer the following questions.*

A. haploid–diploid
B. X–0
C. X–X
D. X–Y
E. Z–W

27) What is the chromosomal system for determining sex in mammals?

Answer: D
*Topic: Concept 15.3*
*Skill: Knowledge*

28) What is the chromosomal system for sex determination in grasshoppers and certain other insects?

Answer: B
*Topic: Concept 15.3*
*Skill: Knowledge*

29) What is the chromosomal system for sex determination in birds?

Answer: E
*Topic: Concept 15.3*
*Skill: Knowledge*

30) What is the chromosomal system of sex determination in most species of ants and bees?

Answer: A
*Topic: Concept 15.3*
*Skill: Knowledge*

31) SRY is
   A) a gene present on the Y chromosome that triggers male development.
   B) a gene present on the X chromosome that triggers female development.
   C) an autosomal gene that is required for the expression of genes on the Y chromosome.
   D) an autosomal gene that is required for the expression of genes on the X chromosome.
   E) required for development, and males or females lacking the gene do not survive past early childhood.

Answer: A
*Topic: Concept 15.3*
*Skill: Knowledge*

32) In cats, black fur color is caused by an X-linked allele; the other allele at this locus causes orange color. The heterozygote is tortoiseshell. What kinds of offspring would you expect from the cross of a black female and an orange male?
   A) tortoiseshell female; tortoiseshell male
   B) black female; orange male
   C) orange female; orange male
   D) tortoiseshell female; black male
   E) orange female; black male

Answer: D
*Topic: Concept 15.3*
*Skill: Application*

33) Red-green color blindness is a sex-linked recessive trait in humans. Two people with normal color vision have a color-blind son. What are the genotypes of the parents?
   A) $X^c X^c$ and $X^c Y$
   B) $X^c X^c$ and $X^C Y$
   C) $X^C X^C$ and $X^c Y$
   D) $X^C X^C$ and $X^C Y$
   E) $X^C X^c$ and $X^C Y$

Answer: E
*Topic: Concept 15.3*
*Skill: Application*

34) In the following list, which term is *least* related to the others?
   A) Duchenne muscular dystrophy
   B) autosome
   C) sex-linked genes
   D) color blindness
   E) hemophilia

Answer: B
*Topic: Concept 15.3*
*Skill: Comprehension*

35) Cinnabar eyes is a sex-linked recessive characteristic in fruit flies. If a female having cinnabar eyes is crossed with a wild-type male, what percentage of the $F_1$ males will have cinnabar eyes?

A) 0%

B) 25%

C) 50%

D) 75%

E) 100%

Answer: E
*Topic: Concept 15.3*
*Skill: Application*

36) Most calico cats are female because

A) a male inherits only one of the two X-linked genes controlling hair color.

B) the males die during embryonic development.

C) the Y chromosome has a gene blocking orange coloration.

D) only females can have Barr bodies.

E) multiple crossovers on the Y chromosome prevent orange pigment production.

Answer: A
*Topic: Concept 15.3*
*Skill: Comprehension*

37) A recessive allele on the X chromosome is responsible for red-green color blindness in humans. A woman with normal vision whose father is color-blind marries a color-blind male. What is the probability that a son of this couple will be color-blind?

A) 0

B) 1/4

C) 1/2

D) 3/4

E) 1

Answer: C
*Topic: Concept 15.3*
*Skill: Application*

38) In birds, sex is determined by a ZW chromosome scheme. Males are ZZ and females are ZW. A lethal recessive allele that causes death of the embryo is sometimes present on the Z chromosome in pigeons. What would be the sex ratio in the offspring of a cross between a male that is heterozygous for the lethal allele and a normal female?

A) 2:1 male to female

B) 1:2 male to female

C) 1:1 male to female

D) 4:3 male to female

E) 3:1 male to female

Answer: A
*Topic: Concept 15.3*
*Skill: Application*

39) A man who carries an X-linked allele will pass it on to

A) all of his daughters.

B) half of his daughters.

C) all of his sons.

D) half of his sons.

E) all of his children.

Answer: A
*Topic: Concept 15.3*
*Skill: Comprehension*

*Refer to the following information to answer the questions below.*

An achondroplastic male dwarf with normal vision marries a color–blind woman of normal height. The man's father was six-feet tall, and both the woman's parents were of average height. Achondroplastic dwarfism is autosomal dominant, and red–green color blindness is X–linked recessive.

40) How many of their daughters might be expected to be color-blind dwarfs?
   A) all
   B) none
   C) half
   D) one out of four
   E) three out of four

Answer: B
*Topic: Concept 15.3*
*Skill: Application*

41) How many of their sons would be color-blind and of normal height?
   A) all
   B) none
   C) half
   D) one out of four
   E) three out of four

Answer: C
*Topic: Concept 15.3*
*Skill: Application*

42) They have a daughter who is a dwarf with normal color vision. What is the probability that she is heterozygous for both genes?
   A) 0
   B) 0.25
   C) 0.50
   D) 0.75
   E) 1.00

Answer: E
*Topic: Concept 15.3*
*Skill: Application*

43) Male calico cats could be the result of
   A) sex–linked inheritance.
   B) nondisjunction, leading to the male calico having two X chromosomes.
   C) incomplete dominance of multiple alleles.
   D) recessive alleles retaining their fundamental natures even when expressed.
   E) a reciprocal translocation.

Answer: B
*Topic: Concept 15.3*
*Skill: Application*

44) A Barr body is normally found in the nucleus of which kind of human cell?
   A) unfertilized egg cells only
   B) sperm cells only
   C) somatic cells of a female only
   D) somatic cells of a male only
   E) both male and female somatic cells

Answer: C
*Topic: Concept 15.3*
*Skill: Knowledge*

45) Which of these syndromes afflicts mostly males?
   A) Turner syndrome
   B) Down syndrome
   C) Duchenne muscular dystrophy
   D) *cri du chat* syndrome
   E) chronic myelogenous leukemia

Answer: C
*Topic: Concept 15.3*
*Skill: Knowledge*

46) If a human interphase nucleus of a person contains three Barr bodies, it can be assumed that the person

    A) has hemophilia.

    B) is a male.

    C) has four X chromosomes.

    D) has Turner syndrome.

    E) has Down syndrome.

Answer: C
*Topic: Concept 15.4*
*Skill: Comprehension*

47) If nondisjunction occurs in meiosis II during gametogenesis, what will be the result at the completion of meiosis?

    A) All the gametes will be diploid.

    B) Two gametes will be $n + 1$, and two will be $n - 1$.

    C) One gamete will be $n + 1$, one will be $n - 1$, and two will be $n$.

    D) There will be three extra gametes.

    E) Two of the four gametes will be haploid, and two will be diploid.

Answer: C
*Topic: Concept 15.4*
*Skill: Comprehension*

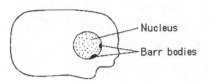

**Figure 15.4**

48) Figure 15.4 represents the stained nucleus from a cheek epithelial cell of an individual whose genotype would probably be

    A) XX.

    B) XY.

    C) XYY.

    D) XXX.

    E) XXY.

Answer: D
*Topic: Concept 15.4*
*Skill: Comprehension*

49) If a pair of homologous chromosomes fails to separate during anaphase of meiosis I, what will be the chromosome number of the four resulting gametes with respect to the normal haploid number ($n$)?

    A) $n + 1; n + 1; n - 1; n - 1$

    B) $n + 1; n - 1; n; n$

    C) $n + 1; n - 1; n - 1; n - 1$

    D) $n + 1; n + 1; n; n$

    E) $n - 1; n - 1; n; n$

Answer: A
*Topic: Concept 15.4*
*Skill: Comprehension*

50) A cell that has $2n + 1$ chromosomes is

    A) trisomic.

    B) monosomic.

    C) aneuploid.

    D) polyploid.

    E) both A and C

Answer: E
*Topic: Concept 15.4*
*Skill: Knowledge*

51) If a chromosome lacks certain genes, what has most likely occurred?

A) disjunction

B) an inversion

C) a deletion

D) a translocation

E) a nonduplication

Answer: C
*Topic: Concept 15.4*
*Skill: Knowledge*

52) One possible result of chromosomal breakage is for a fragment to join a nonhomologous chromosome.  This is called a (an)

A) deletion.

B) disjunction.

C) inversion.

D) translocation.

E) duplication.

Answer: D
*Topic: Concept 15.4*
*Skill: Knowledge*

53) In the following list, which term is *least* related to the others?

A) trisomic

B) monosomic

C) aneuploid

D) triploid

E) nondisjunction

Answer: D
*Topic: Concept 15.4*
*Skill: Comprehension*

54) A nonreciprocal crossover causes which of the following products?

A) deletion

B) duplication

C) nondisjunction

D) A and B

E) B and C

Answer: D
*Topic: Concept 15.4*
*Skill: Comprehension*

55) One possible result of chromosomal breakage can be that a fragment reattaches to the original chromosome in a reverse orientation.  This is called

A) disjunction.

B) translocation.

C) deletion.

D) inversion.

E) aneuploidy.

Answer: D
*Topic: Concept 15.4*
*Skill: Knowledge*

56) A human individual is phenotypically female, but her interphase somatic nuclei do not show the presence of Barr bodies. Which of the following statements concerning her is probably *true*?

A) She has Klinefelter syndrome.

B) She has an extra X chromosome.

C) She has Turner syndrome.

D) She has the normal number of sex chromosomes.

E) She has two Y chromosomes.

Answer: C
*Topic: Concept 15.4*
*Skill: Comprehension*

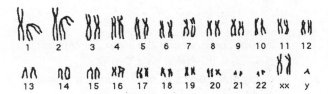

**Figure 15.5**

57) The karyotype shown in Figure 15.5 is associated with which of the following genetic disorders?

A) Turner syndrome

B) Down syndrome

C) Klinefelter syndrome

D) hemophilia

E) male–pattern baldness

Answer: C
*Topic: Concept 15.4*
*Skill: Knowledge*

58) In humans, male–pattern baldness is controlled by a gene that occurs in two allelic forms. Allele *Hn* determines nonbaldness, and allele *Hb* determines pattern baldness. In males, because of the presence of testosterone, allele *Hb* is dominant over *Hn*. If a man and woman both with genotype *HnHb* have a son, what is the chance that he will eventually be bald?

A) 0%

B) 25%

C) 33%

D) 50%

E) 75%

Answer: E
*Topic: Concept 15.4*
*Skill: Application*

59) Of the following human trisomies, the one that generally has the most severe impact on the health of the individual is

A) trisomy 21.

B) Klinefelter syndrome (XXY).

C) trisomy X.

D) XYY.

E) All of the above have equal impact.

Answer: A
*Topic: Concept 15.4*
*Skill: Knowledge*

60) What do all human males inherit from their mother?

A) mitochondrial DNA

B) an X chromosome

C) the SRY gene

D) A and B only

E) A, B, and C

Answer: D
*Topic: Concepts 15.4, 15.5*
*Skill: Knowledge*

61) Which of the following statements is *true* regarding genomic imprinting?

A) It explains cases in which the gender of the parent from whom an allele is inherited affects the expression of that allele.

B) It is greatest in females because of the larger maternal contribution of cytoplasm.

C) It may explain the transmission of Duchenne muscular dystrophy.

D) It involves an irreversible alteration in the DNA sequence of imprinted genes.

E) All of the above are correct.

Answer: A
*Topic: Concept 15.5*
*Skill: Knowledge*

# Media Activity Questions

1) You conduct a dihybrid cross and then testcross the $F_1$ generation. A _____ ratio would make you suspect that the genes are linked.

   A) 3:1

   B) 1:2:1

   C) 1:1:1:1

   D) 7:7:1:1

   E) 9:3:3:1

Answer: D
*Topic: Activity: Linked Genes and Crossing Over*

2) The recombination frequency between gene $A$ and gene $B$ is 8.4%, the recombination frequency between gene $A$ and gene $C$ is 6.8%, and the recombination frequency between gene $B$ and gene $C$ is 15.2%. Which is the correct arrangement of these genes?

   A) $ABC$

   B) $ACB$

   C) $BCA$

   D) $CAB$

   E) $CBA$

Answer: D
*Topic: Activity: Linked Genes and Crossing Over*

3) Hypophosphatemia (vitamin D–resistant rickets) is inherited as a X–linked dominant disorder. An unaffected woman mates with a male with hypophosphatemia. What is the expected phenotypic ratio of their offspring?

   A) 1 normal daughter: 1 daughter with hypophosphatemia

   B) 1 normal daughter : 1 son with hypophosphatemia

   C) 1 daughter with hypophosphatemia : 1 normal son

   D) 2 normal daughters : 1 normal son : 1 son with hypophosphatemia

   E) 3 normal daughters : 1 son with hypophosphatemia

Answer: C
*Topic: Web/CD Activity: Sex–Linked Genes*

4) The sex chromosome complements of both normal human and normal MendAlien males is

   A) XO.

   B) XX.

   C) XY.

   D) YY.

   E) YO.

Answer: C
*Topic: Web/CD Activity: Sex–Linked Genes*

5) Mutant tetraploid plants

   A) are usually sickly.

   B) are able to interbreed with their parents.

   C) have an odd number of chromosomes.

   D) are unable to breed with a diploid plant.

   E) are unable to self–fertilize.

Answer: D
*Topic: Web/CD Activity: Polyploid Plants*

# Self-Quiz Questions

1) A man with hemophilia (a recessive, sex–linked condition) has a daughter of normal phenotype. She marries a man who is normal for the trait. What is the probability that a daughter of this mating will be a hemophiliac? That a son will be a hemophiliac? If the couple has four sons, what is the probability that all four will be born with hemophilia?

   Answer: 0; 1/2, 1/16

2) Pseudohypertrophic muscular dystrophy is an inherited disorder that causes gradual deterioration of the muscles. It is seen almost exclusively in boys born to apparently normal parents and usually results in death in the early teens. Is this disorder caused by a dominant or a recessive allele? Is its inheritance sex–linked or autosomal? How do you know? Explain why this disorder is almost never seen in girls.

   Answer: Recessive. If the disorder were dominant, it would affect at least one parent of a child born with the disorder. The disorder's inheritance is sex–linked because it is seen almost only in boys. For a girl to have the disorder, she would have to inherit the recessive alleles from *both* parents. This would be very rare since males with the recessive allele on their X chromosome die in their early teens.

3) Red–green color blindness is caused by a sex–linked recessive allele. A color-blind man marries a woman with normal vision whose father was color-blind. What is the probability that they will have a color-blind daughter? What is the probability that their first son will be color-blind? (*Note*: The two questions are worded a bit differently.)

   Answer: 1/4 for each daughter (1/2 chance that child will be female × 1/2 chance of a homozygous recessive genotype); 1/2 for first son.

4) A wild–type fruit fly (heterozygous for gray body color and normal wings) is mated with a black fly with vestigial wings. The offspring have the following phenotypic distribution: wild type, 778; black-vestigial, 785; black–normal, 158; gray-vestigial, 162. What is the recombination frequency between these genes for body color and wing size?

   Answer: 17%

5) In another cross, a wild–type fruit fly (heterozygous for gray body color and red eyes) is mated with a black fruit fly with purple eyes. The offspring are as follows: wild type, 721; black-purple, 751; gray-purple, 49; black-red, 45. What is the recombination frequency between these genes for body color and eye color? Using information from problem 4, what fruit flies (genotypes and phenotypes) would you mate to determine the sequence of the body-color, wing-size, and eye-color genes on the chromosome?

   Answer: 6%. Wild type (heterozygous for normal wings and red eyes) × recessive homozygote with vestigial wings and purple eyes

6) What pattern of inheritance would lead a geneticist to suspect that an inherited disorder of cell metabolism is due to a defective mitochondrial gene?

Answer: The disorder would always be inherited from the mother.

7) Women born with an extra X chromosome (XXX) are healthy and phenotypically indistinguishable from normal XX women. What is a likely explanation for this finding? How could you test this explanation?

Answer: The inactivation of two X chromosomes in XXX women would leave them with one genetically active X, as in women with the normal number of chromosomes. Microscopy should reveal two Barr bodies in XXX women.

8) Determine the sequence of genes along a chromosome based on the following recombination frequencies: $A$–$B$, 8 map units; $A$–$C$, 28 map units; $A$–$D$, 25 map units; $B$–$C$, 20 map units; $B$–$D$, 33 map units.

Answer: $D$–$A$–$B$–$C$

9) Assume that genes $A$ and $B$ are linked and are 50 map units apart. An animal heterozygous at both loci is crossed with one that is homozygous recessive at both loci. What percentage of the offspring will show phenotypes resulting from crossovers? If you did not know that genes $A$ and $B$ were linked, how would you interpret the results of this cross?

Answer: Fifty percent of the offspring would show phenotypes that resulted from crossovers. These results would be the same as those from a cross where $A$ and $B$ were not linked. Further crosses involving other genes on the same chromosome would reveal the linkage and map distances.

10) A space probe discovers a planet inhabited by creatures who reproduce with the same hereditary patterns seen in humans. Three phenotypic characters are height ($T$ = tall, $t$ = dwarf), head appendages ($A$ = antennae, $a$ = no antennae), and nose morphology ($S$ = upturned snout, $s$ = downturned snout). Since the creatures are not "intelligent," Earth scientists are able to do some controlled breeding experiments, using various heterozygotes in testcrosses. For tall heterozygotes with antennae, the offspring are: tall-antennae, 46; dwarf-antennae, 7; dwarf–no antennae, 42; tall–no antennae, 5. For heterozygotes with antennae and an upturned snout, the offspring are: antennae-upturned snout, 47; antennae-downturned snout, 2; no antennae-downturned snout, 48; no antennae-upturned snout, 3. Calculate the recombination frequencies for both experiments.

Answer: Between $T$ and $A$, 12%; between $A$ and $S$, 5%

# Chapter 16  The Molecular Basis of Inheritance

1) For a couple of decades, biologists knew the nucleus contained DNA and proteins. The prevailing opinion was that the genetic material was proteins, and not DNA. The reason for this belief was that proteins are more complex than DNA. This is because

   A) proteins have a greater variety of three-dimensional forms than does DNA.

   B) proteins have two different levels of structural organization; DNA has four.

   C) proteins are made of 20 amino acids and DNA is made of four nucleotides.

   D) Only A and C are correct.

   E) A, B, and C are correct.

   Answer: D
   *Topic: Concept 16.1*
   *Skill: Comprehension*

2) In his transformation experiments, Griffith observed that

   A) mutant mice were resistant to bacterial infections.

   B) mixing a heat-killed pathogenic strain of bacteria with a living nonpathogenic strain can convert some of the living cells into the pathogenic form.

   C) mixing a heat-killed nonpathogenic strain of bacteria with a living pathogenic strain makes the pathogenic strain nonpathogenic.

   D) infecting mice with nonpathogenic strains of bacteria makes them resistant to pathogenic strains.

   E) mice infected with a pathogenic strain of bacteria can spread the infection to other mice.

   Answer: B
   *Topic: Concept 16.1*
   *Skill: Knowledge*

3) What does transformation involve in bacteria?

   A) the creation of a strand of DNA from an RNA molecule

   B) the creation of a strand of RNA from a DNA molecule

   C) the infection of cells by a phage DNA molecule

   D) the type of semiconservative replication shown by DNA

   E) assimilation of external DNA into a cell

   Answer: E
   *Topic: Concept 16.1*
   *Skill: Knowledge*

4) Avery and his colleagues purified various chemicals from pathogenic bacteria and showed that _____ was (were) the transforming agent.

A) DNA

B) protein

C) lipids

D) carbohydrates

E) phage

Answer: A
*Topic: Concept 16.1*
*Skill: Knowledge*

5) Tobacco mosaic virus has RNA rather than DNA as its genetic material. In a hypothetical situation where RNA from a tobacco mosaic virus is mixed with proteins from a related DNA virus, the result could be a hybrid virus. If that virus were to infect a cell and reproduce, what would the resulting "offspring" viruses be like?

A) tobacco mosaic virus

B) the related DNA virus

C) a hybrid: tobacco mosaic virus RNA and protein from the DNA virus

D) a hybrid: tobacco mosaic virus protein and nucleic acid from the DNA virus

E) a virus with a double helix made up of one strand of DNA complementary to a strand of RNA surrounded by viral protein

Answer: A
*Topic: Concept 16.1*
*Skill: Application*

6) The following scientists made significant contributions to our understanding of the structure and function of DNA. Place the scientists' names in the correct chronological order, starting with the first scientist(s) to make a contribution.

   I.   Avery, McCarty, and MacLeod

   II.  Griffith

   III. Hershey and Chase

   IV. Meselson and Stahl

   V.  Watson and Crick

A) V, IV, II, I, III

B) II, I, III, V, IV

C) I, II, III, V, IV

D) I, II, V, IV, III

E) II, III, IV, V, I

Answer: B
*Topic: Concept 16.1*
*Skill: Knowledge*

7) After mixing a heat–killed, phosphorescent strain of bacteria with a living non–phosphorescent strain, you discover that some of the living cells are now phosphorescent. The best evidence that the ability to fluoresce is a heritable trait would be an observation that

A) DNA passed from the heat–killed strain to the living strain.

B) protein passed from the heat–killed strain to the living strain.

C) the phosphorescence in the living strain is especially bright.

D) descendants of the living cells are also phosphorescent.

E) both DNA and protein passed from the heat–killed strain to the living strain.

Answer: D
*Topic: Concept 16.1*
*Skill: Application*

8) In trying to determine whether DNA or protein is the genetic material, Hershey and Chase made use of which of the following facts?

A) DNA does not contain sulfur, whereas protein does.

B) DNA contains phosphorus, but protein does not.

C) DNA contains nitrogen, whereas protein does not.

D) A and B only

E) A, B, and C

Answer: D
*Topic: Concept 16.1*
*Skill: Knowledge*

9) For a science fair project, two students decided to repeat the Hershey and Chase experiment, with modifications. They decided to label the nitrogen of the DNA, rather than the phosphate. They reasoned that each nucleotide has only one phosphate and two to five nitrogens. Thus, labeling the nitrogens would provide a stronger signal than labeling the phosphates. Why won't this experiment work?

A) There is no radioactive isotope of nitrogen.

B) Radioactive nitrogen has a half–life of 100,000 years, and the material would be too dangerous for too long.

C) Meselson and Stahl already did this experiment.

D) Although there are more nitrogens in a nucleotide, labeled phosphates actually have 16 extra neutrons; therefore, they are more radioactive.

E) Amino acids (and thus proteins) also have nitrogen atoms; thus, the radioactivity would not distinguish between DNA and proteins.

Answer: E
*Topic: Concept 16.1*
*Skill: Comprehension*

*Match the investigator(s) to the appropriate discovery of about the nature of genes.*

A. Frederick Griffith
B. Alfred Hershey and Martha Chase
C. Oswald Avery, Maclyn McCarty, and Colin MacLeod
D. Erwin Chargaff
E. Matthew Meselson and Franklin Stahl

10) Chemicals from heat–killed S cells were purified. The chemicals were tested for the ability to transform live R cells. The transforming agent was found to be DNA.

Answer: C
*Topic: Concept 16.1*
*Skill: Knowledge*

11) Phage with labeled proteins or DNA was allowed to infect bacteria. It was shown that the DNA, but not the protein, entered the bacterial cells, and was therefore the genetic material.

Answer: B
*Topic: Concept 16.1*
*Skill: Knowledge*

12) In DNA from any species, the amount of adenine equals the amount of thymine, and the amount of guanine equals the amount of cytosine.

Answer: D
*Topic: Concept 16.1*
*Skill: Knowledge*

13) When T2 phages infect bacteria and make more viruses in the presence of radioactive sulfur, what is the result?

   A) The viral DNA will be radioactive.

   B) The viral proteins will be radioactive.

   C) The bacterial DNA will be radioactive.

   D) both A and B

   E) both A and C

Answer: B
*Topic: Concept 16.1*
*Skill: Comprehension*

14) Cytosine makes up 38% of the nucleotides in a sample of DNA from an organism. Approximately, what percentage of the nucleotides in this sample will be thymine?

   A) 12

   B) 24

   C) 31

   D) 38

   E) It cannot be determined from the information provided.

Answer: A
*Topic: Concept 16.1*
*Skill: Application*

15) Chargaff's analysis of the relative base composition of DNA was significant because he was able to show that

   A) the relative proportion of each of the four bases differs from species to species.

   B) the human genome is more complex than that of other species.

   C) the amount of A is always equivalent to T, and C to G.

   D) both A and C

   E) both B and C

Answer: D
*Topic: Concept 16.1*
*Skill: Knowledge*

16) All of the following can be determined directly from X-ray diffraction photographs of crystallized DNA *except* the

   A) diameter of the helix.

   B) helical shape of DNA.

   C) sequence of nucleotides.

   D) spacing of the nitrogenous bases along the helix.

   E) number of strands in a helix.

Answer: C
*Topic: Concept 16.1*
*Skill: Knowledge*

17) The DNA double helix has a uniform diameter because _____, which have two rings, always pair with _____, which have one ring.

   A) purines; pyrimidines

   B) pyrimidines; purines

   C) deoxyribose sugars; ribose sugars

   D) ribose sugars; deoxyribose sugars

   E) nucleotides; nucleoside triphosphates

Answer: A
*Topic: Concept 16.1*
*Skill: Knowledge*

18) What kind of chemical bond is found between paired bases of the DNA double helix?

   A) hydrogen

   B) ionic

   C) covalent

   D) sulfhydryl

   E) phosphate

Answer: A
*Topic: Concept 16.1*
*Skill: Knowledge*

19) Which of the following statements does not apply to the Watson and Crick model of DNA?

A) The two strands of the DNA form a double helix.

B) The distance between the strands of the helix is uniform.

C) The framework of the helix consists of sugar-phosphate units of the nucleotides.

D) The two strands of the helix are held together by covalent bonds.

E) The purines form hydrogen bonds with pyrimidines.

Answer: D
*Topic: Concept 16.1*
*Skill: Knowledge*

20) It became apparent to Watson and Crick after completion of their model that the DNA molecule could carry a vast amount of hereditary information in its

A) sequence of bases.

B) phosphate-sugar backbones.

C) complementary pairing of bases.

D) side groups of nitrogenous bases.

E) different five-carbon sugars.

Answer: A
*Topic: Concept 16.1*
*Skill: Knowledge*

21) In an analysis of the nucleotide composition of DNA, which of the following is *true*?

A) A = C

B) A = G and C = T

C) A + C = G + T

D) G + A = T + C

E) both C and D

Answer: E
*Topic: Concept 16.1*
*Skill: Comprehension*

22) Which of the following statements is *false* when comparing prokaryotes with eukaryotes?

A) The prokaryotic chromosome is circular, whereas eukaryotic chromosomes are linear.

B) Prokaryotic chromosomes have a single origin of replication, whereas eukaryotic chromosomes have many.

C) The rate of elongation during DNA replication is higher in prokaryotes than in eukaryotes.

D) Prokaryotes produce Okazaki fragments during DNA replication, but eukaryotes do not.

E) Eukaryotes have telomeres, and prokaryotes do not.

Answer: D
*Topic: Concept 16.2*
*Skill: Knowledge*

23) The strands that make up DNA are antiparallel. This means that

A) the twisting nature of DNA creates nonparallel strands.

B) the 5' to 3' direction of one strand runs counter to the 5' to 3' direction of the other strand.

C) base pairings create unequal spacing between the two DNA strands.

D) one strand is positively charged and the other is negatively charged.

E) one strand contains only purines and the other contains only pyrimidines.

Answer: B
*Topic: Concept 16.2*
*Skill: Knowledge*

24) Suppose one were provided with an actively dividing culture of *E. coli* bacteria to which radioactive thymine had been added. What would happen if a cell replicated once in the presence of this radioactive base?

  A) One of the daughter cells, but not the other, would have radioactive DNA.

  B) Neither of the two daughter cells would be radioactive.

  C) All four bases of the DNA would be radioactive.

  D) Radioactive thymine would pair with nonradioactive guanine.

  E) DNA in both daughter cells would be radioactive.

Answer: E
*Topic: Concept 16.2*
*Skill: Comprehension*

*Use Figure 16.1 to answer the following questions.*

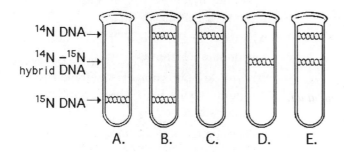

$^{14}$N DNA →
$^{14}$N –$^{15}$N hybrid DNA →
$^{15}$N DNA →

A.    B.    C.    D.    E.

**Figure 16.1**

25) In the late 1950s, Meselson and Stahl grew bacteria in a medium containing "heavy" nitrogen ($^{15}$N) and then transferred them to a medium containing $^{14}$N. Which of the results in Figure 16.1 would be expected after one DNA replication in the presence of $^{14}$N?

Answer: D
*Topic: Concept 16.2*
*Skill: Comprehension*

26) A space probe returns with a culture of a microorganism found on a distant planet. Analysis shows that it is a carbon–based life-form that has DNA. You grow the cells in $^{15}$N medium for several generations and then transfer them to $^{14}$N medium. Which pattern in Figure 16.1 would you expect if the DNA was replicated in a conservative manner?

Answer: B
*Topic: Concept 16.2*
*Skill: Application*

27) Which enzyme catalyzes the elongation of a DNA strand in the 5' → 3' direction?

  A) primase

  B) DNA ligase

  C) DNA polymerase

  D) topoisomerase

  E) helicase

Answer: C
*Topic: Concept 16.2*
*Skill: Knowledge*

28) What determines the nucleotide sequence of the newly synthesized strand during DNA replication?

  A) the particular DNA polymerase catalyzing the reaction

  B) the relative amounts of the four nucleoside triphosphates in the cell

  C) the nucleotide sequence of the template strand

  D) the primase used in the reaction

  E) both A and D

Answer: C
*Topic: Concept 16.2*
*Skill: Knowledge*

29) What is the function of DNA polymerase?

A) to unwind the DNA helix during replication

B) to seal together the broken ends of DNA strands

C) to add nucleotides to the end of a growing DNA strand

D) to degrade damaged DNA molecules

E) to rejoin the two DNA strands (one new and one old) after replication

Answer: C
*Topic: Concept 16.2*
*Skill: Knowledge*

30) Which of the following is *least* related to the others on the list?

A) Okazaki fragments

B) replication fork

C) telomerase

D) DNA polymerase

E) semiconservative model

Answer: C
*Topic: Concept 16.2*
*Skill: Comprehension*

31) You briefly expose bacteria undergoing DNA replication to radioactively labeled nucleotides. When you centrifuge the DNA isolated from the bacteria, the DNA separates into two classes. One class of labeled DNA includes very large molecules (thousands or even millions of nucleotides long), and the other includes short stretches of DNA (several hundred to a few thousand nucleotides in length). These two classes of DNA probably represent

A) leading strands and Okazaki fragments.

B) lagging strands and Okazaki fragments.

C) Okazaki fragments and RNA primers.

D) leading strands and RNA primers.

E) RNA primers and mitochondrial DNA.

Answer: A
*Topic: Concept 16.2*
*Skill: Application*

*Refer to the following list of enzymes to answer the following questions. The answers may be used once, more than once, or not at all.*

A. helicase
B. nuclease
C. ligase
D. DNA polymerase I
E. primase

32) removes the RNA nucleotides from the primer and adds equivalent DNA nucleotides to the 3' end of Okazaki fragments

Answer: D
*Topic: Concept 16.2*
*Skill: Knowledge*

33) separates the DNA strands during replication

Answer: A
*Topic: Concept 16.2*
*Skill: Knowledge*

34) covalently connects segments of DNA

Answer: C
*Topic: Concept 16.2*
*Skill: Knowledge*

35) synthesizes short segments of RNA

Answer: E
*Topic: Concept 16.2*
*Skill: Knowledge*

36) DNA–cutting enzymes used in the repair of DNA damage

Answer: B
*Topic: Concept 16.2*
*Skill: Knowledge*

37) The difference between ATP and the nucleoside triphosphates used during DNA synthesis is that

A) the nucleoside triphosphates have the sugar deoxyribose; ATP has the sugar ribose.

B) the nucleoside triphosphates have two phosphate groups; ATP has three phosphate groups.

C) ATP contains three high–energy bonds; the nucleoside triphosphates have two.

D) ATP is found only in human cells; the nucleoside triphosphates are found in all animal and plant cells.

E) triphosphate monomers are active in the nucleoside triphosphates, but not in ATP.

Answer: A
*Topic: Concept 16.2*
*Skill: Knowledge*

38) The Y-shaped structure where the DNA double helix is actively unwound during DNA replication is called the

A) replication fork.

B) replication Y.

C) elongation junction.

D) unwinding point.

E) Y junction.

Answer: A
*Topic: Concept 16.2*
*Skill: Knowledge*

39) The leading and the lagging strands differ in that

A) the leading strand is synthesized in the same direction as the movement of the replication fork, and the lagging strand is synthesized in the opposite direction.

B) the leading strand is synthesized by adding nucleotides to the 3' end of the growing strand, and the lagging strand is synthesized by adding nucleotides to the 5' end.

C) the leading strand is synthesized continuously, whereas the lagging strand is synthesized in short fragments that are ultimately stitched together.

D) both A and B

E) both A and C

Answer: E
*Topic: Concept 16.2*
*Skill: Comprehension*

40) Which of the following best describes the addition of nucleotides to a growing DNA chain?

   A) A nucleoside triphosphate is added to the 5' end of the DNA, releasing a molecule of pyrophosphate.

   B) A nucleoside triphosphate is added to the 3' end of the DNA, releasing a molecule of pyrophosphate.

   C) A nucleoside diphosphate is added to the 5' end of the DNA, releasing a molecule of phosphate.

   D) A nucleoside diphosphate is added to the 3' end of the DNA, releasing a molecule of phosphate.

   E) A nucleoside monophosphate is added to the 3' end of the DNA.

Answer: B
*Topic: Concept 16.2*
*Skill: Knowledge*

41) A new DNA strand elongates only in the 5' to 3' direction because

   A) DNA polymerase begins adding nucleotides at the 5' end of the template.

   B) Okazaki fragments prevent elongation in the 3' to 5' direction.

   C) the polarity of the DNA molecule prevents addition of nucleotides at the 3' end.

   D) replication must progress toward the replication fork.

   E) DNA polymerase can only add nucleotides to the free 3' end.

Answer: E
*Topic: Concept 16.2*
*Skill: Comprehension*

42) Replicating the lagging strand of DNA—that is, adding bases in the 3' → 5' direction—utilizes which of the following?

   A) DNA ligase

   B) RNA primers

   C) Okazaki fragments

   D) A and B only

   E) A, B, and C

Answer: E
*Topic: Concept 16.2*
*Skill: Knowledge*

43) What kind of molecule or substance is the primer that is used to initiate the synthesis of a new DNA strand?

   A) RNA

   B) DNA

   C) protein

   D) phosphate

   E) sulfur

Answer: A
*Topic: Concept 16.2*
*Skill: Knowledge*

44) What is the function of topoisomerase?

   A) relieving strain in the DNA ahead of the replication fork

   B) elongation of new DNA at a replication fork by addition of nucleotides to the existing chain

   C) the addition of methyl groups to bases of DNA

   D) unwinding of the double helix

   E) stabilizing single-stranded DNA at the replication fork

Answer: A
*Topic: Concept 16.2*
*Skill: Knowledge*

45) What is the role of DNA ligase in the elongation of the lagging strand during DNA replication?

A) synthesize RNA nucleotides to make a primer

B) catalyze the lengthening of telomeres

C) join Okazaki fragments together

D) unwind the parental double helix

E) stabilize the unwound parental DNA

Answer: C
*Topic: Concept 16.2*
*Skill: Knowledge*

46) All of the following are functions of DNA polymerase in DNA replication *except*

A) covalently adding nucleotides to the new strands.

B) proofreading each added nucleotide for correct base pairing.

C) replacing RNA primers with DNA.

D) initiating a polynucleotide strand.

E) none of the above

Answer: D
*Topic: Concept 16.2*
*Skill: Knowledge*

47) Which of the following help to hold the DNA strands apart while they are being replicated?

A) primase

B) ligase

C) DNA polymerase

D) single-strand binding proteins

E) exonuclease

Answer: D
*Topic: Concept 16.2*
*Skill: Knowledge*

48) Which of these mechanisms ensures that the DNA sequence in the genome remains accurate?

A) proofreading during DNA replication

B) mismatch repair

C) excision repair

D) complementary base pairing during DNA replication

E) all of the above

Answer: E
*Topic: Concept 16.2*
*Skill: Knowledge*

49) Individuals with the disorder xeroderma pigmentosum are hypersensitive to sunlight because their cells have an impaired ability to

A) replicate DNA.

B) undergo mitosis.

C) exchange DNA with other cells.

D) repair thymine dimers.

E) recombine homologous chromosomes during meiosis.

Answer: D
*Topic: Concept 16.2*
*Skill: Knowledge*

50) Which of the following is analogous to telomeres?

A) the pull tab on a soft drink can

B) the two ends of a shoelace

C) the central spindle that a CD fits around while in the case

D) the mechanism of a zipper that allows the separated parts to be joined

E) the correct letters used to replace errors in a document after they have been deleted in a word processor

Answer: B
*Topic: Concept 16.2*
*Skill: Application*

51) A eukaryotic cell lacking telomerase would

  A) have a high probability of becoming cancerous.

  B) produce Okazaki fragments.

  C) be unable to repair thymine dimers.

  D) undergo a reduction in chromosome length.

  E) be highly sensitive to sunlight.

Answer: D
*Topic: Concept 16.2*
*Skill: Comprehension*

52) Which of the following statements about telomeres is *correct*?

  A) They contain multiple copies of a short RNA sequence.

  B) They are present at the ends of eukaryotic chromosomes.

  C) They can be extended by an enzyme called telomerase.

  D) both A and B

  E) both B and C

Answer: E
*Topic: Concept 16.2*
*Skill: Knowledge*

# Media Activity Questions

1) Hershey and Chase used _____ to radioactively label the T2 phage's proteins.

   A) 35S

   B) 14C

   C) 222Ra

   D) 32P

   E) 92U

   Answer: A
   *Topic: Activity: The Hershey–Chase Experiment*

2) Which of these is a difference between a DNA and an RNA molecule?

   A) DNA contains uracil, whereas RNA contains thymine.

   B) DNA is a polymer composed of nucleotides, whereas RNA is a polymer composed of nucleic acids.

   C) DNA is double-stranded, whereas RNA is single-stranded.

   D) DNA contains five-carbon sugars, whereas RNA contains six-carbon sugars.

   E) DNA contains nitrogenous bases, whereas RNA contains phosphate groups.

   Answer: C
   *Topic: Web/CD Activity: DNA and RNA Structure*

3) In a nucleotide, the nitrogenous base is attached to the sugar's _____ carbon and the phosphate group is attached to the sugar's _____ carbon.

   A) 1'; 2'

   B) 1'; 5'

   C) 2'; 3'

   D) 1'; 3'

   E) 2'; 1'

   Answer: B
   *Topic: Web/CD Activity: DNA and RNA Structure*

4) After DNA replication is completed,

   A) each new DNA double helix consists of one old DNA strand and one new DNA strand.

   B) each new DNA double helix consists of two new strands.

   C) one DNA double helix consists of two old strands and one DNA double helix consists of two new strands.

   D) each of the four DNA strands consists of some old strand parts and some new strand parts.

   E) there are four double helices.

   Answer: A
   *Topic: Activity: DNA Replication: An Overview*

5) Why is the new DNA strand complementary to the 3' to 5' strands assembled in short segments?

   A) the replication forks block the formation of longer strands

   B) DNA polymerase can assemble DNA only in the 3' to 5' direction

   C) DNA polymerase can assemble DNA only in the 5' to 3' direction

   D) it is more efficient than assembling complete new strands

   E) only short DNA sequences can extend off the RNA primers

   Answer: C
   *Topic: Activity: DNA Replication: A Closer Look*

# Self–Quiz Questions

1) In his work with pneumonia-causing bacteria and mice, Griffith found that

   A) the protein coat from pathogenic cells was able to transform nonpathogenic cells.

   B) heat-killed pathogenic cells caused pneumonia.

   C) some substance from pathogenic cells was transferred to nonpathogenic cells, making them pathogenic.

   D) the polysaccharide coat of bacteria caused pneumonia.

   E) bacteriophages injected DNA into bacteria.

   Answer: C

2) *E. coli* cells grown on $^{15}N$ medium are transferred to $^{14}N$ medium and allowed to grow for two more generations (two rounds of DNA replication). DNA extracted from these cells is centrifuged. What density distribution of DNA would you expect in this experiment?

   A) one high–density and one low–density band

   B) one intermediate–density band

   C) one high–density and one intermediate–density band

   D) one low–density and one intermediate–density band

   E) one low–density band

   Answer: D

3) A biochemist isolates and purifies various molecules needed for DNA replication. When she adds some DNA, replication occurs, but each DNA consists of a normal DNA strand paired with numerous segments of DNA a few hundred nucleotides long. What has she probably left out of the mixture?

   A) DNA polymerase

   B) DNA ligase

   C) nucleotides

   D) Okazaki fragments

   E) primase

   Answer: B

4) What is the basis for the difference in how the leading and lagging strands of DNA molecules are synthesized?

   A) The origins of replication occur only at the 5' end.

   B) Helicases and single-strand binding proteins work at the 5' end.

   C) DNA polymerase can join new nucleotides only to the 3' end of a growing strand.

   D) DNA ligase works only in the 3' → 5' direction.

   E) Polymerase can only work on one strand at a time.

   Answer: C

5) In analyzing the number of different bases in a DNA sample, which result would be consistent with the base–pairing rules?

   A) A = G

   B) A + G = C + T

   C) A + T = G + T

   D) A = C

   E) G = T

   Answer: B

6) Synthesis of a new DNA strand usually begins with
  A) an RNA primer.
  B) a DNA primer.
  C) an Okazaki fragment.
  D) DNA ligase.
  E) a thymine dimer.

Answer: A

7) A eukaryotic cell lacking active telomerase would
  A) be unable to take up DNA from the surrounding solution.
  B) be unable to identify and correct mismatched nucleotides.
  C) experience a gradual reduction of chromosome length with each replication cycle.
  D) have a greater potential to become cancerous.
  E) be unable to connect Okazaki fragments.

Answer: C

8) The elongation of the *leading* strand during DNA synthesis
  A) progresses away from the replication fork.
  B) occurs in the 3' → 5' direction.
  C) produces Okazaki fragments.
  D) depends on the action of DNA polymerase.
  E) does not require a template strand.

Answer: D

9) The spontaneous loss of amino groups from adenine results in hypoxanthine, an unnatural base, opposite thymine. What combination of molecules could the cell use to repair such damage?
  A) nuclease, DNA polymerase, DNA ligase
  B) telomerase, primase, DNA polymerase
  C) telomerase, helicase, single-strand binding protein
  D) DNA ligase, replication fork proteins, adenylyl cyclase
  E) nuclease, telomerase, primase

Answer: A

10) The most reasonable inference from the observation that defects in DNA repair enzymes contribute to some cancers is that
  A) cancer is generally inherited.
  B) uncorrected changes in DNA can lead to cancer.
  C) cancer cannot occur when repair enzymes work properly.
  D) mutations generally lead to cancer.
  E) cancer is caused by environmental factors that damage DNA repair enzymes.

Answer: B

# Chapter 17  From Gene to Protein

1) Garrod hypothesized that "inborn errors of metabolism" such as alkaptonuria occur because

A) genes dictate the production of specific enzymes, and affected individuals have genetic defects that cause them to lack certain enzymes.

B) enzymes are made of DNA, and affected individuals lack DNA polymerase.

C) many metabolic enzymes use DNA as a cofactor, and affected individuals have mutations that prevent their enzymes from interacting efficiently with DNA.

D) certain metabolic reactions are carried out by ribozymes, and affected individuals lack key splicing factors.

E) metabolic enzymes require vitamin cofactors, and affected individuals have significant nutritional deficiencies.

Answer: A
*Topic: Concept 17.1*
*Skill: Knowledge*

*The following questions refer to the following simple metabolic pathway:*

$$A \xrightarrow{\text{enzyme } A} B \xrightarrow{\text{enzyme } B} C$$

2) According to Beadle and Tatum's hypothesis, how many genes are necessary for this pathway?

A) 0

B) 1

C) 2

D) 3

E) It cannot be determined from the pathway.

Answer: C
*Topic: Concept 17.1*
*Skill: Comprehension*

3) A mutation results in a defective enzyme A. Which of the following would be a consequence of that mutation?

A) an accumulation of A and no production of B and C

B) an accumulation of A and B and no production of C

C) an accumulation of B and no production of A and C

D) an accumulation of B and C and no production of A

E) an accumulation of C and no production of A and B

Answer: A
*Topic: Concept 17.1*
*Skill: Comprehension*

4) If A, B, and C are all required for growth, a strain that is mutant for the gene encoding enzyme *A* would be able to grow on which of the following media?

    A) minimal medium

    B) minimal medium supplemented with nutrient "A"

    C) minimal medium supplemented with nutrient "B"

    D) minimal medium supplemented with nutrient "C"

    E) Answers C and D are correct.

Answer: E
*Topic: Concept 17.1*
*Skill: Application*

5) If A, B, and C are all required for growth, a strain mutant for the gene encoding enzyme *B* would be capable of growing on which of the following media?

    A) minimal medium

    B) minimal medium supplemented with "A"

    C) minimal medium supplemented with "B"

    D) minimal medium supplemented with "C"

    E) answers B and C

Answer: D
*Topic: Concept 17.1*
*Skill: Application*

6) We now know that the one gene–one enzyme hypothesis is not entirely accurate because

    A) many genes code for proteins that are not enzymes.

    B) a single gene codes for a single polypeptide chain, and many enzymes are made up of more than one polypeptide chain.

    C) many genes code for RNA molecules that have no enzymatic activity.

    D) A and B only

    E) A, B, and C

Answer: E
*Topic: Concept 17.1*
*Skill: Comprehension*

7) Which of the following represents a similarity between RNA and DNA?

    A) Both are double–stranded.

    B) the presence of uracil

    C) the presence of an OH group on the 2' carbon of the sugar

    D) nucleotides consisting of a phosphate, sugar, and nitrogenous base

    E) Both are found exclusively in the nucleus.

Answer: D
*Topic: Concept 17.1*
*Skill: Comprehension*

8) The nitrogenous base adenine is found in all members of which group?

    A) proteins, triglycerides, and testosterone

    B) proteins, ATP, and DNA

    C) ATP, RNA, and DNA

    D) alpha glucose, ATP, and DNA

    E) proteins, carbohydrates, and ATP

Answer: C
*Topic: Concept 17.1*
*Skill: Knowledge*

9) Using RNA as a template for protein synthesis instead of translating proteins directly from the DNA is advantageous for the cell because

A) RNA is much more stable than DNA.

B) RNA acts as an expendable copy of the genetic material, allowing the DNA to serve as a permanent, pristine repository of the genetic material.

C) many mRNA molecules can be transcribed from a single gene, increasing the potential rate of gene expression.

D) B and C only

E) A, B, and C

Answer: D
*Topic: Concept 17.1*
*Skill: Comprehension*

10) If proteins were composed of only 12 different kinds of amino acids, what would be the smallest possible codon size in a genetic system with four different nucleotides?

A) 1

B) 2

C) 3

D) 4

E) 12

Answer: B
*Topic: Concept 17.1*
*Skill: Application*

11) An extraterrestrial life form is discovered. It has a genetic code much like that of organisms on Earth except that there are five different DNA bases instead of four and the base sequences are translated as doublets instead of triplets. How many different amino acids could be accommodated by this genetic code?

A) 5

B) 10

C) 25

D) 64

E) 32

Answer: C
*Topic: Concept 17.1*
*Skill: Application*

12) The enzyme polynucleotide phosphorylase randomly assembles nucleotides into a polynucleotide polymer. You add polynucleotide phosphorylase to a solution of adenosine triphosphate and guanosine triphosphate. The resulting artificial mRNA molecule would have _____ possible different codons if the code involved two-base sequences and _____ possible different codons if the code involved three-base sequences.

A) 2; 3

B) 2; 4

C) 4; 8

D) 4; 16

E) 16; 64

Answer: C
*Topic: Concept 17.1*
*Skill: Application*

13) A particular triplet of bases in the template strand of DNA is AGT. The corresponding codon for the mRNA transcribed is

   A) AGT.

   B) UGA.

   C) TCA.

   D) ACU.

   E) either UCA or TCA, depending on wobble in the first base

Answer: D
*Topic: Concept 17.1*
*Skill: Application*

*The following questions refer to Figure 17.1, a table of codons.*

   (*Figure 17.1 appears on page 271.*)

14) A possible sequence of nucleotides in the template strand of DNA that would code for the polypeptide sequence phe-leu-ile-val would be

   A) 5' TTG-CTA-CAG-TAG 3'.

   B) 3' AAC-GAC-GUC-AUA 5'.

   C) 5' AUG-CTG-CAG-TAT 3'.

   D) 3' AAA-AAT-ATA-ACA 5'.

   E) 3' AAA-GAA-TAA-CAA 5'.

Answer: E
*Topic: Concept 17.1*
*Skill: Application*

15) What amino acid sequence will be generated, based on the following mRNA codon sequence?
5'AUG-UCU-UCG-UUA-UCC-UUG

   A) met-arg-glu-arg-glu-arg

   B) met-glu-arg-arg-gln-leu

   C) met-ser-leu-ser-leu-ser

   D) met-ser-ser-leu-ser-leu

   E) met-leu-phe-arg-glu-glu

Answer: D
*Topic: Concept 17.1*
*Skill: Application*

16) A peptide has the sequence NH2-phe-pro-lys-gly-phe-pro-COOH. Which of the following sequences in the coding strand of the DNA codes for this peptide?

   A) 3' UUU-CCC-AAA-GGG-UUU-CCC

   B) 3' AUG-AAA-GGG-TTT-CCC-AAA-GGG

   C) 5' TTT-CCC-AAA-GGG-TTT-CCC

   D) 5' GGG-AAA-TTT-AAA-CCC-ACT-GGG

   E) 5' ACT-TAC-CAT-AAA-CAT-TAC-UGA

Answer: C
*Topic: Concept 17.1*
*Skill: Application*

17) What is the sequence of a peptide based on the mRNA sequence
5' UUUUCUUAUUGUCUU3'?

   A) leu-cys-tyr-ser-phe

   B) cyc-phe-tyr-cys-leu

   C) phe-leu-ile-met-val

   D) leu-pro-asp-lys-gly

   E) phe-ser-tyr-cys-leu

Answer: E
*Topic: Concept 17.1*
*Skill: Application*

18) Suppose the following DNA sequence was mutated from 3'AGAGAGAGAGAGAGAGAG5' to 3'AGAAGAGAGATCGAGAGA5'. What amino acid sequence will be generated based on this mutated DNA?

   A) arg-glu-arg-glu-arg-glu

   B) glu-arg-glu-leu-leu-leu

   C) ser-leu-ser-leu-ser-leu

   D) ser-ser-leu

   E) leu-phe-arg-glu-glu-glu

Answer: D
*Topic: Concept 17.1*
*Skill: Application*

19) A particular eukaryotic protein is 300 amino acids long. Which of the following could be the maximum number of nucleotides in the DNA that codes for the amino acids in this protein?

A) 3

B) 100

C) 300

D) 900

E) 1,800

Answer: D
*Topic: Concept 17.1*
*Skill: Application*

20) A codon

A) consists of two nucleotides.

B) may code for the same amino acid as another codon.

C) consists of discrete amino acid regions.

D) catalyzes RNA synthesis.

E) is found in all eukaryotes, but not in prokaryotes.

Answer: B
*Topic: Concept 17.1*
*Skill: Knowledge*

21) If the triplet CCC codes for the amino acid proline in bacteria, then in plants CCC should code for

A) leucine.

B) valine.

C) cystine.

D) phenylalanine.

E) proline.

Answer: E
*Topic: Concept 17.1*
*Skill: Comprehension*

22) The genetic code is essentially the same for all organisms. From this, one can logically assume all of the following *except*

A) a gene from an organism could theoretically be expressed by any other organism.

B) all organisms have a common ancestor.

C) DNA was the first genetic material.

D) the same codons in different organisms usually translate into the same amino acids.

E) different organisms have the same number of different types of amino acids.

Answer: C
*Topic: Concept 17.1*
*Skill: Comprehension*

23) Which of the following is *true* for both prokaryotic and eukaryotic gene expression?

A) After transcription, a 3' poly-A tail and a 5' cap are added to mRNA.

B) Translation of mRNA can begin before transcription is complete.

C) RNA polymerase binds to the promoter region to begin transcription.

D) mRNA is synthesized in the 3' → 5' direction.

E) The mRNA transcript is the exact complement of the gene from which it was copied.

Answer: C
*Topic: Concept 17.2*
*Skill: Knowledge*

24) Which of the following are transcribed from DNA?

A) protein

B) exons

C) rRNA

D) B and C only

E) A, B, and C

Answer: D
*Topic: Concept 17.2*
*Skill: Application*

25) RNA polymerase and DNA polymerase differ in that

A) RNA polymerase uses RNA as a template, and DNA polymerase uses a DNA template.

B) RNA polymerase binds to single-stranded DNA, and DNA polymerase binds to double-stranded DNA.

C) RNA polymerase is much more accurate than DNA polymerase.

D) RNA polymerase can initiate RNA synthesis, but DNA polymerase requires a primer to initiate DNA synthesis.

E) RNA polymerase does not need to separate the two strands of DNA in order to synthesize an RNA copy, whereas DNA polymerase must unwind the double helix before it can replicate the DNA.

Answer: D
*Topic: Concept 17.2*
*Skill: Comprehension*

26) Which of the following is *not* a part of the eukaryotic transcription initiation complex?

A) promoter

B) RNA polymerase

C) transcription factors

D) snRNP

E) TATA box

Answer: D
*Topic: Concept 17.2*
*Skill: Knowledge*

27) Which of the following is *least* related to the other items?

A) translation

B) TATA box

C) transcription

D) template strand

E) RNA polymerase II

Answer: A
*Topic: Concept 17.2*
*Skill: Comprehension*

28) Which of the following statements best describes the termination of transcription in prokaryotes?

A) RNA polymerase transcribes through the polyadenylation signal, causing proteins to associate with the transcript and cut it free from the polymerase.

B) RNA polymerase transcribes through the terminator sequence, causing the polymerase to fall off the DNA and release the transcript.

C) RNA polymerase transcribes through an intron, and the snRNPs cause the polymerase to let go of the transcript.

D) Once transcription has initiated, RNA polymerase transcribes until it reaches the end of the chromosome.

E) RNA polymerase transcribes through a stop codon, causing the polymerase to stop advancing through the gene and release the mRNA.

Answer: B
*Topic: Concept 17.2*
*Skill: Knowledge*

29) RNA polymerase moves along the template strand of DNA in the _____ direction, and adds nucleotides to the _____ end of the growing transcript.

A) 3' to 5'; 5'     B) 3' to 5'; 3'
C) 5' to 3'; 5'     D) 5' to 3'; 3'

Answer: B
*Topic: Concept 17.2*
*Skill: Comprehension*

30) All of the following are found in prokaryotic mRNA *except*

A) the AUG codon.

B) the UGA codon.

C) introns.

D) uracil.

E) cytosine.

Answer: C
*Topic: Concept 17.2*
*Skill: Knowledge*

31) Which of the following helps to stabilize mRNA by inhibiting its degradation?

A) TATA box

B) spliceosomes

C) 5' cap

D) poly-A tail

E) both C and D

Answer: E
*Topic: Concept 17.3*
*Skill: Knowledge*

32) What is a ribozyme?

A) An enzyme that uses RNA as a substrate

B) An enzyme made up of RNA

C) An enzyme that catalyzes the association between the large and small ribosomal subunits

D) An enzyme that synthesizes RNA as part of the transcription process

E) An enzyme that synthesizes RNA primers during DNA replication

Answer: B
*Topic: Concept 17.3*
*Skill: Knowledge*

33) What are the coding segments of a stretch of eukaryotic DNA called?

A) introns

B) exons

C) codons

D) replicons

E) transposons

Answer: B
*Topic: Concept 17.3*
*Skill: Knowledge*

34) A transcription unit that is 8,000 nucleotides long may use 1,200 nucleotides to make a protein consisting of 400 amino acids. This is best explained by the fact that

A) many noncoding nucleotides are present in mRNA.

B) there is redundancy and ambiguity in the genetic code.

C) many nucleotides are needed to code for each amino acid.

D) nucleotides break off and are lost during the transcription process.

E) there are termination exons near the beginning of mRNA.

Answer: A
*Topic: Concept 17.3*
*Skill: Comprehension*

35) Once transcribed, eukaryotic mRNA typically undergoes substantial alteration that includes

A) excision of introns.

B) fusion into circular forms known as plasmids.

C) linkage to histone molecules.

D) union with ribosomes.

E) fusion with other newly transcribed mRNA.

Answer: A
*Topic: Concept 17.3*
*Skill: Knowledge*

36) Introns are significant to biological evolution because

A) their presence allows exons to be moved around more easily, creating proteins with new combinations of functional domains.

B) they protect the mRNA from degeneration.

C) they are translated into essential amino acids.

D) they maintain the genetic code by preventing incorrect DNA base pairings.

E) they correct enzymatic alterations of DNA bases.

Answer: A
*Topic: Concept 17.3*
*Skill: Comprehension*

37) A mutation in which of the following parts of a gene is likely to be most damaging to a cell?

A) intron

B) exon

C) 5' UTR

D) 3' UTR

E) All would be equally damaging.

Answer: B
*Topic: Concept 17.3*
*Skill: Comprehension*

38) Which of the following is (are) true of snRNPs?

A) They are made up of both protein and RNA.

B) They bind to splice sites at each end of the intron.

C) They join together to form a large structure called the spliceosome.

D) Only A and C are true.

E) A, B, and C are true

Answer: E
*Topic: Concept 17.3*
*Skill: Knowledge*

39) During splicing, which molecular component of the spliceosome catalyzes the excision reaction?

A) RNA

B) DNA

C) protein

D) lipid

E) sugar

Answer: A
*Topic: Concept 17.3*
*Skill: Knowledge*

40) Alternative RNA splicing

A) is a mechanism for increasing the rate of transcription.

B) can allow the production of proteins of dramatically different sizes from a single mRNA.

C) can allow the production of proteins of dramatically different amino acid sequences from a single mRNA.

D) B and C only

E) A, B, and C

Answer: D
*Topic: Concept 17.3*
*Skill: Knowledge*

41) Which of the following is *least* related to the other items?

A) snRNP

B) triplet code

C) wobble

D) tRNA

E) anticodon

Answer: A
*Topic: Concept 17.4*
*Skill: Comprehension*

42) All of the following are directly involved in translation *except*

A) mRNA.

B) tRNA.

C) ribosomes.

D) DNA.

E) aminoacyl–tRNA synthetase enzymes.

Answer: D
*Topic: Concept 17.4*
*Skill: Knowledge*

43) A particular triplet of bases in the coding sequence of DNA is AAA. The anticodon on the tRNA that binds the mRNA codon is

A) TTT.

B) UUA.

C) UUU.

D) AAA.

E) either UAA or TAA, depending on first base wobble.

Answer: C
*Topic: Concept 17.4*
*Skill: Application*

44) Accuracy in the translation of mRNA into the primary structure of a protein depends on specificity in the

A) binding of ribosomes to mRNA.

B) shape of the A and P sites of ribosomes.

C) bonding of the anticodon to the codon.

D) attachment of amino acids to tRNAs.

E) both C and D

Answer: E
*Topic: Concept 17.4*
*Skill: Comprehension*

45) What is an anticodon part of?

   A) DNA

   B) tRNA

   C) mRNA

   D) a ribosome

   E) an activating enzyme

Answer: B
*Topic: Concept 17.4*
*Skill: Knowledge*

46) A part of an mRNA molecule with the following sequence is being read by a ribosome: 5' CCG-ACG 3' (mRNA). The following activated transfer RNA molecules (with their anticodons shown in the 3' to 5' direction) are available. Two of them can correctly match the mRNA so that a dipeptide can form.

| tRNA Anticodon | Amino Acid |
| --- | --- |
| GGC | Proline |
| CGU | Alanine |
| UGC | Threonine |
| CCG | Glycine |
| ACG | Cysteine |
| CGG | Alanine |

The dipeptide that will form will be

   A) cysteine–alanine.

   B) proline–threonine.

   C) glycine–cysteine.

   D) alanine–alanine.

   E) threonine–glycine.

Answer: B
*Topic: Concept 17.4*
*Skill: Application*

47) What type of bonding is responsible for maintaining the shape of the tRNA molecule?

   A) covalent bonding between sulfur atoms

   B) ionic bonding between phosphates

   C) hydrogen bonding between base pairs

   D) van der Waals interactions between hydrogen atoms

   E) peptide bonding between amino acids

Answer: C
*Topic: Concept 17.4*
*Skill: Knowledge*

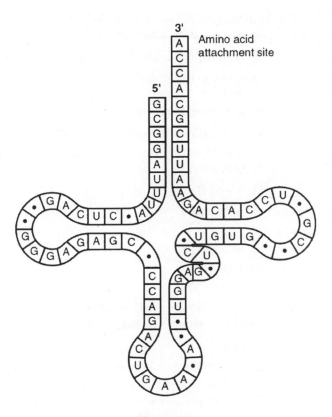

**Figure 17.2**

48) Figure 17.2 represents tRNA that recognizes and binds a particular amino acid (in this instance, phenylalanine). Which codon on the mRNA strand codes for this amino acid?

A) UGG

B) GUG

C) GUA

D) UUC

E) CAU

Answer: D
*Topic: Concept 17.4*
*Skill: Application*

49) A mutant bacterial cell has a defective aminoacyl synthetase that attaches a lysine to tRNAs with the anticodon AAA instead of a phenylalanine. The consequence of this for the cell will be that

A) none of the proteins in the cell will contain phenylalanine.

B) proteins in the cell will include lysine instead of phenylalanine at amino acid positions specified by the codon UUU.

C) the cell will compensate for the defect by attaching phenylalanine to tRNAs with lysine–specifying anticodons.

D) the ribosome will skip a codon every time a UUU is encountered.

E) None of the above will occur; the cell will recognize the error and destroy the tRNA.

Answer: B
*Topic: Concept 17.4*
*Skill: Application*

50) There are 61 mRNA codons that specify an amino acid, but only 45 tRNAs. This is best explained by the fact that

A) some tRNAs have anticodons that recognize two or more different codons.

B) the rules for base pairing between the third base of a codon and tRNA are flexible.

C) many codons are never used, so the tRNAs that recognize them are dispensable.

D) A and B only

E) A, B, and C

Answer: D
*Topic: Concept 17.4*
*Skill: Comprehension*

51) What are ribosomes composed of?

A) rRNA only

B) proteins only

C) both rRNA and protein

D) mRNA, rRNA, and protein

E) mRNA, tRNA, rRNA, and protein

Answer: C
*Topic: Concept 17.4*
*Skill: Knowledge*

52) Where is eukaryotic ribosomal RNA transcribed?

A) the Golgi apparatus

B) ribosomes

C) the nucleolus

D) X chromosomes

E) prokaryotic cells only

Answer: C
*Topic: Concept 17.4*
*Skill: Knowledge*

53) What is the most abundant type of RNA?

A) mRNA

B) tRNA

C) rRNA

D) pre-mRNA

E) hnRNA

Answer: C
*Topic: Concept 17.4*
*Skill: Knowledge*

54) The function of the ribosome in polypeptide synthesis is to

A) hold mRNA and tRNAs together.

B) catalyze the addition of amino acids from tRNAs to the growing polypeptide chain.

C) move along the mRNA and eject tRNAs during the translocation process.

D) A and B only

E) A, B, and C

Answer: E
*Topic: Concept 17.4*
*Skill: Knowledge*

55) From the following list, which is the first event in translation in eukaryotes?

A) elongation of the polypeptide

B) base pairing of activated methionine-tRNA to AUG of the messenger RNA

C) binding of the larger ribosomal subunit to smaller ribosomal subunits

D) covalent bonding between the first two amino acids

E) Both B and D occur simultaneously.

Answer: B
*Topic: Concept 17.4*
*Skill: Knowledge*

56) Choose the answer that has these events of protein synthesis in the proper sequence.
   1. An aminoacyl–tRNA binds to the A site.
   2. A peptide bond forms between the new amino acid and a polypeptide chain.
   3. tRNA leaves the P site, and the P site remains vacant.
   4. A small ribosomal subunit binds with mRNA.
   5. tRNA translocates to the P site.

   A) 1, 3, 2, 4, 5

   B) 4, 1, 2, 5, 3

   C) 5, 4, 3, 2, 1

   D) 4, 1, 3, 2, 5

   E) 2, 4, 5, 1, 3

Answer: B
*Topic: Concept 17.4*
*Skill: Knowledge*

57) Which of the following is *not* directly involved in the process of translation?

   A) ligase

   B) tRNA

   C) rRNA

   D) mRNA

   E) aminoacyl–tRNA synthetase

Answer: A
*Topic: Concept 17.4*
*Skill: Knowledge*

58) Which of the following components are present upon the completion of translation initiation?

   A) small ribosomal subunit

   B) large ribosomal subunit

   C) initiator tRNA

   D) A and C only

   E) A, B, and C

Answer: E
*Topic: Concept 17.4*
*Skill: Knowledge*

59) During translation, chain elongation continues until what happens?

   A) No further amino acids are needed by the cell.

   B) All tRNAs are empty.

   C) The polypeptide is long enough.

   D) A stop codon is encountered.

   E) The ribosomes run off the end of mRNA.

Answer: D
*Topic: Concept 17.4*
*Skill: Knowledge*

60) As a ribosome translocates along an mRNA molecule by one codon, which of the following occurs?

   A) The tRNA that was in the A site moves into the P site.

   B) The tRNA that was in the P site moves into the A site.

   C) The tRNA that was in the P site moves to the E site and is released.

   D) The tRNA that was in the A site departs from the ribosome.

   E) Both A and C are correct.

Answer: E
*Topic: Concept 17.4*
*Skill: Knowledge*

61) Which of the following does *not* occur during the termination phase of translation?

   A) A termination codon causes the A site to accept a release factor.

   B) The newly formed polypeptide is released.

   C) A tRNA with the next amino acid enters the P site.

   D) The two ribosomal subunits separate.

   E) Translation stops.

Answer: C
*Topic: Concept 17.4*
*Skill: Knowledge*

62) What are polyribosomes?

 A) groups of ribosomes reading a single mRNA simultaneously

 B) ribosomes containing more than two subunits

 C) multiple copies of ribosomes associated with giant chromosomes

 D) aggregations of vesicles containing ribosomal RNA

 E) ribosomes associated with more than one tRNA

Answer: A
*Topic: Concept 17.4*
*Skill: Knowledge*

63) What is one function of a signal peptide?

 A) to direct an mRNA molecule into the cisternal space of the ER

 B) to bind RNA polymerase to DNA and initiate transcription

 C) to terminate translation of the messenger RNA

 D) to translocate polypeptides across the ER membrane

 E) to signal the initiation of transcription

Answer: D
*Topic: Concept 17.4*
*Skill: Knowledge*

64) When translating secretory or membrane proteins, ribosomes are directed to the ER membrane by

 A) a specific characteristic of the ribosome itself, which distinguishes free ribosomes from bound ribosomes.

 B) a signal-recognition particle that brings ribosomes to a receptor protein in the ER membrane.

 C) moving through a specialized channel of the nucleus.

 D) a chemical signal given off by the ER.

 E) a signal sequence of RNA that precedes the start codon of the message.

Answer: B
*Topic: Concept 17.4*
*Skill: Knowledge*

65) Which of the following is *least* related to the other items?

 A) exons

 B) introns

 C) RNA splicing

 D) signal-recognition particles (SRPs)

 E) mRNA

Answer: D
*Topic: Concept 17.4*
*Skill: Comprehension*

66) Which of the following is *not* related to ribosomal activity?

 A) A site

 B) spliceosome

 C) codon recognition

 D) peptide bond formation

 E) P site

Answer: B
*Topic: Concept 17.4*
*Skill: Comprehension*

67) When does translation begin in prokaryotic cells?

A) after a transcription initiation complex has been formed

B) during transcription

C) after the 5' caps are converted to mRNA

D) once the pre-mRNA has been converted to mRNA

E) as soon as the DNA introns are removed from the template

Answer: B
*Topic: Concept 17.4*
*Skill: Knowledge*

68) Which of the following is (are) *true* about RNA?

A) snoRNA aids in processing pre-rRNA transcripts in the nucleolus.

B) SRP RNA is an essential component of spliceosomes.

C) It has functional groups that allow it to act as a catalyst (ribozyme).

D) Only A and C are true.

E) A, B, and C are true.

Answer: D
*Topic: Concept 17.5*
*Skill: Comprehension*

69) Which of the following statements are true about protein synthesis in prokaryotes?

A) Translation can begin while transcription is still in progress.

B) Extensive RNA processing is required before prokaryotic transcripts can be translated.

C) Prokaryotic cells have complicated mechanisms for targeting proteins to the appropriate cellular organelles.

D) Only A and B are true.

E) A, B, and C are true.

Answer: A
*Topic: Concept 17.6*
*Skill: Comprehension*

70) Of the following types of mutations, which one is likely to be the *most* common?

A) point mutation

B) missense mutation

C) base–pair substitution

D) nonsense mutation

E) frameshift mutation

Answer: A
*Topic: Concept 17.7*
*Skill: Comprehension*

71) What is the effect of a nonsense mutation in a gene?

A) It changes an amino acid in the encoded protein.

B) It has no effect on the amino acid sequence of the encoded protein.

C) It introduces a stop codon into the mRNA.

D) It alters the reading frame of the mRNA.

E) It prevents introns from being expressed.

Answer: C
*Topic: Concept 17.7*
*Skill: Knowledge*

*Each of the following is a modification of the sentence*
*THECATATETHERAT.*

    A.  THERATATETHECAT
    B.  THETACATETHERAT
    C.  THECATARETHERAT
    D.  THECATATTHERAT
    E.  CATATETHERAT

72) Which of the above is analogous to a frameshift mutation?

Answer: D
*Topic: Concept 17.7*
*Skill: Application*

73) Which of the above is analogous to a single substitution mutation?

Answer: C
*Topic: Concept 17.7*
*Skill: Application*

74) Sickle-cell disease is probably the result of which kind of mutation?

    A) point
    B) frameshift
    C) nonsense
    D) nondisjunction
    E) both B and D

Answer: A
*Topic: Concept 17.7*
*Skill: Application*

75) A frameshift mutation could result from

    A) a base insertion only.
    B) a base deletion only.
    C) a base substitution only.
    D) deletion of three consecutive bases.
    E) either an insertion or a deletion of a base.

Answer: E
*Topic: Concept 17.7*
*Skill: Comprehension*

76) Which of the following DNA mutations is the most likely to be damaging to the protein it specifies?

    A) a base–pair deletion
    B) a codon substitution
    C) a substitution in the last base of a codon
    D) a codon deletion
    E) a point mutation

Answer: A
*Topic: Concept 17.7*
*Skill: Comprehension*

77) Which point mutation would be most likely to have a catastrophic effect on the functioning of a protein?

    A) a base substitution
    B) a base deletion near the start of a gene
    C) a base deletion near the end of the coding sequence, but not in the terminator codon
    D) deletion of three bases near the start of the coding sequence, but not in the initiator codon
    E) a base insertion near the end of the coding sequence, but not in the terminator codon

Answer: B
*Topic: Concept 17.7*
*Skill: Comprehension*

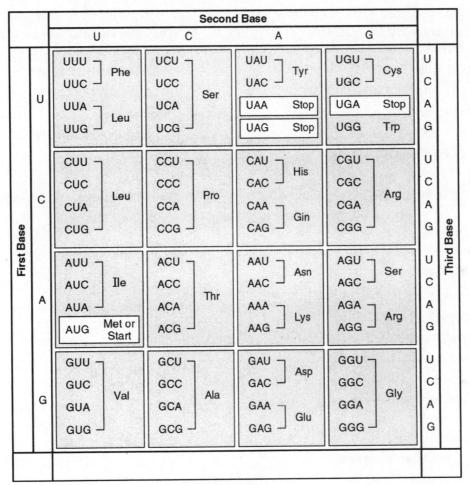

**Figure 17.1**

# Media Activity Questions

1) Which of these correctly illustrates the pairing of DNA and RNA nucleotides?

   A) GTTACG with CAATCG

   B) GTTACG with CAAUGC

   C) GTTACG with GTTACG

   D) GTTACG with ACCGTA

   E) GTTACG with UAACAU

   Answer: B
   *Topic: Web/CD Activity: Transcription*

2) During RNA processing a(n) _____ is added to the 3' end of the RNA.

   A) 3' untranslated region

   B) a long string of adenine nucleotides

   C) 5' untranslated region

   D) coding segment

   E) modified guanine nucleotide

   Answer: B
   *Topic: Web/CD Activity: RNA Processing*

3) Spliceosomes are composed of

   A) snRNPs and other proteins.

   B) polymerases and ligases.

   C) introns and exons.

   D) the RNA transcript and protein.

   E) snRNPs and snurps.

   Answer: A
   *Topic: Web/CD Activity: RNA Processing*

4) Translation occurs in

   A) the cytoplasm.

   B) a lysosome.

   C) the nucleus.

   D) a mitochondrion.

   E) a nucleoplasm.

   Answer: A
   *Topic: Web/CD Activity: RNA Processing*

5) What enzyme catalyzes the attachment of an amino acid to tRNA?

   A) aminoacyl-tRNA synthetase

   B) rubisco

   C) dextrinase

   D) argininosuccinate lyase

   E) nuclease

   Answer: A
   *Topic: Web/CD Activity: Translation*

# Self-Quiz Questions

1) Base-pair substitutions involving the third base of a codon are unlikely to result in an error in the polypeptide. This is because
   A) substitutions are corrected before transcription begins.
   B) substitutions are restricted to introns.
   C) the base-pairing rules are less strict for the third base of codons and anticodons.
   D) a signal-recognition particle corrects coding errors.
   E) transcribed errors attract snRNPs, which then stimulate splicing and correction.

   Answer: C

2) In eukaryotic cells, transcription cannot begin until
   A) the two DNA strands have completely separated and exposed the promoter.
   B) several transcription factors have bound to the promoter.
   C) the 5' caps are removed from the mRNA.
   D) the DNA introns are removed from the template.
   E) DNA nucleases have isolated the transcription unit.

   Answer: B

3) Which of the following is *not* true of a codon?
   A) It consists of three nucleotides.
   B) It may code for the same amino acid as another codon does.
   C) It never codes for more than one amino acid.
   D) It extends from one end of a tRNA molecule.
   E) It is the basic unit of the genetic code.

   Answer: D

4) The metabolic pathway of arginine synthesis is as follows:

   Precursor→Ornithine→Citrulline→Arginine
         A        B        C

   Beadle and Tatum discovered several classes of *Neurospora* mutants that were able to grow on minimal medium with arginine added. Class I mutants were also able to grow on medium supplemented with either ornithine or citrulline, whereas class II mutants could grow on citrulline medium but not on ornithine medium. From the behavior of their mutants, Beadle and Tatum were able to conclude that
   A) one gene codes for the entire metabolic pathway.
   B) the genetic code of DNA is a triplet code.
   C) class I mutants have their mutations later in the nucleotide chain than do class II mutants.
   D) class I mutants have a nonfunctional enzyme at step A, and class II mutants have one at step B.
   E) class III mutants have nonfunctional enzymes for all three steps.

   Answer: D

5) The anticodon of a particular tRNA molecule is
   A) complementary to the corresponding mRNA codon.
   B) complementary to the corresponding triplet in rRNA.
   C) the part of tRNA that bonds to a specific amino acid.
   D) changeable, depending on the amino acid that attaches to the tRNA.
   E) catalytic, making the tRNA a ribozyme.

   Answer: A

6) Which of the following is *not* true of RNA processing?

   A) Exons are cut out before mRNA leaves the nucleus.

   B) Nucleotides may be added at both ends of the RNA.

   C) Ribozymes may function in RNA splicing.

   D) RNA splicing is thought to be catalyzed by spliceosomes.

   E) A primary transcript is often much longer than the final RNA molecule that leaves the nucleus.

   Answer: A

7) Which of the following is true of translation in both prokaryotes and eukaryotes?

   A) Translation is coupled to transcription.

   B) The product of transcription is immediately ready for translation.

   C) The codon UUU codes for phenylalanine.

   D) Ribosomes are affected by streptomycin.

   E) The signal–recognition particle (SRP) binds to the first 20 amino acids of certain polypeptides.

   Answer: C

*The following questions refer to Figure 17.1, a table of codons.*

*(Figure 17.1 appears on page 271.)*

8) Using the genetic code in Figure 17.1, identify a 5' → 3' sequence of nucleotides in the DNA template strand for an mRNA coding for the polypeptide sequence Phe–Pro–Lys.

   A) UUU–GGG–AAA

   B) GAA–CCC–CTT

   C) AAA–ACC–TTT

   D) CTT–CGG–GAA

   E) AAA–CCC–UUU

   Answer: D

9) Which of the following mutations would be *most* likely to have a harmful effect on an organism?

   A) a base–pair substitution

   B) a deletion of three bases near the middle of a gene

   C) a single nucleotide deletion in the middle of an intron

   D) a single nucleotide deletion near the end of the coding sequence

   E) a single nucleotide insertion downstream of, and close to, the start of the coding sequence

   Answer: E

10) Which component is *not directly* involved in the process known as translation?

   A) mRNA

   B) DNA

   C) tRNA

   D) ribosomes

   E) GTP

   Answer: B

# Chapter 18  The Genetics of Viruses and Bacteria

1) Which of the following is (are) *true* about viruses?
   A) Viruses are classified below the cellular level of biological organization.
   B) A single virus particle contains both DNA and RNA.
   C) Even small virus particles are visible with light microscopes.
   D) Only A and B are true.
   E) A, B, and C are true.

   Answer: A
   *Topic: Concept 18.1*
   *Skill: Knowledge*

2) Which of the following is *not* a reason scientists suspected that something other than bacteria was the cause of tobacco mosaic disease?
   A) Passing infectious sap through a fine filter failed to remove the infectious agent.
   B) Treating infectious sap with alcohol failed to remove the infectious agent.
   C) No cells could be seen in the infectious sap using a light microscope.
   D) The infectious agent in the sap could reproduce, as its ability to cause disease was undiluted even after many transfers from plant to plant.
   E) The infectious agent could not be cultivated on nutrient media in petri dishes or in test tubes.

   Answer: D
   *Topic: Concept 18.1*
   *Skill: Knowledge*

3) A researcher lyses a cell that contains nucleic acid molecules and capsomeres of tobacco mosaic virus (TMV). The cell contents are left in a covered test tube overnight. The next day this mixture is sprayed on tobacco plants. Which of the following would be expected to occur?
   A) The plants would develop some but not all of the symptoms of the TMV infection.
   B) The plants would develop symptoms typically produced by viroids.
   C) The plants would develop the typical symptoms of TMV infection.
   D) The plants would not show any disease symptoms.
   E) The plants would become infected, but the sap from these plants would be unable to infect other plants.

   Answer: C
   *Topic: Concept 18.1*
   *Skill: Application*

4) Which of the following is a characteristic of all viruses?
   A) a nucleic acid genome
   B) a protein capsid
   C) a viral envelope
   D) A and B only
   E) A, B, and C

   Answer: D
   *Topic: Concept 18.1*
   *Skill: Knowledge*

5) Viral genomes can consist of any of the following *except*

A) double-stranded DNA.

B) double-stranded RNA.

C) single-stranded DNA.

D) single-stranded RNA.

E) helical capsomeres.

Answer: E
*Topic: Concept 18.1*
*Skill: Knowledge*

6) The host range of a virus is determined by

A) the proteins on its surface.

B) whether its nucleic acid is DNA or RNA.

C) the proteins on the surface of the host cell.

D) the enzymes produced by the virus before it infects the cell.

E) both A and C

Answer: E
*Topic: Concept 18.1*
*Skill: Knowledge*

7) Viruses are referred to as obligate parasites because

A) they cannot reproduce outside of a host cell.

B) viral DNA always inserts itself into host DNA.

C) they invariably kill any cell they infect.

D) they can incorporate nucleic acids from other viruses.

E) they must use enzymes encoded by the virus itself.

Answer: A
*Topic: Concept 18.1*
*Skill: Knowledge*

8) Which of the following is characteristic of the lytic cycle?

A) Many bacterial cells containing viral DNA are produced.

B) Viral DNA is incorporated into the host genome.

C) The viral genome replicates without destroying the host.

D) A large number of phages are released at a time.

E) The virus–host relationship usually lasts for generations.

Answer: D
*Topic: Concept 18.1*
*Skill: Knowledge*

9) Bacteriophage DNA that have become integrated into the host cell chromosome are called

A) intemperate bacteriophages.

B) transposons.

C) prophages.

D) T-even phages.

E) plasmids.

Answer: C
*Topic: Concept 18.1*
*Skill: Knowledge*

10) Which of the following statements about the lysogenic cycle of lambda (λ) phage is *incorrect*?

   A) After infection the viral genes immediately turn the host cell into a lambda-producing factory, and the host cell then lyses.

   B) Most of the prophage genes are silenced by the product of a particular prophage gene.

   C) The phage genome replicates along with the host genome.

   D) Certain environmental triggers can cause the phage to exit the host genome, switching from the lysogenic to the lytic cycle.

   E) The phage DNA is incorporated by genetic recombination (crossing over) into a specific site on the host cell's DNA.

Answer: A
*Topic: Concept 18.1*
*Skill: Knowledge*

11) Virulent phages undergo a(n) _____ life cycle, whereas temperate phages are capable of undergoing a(n) _____ cycle.

   A) infective; retroviral

   B) lysogenic; lytic

   C) lytic; lysogenic

   D) retroviral; infective

   E) infective; benign

Answer: C
*Topic: Concept 18.1*
*Skill: Knowledge*

12) What is the function of the single-stranded RNA in certain animal viruses?

   A) It can serve directly as mRNA.

   B) It can serve as a template for mRNA synthesis.

   C) It can serve as a template for DNA synthesis.

   D) Only A and C are correct.

   E) A, B, and C are correct.

Answer: E
*Topic: Concept 18.1*
*Skill: Knowledge*

13) Viruses with single-stranded RNA that acts as a template for DNA synthesis are known as

   A) retroviruses.

   B) proviruses.

   C) viroids.

   D) bacteriophages.

   E) lytic phages.

Answer: A
*Topic: Concept 18.1*
*Skill: Knowledge*

14) What is the function of reverse transcriptase in retroviruses?

   A) It hydrolyzes the host cell's DNA.

   B) It uses viral RNA as a template for DNA synthesis.

   C) It converts host cell RNA into viral DNA.

   D) It translates viral RNA into proteins.

   E) It uses viral RNA as a template for making complementary RNA strands.

Answer: B
*Topic: Concept 18.1*
*Skill: Knowledge*

15) The membrane making up the viral envelope can come from

A) the virus itself, using enzymes encoded by the virus.

B) the nuclear membrane of an infected cell.

C) the plasma membrane of an infected cell.

D) both A and B

E) both B and C

Answer: E
*Topic: Concept 18.1*
*Skill: Knowledge*

16) Viral envelopes contain proteins with covalently attached carbohydrate groups called

A) glycoproteins.

B) proteosugars.

C) carbopeptides.

D) peptidocarbs.

E) carboproteins.

Answer: A
*Topic: Concept 18.1*
*Skill: Knowledge*

17) The simplest infectious biological systems are

A) bacteria.

B) viruses.

C) viroids.

D) both A and B

E) both B and C

Answer: C
*Topic: Concept 18.2*
*Skill: Knowledge*

18) Which of the following is a *true* statement?

A) Viruses are uncommon.

B) Viruses can cause diarrhea, colds, and measles.

C) All viruses have a similar capsid and membranous envelope.

D) All viruses contain the nucleic acid RNA.

E) Viruses only invade animal cells.

Answer: B
*Topic: Concept 18.2*
*Skill: Knowledge*

19) Which of the following can be effective against viral diseases?

A) vaccination

B) nucleoside analogs that inhibit DNA synthesis

C) antibiotics

D) A and B only

E) A, B, and C

Answer: D
*Topic: Concept 18.2*
*Skill: Knowledge*

20) RNA viruses appear to have higher rates of mutation because

A) RNA nucleotides are more unstable than DNA nucleotides.

B) replication of their genomes does not involve the proofreading steps of DNA replication.

C) RNA viruses replicate faster.

D) RNA viruses can incorporate a variety of nonstandard bases.

E) RNA viruses are more sensitive to mutagens.

Answer: B
*Topic: Concept 18.2*
*Skill: Knowledge*

*Refer to the treatments listed below to answer the following questions.*

You isolate an infectious substance that is capable of causing disease in plants, but you do not know whether the infectious agent is a bacterium, virus, viroid, or prion. You have four methods at your disposal that you can use to analyze the substance in order to determine the nature of the infectious agent.

I.   treating the substance with nucleases that destroy ...ucleic acids and then determining whether it is still infectious

II.  ...... ...g the substance to remove all elements smaller than what can be easily seen under a light microscope

III. culturing the substance by itself on nutritive medium, away from any plant cells

IV.  treating the sample with proteases that digest all proteins and then determining whether it is still infectious

21) Which treatment could definitively determine whether or not the component is a viroid?
   A) I
   B) II
   C) III
   D) IV
   E) first II and then III

Answer: A
*Topic: Concept 18.2*
*Skill: Application*

22) If you already knew that the infectious agent was either bacterial or viral, which treatment would allow you to distinguish between these two possibilities?
   A) I
   B) II
   C) III
   D) IV
   E) either II or IV

Answer: C
*Topic: Concept 18.2*
*Skill: Application*

23) Which treatment would you use to determine if the agent is a prion?
   A) I only
   B) II only
   C) III only
   D) IV only
   E) either I or IV

Answer: D
*Topic: Concept 18.2*
*Skill: Application*

24) Which of the following contributes to the emergence of viral disease?
   A) production of new virus strains through mutation
   B) spread of existing virus from one host species to another
   C) transformation from lytic to lysogenic activity
   D) A and B only
   E) A, B, and C

Answer: D
*Topic: Concept 18.2*
*Skill: Knowledge*

25) Which of the following is *true* of plant virus infections?
   A) They can be controlled by the use of antibiotics.
   B) They are spread throughout a plant by passing through the plasmodesmata.
   C) They have little effect on plant growth.
   D) Only A and B are correct.
   E) A, B, and C are correct.

Answer: B
*Topic: Concept 18.2*
*Skill: Knowledge*

26) Which of the following represents a difference between viruses and viroids?

    A) Viruses infect many types of cells, whereas viroids infect only prokaryotic cells.

    B) Viruses have capsids composed of protein, whereas viroids have no capsids.

    C) Viruses contain introns; viroids have only exons.

    D) Viruses always have genomes composed of DNA, whereas viroids always have genomes composed of RNA.

    E) Viruses cannot pass through plasmodesmata; viroids can.

Answer: B
*Topic: Concept 18.2*
*Skill: Knowledge*

27) The difference between *vertical* and *horizontal* transmission of plant viruses is that

    A) vertical transmission refers to the transmission of a virus from a parent plant to its progeny, and horizontal transmission refers to one plant spreading the virus to another plant.

    B) vertical transmission refers to the spread of viruses from upper leaves to lower leaves of the plant, and horizontal transmission refers to the spread of a virus among leaves at the same general level.

    C) vertical transmission refers to the spread of viruses from trees and tall plants to bushes and other smaller plants, and horizontal transmission refers to the spread of viruses among plants of similar size.

    D) vertical transmission refers to the transfer of DNA from one type of plant virus to another, and horizontal transmission refers to the exchange of DNA between two plant viruses of the same type.

    E) vertical transmission refers to the transfer of DNA from a plant of one species to a plant of a different species, and horizontal transmission refers to the spread of viruses among plants of the same species.

Answer: A
*Topic: Concept 18.2*
*Skill: Knowledge*

28) What are prions?

   A) misfolded versions of normal brain protein

   B) tiny molecules of RNA that infect plants

   C) viral DNA that has had to attach itself to the host genome

   D) viruses that invade bacteria

   E) a mobile segment of DNA

Answer: A
*Topic: Concept 18.2*
*Skill: Knowledge*

29) Most molecular biologists think that viruses originated from fragments of cellular nucleic acid. Which of the following observations supports this theory?

   A) Viruses contain either DNA or RNA.

   B) Viruses are enclosed in protein capsids rather than plasma membranes.

   C) Viruses can reproduce only inside host cells.

   D) Viruses can infect both prokaryotic and eukaryotic cells.

   E) Viral genomes are usually more similar to the genome of the host cell than to the genomes of viruses that infect other cell types.

Answer: E
*Topic: Concept 18.2*
*Skill: Comprehension*

30) Reproduction in bacteria requires

   A) the production of a mitotic spindle.

   B) a plasmid.

   C) cyclic AMP.

   D) replication of DNA.

   E) both B and D

Answer: D
*Topic: Concept 18.3*
*Skill: Comprehension*

31) What is the most common source of genetic diversity in a bacterial colony?

   A) transposons

   B) plasmids

   C) meiotic recombination

   D) crossing over

   E) mutation

Answer: E
*Topic: Concept 18.3*
*Skill: Knowledge*

*Use the following answers for the following questions. The answers may be used once, more than once, or not at all.*

   A.  transduction
   B.  transposition
   C.  translation
   D.  transformation
   E.  conjugation

32) External DNA is assimilated by a cell.

Answer: D
*Topic: Concept 18.3*
*Skill: Knowledge*

33) DNA is transferred from one bacterium to another by a virus.

Answer: A
*Topic: Concept 18.3*
*Skill: Knowledge*

34) A group of $F^+$ bacteria is mixed with a group of $F^-$ bacteria. After several days, all of the bacteria are $F^+$.

Answer: E
*Topic: Concept 18.3*
*Skill: Knowledge*

35) A plasmid is exchanged between bacteria through a pilus.

Answer: E
*Topic: Concept 18.3*
*Skill: Knowledge*

36) A sequence of DNA is moved to alternative locations within the genome.

Answer: B
*Topic: Concept 18.3*
*Skill: Comprehension*

37) In biotechnology, genes are commonly introduced into bacterial cells by incubating the cells together with DNA and high concentrations of calcium ions. This is an example of

A) transformation.

B) translocation.

C) transduction.

D) conjugation.

E) transposition.

Answer: A
*Topic: Concept 18.3*
*Skill: Knowledge*

38) The process by which host cell DNA is accidentally packaged within a phage capsid and transferred to another cell instead of the phage DNA is called

A) translocation.

B) conjugation.

C) specialized transduction.

D) generalized transduction.

E) transformation.

Answer: D
*Topic: Concept 18.3*
*Skill: Knowledge*

39) A scientist is studying a strain of bacteria that commonly transfers genes to other bacteria. Which of the following would provide evidence that the genes are being transferred through *specialized transduction*?

A) Transmission of the genes is always accompanied by transfer of the F plasmid.

B) Transmission of the genes is always accompanied by transfer of the R plasmid.

C) The same one or several gene(s) are always transferred.

D) The transmission of the genes is dramatically enhanced in the presence of calcium.

E) The bacterial strain is often infected by a virulent phage.

Answer: C
*Topic: Concept 18.3*
*Skill: Application*

40) What does bacterial mating involve?

A) exchange of egg and sperm

B) formation of a cytoplasmic bridge for the transfer of "male" DNA

C) sex pili that draw the cells together so that mRNA can be inserted

D) integration of male and female DNA into a cytoplasmic bridge

E) binary fission of a bacterial cell

Answer: B
*Topic: Concept 18.3*
*Skill: Knowledge*

41) An Hfr bacterium is one that has

    A) at least one plasmid present in the cytosol.

    B) a special recognition site that will take up closely related DNA from its environment.

    C) several insertion sequences scattered throughout its chromosome.

    D) several copies of a single transposon repeated randomly throughout its chromosome.

    E) a plasmid that has become integrated into its chromosome.

Answer: E
*Topic: Concept 18.3*
*Skill: Knowledge*

42) Which of the following statements regarding transposons is *not* true?

    A) Transposons are genes that encode sex pili and enable plasmid transfers between bacteria.

    B) Transposons are found in both prokaryotes and eukaryotes.

    C) Transposons can move from a plasmid to the bacterial circular chromosome.

    D) Transposons may replicate at an original site and insert a copy at another site.

    E) Transposons may carry only the genes necessary for insertion.

Answer: A
*Topic: Concept 18.3*
*Skill: Knowledge*

43) An R plasmid can

    A) facilitate bacterial resistance to antibiotics.

    B) adjust the rates of metabolic pathways.

    C) repress gene expression.

    D) convert an $F^+$ to an $F^-$ bacterium.

    E) reverse the direction of transcription.

Answer: A
*Topic: Concept 18.3*
*Skill: Knowledge*

44) What does the operon model attempt to explain?

    A) the coordinated control of gene expression in bacteria

    B) bacterial resistance to antibiotics

    C) how genes move between homologous regions of DNA

    D) the mechanism of viral attachment to a host cell

    E) horizontal transmission of plant viruses

Answer: A
*Topic: Concept 18.4*
*Skill: Comprehension*

45) All of the following are made up of nucleic acid *except* a

    A) repressor.

    B) structural gene.

    C) promoter.

    D) regulatory gene.

    E) operator.

Answer: A
*Topic: Concept 18.4*
*Skill: Knowledge*

46) The role of a metabolite that controls a repressible operon is to

A) bind to the promoter region and decrease the affinity of RNA polymerase for the promoter.

B) bind to the operator region and block the attachment of RNA polymerase to the promoter.

C) increase the production of inactive repressor proteins.

D) bind to the repressor protein and inactivate it.

E) bind to the repressor protein and activate it.

Answer: E
*Topic: Concept 18.4*
*Skill: Comprehension*

47) The tryptophan operon is a repressible operon that is

A) permanently turned on.

B) turned on only when tryptophan is present in the growth medium.

C) turned off only when glucose is present in the growth medium.

D) turned on only when glucose is present in the growth medium.

E) turned off whenever tryptophan is added to the growth medium.

Answer: E
*Topic: Concept 18.4*
*Skill: Comprehension*

*For the following questions, match the following terms with the appropriate phrase or description below. Each term can be used once, more than once, or not at all.*

A. operon
B. inducer
C. promoter
D. repressor
E. corepressor

48) This protein is produced by a regulatory gene.

Answer: D
*Topic: Concept 18.4*
*Skill: Knowledge*

49) A mutation in this section of DNA could influence the binding of RNA polymerase to the DNA.

Answer: C
*Topic: Concept 18.4*
*Skill: Comprehension*

50) A lack of this nonprotein molecule would result in the inability of the cell to "turn off" genes.

Answer: E
*Topic: Concept 18.4*
*Skill: Comprehension*

51) A mutation that inactivates the regulatory gene of a repressible operon in an *E. coli* cell would result in

A) continuous transcription of the structural gene controlled by that regulator.

B) complete inhibition of transcription of the structural gene controlled by that regulator.

C) irreversible binding of the repressor to the operator.

D) inactivation of RNA polymerase.

E) both B and C

Answer: A
*Topic: Concept 18.4*
*Skill: Application*

52) The lactose operon is likely to be transcribed when

  A) there is more glucose in the cell than lactose.

  B) the cyclic AMP levels are low.

  C) there is lactose but no glucose in the cell.

  D) the cyclic AMP and lactose levels are both high within the cell.

  E) both C and D

Answer: E
*Topic: Concept 18.4*
*Skill: Comprehension*

53) Transcription of the structural genes in an inducible operon

  A) occurs all the time.

  B) starts when the pathway's substrate is present.

  C) starts when the pathway's product is present.

  D) stops when the pathway's product is present.

  E) does not produce enzymes.

Answer: B
*Topic: Concept 18.4*
*Skill: Comprehension*

54) Which of the following statements about operons is (are) *true*?

  A) The tryptophan operon is a repressible operon.

  B) Tryptophan itself can bind to the *trp* operator and shut down production of tryptophan pathway enzymes.

  C) The lactose operon repressor binds to the operator and turns on the synthesis of the enzyme β–galactosidase.

  D) Only A and C are correct.

  E) A, B, and C are correct.

Answer: A
*Topic: Concept 18.4*
*Skill: Knowledge*

55) How does active CAP induce expression of the genes of the lactose operon?

  A) It terminates production of repressor molecules.

  B) It degrades the substrate allolactose.

  C) It stimulates splicing of the encoded genes.

  D) It stimulates the binding of RNA polymerase to the promoter.

  E) It binds steroid hormones and controls translation.

Answer: D
*Topic: Concept 18.4*
*Skill: Knowledge*

56) For a repressible operon to be transcribed, which of the following must be *true*?

  A) A corepressor must be present.

  B) RNA polymerase and the active repressor must be present.

  C) RNA polymerase must bind to the promoter, and the repressor must be inactive.

  D) RNA polymerase cannot be present, and the repressor must be inactive.

  E) RNA polymerase must not occupy the promoter, and the repressor must be inactive.

Answer: C
*Topic: Concept 18.4*
*Skill: Comprehension*

57) Allolactose induces the synthesis of the enzyme lactase. An *E. coli* cell is presented for the first time with the sugar lactose (containing allolactose) as a potential food source. Which of the following occurs when the lactose enters the cell?

   A) The repressor protein attaches to the regulator.

   B) Allolactose binds to the repressor protein.

   C) Allolactose binds to the regulator.

   D) The repressor protein and allolactose bind to RNA polymerase.

   E) RNA polymerase attaches to the regulator.

Answer: B
*Topic: Concept 18.4*
*Skill: Comprehension*

58) Of the following, which is *least* related to the others?

   A) corepressor

   B) repressor

   C) inducer

   D) transposon

   E) cAMP receptor protein

Answer: D
*Topic: Concept 18.4*
*Skill: Comprehension*

# Media Activity Questions

1) The lytic cycle of bacteriophage infection ends with the

   A) replication of viral DNA.

   B) entry of the phage protein coat into the host cell.

   C) assembly of viral particles into phages.

   D) the injection of phage DNA into a bacterium.

   E) rupture of the bacterium.

   Answer: E
   *Topic: Web/CD Activity: Phage Lytic Cycle*

2) In the lysogenic cycle

   A) host DNA is destroyed and viral DNA is replicated.

   B) a bacterium replicates without passing viral DNA to its daughter cells.

   C) viral DNA is destroyed and host DNA is replicated.

   D) a bacterium divides once before the lytic cycle is initiated.

   E) viral DNA is replicated along with host DNA

   Answer: E
   *Topic: Activity: Phage Lysogenic and Lytic Cycles*

3) Double-stranded viral DNA is incorporated into a host cell as a

   A) promotor.

   B) provirus.

   C) transposon.

   D) *lac.*

   E) homeoboxes.

   Answer: B
   *Topic: Web/CD Activity: HIV Reproductive Cycle*

4) The operon model of the regulation of gene expression in bacteria was proposed by

   A) Watson and Crick.

   B) Franklin.

   C) Darwin.

   D) Jacob and Monod.

   E) Mendel.

   Answer: D
   *Topic: Web/CD Activity: The lac Operon in E. coli*

5) Which of these is *not* a component of the *lac* operon?

   A) lactose–utilization genes

   B) promoter

   C) regulatory gene

   D) operator

   E) promoter and operator

   Answer: C
   *Topic: Web/CD Activity: The lac Operon in E. coli*

# Self-Quiz Questions

1) A bacterium is infected with an experimentally constructed bacteriophage composed of the T2 phage protein coat and T4 phage DNA. The new phages produced would have

   A) T2 protein and T4 DNA.

   B) T2 protein and T2 DNA.

   C) a mixture of the DNA and proteins of both phages.

   D) T4 protein and T4 DNA.

   E) T4 protein and T2 DNA.

   Answer: D

2) RNA viruses require their own supply of certain enzymes because

   A) host cells rapidly destroy the viruses.

   B) host cells lack enzymes that can replicate the viral genome.

   C) these enzymes translate viral mRNA into proteins.

   D) these enzymes penetrate host cell membranes.

   E) these enzymes cannot be made in host cells.

   Answer: B

3) Which of the following is descriptive of an R plasmid?

   A) Its transfer converts an F$^-$ cell into an F$^+$ cell.

   B) It has genes for antibiotic resistance and maybe for sex pili.

   C) It is transferred between bacteria by transduction.

   D) It is a good example of a composite transposon.

   E) It makes bacteria resistant to phage.

   Answer: B

4) Transposition differs from other mechanisms of genetic recombination because it

   A) occurs only in bacteria.

   B) moves genes between homologous regions of the DNA.

   C) plays little or no role in evolution.

   D) occurs only in eukaryotes.

   E) scatters genes to new loci in the genome.

   Answer: E

5) If a particular operon encodes enzymes for making an essential amino acid and is regulated like the *trp* operon, then

   A) the amino acid inactivates the repressor.

   B) the enzymes produced are called inducible enzymes.

   C) the repressor is active in the absence of the amino acid.

   D) the amino acid acts as a corepressor.

   E) the amino acid turns on transcription of the operon.

   Answer: D

6) What would occur if the repressor of an inducible operon were mutated so it could not bind the operator?

   A) continuous transcription of the operon's genes

   B) reduced transcription of the operon's genes

   C) buildup of a substrate for the pathway controlled by the operon

   D) irreversible binding of the repressor to the promoter

   E) overproduction of catabolite activator protein (CAP)

   Answer: A

7) During conjugation between an Hfr cell and an F⁻ cell,

   A) the F⁻ cell becomes an F⁺ cell.

   B) the F⁻ cell becomes an Hfr cell.

   C) the chromosome of the F⁻cell is degraded.

   D) genes from the Hfr cell may replace genes of the F⁻ cell by recombination.

   E) DNA from the F⁻ cell transfers to the Hfr cell, and DNA from the Hfr cell transfers to the F⁻ cell.

   Answer: D

8) Genetic variation in bacterial populations never results from

   A) transduction.

   B) transformation.

   C) conjugation.

   D) mutation.

   E) meiosis.

   Answer: E

9) Which of the following characteristics or processes is common to *both* bacteria and viruses?

   A) binary fission

   B) ribosomes

   C) genetic material of nucleic acid

   D) mitosis

   E) conjugation

   Answer: C

10) Emerging viruses arise by

   A) mutation of existing viruses.

   B) the spread of existing viruses to new host species.

   C) the spread of existing viruses more widely within host species.

   D) all of the above

   E) none of the above

   Answer: D

# Chapter 19 Eukaryotic Genomes: Organization, Regulation, and Evolution

1) The condensed chromosomes observed in mitosis include all of the following structures *except*

A) nucleosomes.

B) 30–nm fibers.

C) 300–nm fibers.

D) looped domain.

E) ribosomes.

Answer: E
*Topic: Concept 19.1*
*Skill: Knowledge*

2) Under the electron microscope, unfolded chromatin resembles "beads on a string." What do the "beads" represent?

A) nucleosomes

B) ribosomes

C) beadosomes

D) molecules of DNA polymerase

E) molecules of RNA polymerase

Answer: A
*Topic: Concept 19.1*
*Skill: Knowledge*

3) In a nucleosome, what is the DNA wrapped around?

A) polymerase molecules

B) ribosomes

C) mRNA

D) histones

E) nucleolus protein

Answer: D
*Topic: Concept 19.1*
*Skill: Knowledge*

4) Which of the following statements concerning the eukaryotic chromosome is *false*?

A) It is composed of DNA and protein.

B) The nucleosome is the most basic structural subunit.

C) The number of genes on each chromosome is different in different cell types.

D) It consists of a single linear molecule of double–stranded DNA.

E) Active transcription occurs on euchromatin.

Answer: C
*Topic: Concept 19.1*
*Skill: Comprehension*

5) If a cell were unable to produce histone proteins, which of the following would be expected to occur?

A) There would be an increase in the amount of "satellite" DNA produced during centrifugation.

B) The cell's DNA couldn't be packed into its nucleus.

C) Spindle fibers would not form during prophase.

D) Amplification of other genes would compensate for the lack of histones.

E) Pseudogenes would be transcribed to compensate for the decreased protein in the cell.

Answer: B
*Topic: Concept 19.1*
*Skill: Comprehension*

6) Which of the following statements about histones is *incorrect*?

A) Each nucleosome consists of two molecules, each of four types of histone.

B) Histone H1 is not present in the nucleosome bead; instead it is involved in the formation of higher-level chromatin structures.

C) The amino end of each histone extends outward from the nucleosome and is called a "histone tail."

D) Histones are found in mammals, but not in other animals or in plants.

E) The mass of histone in chromatin is approximately equal to the mass of DNA.

Answer: D
*Topic: Concept 19.1*
*Skill: Knowledge*

7) Why do histones bind tightly to DNA?

A) Histones are positively charged, and DNA is negatively charged.

B) Histones are negatively charged, and DNA is positively charged.

C) Both histones and DNA are strongly hydrophobic.

D) Histones are covalently linked to the DNA.

E) Histones are highly hydrophobic, and DNA is hydrophilic.

Answer: A
*Topic: Concept 19.1*
*Skill: Comprehension*

8) Which of the following represents an order of increasingly higher levels of organization?

A) nucleosome, 30–nm chromatin fiber, looped domain

B) looped domain, 30–nm chromatin fiber, nucleosome

C) looped domain, nucleosome, 30–nm chromatin fiber

D) nucleosome, looped domain, 30–nm chromatin fiber

E) 30–nm chromatin fiber, nucleosome, looped domain

Answer: A
*Topic: Concept 19.1*
*Skill: Knowledge*

9) Which of the following statements is *true*?

A) Heterochromatin is composed of DNA, whereas euchromatin is made of DNA and RNA.

B) Both heterochromatin and euchromatin are found in the cytoplasm.

C) Heterochromatin is highly condensed, whereas euchromatin is less compact.

D) Euchromatin is not transcribed, whereas heterochromatin is transcribed.

E) Only euchromatin is visible under the light microscope.

Answer: C
*Topic: Concept 19.1*
*Skill: Knowledge*

10) Which of the following is *least* related to the others?

   A) 30-nm chromatin fiber

   B) pseudogenes

   C) nucleosomes

   D) looped domains

   E) histones

Answer: B
*Topic: Concept 19.1*
*Skill: Comprehension*

11) In a nucleosome, the DNA is wrapped around

   A) polymerase molecules.

   B) ribosomes.

   C) histones.

   D) the nucleolus.

   E) satellite DNA.

Answer: C
*Topic: Concept 19.1*
*Skill: Knowledge*

12) Muscle cells and nerve cells in one species of animal owe their differences in structure to

   A) having different genes.

   B) having different chromosomes.

   C) using different genetic codes.

   D) differential gene expression.

   E) having unique ribosomes.

Answer: D
*Topic: Concept 19.2*
*Skill: Comprehension*

13) Which of the following mechanisms is (are) used to coordinately control the expression of multiple, related genes in eukaryotic cells?

   A) organization of the genes into clusters, with local chromatin structures influencing the expression of all the genes at once

   B) each of the genes sharing a common control element, allowing a single activator to turn on their transcription at once, regardless of their location in the genome

   C) organizing the genes into large operons, allowing them to be transcribed as a single unit

   D) A and B only

   E) A, B , and C

Answer: D
*Topic: Concept 19.2*
*Skill: Comprehension*

14) In which of the following would you expect to find the most methylation of DNA?

   A) tandem arrays for ribosomal genes

   B) pseudogenes

   C) inactivated mammalian X chromosomes

   D) globin genes

   E) transposons

Answer: C
*Topic: Concept 19.2*
*Skill: Knowledge*

15) If you were to observe the activity of methylated DNA, you would expect it to

A) be replicating.

B) be unwinding in preparation for protein synthesis.

C) have turned off or slowed down the process of transcription.

D) be very active in translation.

E) induce protein synthesis by not allowing repressors to bind to it.

Answer: C
*Topic: Concept 19.2*
*Skill: Knowledge*

16) Genomic imprinting, DNA methylation, and histone acetylation are all examples of

A) genetic mutation.

B) chromosomal rearrangements.

C) karyotypes.

D) epigenetic inheritance.

E) translocation.

Answer: D
*Topic: Concept 19.2*
*Skill: Comprehension*

17) A eukaryotic gene typically has all of the following features *except*

A) introns.

B) a promoter.

C) an operator.

D) control elements.

E) a terminator.

Answer: C
*Topic: Concept 19.2*
*Skill: Knowledge*

18) Approximately what proportion of the DNA in the human genome codes for proteins or functional RNA?

A) 83%

B) 46%

C) 32%

D) 13%

E) 2%

Answer: E
*Topic: Concept 19.2*
*Skill: Knowledge*

19) Two potential devices that eukaryotic cells use to regulate transcription are DNA _____ and histone _____.

A) methylation; amplification

B) amplification; methylation

C) acetylation; methylation

D) methylation; acetylation

E) amplification; acetylation

Answer: D
*Topic: Concept 19.2*
*Skill: Knowledge*

20) In both eukaryotes and prokaryotes, gene expression is primarily regulated at the level of

A) transcription.

B) translation.

C) mRNA stability.

D) mRNA splicing.

E) protein stability.

Answer: A
*Topic: Concept 19.2*
*Skill: Knowledge*

21) In eukaryotes, transcription is generally associated with

   A) euchromatin only.

   B) heterochromatin only.

   C) very tightly packed DNA only.

   D) highly methylated DNA only.

   E) both euchromatin and histone acetylation.

Answer: E
*Topic: Concept 19.2*
*Skill: Comprehension*

22) A geneticist introduces a transgene into yeast cells and isolates five independent cell lines in which the transgene has integrated into the yeast genome. In four of the lines, the transgene is expressed strongly, but in the fifth there is no expression at all. A likely explanation for the lack of transgene expression in the fifth cell line is that the

   A) transgene integrated into a heterochromatic region of the genome.

   B) transgene integrated into a euchromatic region of the genome.

   C) transgene was mutated during the process of integration into the host cell genome.

   D) host cell lacks the enzymes necessary to express the transgene.

   E) transgene integrated into a region of the genome characterized by high histone acetylation.

Answer: A
*Topic: Concept 19.2*
*Skill: Application*

23) A significant difference between eukaryotes and prokaryotes is that

   A) DNA is wound around proteins to form chromatin in eukaryotes, but in prokaryotes the DNA is not associated with proteins.

   B) gene expression is largely regulated by transcription in prokaryotes, but not in eukaryotes.

   C) prokaryotic genes do not contain introns.

   D) noncoding DNA sequences are found in prokaryotes, but not in eukaryotes.

   E) prokaryotes have less DNA but more noncoding segments than eukaryotes.

Answer: C
*Topic: Concept 19.2*
*Skill: Knowledge*

24) During DNA replication,

   A) all methylation of the DNA is lost.

   B) DNA polymerase is blocked by methyl groups, and methylated regions of the genome are therefore left uncopied.

   C) methylation of the DNA is maintained because methylation enzymes act at DNA sites where one strand is already methylated and thus correctly methylates daughter strands after replication.

   D) methylation of the DNA is maintained because DNA polymerase directly incorporates methylated nucleotides into the new strand opposite any methylated nucleotides in the template.

   E) methylated DNA is copied in the cytoplasm, and unmethylated DNA in the nucleus.

Answer: C
*Topic: Concept 19.2*
*Skill: Comprehension*

25) Eukaryotic cells control gene expression by which of the following mechanisms?

    A) histone acetylation of nucleosomes

    B) DNA methylation

    C) enzyme modification of chromatin structure

    D) A and B only

    E) A, B, and C

Answer: E
*Topic: Concept 19.2*
*Skill: Knowledge*

26) General transcription factors

    A) are required for the expression of all protein-encoding genes.

    B) bind to other proteins or to a sequence element within the promoter called the TATA box.

    C) help RNA polymerase bind to the promoter and begin transcribing.

    D) usually only lead to a low level of transcription in the absence of additional proteins called *specific* transcription factors.

    E) all of the above

Answer: E
*Topic: Concept 19.2*
*Skill: Knowledge*

*The questions below refer to the following terms. Each term may be used once, more than once, or not at all.*

    A.  enhancer
    B.  promoter
    C.  activator
    D.  repressor
    E.  terminator

27) binds to a site in the DNA far from the promoter to stimulate transcription

Answer: C
*Topic: Concept 19.2*
*Skill: Knowledge*

28) can inhibit transcription by blocking the binding of positively acting transcription factors to the DNA

Answer: D
*Topic: Concept 19.2*
*Skill: Knowledge*

29) site in the DNA located near the end of the final exon, encoding an RNA sequence that determines the 3′ end of the transcript

Answer: E
*Topic: Concept 19.2*
*Skill: Knowledge*

30) Steroid hormones produce their effects in cells by

    A) activating key enzymes in metabolic pathways.

    B) activating translation of certain mRNAs.

    C) promoting the degradation of specific mRNAs.

    D) binding to intracellular receptors and promoting transcription of specific genes.

    E) promoting the formation of looped domains in certain regions of DNA.

Answer: D
*Topic: Concept 19.2*
*Skill: Knowledge*

31) The phenomenon in which RNA molecules in a cell are destroyed if they have a sequence complementary to an introduced double-stranded RNA is called

    A) RNA interference.

    B) RNA obstruction.

    C) RNA blocking.

    D) RNA targeting.

    E) RNA disposal.

Answer: A
*Topic: Concept 19.2*
*Skill: Knowledge*

32) Which of the following is *least* related to the others?

    A) cyclins

    B) ubiquitin

    C) tumor suppression

    D) protein degradation

    E) proteasomes

Answer: C
*Topic: Concept 19.2*
*Skill: Comprehension*

33) Which of the following is *not* a mechanism whereby a proto-oncogene is converted to an oncogene?

    A) methylation of bases

    B) point mutation

    C) gene transposition

    D) gene amplification

    E) chromosome translocation

Answer: A
*Topic: Concept 19.3*
*Skill: Knowledge*

34) Which of the following statements concerning proto-oncogenes is *false*?

    A) They can code for proteins associated with cell growth.

    B) They are similar to oncogenes found in retroviruses.

    C) They are produced by somatic mutations induced by carcinogenic substances.

    D) They can be involved in producing proteins for cell adhesion.

    E) They can code for proteins involved in cell division.

Answer: C
*Topic: Concept 19.3*
*Skill: Knowledge*

35) Which of the following is *not* a characteristic of the product of the *p53* gene? It

    A) is an activator for other genes.

    B) slows down the cell cycle.

    C) causes cell death.

    D) prevents cells from passing on mutations due to DNA damage.

    E) slows down the rate of DNA replication by interfering with the binding of DNA polymerase.

Answer: E
*Topic: Concept 19.3*
*Skill: Knowledge*

36) Tumor suppressor genes

    A) are frequently overexpressed in cancerous cells.

    B) are cancer-causing genes introduced into cells by viruses.

    C) can encode proteins that promote DNA repair or cell-cell adhesion.

    D) often encode proteins that stimulate the cell cycle.

    E) all of the above

Answer: C
*Topic: Concept 19.3*
*Skill: Comprehension*

37) Which of the following events is (are) necessary for the production of a malignant tumor?

    A) activation of an oncogene in the cell

    B) inactivation of tumor-suppressor genes within the cell

    C) presence of mutagenic substances within the cell's environment

    D) presence of a retrovirus within the cell

    E) both A and B

Answer: E
*Topic: Concept 19.3*
*Skill: Comprehension*

38) The incidence of cancer increases dramatically with age because
- A) the Ras protein is more likely to be hyperactive after age sixty.
- B) proteasomes become more active with age.
- C) as we age, normal cell division inhibitors cease to function.
- D) the longer we live, the more mutations accumulate.
- E) tumor-suppressor genes are no longer able to repair damaged DNA.

Answer: D
*Topic: Concept 19.3*
*Skill: Comprehension*

39) The Ras protein is involved in _____, and cancer-causing forms of the protein are usually _____.
- A) relaying a signal from a growth factor receptor; hyperactive
- B) DNA replication; nonfunctional
- C) DNA repair; hyperactive
- D) cell–cell adhesion; nonfunctional
- E) cell division; nonfunctional

Answer: A
*Topic: Concept 19.3*
*Skill: Knowledge*

40) A genetic test to detect predisposition to cancer would likely examine the *APC* gene for _____ cancer and the *BRCA1* and *BRCA2* genes for _____ cancer.
- A) colorectal; breast
- B) lung; breast
- C) breast; lung
- D) colorectal; lung
- E) lung; prostate

Answer: A
*Topic: Concept 19.3*
*Skill: Knowledge*

41) Which of the following can contribute to the development of cancer?
- A) random spontaneous mutations
- B) mutations caused by X-rays
- C) transposition
- D) A and B only
- E) A, B, and C

Answer: E
*Topic: Concept 19.3*
*Skill: Comprehension*

42) One of the unique characteristics of retrotransposons is that
- A) translation of their RNA transcript produces an enzyme that converts the RNA back to DNA.
- B) they are found only in animal cells.
- C) once removed from the DNA, the gene segments for an antibody variable region are rejoined to the constant region.
- D) they contribute a significant portion of the genetic variability seen within a population of gametes.
- E) their amplification is dependent on a concurrent retrovirus infection.

Answer: A
*Topic: Concept 19.4*
*Skill: Comprehension*

43) The most prominent component of the DNA in eukaryotic genomes is
- A) operons.
- B) tandemly repeating DNA.
- C) gene regulatory sequences.
- D) transposable elements and related sequences.
- E) *Alu* elements.

Answer: D
*Topic: Concept 19.4*
*Skill: Knowledge*

44) Which of the following statements concerning transposons is *false*?

A) Transposons may increase the production of a particular protein.

B) Transposons may prevent the normal functioning of a gene.

C) Transposons may decrease the production of a particular protein.

D) Transposons may reduce the amount of DNA within certain cells.

E) Both A and C are false.

Answer: D
*Topic: Concept 19.4*
*Skill: Knowledge*

45) Reverse transcriptase may be present in cells that have not been infected by a retrovirus because of the presence of

A) immunoglobulins.

B) retrotransposons.

C) genomic imprinting.

D) proteasomes.

E) oncogenes.

Answer: B
*Topic: Concept 19.4*
*Skill: Comprehension*

*The questions below refer to the following terms. Each term may be used once, more than once, or not at all.*

A. transposons
B. simple sequence DNA
C. multigene family
D. methylated DNA
E. pseudogenes

46) This is most commonly found in inactivated DNA regions.

Answer: D
*Topic: Concept 19.2*
*Skill: Knowledge*

47) When pieces of DNA are centrifuged, a "satellite" band develops that is separate from the rest of the DNA. This layer is composed of _____.

Answer: B
*Topic: Concept 19.4*
*Skill: Comprehension*

48) α-globins and β-globins are classic examples of which type of DNA?

Answer: C
*Topic: Concept 19.4*
*Skill: Comprehension*

49) This class of DNA was discovered by Barbara McClintock.

Answer: A
*Topic: Concept 19.4*
*Skill: Knowledge*

50) This class of DNA codes for the three largest ribosomal RNA molecules.

Answer: C
*Topic: Concept 19.4*
*Skill: Knowledge*

51) These portions of the genome are nonfunctional nucleotide sequences that are quite similar to the functional genes.

Answer: E
*Topic: Concept 19.4*
*Skill: Knowledge*

52) Multigene families made up of identical genes almost always code for

A) RNA products.

B) restriction enzymes.

C) transposases.

D) proto-oncogenes.

E) deacetylases.

Answer: A
*Topic: Concept 19.4*
*Skill: Knowledge*

53) In humans, the embryonic and fetal forms of hemoglobin have a higher affinity for oxygen than that of adults. This is due to

A) nonidentical genes that produce different versions of globins during development.

B) identical genes that generate many copies of the ribosomes needed for fetal globin production.

C) pseudogenes, which interfere with gene expression in adults.

D) the attachment of methyl groups to cytosine following birth, which changes the type of hemoglobin produced.

E) histone proteins changing shape during embryonic development.

Answer: A
*Topic: Concept 19.4*
*Skill: Knowledge*

54) What do pseudogenes and introns have in common?

A) They code for RNA end products, rather than proteins.

B) They both contain uracil.

C) They have multiple promoter sites.

D) They both code for histones.

E) They are not expressed, nor do they code for functional proteins.

Answer: E
*Topic: Concept 19.4*
*Skill: Comprehension*

55) One of the best pieces of evidence for the process of gene duplication and mutation is the occurrence of

A) pseudogenes.

B) introns.

C) transposons.

D) oncogenes.

E) heterochromatin.

Answer: A
*Topic: Concept 19.5*
*Skill: Comprehension*

56) If a pseudogene were transposed between a functioning gene and its "upstream" regulatory components, which of the following would most likely occur?

A) The functioning gene would not be transcribed.

B) The pseudogene would not be transcribed.

C) The pseudogene would be transcribed.

D) Both genes would be transcribed.

E) Both A and C would probably occur.

Answer: E
*Topic: Concept 19.5*
*Skill: Application*

57) Two genes that are evolutionarily related by gene duplication are likely to have which of the following properties?

A) They will often have related functions.

B) Their sequences will be similar or identical.

C) They will often be located near each other in the genome.

D) Only A and B are correct.

E) A, B, and C are correct.

Answer: E
*Topic: Concept 19.5*
*Skill: Application*

58) Scientists often deduce the evolutionary history of the different members of a gene family by

   A) comparing the sequences of the genes.

   B) determining which of the genes are mutated in human diseases.

   C) comparing the relative enzymatic activities of the proteins encoded by the genes.

   D) overexpressing each of the genes in a cell and determining which has the most destructive effect.

   E) examining the relative stability of the mRNAs produced from the genes.

Answer: A
*Topic: Concept 19.5*
*Skill: Comprehension*

59) The number of repeated units of simple sequence repeat DNA can vary between homologous chromosomes or between individuals. Such variation could be caused by

   A) slippage of DNA polymerase during replication.

   B) unequal crossing over events.

   C) meiotic errors that result in polyploidy.

   D) A and B only

   E) A, B, and C

Answer: D
*Topic: Concept 19.5*
*Skill: Comprehension*

60) Which description below is *not* a way that transposable elements can contribute to genome evolution?

   A) by introducing homologous sequences into various locations within the genome, allowing unequal crossing over to occur during meiosis

   B) by moving genes to new chromosomal locations

   C) by moving exons from one gene to another, creating proteins with novel combinations of exons

   D) by integrating into genes and disrupting their function

   E) All the choices describe how transposable elements can contribute to genome evolution.

Answer: E
*Topic: Concept 19.5*
*Skill: Comprehension*

The table below indicates the exons present in six different genes. Gene 1, for example, contains exons A, B, C, and D, in this order, and gene 2 has a similar structure, although exons A and B have been replaced by related but distinct versions called A' and B'.

| Gene | Exons |
|------|-------|
| 1 | A–B–C–D |
| 2 | A'–B'–C–D |
| 3 | A–B'–C–D |
| 4 | A–A–B–C–D |
| 5 | A–B–C–D' |
| 6 | E–F–B–G |

61) The structural similarity seen in genes 1 through 5 suggests that they were most likely produced by

A) gene duplication.

B) exon shuffling.

C) exon duplication.

D) translocation.

E) polyploidy.

Answer: A
*Topic: Concept 19.5*
*Skill: Application*

62) The repeated A exon in gene 4 is likely a product of

A) exon shuffling.

B) exon duplication.

C) gene duplication.

D) translocation.

E) deletion.

Answer: B
*Topic: Concept 19.5*
*Skill: Comprehension*

63) Gene 6 is mostly unrelated to the other genes, except for the presence of exon B. This is most likely a product of

A) exon shuffling.

B) exon duplication.

C) gene duplication.

D) polyploidy.

E) translocation.

Answer: A
*Topic: Concept 19.5*
*Skill: Application*

# Media Activity Questions

1) Rearrangement of the genome plays an important role in the _____ system.

   A) endocrine

   B) reproductive

   C) nervous

   D) immune

   E) respiratory

   Answer: D
   *Topic: Web/CD Activity: Control of Gene Expression*

2) _____ bind(s) to DNA enhancer regions.

   A) RNA polymerases

   B) Promoters

   C) Introns

   D) Activators

   E) Exons

   Answer: D
   *Topic: Web/CD Activity: Control of Transcription*

3) How can a single RNA transcript lead to the translation of different proteins?

   A) The same RNA transcript may contain one of several different 5′ untranslated regions.

   B) The same RNA transcript may contain one of several different caps.

   C) The same RNA transcript may be spliced in several different ways.

   D) The same RNA transcript may contain one of several different promoters.

   E) The same RNA transcript may contain one of several different 3′ untranslated regions.

   Answer: C
   *Topic: Post-Transcriptional Control Mechanisms*

4) A poly-A tail's resistance to degradation is affected by the characteristics of the

   A) 3′ untranslated region.

   B) promoter.

   C) stop codon.

   D) enhancer.

   E) 5′ untranslated region.

   Answer: A
   *Topic: Post-Transcriptional Control Mechanisms*

5) The nuclear membrane's role in the regulation of gene expression involves

   A) protein activation.

   B) translation.

   C) protein degradation.

   D) regulating the transport of mRNA to the cytoplasm.

   E) RNA processing.

   Answer: D
   *Topic: Activity: Review: Control of Gene Expression*

# Self-Quiz Questions

1) In a nucleosome, the DNA is wrapped around

   A) polymerase molecules.

   B) ribosomes.

   C) histones.

   D) the nucleolus.

   E) satellite DNA.

   Answer: C

2) Muscle cells differ from nerve cells mainly because

   A) they express different genes.

   B) they contain different genes.

   C) they use different genetic codes.

   D) they have unique ribosomes.

   E) they have different chromosomes.

   Answer: A

3) One of the characteristics of retrotransposons is that

   A) they code for an enzyme that synthesizes DNA using an RNA template.

   B) they are found only in animal cells.

   C) they generally move by a cut–and–paste mechanism.

   D) they contribute a significant portion of the genetic variability seen within a population of gametes.

   E) their amplification is dependent on a retrovirus.

   Answer: A

4) The functioning of enhancers is an example of

   A) transcriptional control of gene expression.

   B) a post–transcriptional mechanism for editing mRNA.

   C) the stimulation of translation by initiation factors.

   D) post–translational control that activates certain proteins.

   E) a eukaryotic equivalent of prokaryotic promoter functioning.

   Answer: A

5) Multigene families are

   A) groups of enhancers that control transcription.

   B) usually clustered at the telomeres.

   C) equivalent to the operons of prokaryotes.

   D) sets of genes that are coordinately controlled.

   E) identical or similar genes that have evolved by gene duplication.

   Answer: E

6) Which of the following statements about the DNA in one of your brain cells is *true*?

   A) Some DNA sequences are present in multiple copies.

   B) Most of the DNA codes for protein.

   C) The majority of genes are likely to be transcribed.

   D) Each gene lies immediately adjacent to an enhancer.

   E) Many genes are grouped into operon–like clusters.

   Answer: A

7) Two eukaryotic proteins have one domain in common but are otherwise very different. Which of the following processes is most likely to have contributed to this phenomenon?

A) gene duplication

B) RNA splicing

C) exon shuffling

D) histone modification

E) random point mutations

Answer: C

8) Which of the following is an example of a possible step in the post-transcriptional control of gene expression?

A) the addition of methyl groups to cytosine bases of DNA

B) the binding of transcription factors to a promoter

C) the removal of introns and splicing together of exons

D) gene amplification during a stage in development

E) the folding of DNA to form heterochromatin

Answer: C

9) Within a cell, the amount of protein made using a given mRNA molecule depends partly on

A) the degree of DNA methylation.

B) the rate at which the mRNA is degraded.

C) the presence of certain transcription factors.

D) the number of introns present in the mRNA.

E) the types of ribosomes present in the cytoplasm.

Answer: B

10) Proto-oncogenes can change into oncogenes that cause cancer. Which of the following best explains the presence of these potential time bombs in eukaryotic cells?

A) Proto-oncogenes first arose from viral infections.

B) Proto-oncogenes normally help regulate cell division.

C) Proto-oncogenes are genetic "junk."

D) Proto-oncogenes are mutant versions of normal genes.

E) Cells produce proto-oncogenes as they age.

Answer: B

# Chapter 20  DNA Technology and Genomics

1) Plasmids are important in biotechnology because they are

   A) a vehicle for the insertion of foreign genes into bacteria.

   B) recognition sites on recombinant DNA strands.

   C) surfaces for protein synthesis in eukaryotic recombinants.

   D) surfaces for respiratory processes in bacteria.

   E) proviruses incorporated into the host DNA.

   Answer: A
   *Topic: Concept 20.1*
   *Skill: Knowledge*

2) If you discovered a bacterial cell that contained no restriction enzymes, which of the following would you expect to happen?

   A) The cell would be unable to replicate its DNA.

   B) The cell would create incomplete plasmids.

   C) The cell would be easily infected and lysed by bacteriophages.

   D) The cell would become an obligate parasite.

   E) Both A and D would occur.

   Answer: C
   *Topic: Concept 20.1*
   *Skill: Comprehension*

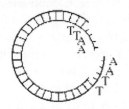

**Figure 20.1**

3) Which enzyme was used to produce the molecule in Figure 20.1?

   A) ligase

   B) transcriptase

   C) a restriction enzyme

   D) RNA polymerase

   E) DNA polymerase

   Answer: C
   *Topic: Concept 20.1*
   *Skill: Comprehension*

4) Assume that you are trying to insert a gene into a plasmid. Someone gives you a preparation of genomic DNA that has been cut with restriction enzyme X. The gene you wish to insert has sites on both ends for cutting by restriction enzyme Y. You have a plasmid with a single site for Y, but not for X. Your strategy should be to

A) insert the fragments cut with X directly into the plasmid without cutting the plasmid.

B) cut the plasmid with restriction enzyme X and insert the fragments cut with Y into the plasmid.

C) cut the DNA again with restriction enzyme Y and insert these fragments into the plasmid cut with the same enzyme.

D) cut the plasmid twice with restriction enzyme Y and ligate the two fragments onto the ends of the DNA fragments cut with restriction enzyme X.

E) cut the plasmid with enzyme X and then insert the gene into the plasmid.

Answer: C
*Topic: Concept 20.1*
*Skill: Application*

5) What is the enzymatic function of restriction enzymes?

A) to add new nucleotides to the growing strand of DNA

B) to join nucleotides during replication

C) to join nucleotides during transcription

D) to cleave nucleic acids at specific sites

E) to repair breaks in sugar–phosphate backbones

Answer: D
*Topic: Concept 20.1*
*Skill: Knowledge*

6) How does a bacterial cell protect its own DNA from restriction enzymes?

A) by adding methyl groups to adenines and cytosines

B) using DNA ligase to seal the bacterial DNA into a closed circle

C) adding histones to protect the double-stranded DNA

D) by forming "sticky ends" of bacterial DNA to prevent the enzyme from attaching

E) by reinforcing the bacterial DNA structure with covalent phosphodiester bonds

Answer: A
*Topic: Concept 20.1*
*Skill: Knowledge*

7) What is a cloning vector?

A) an enzyme that cuts DNA into restriction fragments

B) a DNA probe used to locate a particular gene in the genome

C) an agent, such as a plasmid, used to transfer DNA from an *in vitro* solution into a living cell

D) the laboratory apparatus used to clone genes

E) the sticky end of a DNA fragment

Answer: C
*Topic: Concept 20.1*
*Skill: Knowledge*

8) What are the typical characteristics of a cloning vector?

A) Bacterial cells cannot survive without it when grown under certain conditions.

B) It contains restriction sites that allow the insertion of foreign DNA segments.

C) It can replicate in bacterial cells.

D) Only B and C are correct.

E) A, B, and C are correct.

Answer: E
*Topic: Concept 20.1*
*Skill: Knowledge*

9) What is the most logical sequence of steps for splicing foreign DNA into a plasmid and inserting the plasmid into a bacterium?

I. Transform bacteria with recombinant DNA molecule.
II. Cut the plasmid DNA using restriction enzymes.
III. Extract plasmid DNA from bacterial cells.
IV. Hydrogen-bond the plasmid DNA to nonplasmid DNA fragments.
V. Use ligase to seal plasmid DNA to nonplasmid DNA.

A) I, II, IV, III, V

B) II, III, V, IV, I

C) III, II, IV, V, I

D) III, IV, V, I, II

E) IV, V, I, II, III

Answer: C
*Topic: Concept 20.1*
*Skill: Comprehension*

10) Bacteria containing recombinant plasmids are often identified by which process?

A) examining the cells with an electron microscope

B) using radioactive tracers to locate the plasmids

C) exposing the bacteria to an antibiotic that kills cells lacking the plasmid

D) removing the DNA of all cells in a culture to see which cells have plasmids

E) producing antibodies specific for each bacterium containing a recombinant plasmid

Answer: C
*Topic: Concept 20.1*
*Skill: Knowledge*

*Use the following information to answer the questions below.*

A eukaryotic gene has "sticky ends" produced by the restriction endonuclease *Eco*RI. The gene is added to a mixture containing *Eco*RI and a bacterial plasmid that carries two genes conferring resistance to ampicillin and tetracycline. The plasmid has one recognition site for *Eco*RI located in the tetracycline resistance gene. This mixture is incubated for several hours, exposed to DNA ligase, and then added to bacteria growing in nutrient broth. The bacteria are allowed to grow overnight and are streaked on a plate using a technique that produces isolated colonies that are clones of the original. Samples of these colonies are then grown in four different media: nutrient broth plus ampicillin, nutrient broth plus tetracycline, nutrient broth plus ampicillin and tetracycline, and nutrient broth without antibiotics.

11) Bacteria that contain the plasmid, but without the eukaryotic gene, would grow

   A) in the nutrient broth plus ampicillin, but not in the broth containing tetracycline.

   B) only in the broth containing both antibiotics.

   C) in the broth containing tetracycline, but not in the broth containing ampicillin.

   D) in all four types of broth.

   E) in the nutrient broth without antibiotics only.

Answer: D
*Topic: Concept 20.1*
*Skill: Application*

12) Bacteria containing a plasmid into which the eukaryotic gene has integrated would grow in

   A) the nutrient broth only.

   B) the nutrient broth and the tetracycline broth only.

   C) the nutrient broth, the ampicillin broth, and the tetracycline broth.

   D) all four types of broth.

   E) the ampicillin broth and the nutrient broth.

Answer: E
*Topic: Concept 20.1*
*Skill: Application*

13) Bacteria that do not take up any plasmids would grow on which media?

   A) the nutrient broth

   B) the nutrient broth and the tetracycline broth

   C) the nutrient broth and the ampicillin broth

   D) the tetracycline and ampicillin broth

   E) all four broths

Answer: A
*Topic: Concept 20.1*
*Skill: Application*

14) The principal problem with inserting an unmodified mammalian gene into a bacterial plasmid, and then getting that gene expressed in bacteria, is that

A) prokaryotes use a different genetic code from that of eukaryotes.

B) bacteria translate polycistronic messages only.

C) bacteria cannot remove eukaryotic introns.

D) bacterial RNA polymerase cannot make RNA complementary to mammalian DNA.

E) bacterial DNA is not found in a membrane-bounded nucleus and is therefore incompatible with mammalian DNA.

Answer: C
*Topic: Concept 20.1*
*Skill: Knowledge*

15) A gene that contains introns can be made shorter (but remain functional) for genetic engineering purposes by using

A) RNA polymerase to transcribe the gene.

B) a restriction enzyme to cut the gene into shorter pieces.

C) reverse transcriptase to reconstruct the gene from its mRNA.

D) DNA polymerase to reconstruct the gene from its polypeptide product.

E) DNA ligase to put together fragments of the DNA that codes for a particular polypeptide.

Answer: C
*Topic: Concept 20.1*
*Skill: Comprehension*

16) Yeast cells are frequently used as hosts for cloning because

A) they are easy to grow.

B) they can remove introns from mRNA.

C) they have plasmids.

D) both A and B

E) A, B, and C

Answer: E
*Topic: Concept 20.1*
*Skill: Knowledge*

17) The DNA fragments making up a genomic library are generally contained in

A) recombinant plasmids of bacteria.

B) recombinant viral DNA.

C) eukaryotic chromosomes.

D) both A and B

E) A, B, and C

Answer: D
*Topic: Concept 20.1*
*Skill: Knowledge*

18) A eukaryotic protein can be made in bacteria by inserting the gene encoding the protein into a(n)

A) protein plasmid.

B) expression vector.

C) yeast artificial chromosome (YAC).

D) PCR vector.

E) restriction plasmid.

Answer: B
*Topic: Concept 20.1*
*Skill: Knowledge*

19) How does a genomic library differ from a cDNA library?

    A) A genomic library contains both noncoding sequences and coding sequences, whereas a cDNA library contains only coding sequences.

    B) A genomic library is identical regardless of the cell type used to make it, whereas the content of a cDNA library depends on the cell type used in its construction.

    C) A genomic library can be made using a restriction enzyme and DNA ligase only, whereas a cDNA library requires both of these as well as reverse transcriptase and DNA polymerase.

    D) Only B and C are correct.

    E) A, B and C are correct.

Answer: E
*Topic: Concept 20.1*
*Skill: Comprehension*

20) The polymerase chain reaction is important because it allows us to

    A) insert eukaryotic genes into prokaryotic plasmids.

    B) incorporate genes into viruses.

    C) make DNA from RNA transcripts.

    D) make many copies of a targeted segment of DNA.

    E) insert regulatory sequences into eukaryotic genes.

Answer: D
*Topic: Concept 20.1*
*Skill: Knowledge*

21) Yeast artificial chromosomes contain which of the following elements?

    A) centromere

    B) telomeres

    C) origin of replication

    D) both A and B

    E) A, B, and C

Answer: E
*Topic: Concept 20.1*
*Skill: Knowledge*

22) The polymerase chain reaction (PCR) has been used to amplify DNA from which of the following?

    A) fossils

    B) fetal cells

    C) viruses

    D) bacteria

    E) all of the above

Answer: E
*Topic: Concept 20.1*
*Skill: Knowledge*

23) Which of the following best describes the complete sequence of steps occurring during *every* cycle of PCR?
1. The primers hybridize to the target DNA.
2. The mixture is heated to a high temperature to denature the double stranded target DNA.
3. Fresh DNA polymerase is added.
4. DNA polymerase extends the primers to make a copy of the target DNA.

    A) 2, 1, 4

    B) 1, 3, 2, 4

    C) 3, 4, 1, 2

    D) 3, 4, 2

    E) 2, 3, 4

Answer: A
*Topic: Concept 20.1*
*Skill: Comprehension*

*The following questions refer to the techniques, tools, or substances listed below. Answers may be used once, more than once, or not at all.*

A. restriction enzymes
B. gene cloning
C. DNA ligase
D. gel electrophoresis
E. reverse transcriptase

24) produces multiple identical copies of a gene for basic research or for large-scale production of a gene product

Answer: B
*Topic: Concept 20.1*
*Skill: Knowledge*

25) separates molecules by movement due to size and electrical charge

Answer: D
*Topic: Concept 20.2*
*Skill: Knowledge*

26) seals the sticky ends of restriction fragments to make recombinant DNA

Answer: C
*Topic: Concept 20.1*
*Skill: Knowledge*

27) is used to make complementary DNA (cDNA) from RNA

Answer: E
*Topic: Concept 20.1*
*Skill: Knowledge*

28) cuts DNA molecules at specific locations

Answer: A
*Topic: Concept 20.1*
*Skill: Knowledge*

29) Restriction fragments of DNA are typically separated from one another by which process?
   A) filtering
   B) centrifugation
   C) gel electrophoresis
   D) PCR
   E) electron microscopy

Answer: C
*Topic: Concept 20.2*
*Skill: Knowledge*

30) Which of the following is *least* related to the others?
   A) denaturation
   B) DNA ligase
   C) sticky ends
   D) restriction enzymes
   E) cloning vector

Answer: A
*Topic: Concept 20.2*
*Skill: Comprehension*

31) Probes are short, single-stranded DNA or RNA segments that are used to identify DNA fragments with a particular sequence. In order to identify a specific restriction fragment using a probe, what must be done?
   A) The fragments must be separated by electrophoresis.
   B) The fragments must be treated with heat or chemicals to separate the strands of the double helix.
   C) The probe must be hybridized with the fragment.
   D) Only A and B are correct.
   E) A, B, and C are correct.

Answer: E
*Topic: Concept 20.2*
*Skill: Comprehension*

32) Which of the following modifications is *least* likely to alter the rate at which a DNA fragment moves through a gel during electrophoresis?

    A) altering the nucleotide sequence of the DNA fragment

    B) methylating the cytosine bases within the DNA fragment

    C) increasing the length of the DNA fragment

    D) decreasing the length of the DNA fragment

    E) neutralizing the negative charges within the DNA fragment

Answer: A
*Topic: Concept 20.2*
*Skill: Application*

33) DNA fragments from a gel are transferred to a nitrocellulose paper during the procedure called Southern blotting. The purpose of transferring the DNA from a gel to a nitrocellulose paper is to

    A) permanently attach the DNA fragments to a substrate.

    B) separate the two complementary DNA strands.

    C) transfer only the DNA that is of interest.

    D) prepare the DNA for digestion with restriction enzymes.

    E) separate out the PCRs.

Answer: A
*Topic: Concept 20.2*
*Skill: Comprehension*

34) Which of the following is *least* related to the others?

    A) Southern blotting

    B) denaturation

    C) nucleic acid probe

    D) RNA interference

    E) nucleic acid hybridization

Answer: D
*Topic: Concept 20.2*
*Skill: Comprehension*

35) RFLP analysis can be used to distinguish between alleles based on differences in

    A) restriction enzyme recognition sites between the alleles.

    B) the amount of DNA amplified from the alleles during PCR.

    C) the ability of the alleles to be replicated in bacterial cells.

    D) the proteins expressed from the alleles.

    E) the ability of nucleic acid probes to hybridize to the alleles.

Answer: A
*Topic: Concept 20.2*
*Skill: Comprehension*

36) After being digested with a restriction enzyme, genomic DNA fragments are separated by gel electrophoresis. Specific fragments can then be identified through the use of a

    A) plasmid.

    B) restriction enzyme.

    C) sticky end.

    D) nucleic acid probe.

    E) RFLP.

Answer: D
*Topic: Concept 20.2*
*Skill: Comprehension*

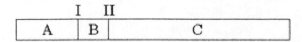

**Figure 20.2**

37) The segment of DNA shown in Figure 20.2 has restriction sites I and II, which create restriction fragments A, B, and C. Which of the gels produced by electrophoresis shown below best represents the separation and identity of these fragments?

A)
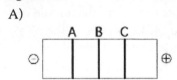

B)
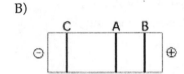

C)
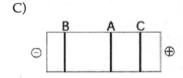

D)
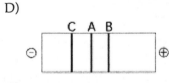

E)
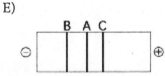

Answer: B
*Topic: Concept 20.2*
*Skill: Application*

38) Which of the following procedures would produce RFLPs?
    A) incubating a mixture of single-stranded DNA from two closely related species
    B) incubating DNA nucleotides with DNA polymerase
    C) incubating DNA with restriction enzymes
    D) incubating RNA with DNA nucleotides and reverse transcriptase
    E) incubating DNA fragments with "sticky ends" with ligase

Answer: C
*Topic: Concept 20.2*
*Skill: Comprehension*

39) Which of these is *not* one of the procedures used in Southern blotting?
    A) electrophoresis
    B) hybridization
    C) autoradiography
    D) restriction fragment preparation
    E) DNA microarray assay

Answer: E
*Topic: Concept 20.2*
*Skill: Knowledge*

40) Which of the following types of genomes have been sequenced?
    A) fungal
    B) plant
    C) bacterial
    D) B and C only
    E) A, B , and C

Answer: E
*Topic: Concept 20.3*
*Skill: Knowledge*

41) The major advantage of using artificial chromosomes such as YACs and BACs instead of plasmids for cloning genes is that

A) plasmids are unable to replicate in cells.

B) only one copy of a plasmid can be present in any given cell, whereas many copies of a YAC or BAC can coexist in a single cell.

C) YACs and BACs can carry much larger DNA fragments than plasmids can.

D) YACs and BACs can be used to express proteins encoded by inserted genes, but plasmids cannot.

E) all of the above

Answer: C
*Topic: Concept 20.3*
*Skill: Knowledge*

42) RFLPs played an important role in the Human Genome Project because they

A) make bacterial cells grow faster, increasing the amount of cloned DNA that was available for sequencing.

B) dramatically enhance the rate at which DNA can be sequenced.

C) increase the amount of DNA that can be produced during PCR.

D) do not vary between individuals, so they were used to produce a "universal" genome sequence representative of all humans.

E) provided genetic markers scattered throughout the genome, allowing the construction of a genome-wide linkage map.

Answer: E
*Topic: Concept 20.3*
*Skill: Comprehension*

43) Dideoxyribonucleotide chain-termination is a method of

A) cloning DNA.

B) sequencing DNA.

C) digesting DNA.

D) synthesizing DNA.

E) separating DNA fragments.

Answer: B
*Topic: Concept 20.3*
*Skill: Knowledge*

44) The "shotgun" approach used by Craig Venter to sequence the human genome skipped which of the following steps that were used by the Human Genome Project?

A) genetic mapping

B) physical mapping

C) DNA sequencing

D) A and B only

E) A, B, and C

Answer: D
*Topic: Concept 20.3*
*Skill: Knowledge*

45) The completion of the Human Genome Project revealed that the human genome contains fewer genes than expected, not so many more than simpler organisms. How can this be reconciled with the greater complexity of humans relative to many other organisms?

A) RNA transcripts of human genes are more likely to undergo alternative splicing.

B) Post-translational processing adds diversity to the resulting polypeptides.

C) Polypeptide domains are combined in a variety of ways.

D) Gene expression patterns in humans are often more complex than those in other organisms.

E) All of the above are correct.

Answer: E
*Topic: Concept 20.4*
*Skill: Comprehension*

46) Genomics includes the study of all of the following *except*

A) identifying the location of all of the genes present in the genome.

B) comparing genomes between different organisms.

C) studying the coordinated expression of groups of genes under various conditions or in different cell types.

D) studying how the genome is duplicated and segregated within the cell cycle.

E) identifying the functions of all of the genes in the genome.

Answer: D
*Topic: Concept 20.4*
*Skill: Comprehension*

47) Upon the completion of genome sequencing projects, how do scientists generally go about asking how many genes there are in the genome and where they are located?

A) mutating nucleotides throughout the genome and looking for phenotypes

B) using software to scan the genome sequence for gene-related sequence elements such as promoters and transcription start and stop sites

C) using RNA interference to pinpoint gene regulatory elements such as enhancers

D) examining the expression of all potential genes using DNA microchips

E) using PCR to amplify sequences throughout the genome and looking for gene-like amplification patterns

Answer: B
*Topic: Concept 20.4*
*Skill: Comprehension*

48) The function of a gene can be determined by

A) comparing its sequence to genes of known function from other organisms.

B) eliminating the function of the gene by *in vitro* mutagenesis and examining the consequences.

C) eliminating the expression of the gene using RNA interference and examining the consequences.

D) A and B only

E) A, B, and C

Answer: E
*Topic: Concept 20.4*
*Skill: Comprehension*

49) DNA microarrays have made a huge impact on genomic studies because they

    A) can be used to eliminate the function of any gene in the genome.

    B) can be used to introduce entire genomes into bacterial cells.

    C) allow the expression of many or even all of the genes in the genome to be compared at once.

    D) allow physical maps of the genome to be assembled in a very short time.

    E) dramatically enhance the efficiency of restriction enzymes.

Answer: C
*Topic: Concept 20.4*
*Skill: Knowledge*

50) Proteomics presents a particular challenge because

    A) the number of proteins in humans probably far exceeds the number of genes.

    B) a cell's proteins differ with cell type.

    C) proteins are extremely varied in structure and chemical properties.

    D) A and B only

    E) A, B, and C

Answer: E
*Topic: Concept 20.4*
*Skill: Comprehension*

*Use Figure 20.3 to answer the following questions. The DNA profiles below represent four different individuals.*

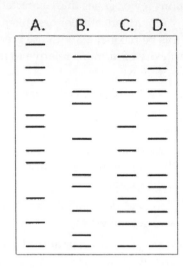

**Figure 20.3**

51) Which of the following statements is consistent with the results?

    A) B is the child of A and C.

    B) C is the child of A and B.

    C) D is the child of B and C.

    D) A is the child of B and C.

    E) A is the child of C and D.

Answer: B
*Topic: Concept 20.5*
*Skill: Application*

52) Which of the following statements is most likely *true*?

    A) D is the child of A and C.

    B) D is the child of A and B.

    C) D is the child of B and C.

    D) A is the child of C and D.

    E) B is the child of A and C.

Answer: B
*Topic: Concept 20.5*
*Skill: Application*

53) Which of the following are probably siblings?

   A) A and B

   B) A and C

   C) A and D

   D) C and D

   E) B and D

Answer: D
*Topic: Concept 20.5*
*Skill: Application*

54) Gene therapy

   A) has proven to be beneficial to HIV patients.

   B) involves replacement of a defective allele in sex cells.

   C) cannot be used to correct genetic disorders.

   D) had apparent success in treating disorders involving bone marrow cells.

   E) is a widely accepted procedure.

Answer: D
*Topic: Concept 20.5*
*Skill: Knowledge*

55) Genetic engineering is being used by the pharmaceutical industry. Which of the following is *not* currently one of the uses?

   A) production of human insulin

   B) production of human growth hormone

   C) production of tissue plasminogen activator

   D) genetic modification of plants to produce vaccines

   E) creation of products that will remove poisons from the human body

Answer: E
*Topic: Concept 20.5*
*Skill: Knowledge*

56) The most powerful way of increasing the specificity of a DNA profile analysis is to

   A) select markers present on the sex chromosomes rather than on the autosomes.

   B) analyze each marker by PCR rather than RFLP analysis.

   C) increase the number of markers used.

   D) repeat the analysis multiple times.

   E) analyze DNA obtained from skin cells rather than blood cells.

Answer: C
*Topic: Concept 20.5*
*Skill: Comprehension*

57) A DNA profile is produced by

   A) treating selected segments of DNA with restriction enzymes.

   B) electrophoresis of restriction fragments.

   C) using a probe to locate specific nucleotide sequences.

   D) A and B only

   E) A, B, and C

Answer: E
*Topic: Concept 20.5*
*Skill: Application*

58) Genetically engineered plants

   A) are more difficult to engineer than animals.

   B) include a transgenic rice plant that could help prevent vitamin A deficiency.

   C) are being rapidly developed, but traditional plant breeding programs are still the only method used to develop new plants.

   D) are able to fix nitrogen themselves.

   E) are banned throughout the world.

Answer: B
*Topic: Concept 20.5*
*Skill: Knowledge*

59) Current applications of biotechnology include

   A) cleaning up toxic waste.

   B) development of artificial photosynthetic machines.

   C) manufacturing human growth hormone.

   D) A and C only

   E) A, B, and C

Answer: D
*Topic: Concept 20.5*
*Skill: Knowledge*


60) Scientists developed a set of guidelines to address the safety of DNA technology. Which of the following is one of the adopted safety measures?

   A) Microorganisms used in recombinant DNA experiments are genetically crippled to ensure that they cannot survive outside of the laboratory.

   B) Genetically modified organisms cannot be part of our food supply.

   C) Transgenic plants are engineered so that the plant genes cannot hybridize.

   D) Experiments involving HIV or other potentially dangerous viruses have been banned.

   E) Recombinant plasmids cannot be replicated.

Answer: A
*Topic: Concept 20.5*
*Skill: Knowledge*

# Media Activity Questions

1) What is the advantage of being able to clone the gene for human insulin?

   A) Human insulin is more variable than other sources of insulin, so cloning would provide a greater chance of obtaining a form that can be used by the diabetic's muscles.

   B) There are too few cows, pigs, and horses to provide an adequate supply of their insulin.

   C) Human insulin is less likely to provoke an allergic reaction than cow, pig, or horse insulin.

   D) Cow, pig, or horse insulin cannot keep a diabetic alive for more than three months.

   E) Using human insulin increases the probability that, in the future, the diabetic can be weaned from a dependence on insulin.

   Answer: C
   *Topic: Activity: Applications of DNA Technology*

2) The unpaired nucleotides produced by the action of restriction enzymes are referred to as

   A) sticky ends.

   B) base sequences.

   C) single strands.

   D) restriction fragments.

   E) ligases.

   Answer: A
   *Topic: Web/CD Activity: Restriction Enzymes*

3) In order to insert a human gene into a plasmid, both must

   A) have identical DNA sequences.

   B) originate from the same type of cell.

   C) code for the same gene product.

   D) be cut by the same restriction enzyme.

   E) be the same length.

   Answer: D
   *Topic: Web/CD Activity: Cloning a Gene in Bacteria*

4) What enzyme forms covalent bonds between restriction fragments?

   A) DNA primase

   B) DNA helicase

   C) single-stranded binding protein

   D) DNA polymerase

   E) DNA ligase

   Answer: E
   *Topic: Web/CD Activity: Cloning a Gene in Bacteria*

5) The *TP53* gene of chromosome 17 codes for a protein

   A) that plays a role in the digestive process.

   B) that, in a particular variant, may play a role in Alzheimer's disease.

   C) involved in glucose transport.

   D) involved in the regulation of the cell cycle.

   E) that is like a white blood cell protein.

   Answer: D
   *Topic: Web/CD Activity: The Human Genome Project*

# Self-Quiz Questions

1) Which of the following tools of recombinant DNA technology is *incorrectly* paired with its use?

   A) restriction enzyme—production of RFLPs

   B) DNA ligase—enzyme that cuts DNA, creating the sticky ends of restriction fragments

   C) DNA polymerase—used in a polymerase chain reaction to amplify sections of DNA

   D) reverse transcriptase—production of cDNA from mRNA

   E) electrophoresis—separation of DNA fragments

   Answer: B

2) Which of the following would *not* be true of cDNA produced using human brain tissue as the starting material?

   A) It could be amplified by the polymerase chain reaction.

   B) It could be used to create a complete genomic library.

   C) It is produced from mRNA using reverse transcriptase.

   D) It could be used as a probe to locate genes expressed in the brain.

   E) It lacks the introns of the human genes and thus can probably be introduced into phage vectors.

   Answer: B

3) Plants are more readily manipulated by genetic engineering than are animals because

   A) plant genes do not contain introns.

   B) more vectors are available for transferring recombinant DNA into plant cells.

   C) a somatic plant cell can often give rise to a complete plant.

   D) genes can be inserted into plant cells by microinjection.

   E) plant cells have larger nuclei.

   Answer: C

4) A paleontologist has recovered a bit of tissue from the 400-year-old preserved skin of an extinct dodo (a bird). The researcher would like to compare DNA from the sample with DNA from living birds. Which of the following would be most useful for increasing the amount of dodo DNA available for testing?

   A) RFLP analysis

   B) polymerase chain reaction (PCR)

   C) electroporation

   D) gel electrophoresis

   E) Southern hybridization

   Answer: B

5) Expression of a cloned eukaryotic gene in a prokaryotic cell involves many difficulties. The use of mRNA and reverse transcriptase is part of a strategy to solve the problem of

   A) post-transcriptional processing.

   B) electroporation.

   C) post-translational processing.

   D) nucleic acid hybridization.

   E) restriction fragment ligation.

   Answer: A

6) DNA technology has many medical applications. Which of the following is *not* done routinely at present?
   A) production of hormones for treating diabetes and dwarfism
   B) production of viral subunits for vaccines
   C) introduction of genetically engineered genes into human gametes
   D) prenatal identification of genetic disease genes
   E) genetic testing for carriers of harmful alleles

Answer: C

7) Which of the following has the largest genome size and the smallest number of genes per million base pairs?
   A) *Hemophilus influenzae* (bacterium)
   B) *Saccharomyces cerevisiae* (yeast)
   C) *Arabidopsis thaliana* (plant)
   D) *Drosophila melanogaster* (fruit fly)
   E) *Homo sapiens* (human)

Answer: E

8) Which of the following sequences in double-stranded DNA is most likely to be recognized as a cutting site for a restriction enzyme?
   A) AAGG
      TTCC
   B) AGTC
      TCAG
   C) GGCC
      CCGG
   D) ACCA
      TGGT
   E) AAAA
      TTTT

Answer: C

9) In recombinant DNA methods, the term *vector* can refer to
   A) the enzyme that cuts DNA into restriction fragments.
   B) the sticky end of a DNA fragment.
   C) a RFLP marker.
   D) a plasmid used to transfer DNA into a living cell.
   E) a DNA probe used to identify a particular gene.

Answer: D

10) When using the shotgun approach to genome mapping, researchers carry out
   A) linkage mapping of each chromosome.
   B) extensive physical mapping of each chromosome, starting with large chromosomal fragments.
   C) DNA sequencing of small fragments and then ordering of the fragments to determine overall nucleotide sequence.
   D) A and B
   E) A, B, and C

Answer: C

# Chapter 21  The Genetic Basis of Development

1) A model organism for genetic studies of development should ideally meet certain criteria. Which of these is *not* one of the criteria?
   A) readily observable embryos
   B) short generation times
   C) relatively small genomes
   D) the presence of unique features not observed in other organisms
   E) availability of detailed knowledge concerning the organism's genes

   Answer: D
   *Topic: Overview*
   *Skill: Knowledge*

2) Which of the following are common model organisms in the study of developmental genetics?
   A) *Homo sapiens*
   B) *Drosophila melanogaster*
   C) *Arabidopsis thaliana*
   D) B and C only
   E) A, B, and C

   Answer: D
   *Topic: Overview*
   *Skill: Comprehension*

3) The nematode *Caenorhabditis elegans* is used as a model organism for genetic studies. One of the key advantages of using *C. elegans* for such studies is that
   A) it is hermaphroditic, making it easy to detect recessive mutations.
   B) it has a great variety of somatic cells.
   C) its genome is as large as ours.
   D) its development is extremely variable.
   E) morphogenesis and growth occur throughout its life.

   Answer: A
   *Topic: Overview*
   *Skill: Knowledge*

4) Which of the following is (are) involved in embryonic development?
   A) cell division
   B) cell differentiation
   C) morphogenesis
   D) A and B only
   E) A, B, and C

   Answer: E
   *Topic: Concept 21.1*
   *Skill: Knowledge*

5) One striking difference between development in plants and development in animals is the importance of cell _____ in animal embryos.
   A) division
   B) differentiation
   C) growth
   D) movement
   E) death

   Answer: D
   *Topic: Concept 21.1*
   *Skill: Knowledge*

6) One striking difference between development in plants and development in animals is that in plant development
   A) growth and morphogenesis continue throughout the life of the plant.
   B) cell differentiation never stops.
   C) once a structure develops, it cannot reverse its path.
   D) cell differentiation is rarely permanent.
   E) chemical signals play a much greater role than in animal development.

   Answer: A
   *Topic: Concept 21.1*
   *Skill: Knowledge*

7) What is the term for the physical processes that give rise to the shape of an organism?

A) morphogenesis

B) differentiation

C) totipotency

D) pluripotency

E) mitosis

Answer: A
*Topic: Concept 21.1*
*Skill: Knowledge*

8) The perpetually embryonic regions of plants responsible for continual growth and formation of new organs are called the

A) stamens.

B) nurse cells.

C) myoblasts.

D) apical meristems.

E) anchor cells.

Answer: D
*Topic: Concept 21.1*
*Skill: Knowledge*

9) "Genomic equivalence" refers to the

A) similarity in genomes among all individuals of the same species.

B) similarity in genomes between males and females of the same species.

C) fact that all the cells of an organism express the same genes, regardless of differences in their genomes.

D) fact that all the somatic cells of an organism have identical genomes, regardless of their state of differentiation.

E) organizational similarity of the genomes of all living organisms, reflecting their common ancestry.

Answer: D
*Topic: Concept 21.2*
*Skill: Comprehension*

10) The process of cellular differentiation is a direct result of

A) differential gene expression.

B) morphogenesis.

C) cell division.

D) apoptosis.

E) differences in cellular genomes.

Answer: A
*Topic: Concept 21.2*
*Skill: Knowledge*

11) The fact that plants can be cloned from somatic cells demonstrates that

A) differentiated cells retain all the genes of the zygote.

B) genes are lost during differentiation.

C) the differentiated state is normally very unstable.

D) differentiated cells contain masked mRNA.

E) differentiation does not occur in plants.

Answer: A
*Topic: Concept 21.2*
*Skill: Comprehension*

12) "Nuclear transplantation" refers to a(n)

A) cloning method involving the transfer of a nucleus from a differentiated cell into an enucleated egg cell or zygote.

B) form of gene therapy involving the transfer of nuclei from a healthy individual to the cells of a patient with a genetic disorder.

C) method of creating new species by injecting diploid nuclei into diploid zygotes in order to produce tetraploid embryos.

D) method of gene therapy in which nuclei are isolated from cells of an individual with a genetic disorder, transfected with recombinant DNA, and reintroduced into the individual's cells.

E) experimental method involving transferring nuclei from cells of an organism of one species into cells of an organism from another species, and examining the resulting phenotype.

Answer: A
*Topic: Concept 21.2*
*Skill: Knowledge*

13) In cloning, the ability of a transplanted nucleus to support development

A) is inversely related to the age of the donor.

B) depends on the DNA base sequence.

C) only occurs in plants.

D) depends on the size of the genome.

E) depends on the nucleus not changing.

Answer: A
*Topic: Concept 21.2*
*Skill: Knowledge*

14) A cell that remains entirely flexible in its developmental possibilities is said to be

A) differentiated.

B) determined.

C) totipotent.

D) genomically equivalent.

E) epigenetic.

Answer: C
*Topic: Concept 21.2*
*Skill: Knowledge*

15) Differentiation of cells is not easily reversible because it involves

A) changes in the nucleotide sequence of genes within the genome.

B) changes in chromatin structure that make certain regions of the genome inaccessible.

C) chemical modifications of histones and DNA methylation.

D) B and C only

E) A, B, and C

Answer: D
*Topic: Concept 21.2*
*Skill: Comprehension*

16) Why was the cloning of "Dolly" considered a major scientific breakthrough?

A) It showed that differentiated adult cells of mammals can dedifferentiate.

B) It showed that cells can be arrested in the cell cycle.

C) It was the first time a surrogate mother was used successfully.

D) It was evidence that DNA methylation regulates gene expression.

E) It proved that the pattern of gene expression is controlled at transcription.

Answer: A
*Topic: Concept 21.2*
*Skill: Knowledge*

17) Despite the extensive success that scientists have had in cloning animals, the process is still quite inefficient and cloned animals often show a variety of defects. This is likely because

A) the epigenetic features of the chromatin in differentiated donor nuclei are not completely erased in the cloning process.

B) cloned animals only have one parent, and therefore carry a high number of homozygous mutations in their genomes.

C) cloned animals have fewer genes than other animals, and often lack proteins required for normal health.

D) the surrogate mothers that give birth to cloned animals tend to neglect cloned animals in favor of their own biological offspring.

E) scientists usually damage the donor cell nuclei in the process of transplantation.

Answer: A
*Topic: Concept 21.2*
*Skill: Comprehension*

18) In animals, embryonic stem cells differ from adult stem cells in that

A) embryonic stem cells are totipotent, and adult stem cells are pluripotent.

B) embryonic stem cells are pluripotent, and adult stem cells are totipotent.

C) embryonic stem cells have more genes than adult stem cells.

D) embryonic stem cells have fewer genes than adult stem cells.

E) embryonic stem cells are localized to specific sites within the embryo, whereas adult stem cells are spread throughout the body.

Answer: A
*Topic: Concept 21.2*
*Skill: Knowledge*

19) Which of the following statements is *not* true about stem cells?

A) Stem cells can continually reproduce themselves.

B) Stem cells can differentiate into specialized cells.

C) Stem cells are found in bone marrow.

D) Stem cells are found in the adult human brain.

E) Stem cell DNA lacks introns.

Answer: E
*Topic: Concept 21.2*
*Skill: Knowledge*

20) What is considered to be the first evidence of differentiation in the cells of an embryo?

A) cell division

B) the occurrence of mRNAs for the production of tissue-specific proteins

C) determination

D) changes in the size and shape of the cell

E) changes resulting from induction

Answer: B
*Topic: Concept 21.2*
*Skill: Comprehension*

21) In most cases, differentiation is controlled at the level of

A) replication of the DNA.

B) nucleosome formation.

C) transcription.

D) translation.

E) post–translational activation of the proteins.

Answer: C
*Topic: Concept 21.2*
*Skill: Knowledge*

22) Which of the following serve as sources of developmental information?

A) cytoplasmic determinants such as mRNAs and proteins produced before fertilization

B) signal molecules produced by neighboring cells

C) ubiquitous enzymes such as DNA polymerase and DNA ligase

D) A and B only

E) A, B, and C

Answer: D
*Topic: Concept 21.2*
*Skill: Comprehension*

23) The MyoD protein

A) can promote muscle development in all cell types.

B) is a transcription factor that binds to and activates the transcription of muscle-related genes.

C) was used by researchers to convert differentiated liver cells into muscle cells.

D) B and C only

E) A, B and C

Answer: D
*Topic: Concept 21.2*
*Skill: Knowledge*

24) The gene for which protein would most likely be expressed as a result of MyoD activity?

A) myosin

B) crystallin

C) albumin

D) hemoglobin

E) DNA polymerase

Answer: A
*Topic: Concept 21.2*
*Skill: Comprehension*

25) The general process that leads to the differentiation of cells is called

A) determination.

B) specialization.

C) identification.

D) differentialization.

E) cellularization.

Answer: A
*Topic: Concept 21.2*
*Skill: Knowledge*

26) Which of the following statements is *false*?

A) Induction involves cells communicating with each other.

B) Induction usually involves transcriptional regulation.

C) Induction can play an essential role in the formation of complex organs.

D) Induction may involve stimulating cells to die as well as to divide and grow.

E) Induction signals are almost always small carbohydrates.

Answer: E
*Topic: Concept 21.2*
*Skill: Knowledge*

27) Which of the following is *least* related to the others?

A) cell division

B) morphogenesis

C) induction

D) differentiation

E) bacterial transformation

Answer: E
*Topic: Concept 21.2*
*Skill: Comprehension*

28) Your brother has just purchased a new plastic model airplane. He places all the parts on the table in approximately the positions in which they will be located when the model is complete. His actions are analogous to which process in development?

A) morphogenesis

B) determination

C) induction

D) differentiation

E) pattern formation

Answer: E
*Topic: Concept 21.3*
*Skill: Comprehension*

29) Of the approximately 13,700 genes in *Drosophila*, how many were found to be essential for embryonic development by Christiane Nüsslein-Volhard and Eric Wieschaus?

A) about 120 genes

B) about 240 genes

C) about 1,200 genes

D) about 6,000 genes

E) about 9,000 genes

Answer: C
*Topic: Concept 21.3*
*Skill: Knowledge*

30) Which of the following is established prior to fertilization in *Drosophila* eggs?

A) the anterior-posterior and dorsal-ventral axes

B) the position of the future segments

C) the position of the future wings, legs, and antennae

D) A and B only

E) A, B, and C

Answer: A
*Topic: Concept 21.3*
*Skill: Knowledge*

31) The product of the *bicoid* gene in *Drosophila* provides essential information about

A) the anterior-posterior axis.

B) the dorsal-ventral axis.

C) the left-right axis.

D) segmentation.

E) lethal genes.

Answer: A
*Topic: Concept 21.3*
*Skill: Knowledge*

32) If a *Drosophila* female has a homozygous mutation for a maternal effect gene,

A) she will not develop past the early embryonic stage.

B) all of her offspring will show the mutant phenotype, regardless of their genotype.

C) only her male offspring will show the mutant phenotype.

D) her offspring will show the mutant phenotype only if they are also homozygous for the mutation.

E) only her female offspring will show the mutant phenotype.

Answer: B
*Topic: Concept 21.3*
*Skill: Application*

*For the following questions, use the following responses:*

A. homeotic genes
B. segmentation genes
C. egg-polarity genes
D. morphogens
E. inducers

33) Mutations in these genes lead to transformations in the identity of entire body parts.

Answer: A
*Topic: Concept 21.3*
*Skill: Knowledge*

34) These genes are expressed by the mother, and their products are deposited into the developing egg.

Answer: C
*Topic: Concept 21.3*
*Skill: Knowledge*

35) These genes map out the basic subdivisions along the anterior-posterior axis of the *Drosophila* embryo.

Answer: B
*Topic: Concept 21.3*
*Skill: Knowledge*

36) These genes form gradients and help establish the axes and other features of an embryo.

Answer: D
*Topic: Concept 21.3*
*Skill: Knowledge*

37) Gap genes and pair-rule genes fall into this category.

Answer: B
*Topic: Concept 21.3*
*Skill: Knowledge*

38) The product of the *bicoid* gene in *Drosophila* could be considered a
   A) tissue-specific protein.
   B) cytoplasmic determinant.
   C) morphogen.
   D) B and C only
   E) A, B, and C

Answer: D
*Topic: Concept 21.3*
*Skill: Comprehension*

39) The *bicoid* gene product is normally localized to the anterior end of the embryo. If large amounts of the product were injected into the posterior end as well, which of the following would occur?
   A) The embryo would grow to an unusually large size.
   B) The embryo would grow extra wings and legs.
   C) The embryo would probably show no anterior development and die.
   D) Anterior structures would form in both sides of the embryo.
   E) The embryo would develop normally.

Answer: D
*Topic: Concept 21.3*
*Skill: Application*

40) What do gap genes, pair-rule genes, segment polarity genes, and homeotic genes all have in common?
   A) Their products act as transcription factors.
   B) They have no counterparts in animals other than *Drosophila*.
   C) Their products are all synthesized prior to fertilization.
   D) They act independently of other positional information.
   E) They apparently can be activated and inactivated at any time of the fly's life.

Answer: A
*Topic: Concept 21.3*
*Skill: Comprehension*

41) Which of the following is *least* related to the others?

A) gap genes

B) cyclin genes

C) pair-rule genes

D) segment polarity genes

E) segmentation genes

Answer: B
*Topic: Concept 21.3*
*Skill: Comprehension*

42) The *fasciated* mutant in tomatoes

A) affects the identity of the floral organs produced by the plant.

B) affects the number of floral organs produced by the plant.

C) affects the overall height of the plant.

D) is an example of an "organ identity gene."

E) both A and D

Answer: B
*Topic: Concept 21.3*
*Skill: Knowledge*

43) One difference between development in plants and development in animals involves pattern formation because

A) pattern formation is continuous in plants and limited to early development in animals.

B) pattern formation is continuous in animals and limited to early development in plants.

C) pattern formation occurs in all parts of the plant, but is limited to specific locations in animals.

D) pattern formation is limited to specific locations in plants, but occurs in all parts of animals.

E) both A and C

Answer: A
*Topic: Concept 21.3*
*Skill: Knowledge*

44) Which of the following is *not* true concerning homeotic genes?

A) They are found in all animals, but nothing like them exists in plants.

B) A specific 180-nucleotide DNA sequence is common to all of the genes.

C) They were first identified in *Drosophila* by Edward Lewis.

D) The peptide gene product is a regulatory protein that controls transcription.

E) A mutation may cause alterations in the identity of body segments.

Answer: A
*Topic: Concept 21.3*
*Skill: Knowledge*

45) A small, impermeable membrane is placed between the anchor cell and the other vulva precursor cells in a larva of *C. elegans*. What would you expect the result to be?

A) The vulva would continue to develop normally.

B) The vulva would not develop at all.

C) The outer part of the vulva would develop, but the inner part would not.

D) The inner part of the vulva would develop, but the outer part would not.

E) Only the posterior part of the vulva would develop.

Answer: B
*Topic: Concept 21.3*
*Skill: Application*

46) Which of the following involves apoptosis?

A) Interactions between muscle cells and bone cells guide the growth of the muscle to a specific location so that it can attach to the bone.

B) Cells from the top of the mouth combine with cells from the base of the brain to form the pituitary.

C) A gonad begins as an undifferentiated organ that can form either an ovary or a testis. The formation depends on the hormonal signals that control the growth of some cells and the death of others.

D) If part of the developing spinal cord in a frog embryo is transplanted to under the skin of its back, it will stimulate development of an eye in that location.

E) The bones of the spinal column develop from blocks of undifferentiated tissue called somites.

Answer: C
*Topic: Concept 21.3*
*Skill: Comprehension*

47) In vertebrates, programmed cell death is essential for all of the following *except*

A) normal development of the nervous system.

B) normal operation of the immune system.

C) normal morphogenesis of human feet.

D) normal removal of damaged cells.

E) normal triggering of the signal transduction pathways.

Answer: E
*Topic: Concept 21.3*
*Skill: Knowledge*

48) The term *homeobox* refers to

A) a group of genes that determine polarity during development.

B) peptide sequences of 60 amino acids that turn other genes on or off.

C) zones of polarizing activity commonly present during limb formation.

D) a specific nucleotide sequence present within certain genes that regulate development.

E) glycoproteins that assist cells during morphogenetic movements.

Answer: D
*Topic: Concept 21.4*
*Skill: Knowledge*

49) Which of the following are true statements about homeobox-containing genes?

A) They are found in both plants and animals.

B) They are involved in the transcriptional regulation of other genes.

C) They encode proteins containing domains called "homeodomains."

D) Only B and C are true.

E) A, B, and C are true.

Answer: E
*Topic: Concept 21.4*
*Skill: Knowledge*

# Media Activity Questions

1) What role does a transcription factor play in a signal transduction pathway?

   A) By binding to a plasma membrane receptor it initiates a cascade.

   B) It relays a signal from the cytoplasm to the plasma membrane.

   C) It activates relay proteins.

   D) By binding to DNA it triggers the transcription of a specific gene.

   E) It is a plasma membrane protein that binds signal molecules.

Answer: D
*Topic: Activity: Signal Transduction Pathway*

2) The *bicoid* gene product is directly responsible for _____ in the developing *Drosophila* embryo.

   A) the establishment of the right–left axis

   B) vulval development

   C) flower development

   D) the establishment of the anterior–posterior axis

   E) apoptosis

Answer: D
*Topic: Activity: Bicoid gene in Drosophila Developmer.*

3) The region of a *Drosophila* embryo with the highest concentration of bicoid protein will develop into the

   A) head.

   B) ovaries.

   C) vulva.

   D) homeobox.

   E) abdomen.

Answer: A
*Topic: Activity: Bicoid gene in Drosophila Developmer.*

4) The *bicoid* gene is a type of _____ gene.

   A) segmentation

   B) pair-rule

   C) segment polarity

   D) egg-polarity

   E) gap

Answer: D
*Topic: Activity: Bicoid gene in Drosophila Developmer.*

5) How does bicoid protein get into a fertilized egg?

   A) exocytosis

   B) phagocytosis

   C) diffusion

   D) pinocytosis

   E) receptor-mediated endocytosis

Answer: C
*Topic: Activity: Bicoid gene in Drosophila Developmer.*

# Self-Quiz Questions

1) Which of the following processes is most directly responsible for the lack of webbing between the fingers of most humans?

A) pattern formation

B) transcriptional regulation

C) apoptosis

D) cell division

E) induction

Answer: C

2) The criteria for a good model organism for studying development would probably include all of the following *except*

A) observable embryonic development.

B) short generation time.

C) a relatively small genome.

D) preexisting knowledge of the organism's life history.

E) a rare pattern of development when compared to most organisms.

Answer: E

3) Totipotency is demonstrated when

A) mutations in homeotic genes result in the development of misplaced appendages.

B) a cell isolated from a plant leaf grows into a normal adult plant.

C) an embryonic cell divides and differentiates.

D) replacing the nucleus of an unfertilized egg with that of an intestinal cell converts the egg to an intestinal cell.

E) segment-specific organs develop along the anterior–posterior axis of a *Drosophila* embryo.

Answer: B

4) Cell differentiation always involves

A) the production of tissue–specific proteins, such as muscle actin.

B) the movement of cells.

C) the transcription of the *myoD* gene.

D) the selective loss of certain genes from the genome.

E) the cell's sensitivity to environmental cues such as light or heat.

Answer: A

5) The development of *Drosophila* is somewhat unusual in that

A) the early mitotic divisions proceed without cytokinesis.

B) metamorphosis occurs during the larval stage rather than the pupal stage, as with other insects.

C) homeotic genes are mutated.

D) cell migration within the embryo does not occur.

E) the initial cell divisions have lengthy $G_1$ phases.

Answer: A

6) In *Drosophila*, which genes initiate a cascade of gene activation that includes all other genes in the list?

A) homeotic genes

B) gap genes

C) pair-rule genes

D) egg-polarity genes

E) segment polarity genes

Answer: D

7) Absence of *bicoid* mRNA from a *Drosophila* egg leads to the absence of anterior larval body parts and mirror-image duplication of posterior parts. This is evidence that the product of the *bicoid* gene

A) is transcribed in the early embryo.

B) normally leads to formation of tail structures.

C) normally leads to formation of head structures.

D) is a protein present in all head structures.

E) leads to programmed cell death.

Answer: C

8) Homeotic genes

A) encode transcription factors that control the expression of genes responsible for specific anatomical structures.

B) are found only in *Drosophila* and other arthropods.

C) specify the anterior–posterior axis for each fruit fly segment.

D) create the basic subdivisions of the anterior–posterior axis of the fly embryo.

E) are responsible for the programmed cell death occurring during morphogenesis.

Answer: A

9) The embryonic development of *C. elegans* illustrates all of the following developmental concepts *except*:

A) An inducer's effect can depend on its concentration gradient.

B) The response of an induced cell involves the establishment of a unique pattern of gene activity.

C) The signal transduction pathways activated by inducers are unique to embryonic cells.

D) Sequential inductions direct the formation of complex structures in the developing embryo.

E) Inducers bring about their effects via the activation or inactivation of genes that code for transcriptional regulators.

Answer: C

10) Although quite different in structure, plants and animals share some basic similarities in their development, such as

A) the importance of cell and tissue movements.

B) the importance of selective cell enlargement.

C) the importance of homeobox-containing homeotic genes.

D) the retention of meristematic tissues in the adult.

E) master regulatory genes that encode DNA-binding proteins.

Answer: E

# Chapter 22  Descent with Modification: A Darwinian View of Life

1) On which of the following did Linnaeus base his classification system?

   A) morphology and anatomy

   B) evolutionary history

   C) the fossil record

   D) A and B only

   E) A, B, and C

   Answer: A
   *Topic: Concept 22.1*
   *Skill: Knowledge*

2) Catastrophism, meaning the regular occurrence of geological or meteorological disturbances (catastrophes), was Cuvier's attempt to explain the existence of

   A) evolution.

   B) the fossil record.

   C) uniformitarianism.

   D) the origin of new species.

   E) natural selection.

   Answer: B
   *Topic: Concept 22.1*
   *Skill: Knowledge*

3) Which of the following events, as described here, is most in agreement with the idea of catastrophism?

   A) the gradual uplift of the Himalayas by the collision of the Australian crustal plate with the Eurasian crustal plate

   B) the formation of the Grand Canyon by the Colorado River over millions of years

   C) the deposition of sediments many kilometers thick on the floors of seas and oceans

   D) the demise of the dinosaurs, and various other groups, by the impact of a large extraterrestrial body with Earth

   E) the development of the Galápagos Islands from underwater seamounts over millions of years

   Answer: D
   *Topic: Concept 22.1*
   *Skill: Comprehension*

4) What was the prevailing notion prior to the time of Lyell and Darwin?

   A) Earth is 6,000 years old, and populations are unchanging.

   B) Earth is 6,000 years old, and populations gradually change.

   C) Earth is millions of years old, and populations rapidly change.

   D) Earth is millions of years old, and populations are unchanging.

   E) Earth is millions of years old, and populations gradually change.

   Answer: A
   *Topic: Concept 22.1*
   *Skill: Knowledge*

5) During a study session about evolution, one of your fellow students remarks, "The giraffe stretched its neck while reaching for higher leaves; its offspring inherited longer necks as a result." Which statement would you use to correct this student's misconception?

A) Characteristics acquired during an organism's life are generally not passed on through genes.

B) Spontaneous mutations can result in the appearance of new traits.

C) Only favorable adaptations have survival value.

D) Disuse of an organ may lead to its eventual disappearance.

E) Overproduction of offspring leads to a struggle for survival.

Answer: A
*Topic: Concept 22.1*
*Skill: Comprehension*

6) "Improving the intelligence of an adult through education will result in that adult's descendants being born with a greater native intelligence." This statement is an example of

A) Darwinism.

B) Lamarckism.

C) uniformitarianism.

D) *scala naturae.*

E) Malthusianism.

Answer: B
*Topic: Concept 22.1*
*Skill: Comprehension*

7) In the mid–1900s, the Soviet geneticist Lysenko exposed winter wheat plants to ever–colder temperatures, collected their seeds, and then exposed the seedlings to ever–colder temperatures. He repeated his attempts over the course of decades in an attempt to evolve cold–tolerant winter wheat. Lysenko's attempts in this regard were most in agreement with the ideas of

A) Cuvier.

B) Hutton.

C) Lamarck.

D) Darwin.

E) Plato.

Answer: C
*Topic: Concept 22.1*
*Skill: Application*

8) Darwin's mechanism of natural selection required long time spans in order to modify species. From whom did Darwin get the concept of Earth's ancient age?

A) Georges Cuvier

B) Charles Lyell

C) Alfred Wallace

D) Thomas Malthus

E) John Henslow

Answer: B
*Topic: Concept 22.2*
*Skill: Knowledge*

9) Darwin had initially expected the living plants of temperate South America to resemble those of temperate Europe, but he was surprised to find that they more closely resembled the plants of *tropical* South America. The biological explanation for this observation is most properly associated with the field of

A) meteorology.

B) embryology.

C) vertebrate anatomy.

D) bioengineering.

E) biogeography.

Answer: E
*Topic: Concept 22.2*
*Skill: Comprehension*

10) Who was the naturalist who synthesized a concept of natural selection independently of Darwin?

A) Charles Lyell

B) Gregor Mendel

C) Alfred Wallace

D) John Henslow

E) Thomas Malthus

Answer: C
*Topic: Concept 22.2*
*Skill: Knowledge*

11) Charles Darwin was the first to propose

A) that evolution occurs.

B) a mechanism for how evolution occurs.

C) that the Earth is older than 6,000 years.

D) a mechanism for evolution that was supported by evidence.

E) a way to use artificial selection as a means of domesticating plants and animals.

Answer: D
*Topic: Concept 22.2*
*Skill: Knowledge*

12) In evolutionary terms, the more closely related two different organisms are, the

A) more similar their habitats are.

B) less similar their DNA sequences are.

C) more recently they shared a common ancestor.

D) less likely they are to be related to fossil forms.

E) more similar they are in size.

Answer: C
*Topic: Concepts 22.1–22.2*
*Skill: Comprehension*

13) Both Darwin's and Lamarck's ideas regarding evolution suggest which of the following?

A) All species were fixed at the time of creation.

B) Acquired physical characteristics can be inherited.

C) The giraffe's long neck is the result of artificial selection.

D) The main mechanism of evolution is natural selection.

E) The interaction of organisms with their environment is important in the evolutionary process.

Answer: E
*Topic: Concepts 22.1–22.2*
*Skill: Knowledge*

14) Natural selection is based on all of the following *except*

    A) variation exists within populations.

    B) the fittest individuals tend to leave the most offspring.

    C) there is differential reproductive success within populations.

    D) populations tend to produce more individuals than the environment can support.

    E) individuals must adapt to their environment.

Answer: E
*Topic: Concept 22.2*
*Skill: Knowledge*

15) Which of the following represents an idea Darwin took from the writings of Thomas Malthus?

    A) All species are fixed in the form in which they are created.

    B) Populations tend to increase at a faster rate than their food supply.

    C) Earth changed over the years through a series of catastrophic upheavals.

    D) The environment is responsible for natural selection.

    E) Earth is more than 10,000 years old.

Answer: B
*Topic: Concept 22.2*
*Skill: Knowledge*

16) Which statement about natural selection is *most* correct?

    A) Adaptations beneficial in one habitat should generally be beneficial in all other habitats as well.

    B) Different species that together occupy the same habitat will adapt to that habitat by undergoing the same genetic changes.

    C) Adaptations beneficial at one time should generally be beneficial during all other times as well.

    D) Well-adapted individuals leave more offspring, and thus contribute more to the gene pool, than poorly adapted individuals.

    E) Natural selection is the sole means by which populations can evolve.

Answer: D
*Topic: Concept 22.2*
*Skill: Comprehension*

17) Given a population that contains genetic variation, what is the correct sequence of the following events, under the influence of natural selection?
    1.  Differential reproduction occurs.
    2.  A new selective pressure arises.
    3.  Allele frequencies within the population change.
    4.  Poorly adapted individuals have decreased survivorship.

    A) 2, 4, 1, 3

    B) 4, 2, 1, 3

    C) 4, 1, 2, 3

    D) 4, 2, 3, 1

    E) 2, 4, 3, 1

Answer: A
*Topic: Concept 22.2*
*Skill: Comprehension*

18) To observe natural selection's effects on a population, what must be true?

    A) One must observe more than one generation of the population.

    B) The population must contain genetic variation.

    C) Members of the population must increase or decrease the use of some portion of their anatomy.

    D) A and C only

    E) A and B only

Answer: E
*Topic: Concept 22.2*
*Skill: Comprehension*

19) If the HMS *Beagle* had completely bypassed the Galápagos Islands, Darwin would have had a much poorer understanding of

    A) the age of Earth.

    B) the ability of populations to undergo modification as they adapt to a particular environment.

    C) the tendency of organisms to produce a larger number of offspring than the environment can support.

    D) the limited resources available to support population growth in most natural environments.

    E) how fossils of marine organisms could be found high in the Andes.

Answer: B
*Topic: Concept 22.2*
*Skill: Comprehension*

20) During drought years on the Galápagos, small, easily eaten seeds become rare leaving only large, hard-cased seeds that only birds with large beaks can eat. If a drought persists for several years, then what should one expect to result from natural selection?

    A) Small birds gaining larger beaks by exercising their mouth parts.

    B) Small birds mutating their beak genes with the result that later-generation offspring have larger beaks.

    C) Small birds anticipating the long drought and eating more to gain weight and, consequently, growing larger beaks.

    D) More small-beaked birds dying than the larger-beaked birds. The offspring produced in subsequent generations have a higher percentage of birds with large beaks.

    E) Larger birds eating less so smaller birds can survive.

Answer: D
*Topic: Concept 22.2*
*Skill: Application*

21) Which of the following statements is *not* an inference of natural selection?

    A) Subsequent generations of a population should have greater proportions of individuals that possess favorable traits.

    B) An individual organism undergoes evolution over the course of its lifetime.

    C) Often only a fraction of offspring survive, because there is a struggle for limited resources.

    D) Individuals whose inherited characteristics best fit them to the environment should leave more offspring.

    E) Unequal reproductive success among its members leads a population to adapt over time.

Answer: B
*Topic: Concept 22.2*
*Skill: Knowledge*

22) Which of the following *must* exist in a population before natural selection can act upon that population?

    A) genetic variation among individuals

    B) variation among individuals caused by environmental factors

    C) sexual reproduction

    D) A and C only

    E) A, B, and C

Answer: D
*Topic: Concept 22.2*
*Skill: Comprehension*

23) In a hypothetical environment, fishes called pike–cichlids are visual predators of algae–eating fish, i.e., they locate their prey by sight. If a population of algae eaters experiences predation pressure from pike–cichlids, which of the following would *least* likely be observed in the algae–eater population over the course of many generations?

    A) Coloration of the algae eaters may become drab.

    B) The algae eaters may become nocturnal (active only at night).

    C) Female algae eaters may become larger, bearing broods composed of more, and larger, young.

    D) The algae eaters may become sexually mature at smaller overall body sizes.

    E) The algae eaters may become faster swimmers.

Answer: C
*Topic: Concept 22.3*
*Skill: Application*

24) A biologist studied a population of squirrels for 15 years. During that time, the population was never fewer than 30 squirrels and never more than 45. Her data showed that over half of the squirrels born did not survive to reproduce, because of competition for food and predation. In a single generation, 90% of the squirrels that were born lived to reproduce, and the population increased to 80. What inferences might you make about this population?

A) The amount of available food may have increased.

B) The number of predators may have decreased.

C) The squirrels of subsequent generations should show greater levels of variation than previous generations because squirrels that would not have survived in the past will now survive.

D) A and B only

E) A, B, and C

Answer: E
*Topic: Concept 22.3*
*Skill: Application*

25) Which of the following is the *best* example of humans undergoing evolution, understood as "descent with modification"?

A) reduction in the amount and coarseness of body hair over millennia

B) reduction in number of hairs on the head of a balding person

C) increased pigment production by the skin of a person who is exposed to increased UV radiation levels

D) increase in weight over an individual's lifetime

E) widening of the pupils of the eyes when one encounters dimly lit conditions

Answer: A
*Topic: Concept 22.3*
*Skill: Comprehension*

26) Which statement best describes how the evolution of pesticide resistance occurs in a population of insects?

A) Individual members of the population slowly adapt to the presence of the chemical by striving to meet the new challenge.

B) All insects exposed to the insecticide begin to use a formerly silent gene to make a new enzyme that breaks down the insecticide molecules.

C) Insects observe the behavior of other insects that survive pesticide application, and adjust their own behaviors to copy those of the survivors.

D) A number of genetically resistant pesticide survivors reproduce. The next generation of insects contains more genes from the survivors than it does from susceptible individuals.

E) B and D only

Answer: D
*Topic: Concept 22.3*
*Skill: Comprehension*

27) DDT was once considered a "silver bullet" that would permanently eradicate insect pests. Today, instead, DDT is largely useless against many insects. What would need to be true for pest eradication efforts to have been successful in the long run?

   A) Larger doses of DDT should have been applied.

   B) All habitats should have received applications of DDT at about the same time.

   C) The frequency of DDT application should have been higher.

   D) All individual insects should have possessed genomes that made them susceptible to DDT.

   E) DDT application should have been continual.

Answer: D
*Topic: Concept 22.3*
*Skill: Application*

28) Some members of a photosynthetic plant species are genetically resistant to an herbicide, while other members of the same species are not resistant to the herbicide. Maintaining resistance against the herbicide is metabolically expensive for the plants. Which combination of events should cause the most effective replacement of the non-herbicide-resistant strain of plants by the resistant strain?
1.   an abundance of sunny weather
2.   an abundance of cloudy weather
3.   the presence of the herbicide in the environment
4.   the absence of the herbicide from the environment
5.   the maintenance of the proper conditions for one generation
6.   the maintenance of the proper conditions for many generations

   A) 2, 4, and 5

   B) 2, 3, and 5

   C) 1, 4, and 6

   D) 1, 3, and 6

   E) 2, 3, and 6

Answer: D
*Topic: Concept 22.3*
*Skill: Application*

*The graph below depicts four possible patterns for the abundance of 3TC–resistant HIV within an infected human over time.*

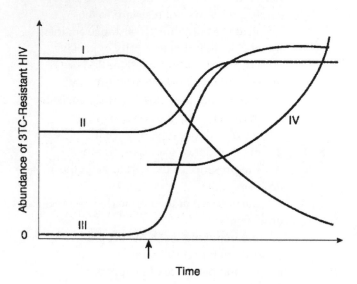

**Figure 22.1**

29) If 3TC resistance is costly for HIV, then which plot (I–IV) best represents the response of a strain of 3TC–resistant HIV over time, if 3TC administration begins at the time indicated by the arrow?

    A) I      B) II      C) III      D) IV

Answer: C
*Topic: Concept 22.3*
*Skill: Application*

30) Of the following anatomical structures, which is homologous to the wing of a bat?

    A) dorsal fin of a shark

    B) tail of a kangaroo

    C) wing of a butterfly

    D) tail fin of a fish

    E) arm of a human

Answer: E
*Topic: Concept 22.3*
*Skill: Knowledge*

31) If two modern organisms are *distantly* related in an evolutionary sense, then one should expect that

    A) they live in very different habitats.

    B) they should share fewer homologous structures than two more closely related organisms.

    C) their chromosomes should be very similar.

    D) they shared a common ancestor relatively recently.

    E) they should be members of the same genus.

Answer: B
*Topic: Concept 22.3*
*Skill: Application*

32) Structures as different as human arms, bat wings, and dolphin flippers contain many of the same bones, these bones having developed from the same embryonic tissues. How do biologists interpret these similarities?

    A) by identifying the bones as being homologous

    B) by the principle of convergent evolution

    C) by proposing that humans, bats, and dolphins share a common ancestor

    D) A and C only

    E) A, B, and C

Answer: D
*Topic: Concept 22.3*
*Skill: Comprehension*

33) Human intestines are held in place by membranes called mesenteries. In bipedal humans, it would be logical for these mesenteries to be attached to the rib cage. Instead, they are attached to the backbone, as they are in quadrupedal mammals. Because of this arrangement, human mesenteries have a tendency to tear more often than mesenteries in other mammals, as frequently observed among truck drivers and jackhammer operators. The same evolutionary modification that causes increased susceptibility to torn mesenteries is responsible for

A) tonsillitis.

B) appendicitis.

C) back and knee problems.

D) susceptibility to HIV infection.

E) vision problems associated with advanced age.

Answer: C
*Topic: Concept 22.3*
*Skill: Application*

34) As adults, certain species of whales possess baleen instead of teeth. Baleen is used to filter the whales' diet of planktonic animals from seawater. As embryos, baleen whales possess teeth, which are later replaced by baleen. The teeth of embryonic baleen whales are evidence that

A) all whales are the descendants of terrestrial mammals.

B) baleen whale embryos pass through a stage when they resemble adult toothed whales.

C) baleen whales are descendants of toothed whales.

D) ontogeny recapitulates phylogeny.

E) among ancient whales, baleen evolved before teeth.

Answer: C
*Topic: Concept 22.3*
*Skill: Application*

35) Over evolutionary time, many cave-dwelling organisms have lost their eyes. Tapeworms have lost their digestive systems. Whales have lost their hind limbs. How can natural selection account for these losses?

A) Natural selection cannot account for losses, only for innovations.

B) It can account for these losses by the principle of use and disuse.

C) Under particular circumstances that persisted for long periods, each of these structures presented greater costs than benefits.

D) These organisms had the misfortune to experience harmful mutations, which caused the loss of these structures.

E) B and D only

Answer: C
*Topic: Concept 22.3*
*Skill: Comprehension*

36) Which of the following pieces of evidence most strongly supports the common origin of all life on Earth?

A) All organisms require energy.

B) All organisms use essentially the same genetic code.

C) All organisms reproduce.

D) All organisms show heritable variation.

E) All organisms have undergone evolution.

Answer: B
*Topic: Concept 22.3*
*Skill: Comprehension*

37) What would be the best technique for determining the evolutionary relationships among several closely related species, each of which still contains living members?

A) examining the fossil record

B) comparison of homologous structures

C) comparative embryology

D) comparative anatomy

E) DNA or RNA analysis

Answer: E
*Topic: Concept 22.3*
*Skill: Application*

38) Logically, which of these should cast the *most* doubt on the relationships depicted by an evolutionary tree?

A) None of the organisms depicted by the tree provided DNA samples for analysis.

B) Some of the organisms depicted by the tree had lived in different habitats.

C) The skeletal remains of the organisms depicted by the tree were incomplete (i.e., some bones were missing).

D) Transitional fossils had not been found.

E) DNA sequence evidence fully disagreed with morphological evidence.

Answer: E
*Topic: Concept 22.3*
*Skill: Application*

39) Which of the following statements gives the *least* support to the claim that the human appendix is a completely vestigial organ?

A) The appendix can be surgically removed with no apparent ill effects.

B) The appendix might have been larger in fossil hominids.

C) The appendix can have a substantial amount of defensive lymphatic tissue in its walls.

D) Individuals with a larger-than-average appendix leave fewer offspring than those with a below-average-sized appendix.

E) In a million years, the human species might completely lack an appendix.

Answer: C
*Topic: Concept 22.3*
*Skill: Comprehension*

40) Members of two different species possess a similar-looking structure that they use in a similar fashion to perform the same function. Which information would shed the *most* light on whether these structures are homologous or whether they are, instead, the result of convergent evolution?

A) The two species live at great distance from each other.

B) The two species share many proteins in common, and the nucleotide sequences that code for these proteins are almost identical.

C) The sizes of the structures in adult members of both species are similar in size.

D) Both species are well adapted to their particular environments.

E) Both species reproduce sexually.

Answer: B
*Topic: Concept 22.3*
*Skill: Application*

41) Ichthyosaurs were aquatic dinosaurs. Fossils show us that they had dorsal fins and tails just as fish do, even though their closest relatives were terrestrial reptiles that had neither dorsal fins nor aquatic tails. The dorsal fins and tails of ichthyosaurs and fish are

A) homologous.

B) examples of convergent evolution.

C) adaptations to a common environment.

D) A and C only

E) B and C only

Answer: E
*Topic: Concept 22.3*
*Skill: Comprehension*

42) It has been observed that organisms on islands are different from, but closely related to, similar forms found on the nearest continent. This is taken as evidence that

A) island forms and mainland forms descended from common ancestors.

B) common environments are inhabited by the same organisms.

C) the islands were originally part of the continent.

D) the island forms and mainland forms are converging.

E) island forms and mainland forms have identical gene pools.

Answer: A
*Topic: Concept 22.3*
*Skill: Comprehension*

43) Monkeys of South and Central America have prehensile tails, meaning that their tails can be used to grasp objects. The tails of African and Asian monkeys are not prehensile. Which discipline is most likely to provide an explanation for how this difference in tails came about?

A) aerodynamics

B) biogeography

C) physiology

D) biochemistry

E) botany

Answer: B
*Topic: Concept 22.3*
*Skill: Application*

44) The theory of evolution is most accurately described as

A) an educated guess about how species originate.

B) one possible explanation, among several scientific alternatives, about how species have come into existence.

C) an opinion that some scientists hold about how living things change over time.

D) an overarching explanation, supported by much evidence, for how populations change over time.

E) an idea about how acquired characteristics are passed on to subsequent generations.

Answer: D
*Topic: Concept 22.3*
*Skill: Knowledge*

# Media Activity Questions

1) The Galápagos Islands are cooled off by the

   A) Equatorial Countercurrent.

   B) Humboldt Current.

   C) Monsoon Drift.

   D) Gulf Stream.

   E) Kurshio Current.

   Answer: B
   *Topic: Web/CD Activity: Darwin and the Galapagos*

2) Which of these is a consequence of uniformitarianism?

   A) Earth is round, not flat.

   B) Populations evolve.

   C) Populations reproduce faster than their food supply.

   D) A Creator made Earth.

   E) Earth is old.

   Answer: E
   *Topic: Web/CD Activity: The Voyage of the Beagle*

3) At the fossil site Punta Alta, Darwin found evidence

   A) that the pampas could support large mammals.

   B) extinction does not happen.

   C) of extinction.

   D) that Brazilian flatworms were a type of slug.

   E) of divine creation.

   Answer: C
   *Topic: Web/CD Activity: The Voyage of the Beagle*

4) His experiences with Fuegians and slavery convinced Darwin that differences among all peoples are primarily _____ differences.

   A) cultural

   B) genetic

   C) cultural and genetic

   D) height

   E) height and genetic

   Answer: A
   *Topic: Web/CD Activity: The Voyage of the Beagle*

5) Which explains variations in homologous structures?

   A) Variations in homologous structures occur because the structures develop from different parts of an embryo.

   B) The traits evolved independently in different ancestors.

   C) The theory of convergent evolution.

   D) Variations in the development of the structures occur as the embryos grow.

   E) All of the above could be true.

   Answer: D
   *Topic: Web/CD Activity: Reconstructing Forelimbs*

# Self-Quiz Questions

1) Which of the following reflect Hutton and Lyell's ideas of gradualism that were incorporated into Darwin's theory of evolution?

A) There is a struggle in populations for survival and reproduction.

B) Natural selection acts on heritable variation.

C) Small changes accumulated over vast spans of time can produce dramatic results.

D) Characteristics acquired gradually over an organism's lifetime can lead to changes in the characteristics of the next generation.

E) Homologous structures are found in organisms with a common ancestor.

Answer: C

2) Which of the following is *not* an observation or inference on which natural selection is based?

A) There is heritable variation among individuals.

B) Poorly adapted individuals never produce offspring.

C) There is a struggle for limited resources, and only a fraction of offspring survive.

D) Individuals whose characteristics are best suited to the environment generally leave more offspring than those that are less well suited.

E) Organisms interact with their environments.

Answer: B

3) Analysis of forelimb anatomy of humans, bats, and whales shows that humans and bats have fairly similar skeletal structures, while whales have diverged considerably in the shapes and proportions of their bones. However, analysis of several genes in these species suggests that all three diverged from a common ancestor at about the same time. Which of the following is the best explanation for these data?

A) Humans and bats evolved by natural selection and whales evolved by Lamarckian mechanisms.

B) Evolution of human and bat forelimbs was adaptive, but not for whales.

C) Natural selection in an aquatic environment resulted in significant changes to whale forelimb anatomy.

D) Genes mutate more rapidly in whales than in humans or bats.

E) Whales are not properly defined as mammals.

Answer: C

4) Which of the following observations helped Darwin shape his concept of descent with modification?

A) Species diversity declines as distance from the equator increases.

B) Fewer species are found living on islands than on the nearest continents.

C) Birds can be found on islands that are farther apart from the mainland than the birds' maximum nonstop flight distance.

D) South American temperate plants are more similar to the tropical plants of South America than to the temperate plants of Europe.

E) Earthquakes reshape life by causing mass extinctions.

Answer: D

5) Darwin synthesized information from several sources in developing his theory of evolution by natural selection. Which of the following did *not* influence his thinking?

A) Linnaeus' hierarchical classification of species

B) Lyell's *Principles of Geology*

C) observations of molecular homologies

D) examples of major changes in domesticated species produced by artificial selection

E) the distribution of species that he observed on the Galápagos Islands and during his journey around South America

Answer: C

6) In science, the term *theory* generally applies to an idea that

A) is a speculation lacking supportive observations or experiments.

B) attempts to explain many related phenomena.

C) is synonymous with what biologists mean by a hypothesis.

D) is considered a law of nature.

E) all of the above.

Answer: B

7) Within a few weeks of treatment with the drug 3TC, a patient's HIV population consists entirely of 3TC-resistant viruses. How can this result best be explained?

A) HIV has the ability to change its surface proteins and resist vaccines.

B) The patient must have become reinfected with 3TC-resistant viruses.

C) HIV began making drug-resistant versions of reverse transcriptase in response to the drug.

D) A few drug-resistant viruses were present at the start of treatment, and natural selection increased their frequency.

E) The drug caused the HIV RNA to change.

Answer: D

8) The smallest biological unit that can evolve over time is

A) a cell.

B) an individual organism.

C) a population.

D) a species.

E) an ecosystem.

Answer: C

9) Which of the following ideas is common to both Darwin's and Lamarck's theories of evolution?

A) Adaptation results from differential reproductive success.

B) Evolution drives organisms to greater and greater complexity.

C) Evolutionary adaptation results from interactions between organisms and their environments.

D) Adaptation results from the use and disuse of anatomical structures.

E) The fossil record supports the view that species are fixed.

Answer: C

10) Which of the following pairs of structures is *least* likely to represent homology?

A) the wings of a bat and the forelimbs of a human

B) the hemoglobin of a baboon and that of a gorilla

C) the mitochondria of a plant and those of an animal

D) the wings of a bird and those of an insect

E) the brain of a cat and that of a dog

Answer: D

# Chapter 23  The Evolution of Populations

1) What is the most important missing evidence or observation in Darwin's theory of 1859?
   A) the source of genetic variation
   B) evidence of the overproduction of offspring
   C) evidence that some organisms became extinct
   D) observation that variation is common in populations
   E) observation that competition exists in populations

   Answer: A
   *Topic: Concept 23.1*
   *Skill: Knowledge*

2) Which hypothesis of inheritance, common at Darwin's time, caused many to question the ability of natural selection to bring about adaptation in populations?
   A) particulate hypothesis
   B) blending hypothesis
   C) chromosomal hypothesis
   D) nucleic acid hypothesis
   E) proofreading hypothesis

   Answer: B
   *Topic: Concept 23.1*
   *Skill: Knowledge*

3) Which definition of evolution would have been most foreign to Charles Darwin during his lifetime?
   A) change in gene frequency in gene pools
   B) descent with modification
   C) the gradual change of a population's heritable traits over generations
   D) populations becoming better adapted to their environments over the course of generations
   E) the appearance of new varieties and new species with the passage of time

   Answer: A
   *Topic: Concept 23.1*
   *Skill: Knowledge*

4) Even in Darwin's time, the blending hypothesis was incompatible with observed facts.  If the blending hypothesis were true, then what should one expect to observe over the course of generations?
   A) Phenotypic polymorphisms should increase.
   B) Genetic variation should increase.
   C) Members of a breeding population should become more uniform in phenotype.
   D) Neutral variation should decrease.
   E) Genetic polymorphisms should increase.

   Answer: C
   *Topic: Concepts 23.1, 23.4*
   *Skill: Comprehension*

5) What is true of the modern evolutionary synthesis?

A) It is about to be declared a scientific law.

B) It is nearing final completion.

C) It has not been able to improve upon Darwin's original ideas about evolution.

D) It remains unable to account for Mendel's findings concerning the genetics of pea plants.

E) It exemplifies the tentative nature of scientific knowledge.

Answer: E
*Topic: Concept 23.1*
*Skill: Knowledge*

*Use the following information to answer the questions below.*

A large population of laboratory animals has been allowed to breed randomly for a number of generations. After several generations, 36% of the animals display a recessive trait (*aa*), the same percentage as at the beginning of the breeding program. The rest of the animals show the dominant phenotype, with heterozygotes indistinguishable from the homozygous dominants.

6) What is the most reasonable conclusion that can be drawn from the fact that the frequency of the recessive trait (*aa*) has *not* changed over time?

A) The population is undergoing genetic drift.

B) The two phenotypes are about equally adaptive under laboratory conditions.

C) The genotype *AA* is lethal.

D) There has been a high rate of mutation of allele *A* to allele *a*.

E) There has been sexual selection favoring allele *a*.

Answer: B
*Topic: Concept 23.1*
*Skill: Comprehension*

7) What is the estimated frequency of allele *a* in the gene pool?

A) 0.18

B) 0.40

C) 0.60

D) 0.70

E) 0.80

Answer: C
*Topic: Concept 23.1*
*Skill: Application*

8) What proportion of the population is probably heterozygous (*Aa*) for this trait?

A) 0.18

B) 0.36

C) 0.48

D) 0.60

E) 0.72

Answer: C
*Topic: Concept 23.1*
*Skill: Application*

9) All of the following are criteria for maintaining Hardy–Weinberg equilibrium involving two alleles *except*

A) the frequency of all genotypes must be equal.

B) there should be no natural selection.

C) matings must be random.

D) populations must be large.

E) gene flow from other populations must be zero.

Answer: A
*Topic: Concept 23.1*
*Skill: Comprehension*

10) In a Hardy–Weinberg population with two alleles, *A* and *a*, that are in equilibrium, the frequency of the allele *a* is 0.7. What is the percentage of the population that is homozygous for this allele?

 A) 3

 B) 9

 C) 30

 D) 42

 E) 49

Answer: E
*Topic: Concept 23.1*
*Skill: Application*

11) In a Hardy–Weinberg population with two alleles, *A* and *a*, that are in equilibrium, the frequency of allele *a* is 0.7. What is the percentage of the population that is heterozygous for this allele?

 A) 3

 B) 9

 C) 21

 D) 30

 E) 42

Answer: E
*Topic: Concept 23.1*
*Skill: Application*

12) In a Hardy–Weinberg population with two alleles, *A* and *a*, that are in equilibrium, the frequency of allele *a* is 0.2. What is the frequency of individuals with *Aa* genotype?

 A) 0.20

 B) 0.32

 C) 0.42

 D) 0.80

 E) Genotype frequency cannot be determined from the information provided.

Answer: B
*Topic: Concept 23.1*
*Skill: Application*

13) In a population with two alleles, *A* and *a*, the frequency of *a* is 0.50. What would be the frequency of heterozygotes if the population is in Hardy–Weinberg equilibrium?

 A) 1.00

 B) 0.75

 C) 0.50

 D) 0.25

 E) 0.10

Answer: C
*Topic: Concept 23.1*
*Skill: Application*

14) Most copies of harmful recessive alleles in a sexual species are carried by individuals that are

 A) haploid.

 B) polymorphic.

 C) homozygous for the allele.

 D) heterozygous for the allele.

 E) B and C

Answer: D
*Topic: Concept 23.1*
*Skill: Knowledge*

15) In a population with two alleles, *A* and *a*, the frequency of *A* is 0.2. Organisms that are homozygous for *A* die before reaching sexual maturity. In five generations, what would be the frequency of individuals with *aa* genotypes?

A) less than 0.04

B) 0.04

C) 0.32

D) 0.64

E) greater than 0.64

Answer: E
*Topic: Concept 23.1*
*Skill: Application*

16) You sample a population of butterflies and find that 42% are heterozygous for a particular gene. What would be the frequency of the recessive allele in this population?

A) 0.09

B) 0.30

C) 0.49

D) 0.70

E) Allele frequency cannot be estimated from this information.

Answer: E
*Topic: Concept 23.1*
*Skill: Application*

*Use the following information to answer the questions below.*

In a hypothetical population of 1,000 people, tests of blood–type genes show that 160 have the genotype *AA*, 480 have the genotype *AB*, and 360 have the genotype *BB*.

17) What is the frequency of the *A* allele?

A) 0.001

B) 0.002

C) 0.100

D) 0.400

E) 0.600

Answer: D
*Topic: Concept 23.1*
*Skill: Application*

18) What is the frequency of the *B* allele?

A) 0.001

B) 0.002

C) 0.100

D) 0.400

E) 0.600

Answer: E
*Topic: Concept 23.1*
*Skill: Application*

19) What percentage of the population has type O blood?

A) 0

B) 10

C) 24

D) 48

E) 60

Answer: A
*Topic: Concept 23.1*
*Skill: Application*

20) If there are 4,000 children born to this generation, how many would be expected to have AB blood under the conditions of Hardy-Weinberg equilibrium?

A) 100

B) 960

C) 1,920

D) 2,000

E) 2,400

Answer: C
*Topic: Concept 23.1*
*Skill: Application*

21) In peas, a gene controls flower color such that $R$ = purple and $r$ = white. In an isolated pea patch, there are 36 purple flowers and 64 white flowers. Assuming Hardy-Weinberg equilibrium, what is the value of $q$ for this population?

A) 0.36

B) 0.60

C) 0.64

D) 0.75

E) 0.80

Answer: E
*Topic: Concept 23.1*
*Skill: Application*

22) Which of the following is *not* a requirement for maintenance of Hardy-Weinberg equilibrium?

A) an increasing mutation rate

B) random mating

C) large population size

D) no migration

E) no natural selection

Answer: A
*Topic: Concept 23.1*
*Skill: Knowledge*

*The following questions refer to this information:*

You are studying three populations of birds. Population 1 has ten birds, of which one is brown (a recessive trait) and nine are red. Population 2 has 100 birds. In that population, ten of the birds are brown. Population 3 has 30 birds, and three of them are brown. Use the following options to answer the questions:

A. Population 1
B. Population 2
C. Population 3
D. They are all the same.
E. It is impossible to tell from the information given.

23) In which population is the frequency of the allele for brown feathers highest?

Answer: D
*Topic: Concept 23.1*
*Skill: Application*

24) In which population would it be *least* likely that an accident would significantly alter the frequency of the brown allele?

Answer: B
*Topic: Concepts 23.1, 23.3*
*Skill: Application*

25) Which population is *most* likely to be subject to the bottleneck effect?

Answer: A
*Topic: Concepts 23.1, 23.3*
*Skill: Comprehension*

26) The probability of a mutation at a particular gene locus is _____, and the probability of a mutation in the genome of a particular individual is _____.

A) high; low

B) low; high

C) low; low

D) high; high

E) moderate; moderate

Answer: B
*Topic: Concept 23.2*
*Skill: Knowledge*

27) Which factor is the *most* important in producing the variability that occurs in each generation of humans?

A) mutation

B) sexual recombination

C) genetic drift

D) nonrandom mating

E) natural selection

Answer: B
*Topic: Concept 23.2*
*Skill: Knowledge*

28) In modern terminology, diversity is understood to be a result of genetic variation. Sources of variation for evolution include all of the following *except*

A) mistakes in translation of structural genes.

B) mistakes in DNA replication.

C) translocations and mistakes in meiosis.

D) recombination at fertilization.

E) recombination by crossing over in meiosis.

Answer: A
*Topic: Concept 23.2*
*Skill: Comprehension*

29) Which of the following chromosomal mutations can increase the mass of DNA present in an organism's genome, creating superfluous DNA that may undergo further changes producing entirely new genes?

A) transposition

B) translocation

C) inversion

D) duplication

E) crossing over

Answer: D
*Topic: Concept 23.2*
*Skill: Knowledge*

30) Genetic recombination is a crucial process in evolution. This statement is supported by the continuous existence of which of the following in evolving populations?

A) sexual reproduction

B) bacterial conjugation

C) exchange of chromosome regions in meiosis (crossing over)

D) A and C only

E) A, B, and C

Answer: E
*Topic: Concept 23.2*
*Skill: Comprehension*

31) Which is true regarding genetic variation in prokaryotes, where cell reproduction occurs via binary fission?

A) Prokaryotes lack any ability to increase their genetic variation.

B) Prokaryotes are limited to the rare-chance mutation to increase their genetic variation.

C) Only when binary fission occurs by meiosis do prokaryotes have the ability to undergo genetic recombination.

D) Prokaryotic genomes can experience increased genetic variation via both mutation and genetic recombination.

E) Prokaryotic genomes gain genetic variation solely through the action of bacteriophages.

Answer: D
*Topic: Concept 23.2*
*Skill: Knowledge*

32) In DNA molecules, A–T base pairs are held to each other by two hydrogen bonds, whereas the more stable G–C base pairs are held to each other by three hydrogen bonds. If DNA mutability increases as DNA stability decreases, then which of the five exons of a hypothetical gene should be most highly conserved over evolutionary time (assuming no selection and no transposition occurs)?

| Exon | % of A–T pairs | % of G–C pairs |
| --- | --- | --- |
| A | 50 | 50 |
| B | 46 | 54 |
| C | 40 | 60 |
| D | 70 | 30 |
| E | 62 | 38 |

A) Exon A

B) Exon B

C) Exon C

D) Exon D

E) Exon E

Answer: C
*Topic: Concept 23.2*
*Skill: Application*

33) Non-replicative transposons are sections of a DNA molecule that can remove themselves, seal the nicked ends of their former site, and reintegrate themselves somewhere else in the genome. On the other hand, retrotransposons do not remove themselves but, rather, once transcribed as RNA, act as a template for reverse transcriptase. The resulting cDNA can then integrate itself somewhere else in the genome. What is true of retrotransposons that is *not* generally true of non-replicative transposons?

A) They temporarily exist as RNA intermediates.

B) They can increase the size of an organism's genome.

C) They can cause gene duplication to occur.

D) A, B, and C are true.

E) Only B and C are true.

Answer: D
*Topic: Concept 23.2*
*Skill: Comprehension*

34) Non-replicative transposons are sections of a DNA molecule that can remove themselves, seal the nicked ends of their former site, and reintegrate themselves somewhere else in the genome. On the other hand, retrotransposons do not remove themselves but, rather, once transcribed as RNA, act as a template for reverse transcriptase. The resulting cDNA can then integrate itself somewhere else in the genome. Unlike other DNA polymerases, reverse transcriptase lacks proofreading capability. In which way(s) should retrotransposons affect the genome that non-replicative transposons do *not*?

A) They should maintain the amount of DNA in the genome.

B) They should increase the nucleotide variability of the genome.

C) They should increase the number of base-pairs in the genome.

D) Both A and B are true.

E) Both B and C are true.

Answer: E
*Topic: Concept 23.2*
*Skill: Application*

35) In a large, sexually reproducing population, the frequency of an allele changes from 0.6 to 0.2. From this change, one can most logically assume that, in this environment,

A) the allele is neutral.

B) the allele mutates readily.

C) random processes have changed allelic frequencies.

D) there is no sexual selection.

E) the allele reduces fitness.

Answer: E
*Topic: Concepts 23.2, 23.3*
*Skill: Comprehension*

36) The following important concepts of population genetics are due to random events or chance *except*

A) mutation.

B) the bottleneck effect.

C) the founder effect.

D) natural selection.

E) sexual recombination.

Answer: D
*Topic: Concepts 23.2, 23.3*
*Skill: Comprehension*

37) You are maintaining a small population of fruit flies in the laboratory by transferring the flies to a new culture bottle after each generation. After several generations, you notice that the viability of the flies has decreased greatly. Recognizing that small population size is likely to be linked to decreased viability, the best way to reverse this trend is to

A) cross your flies with flies from another lab.

B) reduce the number of flies that you transfer at each generation.

C) transfer only the largest flies.

D) change the temperature at which you rear the flies.

E) shock the flies with a brief treatment of heat or cold to make them more hardy.

Answer: A
*Topic: Concepts 23.2, 23.3*
*Skill: Application*

38) If the frequency of a particular allele that is present in a small, isolated population of alpine plants should change due to a landslide that leaves an even smaller remnant of surviving plants, then what has occurred?

A) a bottleneck

B) genetic drift

C) microevolution

D) A and B only

E) A, B, and C

Answer: D
*Topic: Concept 23.3*
*Skill: Comprehension*

39) Natural selection is most nearly the same as

A) diploidy.

B) gene flow.

C) genetic drift.

D) nonrandom mating.

E) differential reproductive success.

Answer: E
*Topic: Concept 23.3*
*Skill: Knowledge*

40) Through time, the movement of people on Earth has steadily increased. This has altered the course of human evolution by increasing

A) nonrandom reproduction.

B) geographic isolation.

C) genetic drift.

D) mutations.

E) gene flow.

Answer: E
*Topic: Concept 23.3*
*Skill: Knowledge*

41) Gene flow is a concept best used to describe an exchange between

A) species.

B) males and females.

C) populations.

D) individuals.

E) chromosomes.

Answer: C
*Topic: Concept 23.3*
*Skill: Knowledge*

*The following questions refer to this information:*

In the year 2500, five male space colonists and five female space colonists (all unrelated to each other) settle on an uninhabited Earthlike planet in the Andromeda galaxy. The colonists and their offspring randomly mate for generations. All ten of the original colonists had free earlobes, and two were heterozygous for that trait. The allele for free earlobes is dominant to the allele for attached earlobes.

42) Which of these is closest to the allele frequency in the founding population?

A) 0.1 *a*, 0.9 *A*

B) 0.2 *a*, 0.8 *A*

C) 0.5 *a*, 0.5 *A*

D) 0.8 *a*, 0.2 *A*

E) 0.4 *a*, 0.6 *A*

Answer: A
*Topic: Concept 23.2*
*Skill: Application*

43) If one assumes that Hardy–Weinberg equilibrium applies to the population of colonists on this planet, about how many people will have attached earlobes when the planet's population reaches 10,000?

A) 100

B) 400

C) 800

D) 1,000

E) 10,000

Answer: A
*Topic: Concept 23.2*
*Skill: Application*

44) If four of the original colonists died before they produced offspring, the ratios of genotypes could be quite different in the subsequent generations. This is an example of

A) diploidy.

B) gene flow.

C) genetic drift.

D) disruptive selection.

E) stabilizing selection.

Answer: C
*Topic: Concept 23.3*
*Skill: Application*

45) A trend toward the decrease in the size of plants on the slopes of mountains as altitudes increase is an example of

A) a cline.

B) a bottleneck.

C) relative fitness.

D) genetic drift.

E) speciation.

Answer: A
*Topic: Concept 23.4*
*Skill: Knowledge*

46) Which of the following is one important evolutionary feature of the diploid condition?

A) An extra set of genes facilitates the inheritance of characteristics acquired by the previous generation.

B) Recombination can only occur in diploid organisms.

C) DNA in diploid cells is more resistant to mutation than is the DNA of haploid cells.

D) Diploid organisms express less of their genetic variability than haploid organisms.

E) Diploid organisms are more likely to clone successfully than are haploid organisms.

Answer: D
*Topic: Concept 23.4*
*Skill: Comprehension*

The restriction enzymes of bacteria protect the bacteria from successful attack by bacteriophages, whose genomes can be degraded by the restriction enzymes. The bacterial genomes are not vulnerable to these restriction enzymes because bacterial DNA is methylated. This situation selects for bacteriophages whose genomes are also methylated. As new strains of resistant bacteriophages become more prevalent, this in turn selects for bacteria whose genomes are not methylated and whose restriction enzymes instead degrade methylated DNA.

47) The outcome of the conflict between bacteria and bacteriophage at any point in time results from

A) frequency–dependent selection.

B) evolutionary imbalance.

C) heterozygote advantage.

D) neutral variation.

E) genetic variation being preserved by diploidy.

Answer: A
*Topic: Concept 23.4*
*Skill: Comprehension*

48) Over the course of evolutionary time, what should occur?

A) Methylated DNA should become fixed in the gene pools of bacterial species.

B) Nonmethylated DNA should become fixed in the gene pools of bacteriophages.

C) Methylated DNA should become fixed in the gene pools of bacteriophages.

D) Methylated and nonmethylated strains should be maintained among both bacteria and bacteriophages, with ratios that vary over time.

E) Both A and B are correct.

Answer: D
*Topic: Concept 23.4*
*Skill: Application*

49) The Darwinian fitness of an individual is measured by

A) the number of its offspring that survive to reproduce.

B) the number of supergenes in the genotype.

C) the number of mates it attracts.

D) its physical strength.

E) how long it lives.

Answer: A
*Topic: Concept 23.4*
*Skill: Knowledge*

50) If a phenotypic polymorphism lacks a genetic component, then

    A) the environment cannot affect its abundance.

    B) natural selection cannot act upon it to make a population better adapted over the course of generations.

    C) it cannot affect an individual's ability to survive.

    D) it must exhibit quantitative variation.

    E) all of the above.

Answer: B
*Topic: Concept 23.4*
*Skill: Comprehension*

51) When we say that an individual organism has a greater fitness than another individual, we specifically mean that the organism

    A) lives longer than others of its species.

    B) competes for resources more successfully than others of its species.

    C) mates more frequently than others of its species.

    D) utilizes resources more efficiently than other species occupying similar niches.

    E) leaves more viable offspring than others of its species.

Answer: E
*Topic: Concept 23.4*
*Skill: Knowledge*

52) Which of the following statements best summarizes evolution as it is viewed today?

    A) It is goal-directed.

    B) It represents the result of selection for acquired characteristics.

    C) It is synonymous with the process of gene flow.

    D) It is the descent of humans from the present-day great apes.

    E) It is the differential survival and reproduction of the most fit phenotypes.

Answer: E
*Topic: Concept 23.4*
*Skill: Comprehension*

53) The higher the proportion of loci that are "fixed" in a population, the lower is that population's

    A) nucleotide variability.

    B) genetic polymorphism.

    C) average heterozygosity.

    D) A, B, and C

    E) A and B only

Answer: D
*Topic: Concept 23.4*
*Skill: Comprehension*

54) If neutral variation is truly "neutral," then it should have no effect on

    A) nucleotide diversity.

    B) average heterozygosity.

    C) our ability to measure the rate of evolution.

    D) relative fitness.

    E) gene diversity.

Answer: D
*Topic: Concept 23.4*
*Skill: Comprehension*

Choose among these options to answer the following questions. Each option may be used once, more than once, or not at all.

A. random selection
B. directional selection
C. stabilizing selection
D. disruptive selection
E. sexual selection

55) An African butterfly species exists in two strikingly different color patterns.

Answer: D
Topic: Concept 23.4
Skill: Knowledge

56) Brightly colored peacocks mate more frequently than do drab peacocks.

Answer: E
Topic: Concept 23.4
Skill: Knowledge

57) Most Swiss starlings produce four to five eggs in each clutch.

Answer: C
Topic: Concept 23.4
Skill: Knowledge

58) Fossil evidence indicates that horses have gradually increased in size over geologic time.

Answer: B
Topic: Concept 23.4
Skill: Application

59) The average birth weight for human babies is about 3 kg.

Answer: C
Topic: Concept 23.4
Skill: Knowledge

60) A certain species of land snail exists as either a cream color or a solid brown color. Intermediate individuals are relatively rare.

Answer: D
Topic: Concept 23.4
Skill: Knowledge

61) Pathogenic bacteria found in many hospitals are antibiotic resistant.

Answer: B
Topic: Concept 23.4
Skill: Application

62) Cattle breeders have improved the quality of meat over the years by which process?

A) artificial selection
B) directional selection
C) stabilizing selection
D) A and B
E) A and C

Answer: D
Topic: Concept 23.4
Skill: Comprehension

63) The allele that causes phenylketonuria (PKU) is harmful, except when an infant's diet lacks the amino acid, phenylalanine. What maintains the presence of this harmful allele in a population's gene pool?

A) heterozygote advantage
B) stabilizing selection
C) balanced polymorphism
D) diploidy
E) balancing selection

Answer: D
Topic: Concept 23.4
Skill: Comprehension

64) Mules are relatively long-lived and hardy organisms that cannot, generally speaking, perform successful meiosis. Which statement about mules is true?

A) They have a relative evolutionary fitness of zero.

B) Their offspring have less genetic variation than the parents.

C) Mutations cannot occur in their genomes.

D) If crossing over happens in mules, then it must be limited to prophase of binary fission.

E) When two mules interbreed, genetic recombination cannot occur by meiotic crossing over, but only by the act of fertilization.

Answer: A
*Topic: Concept 23.4*
*Skill: Comprehension*

65) Heterozygote advantage should be most closely linked to which of the following?

A) sexual selection

B) stabilizing selection

C) random selection

D) directional selection

E) disruptive selection

Answer: B
*Topic: Concept 23.4*
*Skill: Knowledge*

66) In equatorial Africa, all of the following factors contribute to keeping the sickle-cell allele at a high frequency in the population, *except*

A) stabilizing selection.

B) heterozygote advantage.

C) diploidy.

D) balancing selection.

E) frequency-dependent selection.

Answer: E
*Topic: Concept 23.4*
*Skill: Comprehension*

67) Which statement about variation is most true?

A) All phenotypic variation is the result of genotypic variation.

B) All genetic variation produces phenotypic variation.

C) All nucleotide variability results in neutral variation.

D) All new alleles are the result of nucleotide variability.

E) All geographic variation results from the existence of clines.

Answer: D
*Topic: Concept 23.4*
*Skill: Comprehension*

68) A balanced polymorphism exists through disruptive selection in seedcracker finches from Cameroon in which small- and large-billed birds specialize in cracking soft and hard seeds, respectively. If long-term climatic change resulted in all seeds becoming hard, what type of selection would then operate on the finch population?

A) disruptive selection

B) directional selection

C) stabilizing selection

D) sexual selection

E) No selection would operate because the population is in Hardy-Weinberg equilibrium.

Answer: B
*Topic: Concept 23.4*
*Skill: Application*

*In a very large population, a quantitative trait has the following distribution pattern:*

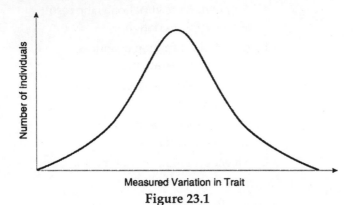

Number of Individuals

Measured Variation in Trait

**Figure 23.1**

69) What is true of the trait whose frequency distribution in a large population appears above? It has probably undergone

   A) directional selection.

   B) stabilizing selection.

   C) disruptive selection.

   D) sexual selection.

   E) random selection.

   Answer: B
   *Topic: Concept 23.4*
   *Skill: Knowledge*

70) If the unimodal distribution shown above becomes a bimodal distribution over time, then

   A) there must be some advantage to being heterozygous at all of the contributing gene loci.

   B) a situation of balanced polymorphism may be produced.

   C) directional selection is operating on this trait.

   D) the two-fold disadvantage of sex is the cause of the switch.

   E) the trait must be neutral.

   Answer: B
   *Topic: Concept 23.4*
   *Skill: Comprehension*

71) If the curve shifts to the left or to the right, there is no gene flow, and the population size consequently increases over successive generations, then which of these is (are) probably occurring?
   1. immigration or emigration
   2. directional selection
   3. adaptation
   4. genetic drift
   5. disruptive selection

   A) 1 only

   B) 4 only

   C) 2 and 3

   D) 4 and 5

   E) 1, 2, and 3

   Answer: C
   *Topic: Concept 23.4*
   *Skill: Comprehension*

72) Male satin bowerbirds adorn structures that they build, called "bowers," with parrot feathers, flowers, and other bizarre ornaments in order to attract females. Females inspect the bowers and, if suitably impressed, allow males to mate with them, after which they go off to nest by themselves. The evolution of this behavior is best described as due to

   A) survival of the fittest.

   B) artificial selection.

   C) sexual selection.

   D) natural selection.

   E) disruptive selection.

   Answer: C
   *Topic: Concept 23.4*
   *Skill: Comprehension*

73) In many animal species, mature males are much larger than mature females. This size difference can be attributed to

A) male hormones having a more positive effect on body size than female hormones do.

B) the operation of intrasexual selection.

C) females preferentially selecting larger males as mates.

D) A and B only

E) A, B, and C

Answer: E
*Topic: Concept 23.4*
*Skill: Application*

74) Adult male vervet monkeys have red penises and blue scrotums. Males use their colorful genitalia in dominance displays wherein they compete with each other for access to females. The coloration of the male genitalia is best explained as the result of _____, and specifically of _____.

A) natural selection; stabilizing selection

B) disruptive selection; intrasexual selection

C) sexual selection; intrasexual selection

D) natural selection; intersexual selection

E) sexual selection; disruptive selection

Answer: C
*Topic: Concept 23.4*
*Skill: Application*

75) Which of the following is most likely to have been produced by sexual selection?

A) a male lion's mane

B) bright colors of female flowers

C) the ability of desert animals to concentrate their urine

D) different sizes of male and female pinecones

E) camouflage coloration in animals

Answer: A
*Topic: Concept 23.4*
*Skill: Knowledge*

76) When imbalances occur in the sex ratio of sexual species that have two sexes (i.e., other than a 50:50 ratio), the members of the minority sex often receive a greater proportion of care and resources from parents than do the offspring of the majority sex. This is most clearly an example of

A) sexual selection.

B) disruptive selection.

C) balancing selection.

D) stabilizing selection.

E) frequency-dependent selection.

Answer: E
*Topic: Concept 23.4*
*Skill: Comprehension*

77) Female wasps, which are protected by the use of a painful stinger, often make their presence conspicuous by rapidly moving their usually long antennae. These wasps are often mimicked by flies with short antennae who give the appearance of rapidly moving long antennae by waving their forelegs in front of their bodies. Which of the following statements concerning this behavior is *not* consistent with current evolutionary theory?

A) Natural selection cannot fashion perfect organisms.

B) The behavior of the flies may be a compromise if their short antennae are adapted for other uses.

C) Variation in leg-waving behavior may have been present in ancestral populations and available for natural selection, while variation in antennae length may not have.

D) Given enough time, these flies will develop longer antennae and become perfect mimics.

E) Organisms are often locked into historic genetic constraints.

Answer: D
*Topic: Concept 23.4*
*Skill: Comprehension*

78) The same gene that causes various coat patterns in wild and domesticated cats also causes the cross–eyed condition in these cats, the cross–eyed condition being slightly maladaptive. In a hypothetical environment, the coat pattern that is associated with crossed eyes is highly adaptive, with the result that both the coat pattern and the cross–eyed condition increase in a feline population over time. Which statement is best supported by these observations?

A) Evolution is progressive and tends toward a more perfect population.

B) Phenotype is often the result of compromise.

C) Natural selection reduces the frequency of maladaptive genes in populations over the course of time.

D) Polygenic inheritance is generally maladaptive, and should become less common in future generations.

E) In all environments, coat pattern is a more important survival factor than is eye-muscle tone.

Answer: B
*Topic: Concept 23.4*
*Skill: Comprehension*

79) A proficient engineer can easily design skeletal structures that are more functional than those currently found in the forelimbs of such diverse mammals as horses, whales, and bats.  That the actual forelimbs of these mammals do not seem to be optimally arranged is because

A) natural selection has not had sufficient time to create the optimal design in each case, but will do so given enough time.

B) natural selection operates in ways that are beyond the capability of the human mind to comprehend.

C) in many cases, phenotype is not merely determined by genotype, but by the environment as well.

D) though we may not consider the fit between the current skeletal arrangements and their functions excellent, we should not doubt that natural selection ultimately produces the best design.

E) natural selection is generally limited to modifying structures that were present in previous generations and in previous species.

Answer: E
*Topic: Concept 23.4*
*Skill: Comprehension*

# Media Activity Questions

1) In the hypothetical insect population you examined in the activity "Causes of Microevolution," the genotypic frequency of the green and red bugs changed significantly after a windstorm randomly blew away individuals from the home plant. This change in genotypic frequency can be attributed to

   A) gene flow.

   B) mutation.

   C) genetic drift.

   D) natural selection.

   E) disruptive selection.

   Answer: C
   *Topic: Activity: Causes of Evolutionary Change*

2) What is the result of natural selection?

   A) a chance change in the gene pool of a small population

   B) the entry of alleles into a population due to immigration

   C) a change in the gene pool of a population due to differential reproductive success

   D) a change in allelic frequencies due to mutation

   E) the loss of alleles from a population due to emigration

   Answer: C
   *Topic: Activity: Causes of Evolutionary Change*

3) All the genes in a population are the population's

   A) gene pool.

   B) fitness.

   C) genotype.

   D) gene flow.

   E) phenotype.

   Answer: A
   *Topic: Activity: Causes of Evolutionary Change*

4) In a cell in which $2n = 6$, the independent assortment of chromosomes during meiosis can by itself give rise to _____ genetically different gametes.

   A) two

   B) four

   C) six

   D) eight

   E) ten

   Answer: D
   *Topic: Activity: Genetic Variation from Recombination*

5) In sexually reproducing organisms, the events of _____ do *not* contribute to an increase in genetic variation.

   A) prophase I

   B) random fertilization

   C) metaphase I

   D) interphase

   E) All of these events *do* contribute to an increase in genetic variation.

   Answer: D
   *Topic: Activity: Genetic Variation from Recombination*

# Self–Quiz Questions

1) In the gene pool of a population with 100 individuals, a fixed allele for a particular gene locus has a frequency of

A) 0.

B) 0.5.

C) 1.

D) 100.

E) cannot be calculated based on this information

Answer: C

2) Researchers examining a particular gene in a fruit fly population discovered that the gene can have either of two slightly different sequences, designated A1 and A2. Further tests showed that 70% of the gametes produced in the population contained the A1 sequence. If the population is at Hardy–Weinberg equilibrium, what proportion of the flies carries both A1 and A2?

A) 0.7

B) 0.49

C) 0.21

D) 0.42

E) 0.09

Answer: D

3) At a locus with a dominant and a recessive allele in Hardy–Weinberg equilibrium, 16% of the individuals are homozygous for the recessive allele. What is the frequency of the dominant allele in the population?

A) 0.84

B) 0.36

C) 0.6

D) 0.4

E) 0.48

Answer: C

4) The average length of jackrabbit ears decreases gradually with increasing latitude. This variation is an example of

A) directional selection.

B) discrete variation.

C) polymorphism.

D) genetic drift.

E) disruptive selection.

Answer: A

5) Which of the following is a polymorphic trait in humans?

A) variation in height

B) variation in intelligence

C) free versus attached earlobes

D) variation in the number of fingers

E) variation in fingerprints

Answer: C

6) Natural selection changes allele frequencies in populations because some _____ survive and reproduce more successfully than others.

A) alleles

B) individual organisms

C) gene pools

D) gene loci

E) species

Answer: B

7) Longer tails of male barn swallows evolve because female barn swallows prefer to mate with the males that have the longest tails. This process is best described as

A) genetic drift that changes the frequencies of the alleles for tail length.

B) natural selection for sexual reproduction that maintains variation in the genes that influence tail length.

C) intersexual selection for traits, such as long tails, that help males attract mates.

D) intrasexual selection for traits, such as long tails, that help males win contests for females.

E) directional selection for traits, such as long tails, that improve males' ability to fly strongly and forage for food over large areas.

Answer: C

8) No two human individuals are alike, except for identical twins. The chief cause of the variation among individuals is

A) new mutations that occurred in the preceding generation.

B) sexual recombination.

C) genetic drift due to the small size of the population.

D) geographic variation within the population.

E) environmental effects.

Answer: B

9) Road construction has isolated a small portion of a beetle population from the main population. After a few generations, this new population exhibits dramatic genetic differences from the old one, most likely because

A) mutations are more common in the new environment.

B) allele frequencies among the stranded beetles differed by chance from those in the parent population's gene pool and subsequent genetic drift caused even more divergence from the original gene pool.

C) the new environment is different from the old, favoring directional selection.

D) gene flow increases in a new environment.

E) members of a small population tend to migrate, removing alleles from the gene pool.

Answer: B

10) Sparrows with average-sized wings survive severe storms better than those with longer or shorter wings, illustrating

A) the bottleneck effect.

B) stabilizing selection.

C) frequency-dependent selection.

D) natural variation.

E) disruptive selection.

Answer: B

# Chapter 24 The Origin of Species

1) Which of the following applies to *both* anagenesis and cladogenesis?

A) branching

B) increased diversity

C) speciation

D) more species

E) adaptive radiation

Answer: C
*Topic: Concept 24.1*
*Skill: Comprehension*

2) Which of the following statements about species, as defined by the biological species concept, is (are) correct?

    I.    Biological species are defined by reproductive isolation.

    II.   Biological species are the model used for grouping extinct forms of life.

    III.  The biological species is the largest unit of population in which successful reproduction is possible.

A) I only

B) II only

C) I and III

D) II and III

E) I, II, and III

Answer: C
*Topic: Concept 24.1*
*Skill: Comprehension*

3) What is generally true of two sibling species?

A) They shared a common ancestor recently in evolutionary time.

B) Genes are unable to pass from one sibling species' gene pool to the other's.

C) They are unable to produce hybrid offspring upon interbreeding.

D) Their reproductive isolation from each other is complete.

E) They are the result of anagenesis.

Answer: A
*Topic: Concept 24.1*
*Skill: Comprehension*

4) Which of the various species concepts identifies species based on the degree of genetic exchange between their gene pools?

A) phylogenetic

B) ecological

C) biological

D) morphological

E) paleontological

Answer: C
*Topic: Concept 24.1*
*Skill: Knowledge*

5) For which two species concepts are anatomical features the primary criterion for determining species identities?
   1. biological
   2. ecological
   3. morphological
   4. phylogenetic
   5. paleontological

   A) 1 and 2

   B) 1 and 3

   C) 2 and 3

   D) 3 and 5

   E) 4 and 5

   Answer: D
   *Topic: Concept 24.1*
   *Skill: Comprehension*

6) Successfully breeding two individual organisms at a zoo and obtaining fertile offspring for several generations is no guarantee that the same could occur in nature (i.e., in the wild). Which species concept becomes difficult to confirm because of this fact?

   A) biological

   B) ecological

   C) morphological

   D) phylogenetic

   E) paleontological

   Answer: A
   *Topic: Concept 24.1*
   *Skill: Knowledge*

7) There is still some controversy among biologists about whether Neanderthals should be placed within the same species as modern humans, or into a separate species of their own. Most DNA sequence data analyzed so far indicate that there was probably little or no gene flow between Neanderthals and *Homo sapiens*. Which species concept is most applicable in this example?

   A) paleontological

   B) phylogenetic

   C) ecological

   D) morphological

   E) biological

   Answer: E
   *Topic: Concept 24.1*
   *Skill: Application*

8) A biologist discovers two populations of wolf spiders whose members appear identical. Members of one population are found in the leaf litter deep within a woods. Members of the other population are found in the grass at the edge of the woods. The biologist decides to designate the members of the two populations as two separate species. Which species concept is this biologist most closely utilizing?

   A) ecological

   B) biological

   C) morphological

   D) paleontological

   E) phylogenetic

   Answer: A
   *Topic: Concept 24.1*
   *Skill: Application*

9) What was the species concept used by Linnaeus?

 A) biological

 B) morphological

 C) paleontological

 D) ecological

 E) phylogenetic

Answer: B
*Topic: Concept 24.1*
*Skill: Knowledge*

10) You are confronted with a box of preserved grasshoppers of various species that are new to science and have not been described. Your assignment is to separate them into species. There is no accompanying information as to where or when they were collected. Which species concept will you have to use?

 A) biological

 B) phylogenetic

 C) ecological

 D) paleontological

 E) morphological

Answer: E
*Topic: Concept 24.1*
*Skill: Application*

11) Which of the following is *not* considered an intrinsic isolating mechanism?

 A) sterile offspring

 B) ecological isolation

 C) geographic isolation

 D) gametic incompatibility

 E) timing of courtship display

Answer: C
*Topic: Concept 24.1*
*Skill: Knowledge*

12) Some species of *Anopheles* mosquito live in brackish water, some in running fresh water, and others in stagnant water. What type of reproductive barrier is most obviously separating these different species?

 A) habitat isolation

 B) temporal isolation

 C) behavioral isolation

 D) gametic isolation

 E) postzygotic isolation

Answer: A
*Topic: Concept 24.1*
*Skill: Comprehension*

13) Which of the following *must* occur during a period of geographic isolation in order for two sibling species to remain genetically distinct following their geographic reunion in the same home range?

 A) prezygotic barriers

 B) postzygotic barriers

 C) ecological isolation

 D) reproductive isolation

 E) temporal isolation

Answer: D
*Topic: Concept 24.1*
*Skill: Comprehension*

Use the following options to answer the following questions. For each description of reproductive isolation, select the option that best describes it. Options may be used once, more than once, or not at all.

A. gametic
B. temporal
C. behavioral
D. habitat
E. mechanical

14) two species of orchids with different floral anatomy

Answer: E
*Topic: Concept 24.1*
*Skill: Application*

15) two species of trout that breed in different seasons

Answer: B
*Topic: Concept 24.1*
*Skill: Knowledge*

16) two species of meadowlarks with different mating songs

Answer: C
*Topic: Concept 24.1*
*Skill: Knowledge*

17) two species of garter snakes live in the same region, but one lives in water and the other lives on land

Answer: D
*Topic: Concept 24.1*
*Skill: Knowledge*

18) two species of pine shed their pollen at different times

Answer: B
*Topic: Concept 24.1*
*Skill: Knowledge*

19) mating fruit flies recognize the appearance, odor, tapping motions, and sounds of members of their own species, but not of other species

Answer: C
*Topic: Concept 24.1*
*Skill: Application*

20) the scarlet oak is adapted to moist bottomland, whereas the black oak is adapted to dry upland soils

Answer: D
*Topic: Concept 24.1*
*Skill: Application*

*The questions below are based on the following description:*

Several closely related frog species of the genus *Rana* can be found in the forests of the southeastern United States. The species boundaries are maintained by reproductive barriers. In each case, match the various descriptions of frogs below with the appropriate reproductive barrier listed. Options may be used once, more than once, or not at all.

A) behavioral
B) gametic
C) habitat
D) temporal
E) mechanical

21) Males of one species sing only during rainy conditions; males of another species sing only when it is not raining.

Answer: A
*Topic: Concept 24.1*
*Skill: Application*

22) One species lives only in tree holes; another species lives only in streams.

Answer: C
*Topic: Concept 24.1*
*Skill: Application*

23) Females of one species choose mates based on song quality; females of another species choose mates on the basis of size.

Answer: A
*Topic: Concept 24.1*
*Skill: Application*

24) One species mates for two weeks in early April; another species mates for three weeks in early May.

Answer: D
*Topic: Concept 24.1*
*Skill: Application*

25) Males of one species are too small to perform amplexus (an action that stimulates ovulation) with females of all other species.

Answer: E
*Topic: Concept 24.1*
*Skill: Application*

26) Dog breeders maintain the purity of breeds by keeping dogs of different breeds apart when they are fertile. This kind of isolation is most similar to which of the following reproductive isolating mechanisms?
   A) reduced hybrid fertility
   B) hybrid breakdown
   C) mechanical isolation
   D) habitat isolation
   E) gametic isolation

Answer: D
*Topic: Concept 24.1*
*Skill: Comprehension*

27) Two species of frogs belonging to the same genus occasionally mate, but the offspring do not complete development. What is the mechanism for keeping the two frog species separate?
   A) the postzygotic barrier called hybrid inviability
   B) the postzygotic barrier called hybrid breakdown
   C) the prezygotic barrier called hybrid sterility
   D) gametic isolation
   E) adaptation

Answer: A
*Topic: Concept 24.1*
*Skill: Knowledge*

28) Theoretically, the production of sterile mules by interbreeding between female horses and male donkeys should
   A) result in the extinction of one of the two parental species.
   B) cause convergent evolution.
   C) reinforce postzygotic barriers between horses and donkeys.
   D) weaken the intrinsic reproductive barriers between horses and donkeys.
   E) eventually result in the formation of a single species from the two parental species.

Answer: C
*Topic: Concept 24.1*
*Skill: Comprehension*

29) The biological species concept is inadequate for grouping

   A) plants.

   B) parasites.

   C) asexual organisms.

   D) animals that migrate.

   E) sympatric populations.

Answer: C
*Topic: Concept 24.1*
*Skill: Knowledge*

30) Races of humans are unlikely to evolve extensive differences in the future for which of the following reasons?
   I.   The environment is unlikely to change.
   II.  Human evolution is complete.
   III. The human races are incompletely isolated.

   A) I only

   B) III only

   C) I and II only

   D) II and III only

   E) I, II, and III

Answer: B
*Topic: Concept 24.1*
*Skill: Comprehension*

*Use the graphs in Figure 24.1 to answer the following question.*

*(See page 387 for Figure 24.1.)*

31) In an environment in which members of a population compete with each other for resources, a change occurs that selects against members that exhibit a particular dominant trait (the trait exhibits complete dominance). Which graph best depicts the trends in genotypic frequencies that would be expected to occur over time?

   A) graph A            B) graph B

   C) graph C            D) graph D

Answer: B
*Topic: Concept 24.2*
*Skill: Comprehension*

32) In a hypothetical situation, a certain species of flea feeds only on pronghorn antelopes. In rangelands of the western United States, pronghorns and cattle often associate with one another. If it should happen that some of these fleas develop a strong preference, instead, for cattle blood and mate only with fleas that, likewise, prefer cattle blood, it is possible that over time _____ will occur.
   1.  reproductive isolation
   2.  sympatric speciation
   3.  habitat isolation
   4.  prezygotic barriers
   5.  cladogenesis

   A) 1 only

   B) 2 and 3

   C) 1, 2, and 3

   D) 1, 2, 3, and 5

   E) 1 through 5

Answer: E
*Topic: Concepts 24.1, 24.2*
*Skill: Comprehension*

33) Which example below will most likely guarantee that two closely related species will remain distinct biological species?

A) colonization of new habitats

B) convergent evolution

C) hybridization

D) geographic isolation from one another

E) reproductive isolation from one another

Answer: E
*Topic: Concept 24.2*
*Skill: Knowledge*

34) A defining characteristic of allopatric speciation is

A) the appearance of new species in the midst of old ones.

B) asexually reproducing populations.

C) geographic isolation.

D) artificial selection.

E) large populations.

Answer: C
*Topic: Concept 24.2*
*Skill: Knowledge*

35) The Hawaiian islands are a great showcase of evolution because of intense

A) ecological isolation and sympatric speciation.

B) adaptive radiation and allopatric speciation.

C) allopolyploidy and sympatric speciation.

D) cross-specific mating and reinforcement.

E) hybrid vigor and allopatric speciation.

Answer: B
*Topic: Concept 24.2*
*Skill: Knowledge*

36) All of the following have contributed to the diversity of organisms on the Hawaiian archipelago *except* that

A) the islands are distant from the mainland.

B) multiple invasions have occurred.

C) adaptive radiation has occurred.

D) the islands are very young in geologic time.

E) environmental conditions differ from one island to the next.

Answer: D
*Topic: Concept 24.2*
*Skill: Comprehension*

37) The Galápagos archipelago appeared about 2 million years ago, when submerged volcanoes (seamounts) rose above the ocean's surface. A single hypothetical colonization event introduced a species of finch to one island in the distant past. Today, several islands in the archipelago contain unique species of finches. What must have happened following the initial colonization event to account for the current situation?

1. cladogenesis
2. anagenesis
3. allopatric speciation
4. adaptive radiation

A) 1 and 3

B) 1 and 4

C) 2 and 3

D) 1, 3, and 4

E) 2, 3, and 4

Answer: D
*Topic: Concept 24.2*
*Skill: Comprehension*

38) A rapid method of speciation that has been important in the history of flowering plants is

    A) genetic drift.

    B) paedomorphosis.

    C) a mutation in the gene controlling the timing of flowering.

    D) behavioral isolation.

    E) polyploidy.

Answer: E
*Topic: Concept 24.2*
*Skill: Knowledge*

39) Plant species A has a diploid number of 8. A new species, B, arises as an autopolyploid from A. The diploid number of B would probably be

    A) 4.

    B) 8.

    C) 16.

    D) 32.

    E) 64.

Answer: C
*Topic: Concept 24.2*
*Skill: Application*

40) Autopolyploidy is a speciation process that begins with an event during

    A) habitat selection.

    B) copulation.

    C) meiosis.

    D) embryonic development.

    E) hybridization.

Answer: C
*Topic: Concept 24.2*
*Skill: Knowledge*

41) Which of the following is a way that allopolyploidy can most directly cause speciation?

    A) It can improve success in island habitats.

    B) It can overcome hybrid sterility.

    C) It can change the mating behavior of animals.

    D) It can generate geographic barriers.

    E) It can produce heterochrony.

Answer: B
*Topic: Concept 24.2*
*Skill: Comprehension*

42) A new plant species formed from the hybridization between a plant with a diploid number of 16 and a plant with a diploid number of 12 would probably have a gamete chromosome number of

    A) 12.

    B) 14.

    C) 16.

    D) 22.

    E) 28.

Answer: B
*Topic: Concept 24.2*
*Skill: Application*

43) Plant species A has a diploid number of 28. Plant species B has a diploid number of 14. A new, sexually reproducing species C arises as an allopolyploid from hybridization of A and B. The diploid number of C would probably be

    A) 14.

    B) 21.

    C) 28.

    D) 42.

    E) 63.

Answer: D
*Topic: Concept 24.2*
*Skill: Application*

44) Two closely related populations of mice have been separated for a long period by a river. Climatic change causes the river to dry up, thereby bringing the mice populations back into contact in a zone of overlap. Which of the following is *not* a possible outcome when they meet?

A) They interbreed freely and produce fertile hybrid offspring.

B) They no longer attempt to interbreed.

C) They interbreed in the region of overlap, producing an inferior hybrid. Subsequent interbreeding between inferior hybrids produces progressively superior hybrids over several generations.

D) They remain separate in the extremes of their ranges but develop a hybrid zone in the area of overlap.

E) They interbreed in the region of overlap, but produce sterile offspring.

Answer: C
*Topic: Concept 24.2*
*Skill: Comprehension*

45) As a result of deforestation, the number of different habitats in a particular locale declines while, at the same time, the rate of cladogenesis in a particular lineage of animals in this locale increases. Choose the feature that most likely accounts for this observation.

A) adaptive radiation

B) allopolyploidy

C) autopolyploidy

D) increased habitat differentiation

E) increased sexual selection

Answer: E
*Topic: Concept 24.2*
*Skill: Comprehension*

46) Beetle pollinators of a particular plant are attracted to its flowers by their bright orange color. The beetles not only pollinate the flowers, but they mate while inside of the flowers. A mutant version of the plant with red flowers becomes more common with the passage of time. A particular variant of the beetle prefers the red flowers to the orange flowers. Over time, these two beetle variants diverge from each other to such an extent that interbreeding is no longer possible. What kind of speciation has occurred in this example, and what has driven it?

A) allopatric speciation, ecological isolation

B) sympatric speciation, habitat differentiation

C) allopatric speciation, behavioral isolation

D) sympatric speciation, sexual selection

E) sympatric speciation, allopolyploidy

Answer: B
*Topic: Concept 24.2*
*Skill: Application*

47) According to the concept of punctuated equilibrium, the "sudden" appearance of a new species in the fossil record means that

A) the species is now extinct.

B) speciation occurred instantaneously.

C) speciation occurred in one generation.

D) speciation occurred rapidly in geologic time.

E) the species will consequently have a relatively short existence, compared with other species.

Answer: D
*Topic: Concept 24.2*
*Skill: Knowledge*

48) According to the concept of punctuated equilibrium,

A) natural selection is unimportant as a mechanism of evolution.

B) given enough time, most existing species will branch gradually into new species.

C) a new species accumulates most of its unique features as it comes into existence.

D) evolution of new species features long periods during which changes are occurring, interspersed with short periods of equilibrium or stasis.

E) transitional fossils, intermediate between newer species and their parent species, should be abundant.

Answer: C
*Topic: Concept 24.2*
*Skill: Comprehension*

49) Which of the following would be a position held by an adherent of the punctuated equilibrium theory?

A) A new species forms most of its unique features as it comes into existence and then changes little for the duration of its existence.

B) One should expect to find many transitional fossils left by organisms in the process of forming new species.

C) Given enough time, most existing species will gradually evolve into new species.

D) Natural selection is unimportant as a mechanism of evolution.

E) Most speciation is anagenetic.

Answer: A
*Topic: Concept 24.2*
*Skill: Knowledge*

50) Speciation

A) occurs at such a slow pace that no one has ever observed the emergence of new species.

B) occurs only by the accumulation of genetic change over vast expanses of time.

C) must begin with the geographic isolation of a small, frontier population.

D) proceeds at a uniform tempo across all taxa.

E) occurs via anagenesis and cladogenesis, but only the latter increases biodiversity.

Answer: E
*Topic: Concept 24.2*
*Skill: Knowledge*

51) The origin of a new plant species by hybridization coupled with nondisjunction is an example of

A) allopatric speciation.

B) sympatric speciation.

C) autopolyploidy.

D) heterochrony.

E) habitat selection.

Answer: B
*Topic: Concepts 24.2, 24.3*
*Skill: Comprehension*

*The following questions refer to this hypothetical situation:*

A female fly, full of fertilized eggs, is swept by high winds to an island far out to sea. She is the first fly to arrive on this island, and the only fly to arrive in this way. Thousands of years later, her numerous offspring occupy the island, but none of them resemble her. There are, instead, several species each of which eats only certain type of food. None of the species can fly, for their flight wings are absent, and their balancing organs (i.e., the halteres) are now used in courtship displays. The male members of each species bear modified halteres that are unique in appearance to their species. Females bear vestigial halteres. The ranges of all of the daughter species overlap.

52) If these fly species lost the ability to fly independently of each other (the result of separate mutation events in each lineage), then the flightless condition in these species could be an example of

A) adaptive radiation.

B) species selection.

C) sexual selection.

D) allometric growth.

E) habitat differentiation.

Answer: B
*Topic: Concepts 24.2, 24.3*
*Skill: Application*

53) In each fly species, the entire body segment that gave rise to the original flight wings is missing. The mutation(s) that led to the flightless condition probably affected the _____ genes, making the initial mutants examples of _____.

A) thorax; complete metamorphosis

B) exoskeleton; exaptations

C) *Hox*; complete metamorphosis

D) thorax; exaptations

E) *Hox*; adaptive radiants

Answer: C
*Topic: Concepts 24.2, 24.3*
*Skill: Comprehension*

54) If the foods preferred by each species are found on different parts of the island, and if the flies mate and lay eggs on their food sources, regardless of the location of the food sources, then the speciation events involving these fly species may have been driven, at least in part, by which of the following?

A) autopolyploidy

B) allopolyploidy

C) species selection

D) genetic drift

E) habitat differentiation

Answer: E
*Topic: Concepts 24.2, 24.3*
*Skill: Application*

55) If the males' halteres have species-specific size, shape, color, and use in courtship displays, and if the species' ranges overlap, then the speciation events may have been driven, at least in part, by which of the following?

A) autopolyploidy

B) allopolyploidy

C) species selection

D) sexual selection

E) habitat differentiation

Answer: D
*Topic: Concepts 24.2, 24.3*
*Skill: Application*

56) Which of these events seem(s) to have occurred among the fly populations on the island?
1. cladogenesis
2. adaptive radiation
3. sympatric speciation

A) 1 only

B) 2 only

C) 3 only

D) 1 and 2 only

E) 1, 2, and 3

Answer: E
*Topic: Concepts 24.2, 24.3*
*Skill: Comprehension*

57) Fly species W, found in a certain part of the island, produces fertile offspring with species Y. Species W does not produce fertile offspring with species X or Z. If no other species can hybridize, then species W and Y

A) are still sibling species.

B) shared a common ancestor more recently with each other than either did with the other two species.

C) may merge into a single species if their hybrids remain fertile over the course of many generations.

D) A and B only

E) A, B, and C

Answer: E
*Topic: Concepts 24.2, 24.3*
*Skill: Comprehension*

58) Which of these fly organs, as they exist in current fly populations, best fits the description of an *exaptation*?

A) wings

B) halteres

C) mouthparts

D) thoraxes

E) walking appendages

Answer: B
*Topic: Concepts 24.2, 24.3*
*Skill: Comprehension*

59) Which of the following statements about speciation is *correct*?

A) The goal of natural selection is speciation.

B) When reunited, two allopatric populations will not interbreed.

C) Natural selection chooses the reproductive barriers for populations.

D) Prezygotic reproductive barriers usually evolve before postzygotic barriers.

E) Speciation is included within the concept of macroevolution.

Answer: E
*Topic: Concept 24.3*
*Skill: Knowledge*

60) Which of the following would be an example of macroevolution?

 A) evolution of antibiotic resistance in a strain of *E. coli*

 B) evolution of polymorphism in *Papilio dardanus*, with each morph mimicking a different protected butterfly

 C) evolution of modern humans, *Homo sapiens*, from australopithecine ancestors

 D) evolution of insecticide resistance in populations of insect pests treated through the years with DDT

 E) replacement of a melanin-poor morph by a melanin-rich morph over many generations under conditions of increased UV exposure

Answer: C
*Topic: Concept 24.3*
*Skill: Application*

*The following questions are based on the observation that several dozen different proteins comprise the prokaryotic flagellum and its attachment to the prokaryotic cell wall, producing an incredibly complex structure.*

61) If the complex protein assemblage of the prokaryotic flagellum arose by the same general processes as those of the complex eyes of advanced molluscs (such as squids), then

 A) natural selection cannot account for the rise of the prokaryotic flagellum.

 B) ancestral versions of this protein assemblage were either less functional, or had different functions, than modern prokaryotic flagella.

 C) science should accept the conclusion that neither of these structures could have arisen by evolution.

 D) we can conclude that both of these structures must have arisen through the direct action of an intelligent "designer."

 E) Both A and C are true.

Answer: B
*Topic: Concept 24.3*
*Skill: Comprehension*

62) If the prokaryotic flagellum developed from assemblages of proteins that originally were *not* involved with cell motility but with some other function instead, then the modern prokaryotic flagellum is an example of a(n)

 A) vestigial organ.

 B) adoption.

 C) exaptation.

 D) homogeneous organ.

 E) allometric organ.

Answer: C
*Topic: Concept 24.3*
*Skill: Comprehension*

63) An explanation for the evolution of insect wings suggests that wings began as lateral extensions of the body that were used as heat dissipaters for thermoregulation. When they had become sufficiently large, these extensions became useful for gliding through the air, and selection later refined them as flight-producing wings. If this hypothesis is correct, insect wings could best be described as

A) adaptations.

B) mutations.

C) exaptations.

D) isolating mechanisms.

E) examples of natural selection's predictive ability.

Answer: C
*Topic: Concept 24.3*
*Skill: Application*

64) If one organ is an exaptation of another organ, then what must be true of these two organs?

A) They are both vestigial organs.

B) They are homologous organs.

C) They are undergoing convergent evolution.

D) They are found together in the same hybrid species.

E) They have the same function.

Answer: B
*Topic: Concept 24.3*
*Skill: Comprehension*

65) Which of the following examples would be most likely to result in macroevolution?

A) a change in a regulatory gene, which has a major and adaptive impact on morphology

B) a point mutation deep within an intron

C) DNA-DNA hybridization

D) gene flow

E) genetic drift involving a trait that seems to exhibit neutral variation

Answer: A
*Topic: Concept 24.3*
*Skill: Comprehension*

66) An organism has a relatively large number of *Hox* genes in its genome. Which of the following is *not* true of this organism?

A) It evolved from evolutionary ancestors that had fewer *Hox* genes.

B) It must have multiple paired appendages along the length of its body.

C) It has the genetic potential to have a relatively complex anatomy.

D) At least some of its *Hox* genes owe their existence to gene duplication events.

E) Its *Hox* genes cooperated to produce the positional patterns of this organism as it developed.

Answer: B
*Topic: Concept 24.3*
*Skill: Comprehension*

67) Bagworm moth caterpillars feed on evergreens and carry a silken case or bag around with them in which they eventually pupate. Adult female bagworm moths are larval in appearance; they lack the wings and other structures of the adult male and instead retain the appearance of a caterpillar even though they are sexually mature and can lay eggs within the bag. This is a good example of

A) anagenesis.

B) paedomorphosis.

C) sympatric speciation.

D) adaptive radiation.

E) changes in homeotic genes.

Answer: B
*Topic: Concept 24.3*
*Skill: Comprehension*

68) As rat pups mature growth of their snouts and tails outpaces growth of the rest of their bodies, producing the appearance of sexually mature males. It is found that sexually mature female rats prefer to mate with mutant, sexually mature males that possess snouts and tails with juvenile proportions. Which of the following terms is (are) appropriately applied to this situation?

A) sexual selection

B) paedomorphosis

C) allometric growth

D) B and C only

E) A, B, and C

Answer: E
*Topic: Concept 24.3*
*Skill: Comprehension*

69) A hypothetical mutation in a squirrel population produces organisms with eight legs rather than four. Further, these mutant squirrels survive, successfully invade new habitats, and eventually give rise to a new species. The initial event giving rise to extra legs would be a good example of

A) punctuated equilibrium.

B) species selection.

C) habitat selection.

D) changes in homeotic genes.

E) allometry.

Answer: D
*Topic: Concept 24.3*
*Skill: Comprehension*

70) Many species of snakes lay eggs, but in the forests of northern Minnesota where growing seasons are short, only live-bearing snake species are present. This trend toward species that perform live birth is an example of

A) natural selection.

B) sexual selection.

C) species selection.

D) goal direction in evolution.

E) directed selection.

Answer: C
*Topic: Concept 24.3*
*Skill: Comprehension*

71) In the 5-6 million years that the hominid lineage has been diverging from its common ancestor with the great apes, dozens of hominid species have arisen, often with several species coexisting in time and space. As recently as 30,000 years ago, *Homo sapiens* coexisted with *Homo neanderthalensis*. Both species had large brains and advanced intellects. That these traits were common to both species is most easily explained by which of the following?

   A) species selection

   B) uniformitarianism

   C) sexual selection

   D) A and B only

   E) A, B, and C

Answer: A
*Topic: Concept 24.3*
*Skill: Comprehension*

72) The existence of evolutionary trends, such as increasing body sizes among horse species, is evidence that

   A) a larger volume-to-surface area ratio is beneficial to all mammals.

   B) an unseen guiding force is at work.

   C) evolution always tends toward increased complexity or increased size.

   D) in particular environments, similar adaptations can be beneficial in more than one species.

   E) evolution generally progresses toward some predetermined goal.

Answer: D
*Topic: Concept 24.3*
*Skill: Comprehension*

73) In certain motile prokaryotes, dozens of different proteins comprise the motor that powers the prokaryotic flagellum. The motor has a complicated structure, and its various proteins interact to carry out its function. Based on Darwin's explanation for the existence of human eyes, how would he probably have explained the existence of such motors?

   A) Because he could not have explained their existence, he would have used supernatural agents as a temporary explanation until the gap in scientific knowledge had been filled.

   B) Because he could not have explained their existence, he would have concluded that the human brain has not (and probably cannot) evolve the capability to solve such complex problems.

   C) He would have proposed that these motors were the products of aliens, and had been delivered to Earth by extraterrestrial visitors.

   D) Faced with such complexity, he would have given up science.

   E) He would have proposed that less complicated, but still functional, versions (though maybe with a different function) had existed in ancestral prokaryotes.

Answer: E
*Topic: Concept 24.3*
*Skill: Comprehension*

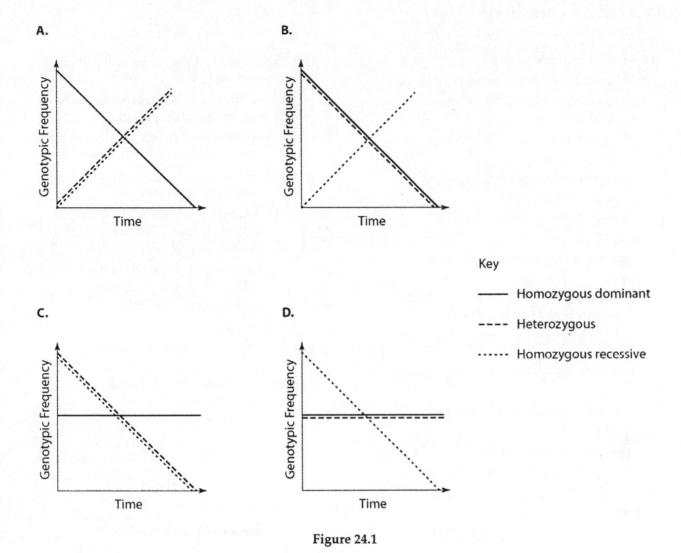

Figure 24.1

# Media Activity Questions

1) What is macroevolution?

   A) evolution as it occurs on a large scale

   B) it is a synonym for "stabilizing selection"

   C) population-level changes in gene frequencies

   D) a uniform change in the rate and pattern of evolution

   E) change on the subspecies level

   Answer: A
   *Topic: Web/CD Activity: Macroevolution*

2) Which is one way that the skulls of adult chimpanzees and humans differ?

   A) Adult chimpanzees have a less angled skull.

   B) Adult chimpanzees have less massive jaws.

   C) Adult chimpanzees have heavier brow ridges.

   D) Adult chimpanzees have flatter faces.

   E) Adult chimpanzees have rounded faces.

   Answer: C
   *Topic: Web/CD Activity: Allometric Growth*

3) "Allometric" growth refers to

   A) the retention of juvenile characteristics in the adult.

   B) growth in height.

   C) large genetic changes.

   D) the variation in growth rate of various parts of the body.

   E) growth in girth.

   Answer: D
   *Topic: Web/CD Activity: Allometric Growth*

4) Variations in allometric growth patterns demonstrate how

   A) relative large genetic change can have minor impact on phenotype.

   B) relative small genetic change can have a major impact on phenotype.

   C) chimpanzees and humans could not have a common ancestor.

   D) adult chimpanzees are basically juvenile humans that have gained the ability to reproduce.

   E) differences in the fetal skulls of chimpanzees and humans lead to very similar adult skulls.

   Answer: B
   *Topic: Web/CD Activity: Allometric Growth*

5) The fetal skulls of chimpanzees and humans both have

   A) massive jaws.

   B) heavy brow ridges.

   C) small jaws.

   D) sharp angular skulls.

   E) three eyes.

   Answer: C
   *Topic: Web/CD Activity: Allometric Growth*

# Self-Quiz Questions

1) The biological species concept is *not* useful for organisms known only from fossils because
   A) fossils are rarely preserved well enough to distinguish species based on morphology.
   B) it is not possible to test reproductive isolation in fossil forms.
   C) it is not possible to infer the types of habitats occupied by fossil forms before their extinction.
   D) in examining fossil organisms, it is not possible to distinguish males from females.
   E) the fossil record can only be used for studying anagenesis, but not cladogenesis.

   Answer: B

2) The *largest* unit in which gene flow can readily occur is a
   A) population.
   B) species.
   C) genus.
   D) hybrid.
   E) phylum.

   Answer: B

3) Bird guides once listed the myrtle warbler and Audubon's warbler as distinct species. Recently, these birds have been classified as eastern and western forms of a single species, the yellow-rumped warbler. Which of the following pieces of evidence, if true, would be cause for this reclassification?
   A) The two forms are observed to interbreed successfully where their habitats overlap.
   B) The two forms live in similar habitats.
   C) The two forms have many genes in common.
   D) The two forms have similar food requirements.
   E) The two forms are very similar in coloration.

   Answer: A

4) Males of different species of the fruit fly *Drosophila* that live in the same parts of the Hawaiian islands have different elaborate courtship rituals that involve fighting other males and stylized movements that attract females. What type of reproductive isolation does this represent?
   A) habitat isolation
   B) temporal isolation
   C) behavioral isolation
   D) gametic isolation
   E) postzygotic barriers

   Answer: C

5) Which of the following factors would *not* contribute to allopatric speciation?

   A) A population becomes geographically isolated from the parent population.

   B) The separated population is small, and genetic drift occurs.

   C) The isolated population is exposed to different selection pressures than the ancestral population.

   D) Different mutations begin to distinguish the gene pools of the separated populations.

   E) Gene flow between the two populations is extensive.

   Answer: E

6) Plant species A has a diploid number of 12. Plant species B has a diploid number of 16. A new species, C, arises as an allopolyploid from A and B. The likely diploid number for species C would probably be

   A) 12.

   B) 14.

   C) 16.

   D) 28.

   E) 56.

   Answer: D

7) The speciation episode described in question 6 is most likely a case of

   A) allopatric speciation.

   B) sympatric speciation.

   C) speciation based on sexual selection.

   D) adaptive radiation.

   E) anagenesis.

   Answer: B

8) *Mimulus lewisii* and *M. cardinalis* are plants that do not hybridize in nature but can be readily crossed in the laboratory to produce fertile offspring. Which of the following is *least* likely to keep the gene pools of these two plants separate in nature?

   A) gametic incompatibility

   B) different attractiveness to pollinators

   C) different ecological niches

   D) different geographic ranges

   E) seasonal differences in flowering

   Answer: A

9) According to the punctuated equilibrium model,

   A) natural selection is unimportant as a mechanism of evolution.

   B) given enough time, most existing species will branch gradually into new species.

   C) most new species accumulate their unique features as they comes into existence, then change little for the rest of their duration as a species.

   D) most evolution is goal oriented.

   E) speciation is usually due to a single mutation.

   Answer: C

10) A genetic change that caused a certain *Hox* gene to be expressed along the tip of a vertebrate limb bud instead of farther back made possible the evolution of the tetrapod limb. This type of change is illustrative of

A) the influence of environment on an individual's development.

B) paedomorphosis, or retention of ancestral juvenile structures in an adult organism.

C) a change in a developmental gene or in its regulation that altered the spatial organization of body parts.

D) punctuated equilibrium.

E) the origin of a new species due to allopolyploidy.

Answer: C

# Chapter 25  Phylogeny and Systematics

1) Which combination of the following species characteristics would cause the greatest likelihood of fossilization in sedimentary rock?
   I.   The species was abundant.
   II.  The species was widespread.
   III. The species had hard body parts.
   IV.  The species was adapted to desert life.
   V.   The species had a long duration in geologic time.

   A) III only
   B) III and IV
   C) I, II, and III
   D) I, II, and V
   E) I, II, III, and V

   Answer: E
   *Topic: Concept 25.1*
   *Skill: Comprehension*

2) The ostrich and the emu look very similar and live in similar habitats, however they are not very closely related. This is an example of

   A) divergent evolution.
   B) convergent evolution.
   C) exaptation.
   D) adaptive radiation.
   E) sympatric speciation.

   Answer: B
   *Topic: Concept 25.1*
   *Skill: Comprehension*

3) Which of the following pairs are homologous?

   A) bat wing and human hand
   B) owl wing and hornet wing
   C) porcupine quill and cactus spine
   D) bat forelimb and bird wing
   E) Australian mole and North American mole

   Answer: A
   *Topic: Concept 25.1*
   *Skill: Comprehension*

4) Some molecular data place the giant panda in the bear family (Ursidae) but place the lesser panda in the raccoon family (Procyonidae). The morphological similarities of these two species must therefore be due to

   A) inheritance of acquired characteristics.
   B) sexual selection.
   C) inheritance of shared derived characters.
   D) convergent evolution.
   E) possession of shared primitive characters.

   Answer: D
   *Topic: Concept 25.1*
   *Skill: Comprehension*

5) The correct sequence from the most to the least comprehensive of the taxonomic levels listed here is

   A) family, phylum, class, kingdom, order, species, and genus.

   B) kingdom, phylum, class, order, family, genus, and species.

   C) kingdom, phylum, order, class, family, genus, and species.

   D) phylum, kingdom, order, class, species, family, and genus.

   E) phylum, family, class, order, kingdom, genus, and species.

Answer: B
*Topic: Concept 25.2*
*Skill: Knowledge*

6) The common house fly belongs to all of the following taxa. Assuming you had access to textbooks or other scientific literature, knowing which of the following should provide you with the greatest amount of *detailed* information about this specific organism?

   A) order Diptera

   B) family Muscidae

   C) genus *Musca*

   D) class Hexapoda

   E) phylum Arthropoda

Answer: C
*Topic: Concept 25.2*
*Skill: Application*

7) *Panthera* is a taxon at which level?

   A) order

   B) family

   C) phylum

   D) genus

   E) class

Answer: D
*Topic: Concept 25.2*
*Skill: Knowledge*

8) If organisms A, B, and C belong to the same class but to different orders and if organisms D, E, and F belong to the same order but to different families, which of the following pairs of organisms would be expected to show the greatest degree of structural homology?

   A) A and B

   B) A and C

   C) B and D

   D) C and F

   E) D and F

Answer: E
*Topic: Concept 25.2*
*Skill: Comprehension*

9) On the basis of their morphologies, how might Linnaeus have classified the Hawaiian silverswords?

   A) He would have placed them all in the same species.

   B) He probably would have classified them the same way that modern botanists do.

   C) He would have placed them in more species than modern botanists do.

   D) He would have used evolutionary relatedness as the primary criterion for their classification.

   E) Both B and D are correct.

Answer: C
*Topic: Concept 25.2*
*Skill: Application*

10) Darwin analogized the effects of evolution as the above-ground portion of a many-branched tree, with extant species being the tips of the twigs. The common ancestor of two species is most analogous to which anatomical tree part?

   A) a single twig that gets longer with time

   B) a node where two twigs diverge

   C) a twig that branches with time

   D) the trunk

   E) neighboring twigs attached to the same stem

   Answer: B
   *Topic: Concept 25.2*
   *Skill: Comprehension*

*Match the individuals below with their accomplishments. Options may be used once, more than once, or not at all.*

   A. Carolus Linnaeus
   B. Charles Darwin
   C. Matoo Kimura
   D. both A and B
   E. both B and C

11) first to think of the hierarchical classification system as a genealogy

   Answer: B
   *Topic: Concept 25.2*
   *Skill: Knowledge*

12) used a classification scheme that did *not* sort homology from analogy

   Answer: A
   *Topic: Concept 25.2*
   *Skill: Knowledge*

13) an originator of neutral theory

   Answer: C
   *Topic: Concept 25.5*
   *Skill: Knowledge*

14) unaware of the existence of genetic mutations

   Answer: D
   *Topic: Concept 25.2*
   *Skill: Knowledge*

15) the originator of the binomial designation for species

   Answer: A
   *Topic: Concept 25.2*
   *Skill: Knowledge*

16) based rate of evolutionary change on the assertion that most genetic mutations in populations are neither harmful nor helpful and therefore are not influenced by natural selection

   Answer: C
   *Topic: Concept 25.5*
   *Skill: Knowledge*

*Match the types of tree diagrams below with the descriptions.*

   A. phlyogenetic tree
   B. phylogram
   C. ultrametric tree
   D. A and B only
   E. A, B, and C

17) Time is represented along at least one axis of the tree.

   Answer: E
   *Topic: Concept 25.3*
   *Skill: Knowledge*

18) Branch length indicates amount of change.

   Answer: B
   *Topic: Concept 25.3*
   *Skill: Knowledge*

19) Branch length distinguishes extant taxa from extinct taxa.

Answer: C
*Topic: Concept 25.3*
*Skill: Knowledge*

20) Provides information only about relative sequence of branch points in time.

Answer: A
*Topic: Concept 25.3*
*Skill: Knowledge*

21) Can provide information about rates of change.

Answer: D
*Topic: Concept 25.3*
*Skill: Knowledge*

22) Can depict phylogeny if based on homologous characters.

Answer: E
*Topic: Concept 25.3*
*Skill: Knowledge*

23) Generally, within a lineage, the largest number of shared derived characters should be found among two organisms that are members of the same

A) kingdom.
B) class.
C) domain.
D) family.
E) order.

Answer: D
*Topic: Concept 25.3*
*Skill: Comprehension*

*Use Figure 25.1 to answer the following questions.*

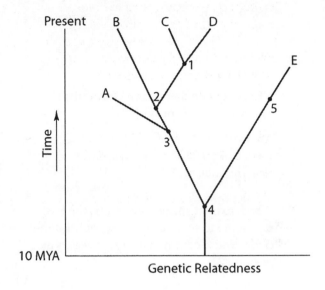

**Figure 25.1**

24) A common ancestor for both species C and E could be at position number

A) 1.
B) 2.
C) 3.
D) 4.
E) 5.

Answer: D
*Topic: Concept 25.3*
*Skill: Application*

25) The two extant species that are most closely related to each other are

A) A and B.
B) B and C.
C) C and D.
D) D and E.
E) E and A.

Answer: C
*Topic: Concept 25.3*
*Skill: Application*

26) Which species are extinct?

   A) A and E

   B) A and B

   C) C and D

   D) D and E

   E) cannot be determined from the information provided

Answer: A
*Topic: Concept 25.3*
*Skill: Application*

27) Which extinct species should be the best candidate to serve as the outgroup for the clade whose common ancestor occurs at position 2?

Answer: A
*Topic: Concept 25.3*
*Skill: Application*

28) If this evolutionary tree is an accurate depiction of relatedness, then which of the following should be *correct*?
1. The entire tree is based on maximum parsimony.
2. If all species depicted here make up a taxon, this taxon is monophyletic.
3. The last common ancestor of species B and C occurred more recently than the last common ancestor of species D and E.
4. Species A is the *direct* ancestor of both species B and species C.
5. The species present at position 3 is ancestral to C, D, and E.

   A) 2 and 5

   B) 1 and 3

   C) 3 and 4

   D) 2, 3, and 4

   E) 1, 2, and 3

Answer: E
*Topic: Concept 25.3*
*Skill: Application*

*The following questions refer to the hypothetical patterns of taxonomic hierarchy shown in Figure 25.2.*

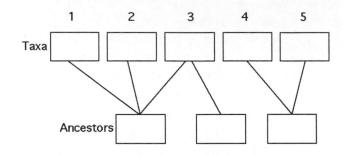

**Figure 25.2**

29) Which of the following numbers represents a polyphyletic taxon?

   A) 2

   B) 3

   C) 4

   D) 5

   E) more than one of these

Answer: B
*Topic: Concept 25.3*
*Skill: Application*

30) If this figure is an accurate depiction of relatedness, then which taxon is unacceptable, based on cladistics?

   A) 1

   B) 2

   C) 3

   D) 4

   E) 5

Answer: C
*Topic: Concept 25.3*
*Skill: Application*

31) Which of the following is *not* true of vertically oriented phylogenetic trees?

A) Each branch point represents a point in absolute time.

B) Organisms represented at the base of such trees are ancestral to those represented at higher levels.

C) The more branch points that occur between two taxa, the more divergent their DNA sequences should be.

D) The common ancestor represented by the highest branch point existed more recently in time than the common ancestors represented at lower branch points.

E) The more branch points there are, the more instances of cladogenesis are represented.

Answer: A
*Topic: Concept 25.3*
*Skill: Comprehension*

32) Ultimately, which of these is the basis for both the principle of maximum parsimony and the principle that shared complexity indicates homology rather than analogy?

A) the laws of thermodynamics

B) Boyle's law

C) the laws of probability

D) chaos theory

E) Hutchinson's law

Answer: C
*Topic: Concept 25.3*
*Skill: Comprehension*

33) The camera–type eyes of octopuses are very complicated and have many of the same features as the camera–type eyes of vertebrates. Yet, the eyes of invertebrates and vertebrates are *not* homologous. This situation is an example of

A) misalignment of sequences.

B) homoplasy.

C) substitution mutations.

D) gene duplication.

E) homogeneity.

Answer: B
*Topic: Concept 25.3*
*Skill: Comprehension*

34) Upon their discovery by Europeans, koalas were classified as bears (Ursidae). Later, it became apparent that koalas are not bears, but marsupial mammals of the family Phascolarctidae. For as long as the koalas were classified as bears, what was true of the family Ursidae?

A) It was polyphyletic.

B) Its classification had a better basis in fact than the current one.

C) Its classification was more in line with molecular evidence than the current one.

D) A and B only

E) A, B, and C

Answer: A
*Topic: Concept 25.3*
*Skill: Comprehension*

*The questions below refer to the following terms. Each term may be used once, more than once, or not at all.*

    A. nonadaptive
    B. analogous
    C. homologous
    D. polyphyletic
    E. monophyletic

35) shared derived characters

    Answer: C
    *Topic: Concept 25.3*
    *Skill: Knowledge*

36) shared primitive characters

    Answer: C
    *Topic: Concept 25.3*
    *Skill: Knowledge*

37) a taxon, all of whose members have the same common ancestor

    Answer: E
    *Topic: Concept 25.3*
    *Skill: Knowledge*

38) bat wing and butterfly wing

    Answer: B
    *Topic: Concept 25.3*
    *Skill: Application*

39) whale pectoral flipper and horse foreleg

    Answer: C
    *Topic: Concept 25.3*
    *Skill: Application*

40) the term that is most appropriately associated with *clade*

    Answer: E
    *Topic: Concept 25.3*
    *Skill: Knowledge*

41) When using a cladistic approach to systematics, which of the following is considered most important for classification?

    A) shared primitive characters

    B) analogous primitive characters

    C) shared derived characters

    D) the degree of evolutionary divergence

    E) overall phenotypic similarity

    Answer: C
    *Topic: Concept 25.3*
    *Skill: Comprehension*

42) The four-chambered hearts of birds and the four-chambered hearts of mammals evolved independently of each other. If one were unaware of this independence, then one might logically conclude that

    A) the common ancestor of birds and mammals had a three-chambered heart.

    B) birds and mammals are more distantly related than is actually the case.

    C) early mammals possessed feathers.

    D) the common ancestor of birds and mammals had a four-chambered heart.

    E) birds and mammals should be placed in the same class.

    Answer: D
    *Topic: Concept 25.3*
    *Skill: Comprehension*

43) Phylogenetic hypotheses (such as those represented by phylogenetic trees) are strongest when

   A) they are based on amino acid sequences from homologous proteins, as long as the genes that code for such proteins contain no introns.

   B) each clade is defined by a single derived character.

   C) they are supported by more than one kind of evidence (such as when fossil evidence corroborates molecular evidence).

   D) they are accepted by the foremost authorities in the field.

   E) they are based on a single putatively homologous DNA sequence.

Answer: C
*Topic: Concept 25.3*
*Skill: Comprehension*

44) Some claim that the birds should continue to be placed in a class (Aves) separate from the Reptilia, despite evidence from molecular systematics indicating a close relationship between birds and crocodiles. Their claim is based on the extent of the adaptations that birds have undergone for flight. The logic of their claim is most similar to that found in which statement?

   A) Dolphins should be classified as fish because of their streamlined bodies and dorsal fins.

   B) Humans should be placed in their own order because no other member of the order Primates features so many modifications for bipedalism.

   C) Koalas (Australian marsupials that feed on Eucalyptus leaves) should be placed in a new family because they are so similar in appearance to true (eutherian) bears.

   D) Convergent evolution has made the cacti of the New World and the euphorbs of the Old World so alike in appearance that they ought to be placed together in the same taxon.

   E) Pterodactyls are an extinct group of reptiles that were well-adapted for flight and, thus, were the first birds.

Answer: B
*Topic: Concept 25.3*
*Skill: Comprehension*

Morphologically, Species A is very similar to four other species, B–E. Yet the nucleotide sequence deep within an intron in a gene shared by all five of these eukaryotic species is quite different in Species A compared to that of the other four species when one studies the nucleotides present at each position.

*(See page 406 for Figure 25.3.)*

45) If the sequence of Species A differs from that of the other four species due to simple misalignment, then what should the computer software find when it compares the sequence of Species A to those of the other four species?

    A) The nucleotide at position 1 should be different in Species A, but the same in species B–E.

    B) The nucleotide sequence of Species A should have long sequences that are nearly identical to those of the other species, but offset in terms of position number.

    C) The sequences of species B–E, though different from that of Species A, should be identical to each other, without exception.

    D) If the software compares, not nucleotide sequence, but rather the amino acid sequence of the actual protein product, then the amino acid sequences of species B–E should be similar to each other, but very different from that of Species A.

    E) Computer software is useless in determining sequences of introns; it can only be used with exons.

Answer: B
*Topic: Concept 25.3*
*Skill: Application*

46) Assuming that misalignment has occurred at one time in the sequence of Species A, what kinds of mutations seem to be connected to this misalignment?

    I.   insertion
    II.   substitution
    III.  deletion
    IV.  point
    V.   neutral

    A) I and IV

    B) II and V

    C) III and V

    D) I, IV, and V

    E) III, IV, and V

Answer: D
*Topic: Concept 25.3*
*Skill: Application*

47) A researcher wants to determine the genetic relatedness of several breeds of dog (*Canis familiaris*). The researcher should compare homologous sequences of _____ that are known to be _____.

    A) carbohydrates; poorly conserved

    B) fatty acids; highly conserved

    C) lipids; poorly conserved

    D) proteins or nucleic acids; poorly conserved

    E) amino acids; highly conserved

Answer: D
*Topic: Concept 25.4*
*Skill: Knowledge*

48) Nucleic acid sequences that undergo few changes over the course of evolutionary time are said to be *conserved*. Conserved nucleic acids should

  A) be found in the most crucial portions of proteins.

  B) include all mitochondrial DNA.

  C) be abundant in ribosomes.

  D) be proportionately more common in eukaryotic introns than in eukaryotic exons.

  E) comprise a larger proportion of pre–mRNA (immature mRNA) than of mature mRNA.

Answer: C
*Topic: Concept 25.4*
*Skill: Knowledge*

49) Species that are *not* closely related and that do *not* share many anatomical similarities can still be placed together on the same phylogenetic tree by comparing their

  A) plasmids.

  B) chloroplast genomes.

  C) mitochondrial genomes.

  D) homologous genes that are poorly conserved.

  E) homologous genes that are highly conserved.

Answer: E
*Topic: Concept 25.4*
*Skill: Comprehension*

*The following questions refer to the information below.*

A researcher compared the nucleotide sequences of a homologous gene from five different species of mammals with the homologous human gene. The sequence homology between each species' version of the gene and the human gene is presented as a percentage of similarity.

| Species | Percentage |
|---|---|
| Chimpanzee | 99.7 |
| Orangutan | 98.6 |
| Baboon | 97.2 |
| Rhesus Monkey | 96.9 |
| Rabbit | 93.7 |

50) What probably explains the inclusion of rabbits in this research?

  A) Their short generation time provides a ready source of DNA.

  B) They possess all of the shared derived characters as do the other species listed.

  C) They are the closest known relatives of rhesus monkeys.

  D) They are the outgroup.

  E) They are the most recent common ancestor of the primates.

Answer: D
*Topic: Concept 25.4*
*Skill: Application*

51) What conclusion can be drawn validly from these data?

   A) Humans and other primates evolved from rabbits within the past 10 million years.

   B) Most of the genes of other organisms are paralogous to human genes, or with chimpanzee genes.

   C) Among the organisms listed, humans shared a common ancestor most recently with chimpanzees.

   D) Humans evolved from chimpanzees somewhere in Africa within the last 6 million years.

   E) Both B and C are correct.

Answer: C
*Topic: Concept 25.4*
*Skill: Application*

52) Typically, mutations that modify the active site of an enzyme are more likely to be harmful than mutations that affect other parts of the enzyme. A hypothetical enzyme consists of four domains (A-D), and the amino acid sequences of these four domains have been determined in five related species. Given the proportion of amino acid homologies among the five species at each of the four domains, which domain probably contains the active site?

| Domain | Percentage of Homologous Amino Acids |
|--------|-------------------------------------|
| A | 32% |
| B | 8% |
| C | 78% |
| D | 45% |

Answer: C
*Topic: Concept 25.4*
*Skill: Application*

53) When sufficient heat is applied, double-stranded DNA denatures into two single-stranded molecules as the heat breaks all of the hydrogen bonds. In an experiment, molecules of single-stranded DNA from species X are separately hybridized with putatively homologous single-stranded DNA molecules from five species (A-E). The hybridized DNAs are then heated, and the temperature at which complete denaturation occurs is recorded. Based on the data below, which species is probably most closely related to species X?

| Species | Temperature at Which Hybridized DNA Denatures |
|---------|----------------------------------------------|
| A | 30°C |
| B | 85°C |
| C | 74°C |
| D | 60°C |
| E | 61°C |

Answer: B
*Topic: Concept 25.4*
*Skill: Application*

54) The lakes of northern Minnesota contain many similar species of damselflies of the genus *Enallagma* that have apparently undergone speciation from ancestral stock since the last glacial retreat about 10,000 years ago. Sequencing which of the following would probably be most useful in sorting out evolutionary relationships among these closely related species?

   A) nuclear DNA

   B) mitochondrial DNA

   C) small nuclear RNA

   D) ribosomal RNA

   E) amino acids in proteins

Answer: B
*Topic: Concept 25.4*
*Skill: Comprehension*

55) Cladograms based on evidence from molecular systematics are based on similarities in

A) morphology.

B) the pattern of embryological development.

C) biochemical pathways.

D) habitat and lifestyle choices.

E) mutations to homologous genes.

Answer: E
*Topic: Concept 25.4*
*Skill: Knowledge*

56) Which statement represents the best explanation for the observation that the nuclear DNA of wolves and domestic dogs has a very high degree of homology?

A) Dogs and wolves have very similar morphologies.

B) Dogs and wolves belong to the same order.

C) Dogs and wolves are both members of the family Canidae.

D) Dogs and wolves shared a common ancestor very recently.

E) Convergent evolution has occurred.

Answer: D
*Topic: Concept 25.4*
*Skill: Comprehension*

57) The reason that paralogous genes can diverge from each other within the same gene pool, whereas orthologous genes diverge after gene pools are isolated from each other, is that

A) having multiple copies of genes is essential for sympatric speciation.

B) paralogous genes can occur only in diploid species.

C) polyploidy is a necessary precondition for sympatric speciation.

D) having an extra copy of a gene permits modifications to the copy without loss of the original gene product.

E) both A and C

Answer: D
*Topic: Concept 25.4*
*Skill: Comprehension*

58) If the genes of yeast are 50% orthologous to those of humans, and if the genes of mice are 99% orthologous to those of humans, then one might validly expect _____ % of the genes of fish to be orthologous to the genes of humans.

A) 10

B) 30

C) 40

D) 50

E) 80

Answer: E
*Topic: Concept 25.4*
*Skill: Application*

59) What is true of gene duplication?

A) It is a type of point mutation.

B) Its occurrence is limited to diploid species.

C) Its occurrence is limited to organisms without functional DNA-repair enzymes.

D) It is most similar in its effects to a deletion mutation.

E) It can increase the size of a genome over evolutionary time.

Answer: E
*Topic: Concept 25.4*
*Skill: Comprehension*

60) Mutations that occur deep within intronic sequences that are not subject to alternative splicing, and not subject to DNA-repair enzyme activity, should usually be _____ mutations.

A) point

B) neutral

C) deletion

D) beneficial

E) harmful

Answer: B
*Topic: Concept 25.5*
*Skill: Comprehension*

61) Which of these theoretically permit(s) a large proportion of base-pair substitutions to be neutral in their effect?

A) the observation that in eukaryotes, 90–95% of gene sequences are intronic

B) the prevalence of third-base-wobble and the redundancy of the genetic code

C) natural selection eliminating the harmful mutations

D) A and B only

E) A, B, and C

Answer: D
*Topic: Concept 25.5*
*Skill: Comprehension*

62) Which of these is most likely to increase the rate of a molecular clock?

A) genes being replicated by DNA polymerases that have no proofreading capability

B) genes with a high proportion of guanine-cytosine pairs

C) the absence of introns from genes

D) when the amino acid sequence of the gene product is critical for proper functioning

E) the absence of functional telomerases

Answer: A
*Topic: Concept 25.5*
*Skill: Comprehension*

63) Which process hinders clarification of the deepest branchings in a phylogenetic tree that depicts the origins of the three domains?

A) binary fission

B) mitosis

C) meiosis

D) horizontal gene transfer

E) gene duplication

Answer: D
*Topic: Concept 25.5*
*Skill: Knowledge*

64) The average mutation rate of a gene can be used as a molecular clock. Which type of mutation would cause an underestimate of the time that elapsed since two related species diverged from their common ancestor?

A) a mutation to the third base of a nucelotide codon

B) a mutation to the second base of a nucleotide codon

C) a mutation to the first base of a nucleotide codon

D) a mutation that returns a mutated nucleotide to its original state

E) a mutation that substitutes a different amino acid in place of the original amino acid

Answer: D
*Topic: Concept 25.5*
*Skill: Comprehension*

*The graph in Figure 25.4 depicts the number of mutations occurring over time (mutation rate) in five possible patterns (A–E).*

*(See page 406 for Figure 25.4.)*

65) Which pattern of mutation rate would be most helpful if one desires to use a gene as a molecular clock to determine evolutionary relatedness of species that are *not* closely related to each other?

Answer: D
*Topic: Concept 25.5*
*Skill: Application*

66) Which pattern of mutation rate would be most helpful if one desires to use a gene as a molecular clock to determine evolutionary relatedness of species that *are* closely related to each other?

Answer: A
*Topic: Concept 25.5*
*Skill: Application*

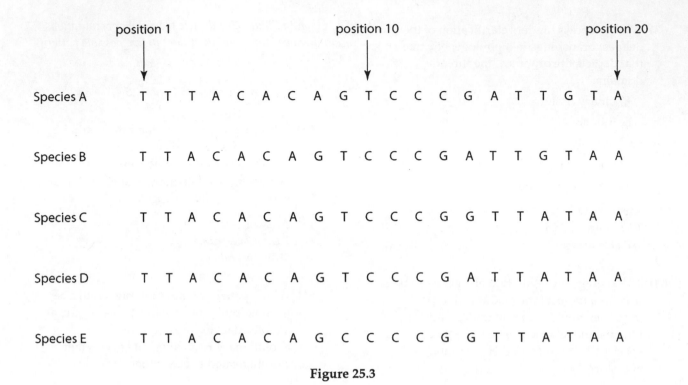

**Figure 25.3**

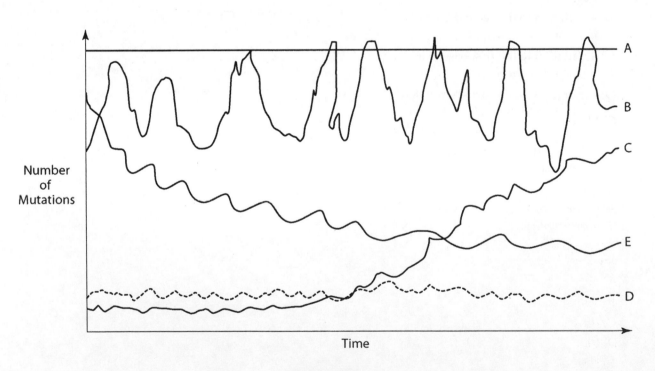

**Figure 25.4**

# Media Activity Questions

1) We are living during the _____ era.

   A) Neogene

   B) Cenozoic

   C) Paleozoic

   D) Paleogene

   E) Mesozoic

   Answer: B
   *Topic: Activity: A Scrolling Geologic Time Scale*

2) _____ were the dominant vertebrate life form during the Paleozoic era.

   A) Amphibians

   B) Reptiles

   C) Sponges

   D) Dinosaurs

   E) Mammals

   Answer: A
   *Topic: Activity: A Scrolling Geologic Time Scale*

3) Flowering plants first appeared during the _____.

   A) Devonian

   B) Precambrian

   C) Mesozoic

   D) Cenozoic

   E) Carboniferous

   Answer: C
   *Topic: Activity: A Scrolling Geologic Time Scale*

4) There is (are) _____ prokaryotic domain(s).

   A) one

   B) two

   C) three

   D) four

   E) five

   Answer: B
   *Topic: Web/CD Activity: Classification Schemes*

5) In the two-kingdom system, why were prokaryotes classified in the kingdom Plantae?

   A) They are sedentary.

   B) They are heterotrophs.

   C) They have cell walls.

   D) They are unicellular.

   E) They are autotrophs.

   Answer: C
   *Topic: Web/CD Activity: Classification Schemes*

# Self-Quiz Questions

1) If humans and pandas belong to the same class, then they must also belong to the same
   A) order.
   B) phylum.
   C) family.
   D) genus.
   E) species.

   Answer: B

2) Three living species X, Y, and Z share a common ancestor T, as do extinct species U and V. A grouping of species T, X, Y, and Z make up
   A) a valid taxon.
   B) a monophyletic clade.
   C) a paraphyletic clade.
   D) a polyphyletic grouping.
   E) an ingroup for comparison with species U as the outgroup.

   Answer: C

3) In a comparison of birds with mammals, having four appendages is
   A) a shared primitive character.
   B) a shared derived character.
   C) a character useful for distinguishing the birds from mammals.
   D) an example of analogy rather than homology.
   E) a character useful for sorting bird species.

   Answer: A

4) How would one apply the principle of parsimony to the construction of a phylogenetic tree?
   A) Choose the tree that assumes all evolutionary changes are equally probable.
   B) Choose the tree in which the branch points are based on as many shared derived characters as possible.
   C) Base phylogenetic trees only on the fossil record, as this provides the simplest explanation for evolution.
   D) Choose the tree that represents the fewest evolutionary changes, either in DNA sequences or morphology.
   E) Choose the tree with the fewest branch points.

   Answer: D

5) What would be the best source of data for determining phylogenetic relationships of lineages of protists that diverged hundreds of millions of years ago?
   A) fossils from the Proterozoic eon
   B) morphological characters that are shared and derived
   C) amino acid sequences of their various chlorophyll molecules
   D) mtDNA sequences
   E) rRNA gene sequences

   Answer: E

6) If you were using cladistic analysis to build a phylogenetic tree of cats, which of the following would make the best outgroup?
   A) lion
   B) domestic cat
   C) wolf
   D) leopard
   E) tiger

   Answer: C

7) Which of the following would be most useful for constructing a phylogenetic tree for several fish species?

A) several analogous characteristics shared by all the fishes

B) a single homologous characteristic shared by all the fishes

C) the total degree of morphological similarity among various fish species

D) several characteristics thought to have evolved after different fishes diverged from one another

E) a single characteristic that is different in all the fishes

Answer: D

8) The relative lengths of the amphibian and mouse branches in the phylogram in Figure 25.12 in your text indicate that

A) amphibians evolved before mice.

B) mice evolved before amphibians.

C) the genes of amphibians and mice have only coincidental homoplasies.

D) the homologous gene has evolved more rapidly in amphibians.

E) the homologous gene has evolved more rapidly in mice.

Answer: D

9) Choose the pair of orthologous genes from the following list.

A) human α hemoglobin and chimpanzee α hemoglobin genes

B) two alleles of the human α hemoglobin gene

C) mouse insulin gene and yeast mating-type gene

D) two different rat olfactory receptor genes

E) the multiple copies of rRNA genes in a eukaryotic genome

Answer: A

10) The recent estimate that HIV–1 M first jumped from chimpanzees to humans in the 1930s is based on

A) the first clinical evidence of AIDS recorded in local village records in Africa.

B) a molecular clock that used changes in sequences of an HIV gene sampled from patients over the past 40 years to project backward to an estimated origin.

C) a comparison of homologous genes in HIV found in chimpanzees and in humans.

D) a parsimonious explanation of the evolutionary relationships among the various strains of the virus found in humans at the present time.

E) the recent discovery of HIV in a blood sample saved from the 1930s.

Answer: B

# Chapter 26   The Tree of Life: An Introduction to Biological Diversity

1) The first genetic material was most likely a(n)
   A) DNA polymer.
   B) DNA oligonucleotide.
   C) RNA polymer.
   D) protein.
   E) protein enzyme.

   Answer: C
   *Topic: Concept 26.1*
   *Skill: Knowledge*

2) Which gas was probably *least* abundant in Earth's early atmosphere?
   A) $O_2$
   B) CO
   C) $CH_4$
   D) $H_2O$
   E) $NH_3$

   Answer: A
   *Topic: Concept 26.1*
   *Skill: Knowledge*

3) In their laboratory simulations of the early Earth, Miller and Urey observed the abiotic synthesis of
   A) amino acids.
   B) complex organic polymers.
   C) DNA.
   D) liposomes.
   E) nucleoli.

   Answer: A
   *Topic: Concept 26.1*
   *Skill: Knowledge*

4) Which putative early Earth condition did Miller and Urey's experimental apparatus *not* attempt to simulate directly?
   A) presence of water vapor
   B) intense lightning storms
   C) warm seas
   D) intense UV bombardment
   E) reducing atmosphere

   Answer: D
   *Topic: Concept 26.1*
   *Skill: Comprehension*

5) Which of the factors below weaken the hypothesis of abiotic synthesis of organic monomers in early Earth's atmosphere?
   1.  the relatively short time between intense meteor bombardment and appearance of the first life forms
   2.  the lack of experimental evidence that organic monomers can form by abiotic synthesis
   3.  uncertainty about which gases comprised early Earth's atmosphere
   A) 1
   B) 2
   C) 3
   D) 1 and 3
   E) 2 and 3

   Answer: D
   *Topic: Concept 26.1*
   *Skill: Comprehension*

6) The early atmosphere of Earth probably retained all of the following molecules in substantial amounts *except*

A) $H_2$.

B) $CH_4$.

C) $CO_2$.

D) $N_2$.

E) $H_2O$.

Answer: A
*Topic: Concept 26.1*
*Skill: Knowledge*

7) Which of the following has not yet been synthesized in laboratory experiments studying the origin of life?

A) liposomes

B) liposomes with selectively permeable membranes

C) oligopeptides and other oligomers

D) protobionts that use DNA to program protein synthesis

E) amino acids

Answer: D
*Topic: Concept 26.1*
*Skill: Comprehension*

8) In what way were conditions on Earth more than 2 billion years ago different from those on Earth today?

A) The early Earth had water vapor in its atmosphere.

B) The early Earth was intensely bombarded by large space debris.

C) The early Earth had an oxidizing atmosphere.

D) Less ultraviolet radiation penetrated the early atmosphere.

E) The early atmosphere had significant quantities of ozone.

Answer: B
*Topic: Concept 26.1*
*Skill: Knowledge*

9) What condition would have made the primitive atmosphere of Earth more conducive to the origin of life than the present one? The primitive atmosphere

A) had a layer of ozone that shielded the first fragile cells.

B) removed electrons that impeded the formation of protobionts.

C) may have been a reducing one that facilitated the formation of complex substances from simple molecules.

D) had more oxygen than the modern atmosphere, and thus it successfully sustained the first living organisms.

E) had less free energy than the modern atmosphere, and thus newly formed organisms were less likely to be destroyed.

Answer: C
*Topic: Concept 26.1*
*Skill: Comprehension*

10) What is true of the amino acids delivered to Earth within carbonaceous chondrites?

A) They have the same proportion of L and D isomers as Earth does today.

B) The proportion of the amino acids are similar to those produced in the Miller–Urey experiment.

C) There were fewer kinds of amino acids on the chondrites than are found in living organisms today.

D) They were delivered in the form of polypeptides.

E) Upon entry into Earth's oxidizing atmosphere, most were destroyed.

Answer: B
*Topic: Concept 26.1*
*Skill: Comprehension*

11) Which of the following is the *correct* sequence of these events in the origin of life?

    I.   Formation of protobionts
    II.  Synthesis of organic monomers
    III. Synthesis of organic polymers

A) I, II, III

B) I, III, II

C) II, III, I

D) III, I, II

E) III, II, I

Answer: C
*Topic: Concept 26.1*
*Skill: Comprehension*

12) What characteristic would all protobionts have had in common?

A) the ability to synthesize enzymes

B) a surrounding membrane or membrane-like structure

C) RNA genes

D) a nucleus

E) the ability to replicate RNA

Answer: B
*Topic: Concept 26.1*
*Skill: Comprehension*

13) Although absolute distinctions between the "most evolved" protobiont and the first living cell are unclear, biologists generally agree that one major difference is that protobionts could *not*

A) possess a selectively permeable membrane boundary.

B) perform osmosis.

C) grow in size.

D) perform controlled, precise reproduction.

E) absorb compounds from the external environment.

Answer: D
*Topic: Concept 26.1*
*Skill: Comprehension*

14) Which of the following statements about the origin of genetic material is most probably *correct*? The first genes were

A) DNA produced by reverse transcriptase from abiotically produced RNA.

B) DNA molecules whose information was transcribed to RNA and later translated in polypeptides.

C) self-replicating, catalytic RNA molecules.

D) RNA produced by autocatalytic, proteinaceous enzymes called ribozymes.

E) protobionts produced by dehydration syntheses of nucleic acids.

Answer: C
*Topic: Concept 26.1*
*Skill: Comprehension*

15) RNA molecules can be both self-replicating and catalytic. This probably means that

A) RNA was the first hereditary information.

B) protobionts had an RNA membrane.

C) RNA could make energy.

D) free nucleotides would not have been necessary ingredients in the synthesis of new RNA molecules.

E) RNA is a polymer of amino acids.

Answer: A
*Topic: Concept 26.1*
*Skill: Comprehension*

16) What probably accounts for the switch to DNA-based genetic systems during the evolution of life on Earth?

A) DNA is chemically more stable and replicates with fewer errors (mutations) than RNA.

B) Only DNA can replicate during cell division.

C) RNA is too involved with translation of proteins and cannot provide multiple functions.

D) DNA forms the rod-shaped chromosomes necessary for cell division.

E) Replication of RNA occurs too quickly.

Answer: A
*Topic: Concept 26.1*
*Skill: Knowledge*

17) The synthesis of new DNA requires the prior existence of oligonucleotides to serve as primers. On Earth, these primers are small RNA molecules. This latter observation is evidence in support of the hypothesized existence of

A) a snowball Earth.

B) an RNA world.

C) the abiotic synthesis of organic monomers.

D) the delivery of organic matter to Earth by meteors and comets.

E) the endosymbiotic origin of mitochondria and chloroplasts.

Answer: B
*Topic: Concept 26.1*
*Skill: Comprehension*

18) How could RNA have become involved in the mechanism for protein translation?

A) Only ribozymes were available as catalysts.

B) RNA replication is enhanced if proteins are produced.

C) Natural selection acted against autocatalytic protein formation.

D) DNA was not available for protein translation.

E) Natural selection favored RNA molecules that synthesized catalytic proteins.

Answer: E
*Topic: Concept 26.1*
*Skill: Comprehension*

19) If the half-life of carbon-14 is about 5,730 years, then a fossil that has one-eighth the normal proportion of carbon-14 to carbon-12 is probably _____ years old.

A) 1,400

B) 2,800

C) 11,200

D) 16,800

E) 22,400

Answer: D
*Topic: Concept 26.2*
*Skill: Application*

20) Which measurement would help determine absolute dates by radiometric means?

A) the accumulation of the daughter isotope

B) the loss of parent isotopes

C) the loss of daughter isotopes

D) all three of these

E) only A and B

Answer: E
*Topic: Concept 26.2*
*Skill: Comprehension*

21) How many half-lives should have elapsed if 12.5% of the parent isotope remains in a fossil at the time of analysis?

A) one

B) two

C) three

D) four

E) five

Answer: C
*Topic: Concept 26.2*
*Skill: Application*

22) Approximately how far back in time does the fossil record extend?

A) 6,000 years

B) 3,500,000 years

C) 6,000,000 years

D) 3,500,000,000 years

E) 5,000,000,000,000 years

Answer: D
*Topic: Concept 26.2*
*Skill: Knowledge*

23) What was the consequence of the release of oxygen gas by plant and bacterial photosynthesis? It

A) made life on land difficult for aerobic organisms.

B) changed the atmosphere from oxidizing to reducing.

C) made it easier to maintain reduced molecules.

D) made Earth an oxidizing environment.

E) prevented the formation of an ozone layer.

Answer: D
*Topic: Concept 26.3*
*Skill: Comprehension*

24) Arrange these events from earliest to most recent.

1. emission of lava in what is now Siberia at time of Permian extinctions

2. emission of lava that solidified at the same time as iron-bearing terrestrial rocks began to rust

3. emission of lava that solidified at the same time as the first banded iron formations formed

4. emission of lava in what is now India at time of Cretaceous extinctions

A) 3, 1, 2, 4

B) 3, 2, 1, 4

C) 3, 1, 4, 2

D) 1, 3, 2, 4

E) 1, 2, 3, 4

Answer: B
*Topic: Concept 26.3*
*Skill: Comprehension*

25) The ancestors of which free-living cells were the earliest autotrophs to contribute to the formation of Earth's oxidizing atmosphere?

A) cyanobacteria

B) chloroplasts

C) mitochondria

D) seaweeds

E) endosymbionts

Answer: A
*Topic: Concept 26.3*
*Skill: Knowledge*

26) Elemental sulfur is to hydrogen–sulfide–splitting prokaryotes as _____ is to water–splitting prokaryotes.

A) $H^+$

B) $H_2$

C) $OH^-$

D) $O_2$

E) $H_2O$

Answer: D
*Topic: Concept 26.3*
*Skill: Comprehension*

27) All are true of the photosynthetic machinery of cyanobacteria, *except*

A) it involved a modified version of electron transport.

B) it was assembled from two anaerobic systems that had originated in different types of bacteria.

C) it evolved relatively late in the evolution of prokaryotes, sometime after eukaryotes had arisen.

D) it obtains electrons by splitting water.

E) it caused Earth's atmosphere to become an oxidizing one.

Answer: C
*Topic: Concept 26.3*
*Skill: Comprehension*

28) At the time when Earth's atmosphere was becoming increasingly oxidizing, which reaction could have helped to prevent damage to oxygen-sensitive enzymes and structures. In which prokaryotes might such a reaction have been expected to occur? (*Note*: these reactions are not balanced.)

A) $e^- + H^+ + O_2 \rightarrow H_2O$, alpha proteobacteria

B) $e^- + H^+ + S \rightarrow H_2S$, non–purple sulfur bactria

C) $e^- + H^+ + CO_2 \rightarrow H_2CO_3$, obligate anaerobes

D) $H_2O \rightarrow e^- + H^+ + O_2$, cyanobacteria

E) $H_2S \rightarrow e^- + H^+ + S$, purple sulfur bacteria

Answer: A
*Topic: Concept 26.3*
*Skill: Comprehension*

29) Which of the following statements provides the strongest evidence that prokaryotes evolved before eukaryotes?

A) the primitive structure of plants

B) meteorites that have struck Earth

C) abiotic laboratory experiments that produced liposomes

D) Liposomes resemble prokaryotic cells.

E) The oldest fossilized cells resemble prokaryotes.

Answer: E
*Topic: Concept 26.3*
*Skill: Comprehension*

30) How would the chief hypothesis concerning the origin of the ER and Golgi apparatus be described?

    A) endosymbiosis

    B) serial endosymbiosis

    C) genetic annealing

    D) infolding of the plasma membrane

    E) outfolding of the nuclear lamina

    Answer: D
    *Topic: Concept 26.4*
    *Skill: Knowledge*

31) Which is an actual observation that provides the strongest evidence for the possible origin of the eukaryotic cytoskeleton?

    A) Prokaryotic flagella possess microtubules in the 9 + 2 pattern.

    B) Only certain bacteria possess flagella.

    C) Homologs of actin and tubulin are found in certain bacteria.

    D) There is a lamina located within prokaryotic nuclei.

    E) The flagella of prokaryotes are hollow, like the microtubules of eukaryotic flagella.

    Answer: C
    *Topic: Concept 26.4*
    *Skill: Comprehension*

32) Certain protists, namely the parabasalids and diplomonads, have tiny mitochondrial "remnants" that lack DNA. Where, in these organisms, would one look if one were trying to confirm the hypothesis that the lack of mitochondrial DNA is due to horizontal gene transfer?

    A) centrioles

    B) cilia and flagella

    C) chloroplasts

    D) transport vesicles

    E) nucleus

    Answer: E
    *Topic: Concept 26.4*
    *Skill: Application*

33) The photosystems of cyanobacteria are embedded in plasma membranes and, in some cases, in internal membranes derived from the plasma membrane. Where would one expect to find the homologous photosystems in green plant cells?

    A) plasma membrane

    B) outer membrane of chloroplasts

    C) inner compartments (stroma) of chloroplasts

    D) inner membranes of chloroplasts

    E) the membranes of other organelles (amyloplasts and tonoplasts)

    Answer: D
    *Topic: Concept 26.4*
    *Skill: Knowledge*

34) The ATP synthase of most mitochondria

A) consists of protein subunits synthesized by ribosomes within the mitochondria.

B) consists of protein subunits synthesized by ribosomes in the surrounding cytoplasm.

C) is a component of a metabolic process that requires oxygen as a final electron acceptor.

D) both A and C

E) A, B, and C

Answer: E
*Topic: Concept 26.4*
*Skill: Knowledge*

35) The hypothesis of "genetic annealing" is used to account for the origin of

A) double-stranded DNA.

B) the mitochondrial genome.

C) the processes of mitosis and meiosis.

D) the nuclear genome.

E) DNA ligases.

Answer: D
*Topic: Concept 26.4*
*Skill: Knowledge*

36) Which process is most directly associated with genetic annealing?

A) binary fission

B) horizontal gene transfer

C) mitosis

D) meiosis

E) membrane invagination

Answer: B
*Topic: Concept 26.4*
*Skill: Comprehension*

37) Which genetic process *requires* one cell or structure to lose genetic material to another cell or structure to which it was *not* previously genetically identical?
1. binary fission
2. mitosis
3. bacterial conjugation
4. horizontal gene transfer

A) 1 only

B) 3 only

C) 1 and 2

D) 1 and 3

E) 3 and 4

Answer: E
*Topic: Concept 26.4*
*Skill: Comprehension*

38) What is the correct sequence of these events, from earliest to most recent, in the evolution of life on Earth?
1. origin of mitochondria
2. origin of multicellular eukaryotes
3. origin of chloroplasts
4. origin of cyanobacteria
5. origin of fungal–plant symbioses

A) 4, 3, 2, 1, 5

B) 4, 1, 2, 3, 5

C) 4, 1, 3, 2, 5

D) 4, 3, 1, 5, 2

E) 3, 4, 1, 2, 5

Answer: C
*Topic: Concept 26.4*
*Skill: Comprehension*

39) Recent evidence indicates that the first major diversification of multicellular eukaryotes may have coincided in time with the

A) origin of prokaryotes.

B) switch to an oxidizing atmosphere.

C) melting that ended the "snowball Earth" period.

D) origin of multicellular organisms.

E) massive eruptions of deep-sea vents.

Answer: C
*Topic: Concept 26.5*
*Skill: Knowledge*

40) Which event may be associated in time with the end of the period known as snowball Earth?

A) oxygenation of Earth's seas and atmosphere

B) evolution of mitochondria

C) Cambrian explosion

D) evolution of true multicellularity

E) Permian extinction

Answer: C
*Topic: Concept 26.5*
*Skill: Knowledge*

41) Assuming total ice cover, which of these would have been the most likely location for the oxygenic photosynthesizers to have survived snowball Earth?

A) deep-sea vents

B) shallow alpine "lakes"

C) at mid-depth in oceans

D) at depth, distant from deep-sea vents

E) in close association with oceanic ice flows

Answer: E
*Topic: Concept 26.5*
*Skill: Comprehension*

42) In order for a beneficial mutation to be transmitted across generations, the mutation must occur in

A) a zygote.

B) a sperm cell.

C) an egg cell.

D) a mother cell about to undergo meiosis.

E) any of the above.

Answer: E
*Topic: Concept 26.5*
*Skill: Comprehension*

43) The snowball Earth hypothesis provides a possible explanation for the

A) diversification of animals at the start of the late Proterozoic.

B) oxygenation of Earth's seas and atmosphere.

C) colonization of land by plants and fungi.

D) origin of $O_2$-releasing photosynthesis.

E) existence of hydrothermal vents on the ocean floor.

Answer: A
*Topic: Concept 26.5*
*Skill: Comprehension*

44) If two continental land masses converge and are united during continental drift, then the collision should bring about

   A) a net loss of intertidal zone and coastal habitat.

   B) the extinction of species adapted to intertidal and coastal habitats.

   C) an overall increase in the surface area located in the continental interior.

   D) an increase in climatic extremes in the interior of the new supercontinent.

   E) all of the above

Answer: E
*Topic: Concept 26.5*
*Skill: Comprehension*

45) A major evolutionary episode that corresponded in time most closely with the formation of Pangaea was the

   A) origin of humans.

   B) Cambrian explosion.

   C) Permian extinctions.

   D) Pleistocene ice ages.

   E) Cretaceous extinctions.

Answer: C
*Topic: Concept 26.5*
*Skill: Knowledge*

46) What kind of evidence has recently made it necessary to assign the prokaryotes to either of two different domains, rather than assigning all prokaryotes to the same kingdom?

   A) molecular

   B) behavioral

   C) nutritional

   D) anatomical

   E) ecological

Answer: A
*Topic: Concept 26.6*
*Skill: Knowledge*

47) What important criterion was used in the late 1960s to distinguish between the three multicellular eukaryotic kingdoms of the five–kingdom classification system?

   A) the number of cells present in individual organisms

   B) the geological stratum in which fossils first appear

   C) the nutritional modes they employ

   D) the biogeographic province where each first appears

   E) the features of their embryos

Answer: C
*Topic: Concept 26.6*
*Skill: Knowledge*

48) As the number of kingdoms increased from two to three, what was true of the kingdom Protista?

   A) It was used to harbor all prokaryotes.

   B) All photosynthetic organisms were assigned to it.

   C) Viruses were assigned to this kingdom.

   D) Unicellular organisms of all kinds were placed here.

   E) It was used for organisms that did not fit clearly into the other two kingdoms.

Answer: E
*Topic: Concept 26.6*
*Skill: Comprehension*

49) The best classification system is that which most closely

    A) unites organisms that possess similar morphologies.

    B) conforms to traditional, Linnaean taxonomic practices.

    C) reflects evolutionary history.

    D) corroborates the classification scheme in use at the time of Charles Darwin.

    E) reflects the basic separation of prokaryotes from eukaryotes.

Answer: C
*Topic: Concept 26.6*
*Skill: Comprehension*

*The questions below refer to the following list, which uses the five-kingdom classification system.*

1. Plantae
2. Fungi
3. Animalia
4. Protista
5. Monera

50) Which obsolete kingdom includes prokaryotic organisms?

    A) 1

    B) 2

    C) 3

    D) 4

    E) 5

Answer: E
*Topic: Concept 26.6*
*Skill: Knowledge*

51) Members of which kingdom have cell walls and are all heterotrophic?

    A) 1

    B) 2

    C) 3

    D) 4

    E) 5

Answer: B
*Topic: Concept 26.6*
*Skill: Knowledge*

52) Which kingdom has been replaced with two domains?

    A) 1

    B) 2

    C) 3

    D) 4

    E) 5

Answer: E
*Topic: Concept 26.6*
*Skill: Knowledge*

53) Which eukaryotic kingdom is polyphyletic and therefore not acceptable, based on cladistics?

    A) 1

    B) 2

    C) 3

    D) 4

    E) 5

Answer: D
*Topic: Concept 26.6*
*Skill: Knowledge*

54) Which kingdoms include free-living photosynthetic organisms?
   A) 1 and 5
   B) 2 and 4
   C) 1, 2, and 5
   D) 1, 4, and 5
   E) 1, 2, 3, 4, and 5

   Answer: D
   *Topic: Concept 26.6*
   *Skill: Knowledge*

*Match the scientists below with their accomplishments.*

   A.  Carl Woese
   B.  Cech and Altman
   C.  Oparin and Haldane
   D.  Miller and Urey
   E.  Robert Whittaker

55) discovered ribozymes

   Answer: B
   *Topic: Concept 26.2*
   *Skill: Knowledge*

56) used SSU–rRNA sequences to propose major modifications to the "tree of life"

   Answer: A
   *Topic: Concept 26.4*
   *Skill: Knowledge*

57) synthesized organic monomers in an apparatus designed to simulate early Earth's conditions

   Answer: D
   *Topic: Concept 26.2*
   *Skill: Knowledge*

58) proposed the five-kingdom classification system

   Answer: E
   *Topic: Concept 26.6*
   *Skill: Knowledge*

59) early proponent(s) of the idea that a reducing atmosphere and energy inputs might have been sufficient to introduce organic monomers to Earth's environment

   Answer: C
   *Topic: Concept 26.1*
   *Skill: Knowledge*

# Media Activity Questions

1) The first prokaryotic cells appeared during the

   A) Jurassic.

   B) Cretaceous.

   C) Paleozoic.

   D) Triassic.

   E) Precambrian.

   Answer: E
   *Topic: Web/CD Activity: A Scrolling Geologic Record*

2) Most modern animal phyla evolved during the _____ era.

   A) Paleozoic

   B) Permian

   C) Cenozoic

   D) Mesozoic

   E) Precambrian

   Answer: A
   *Topic: Web/CD Activity: A Scrolling Geologic Record*

3) Which of these events occurred earliest in the history of Earth?

   A) formation of oxygen

   B) first humans

   C) evolution of land plants, fungi , and land animals

   D) origin of eukaryotes

   E) origin of multicellularity

   Answer: A
   *Topic: Web/CD Activity: The History of Life*

4) Which of these events occurred during the Paleozoic?

   A) origin of Earth

   B) colonization of land by plants

   C) origin of eukaryotes

   D) origin of multicellularity

   E) first humans

   Answer: B
   *Topic: Web/CD Activity: The History of Life*

5) In the two–kingdom system, why were fungi classified in the kingdom Plantae?

   A) They are sedentary.

   B) They are heterotrophs.

   C) They lack cell walls.

   D) They are unicellular.

   E) They are autotrophs.

   Answer: A
   *Topic: Web/CD Activity: Classification Schemes*

# Self–Quiz Questions

1) A paleontologist estimates that when a particular rock formed, it contained 12 mg of the radioactive isotope potassium–40. The rock now contains 3 mg of potassium–40. The half–life of potassium–40 is 1.3 billion years. About how old is the rock?

A) 0.4 billion years

B) 0.3 billion years

C) 1.3 billion years

D) 2.6 billion years

E) 5.2 billion years

Answer: D

2) The animals and plants of India show large differences from species in nearby Southeast Asia. Why might this be true?

A) The species have become separated by convergent evolution.

B) The climates of the two regions are completely different.

C) India is in the process of separating from the rest of Asia.

D) Life in India was wiped out by ancient volcanic eruptions.

E) India was a separate continent until relatively recently.

Answer: E

3) Which statement does *not* lend support to the hypothesis that RNA functioned as the first genetic material of early protobionts?

A) Short RNA sequences can add limited numbers of complementary bases in the presence of nucleotide monomers.

B) Catalytic activity has been demonstrated for RNA in modern cells.

C) Variations in base sequences produce molecules with variable stabilities in different environments.

D) Modern cells use an RNA template when synthesizing proteins.

E) In modern cells, RNA provides the template on which DNA nucleotides are assembled.

Answer: E

4) Populations of protobionts could begin to undergo evolutionary change by natural selection only when

A) they were first able to catalyze chemical reactions.

B) some kind of heredity mechanism developed.

C) they were able to grow and split in two.

D) photosynthesis evolved.

E) DNA first appeared.

Answer: B

5) One current view of the origin of life proposes that, rather than forming in the atmosphere, the first organic compounds on Earth my have formed

A) on dry land.

B) near deep-sea vents.

C) from viruses.

D) in northern Africa.

E) when chunks that broke off from the moon bombarded Earth.

Answer: B

6) Which of the following steps has *not* yet been accomplished by scientists studying the origin of life?

A) synthesis of small RNA polymers by ribozymes

B) abiotic synthesis of polypeptides

C) formation of molecular aggregates with selectively permeable membranes

D) formation of protobionts that use DNA to direct the polymerization of amino acids

E) abiotic synthesis of organic molecules

Answer: D

7) Fossilized mats called stromatolites

A) all date from 2.7 billion years ago.

B) formed around deep-sea vents and provide the first evidence of life on Earth.

C) resemble bacterial communities that are found today in some warm, shallow, salty bays.

D) provide evidence that plants moved onto land in the company of fungi around 500 million years ago.

E) contain the first undisputed fossils of eukaryotes and date from 2.1 billion years ago.

Answer: C

8) The oxygen revolution changed Earth's environment dramatically. Which of the following adaptations took advantage of this change?

A) the evolution of chloroplasts after early protists engulfed photosynthetic cyanobacteria

B) the persistence of some animal groups in anaerobic habitats

C) the evolution of photosynthetic pigments that protected early algae from the corrosive effects of oxygen

D) the evolution of cellular respiration, which used oxygen to help harvest energy from fuel molecules

E) the evolution of multicellular eukaryotic colonies from symbiotic communities of prokaryotes

Answer: D

9) Which of the following represents a probable order in the biological history of Earth?

A) metabolism before mitosis

B) an oxidizing atmosphere followed before a reducing atmosphere

C) eukaryotes before prokaryotes

D) DNA genes before RNA genes

E) animals before algae

Answer: A

10) Current debates about the number and boundaries of the kingdoms of life center *mainly* on which groups of organisms?

A) plants and animals

B) plants and fungi

C) prokaryotes and single-celled eukaryotes

D) fungi and animals

E) amphibians and reptiles

Answer: C

# Chapter 27  Prokaryotes

1) Mycoplasmas are bacteria that lack cell walls. On the basis of this structural feature, which of the statements below is true about mycoplasmas?
   A) They are gram-negative.
   B) They are subject to lysis in hypotonic conditions.
   C) They lack a cell membrane as well.
   D) They undergo ready fossilization in sedimentary rock.
   E) They possess typical prokaryotic flagella.

Answer: B
*Topic: Concept 27.1*
*Skill: Comprehension*

2) Though plants, fungi, and prokaryotes all have cell walls, we classify them under different taxonomic units. Which of the observations below comes closest to explaining *the basis for placing* these organisms in different taxa?
   A) Some closely resemble animals, which lack cell walls.
   B) Their cell walls are constructed from very different biochemicals.
   C) Some have cell walls only for support.
   D) Some have cell walls only for protection from herbivores.
   E) Some have cell walls only to control osmotic balance.

Answer: B
*Topic: Concept 27.1*
*Skill: Comprehension*

3) Which of the following have been present in Earth's living organisms for the *least* amount of evolutionary time?
   A) enzymes that catalyze glycolysis
   B) photosystems I and II
   C) cell walls
   D) nuclei
   E) genes composed of DNA

Answer: D
*Topic: Concept 27.1*
*Skill: Comprehension*

4) Which of the following statements about bacterial cell walls is *false*?
   A) Bacterial cell walls differ in molecular composition from plant cell walls.
   B) Cell walls prevent cells from bursting in hypotonic environments.
   C) Cell walls prevent cells from dying in hypertonic conditions.
   D) Bacterial cell walls are similar in function to the cell walls of many protists, fungi, and plants.
   E) Cell walls provide the cell with a degree of physical protection from the environment.

Answer: C
*Topic: Concept 27.1*
*Skill: Knowledge*

5) Which of the following statements is *correct* about gram-negative bacteria?

   A) Penicillins are the best antibiotics to use against them.

   B) They often possess an outer membrane containing toxic lipopolysaccharides.

   C) On a cell-to-cell basis, they possess more DNA than do the cells of any taxonomically higher organism.

   D) Their chromosomes are composed of DNA tightly wrapped around large amounts of histone proteins.

   E) Their cell walls are primarily composed of peptidoglycan.

Answer: B
*Topic: Concept 27.1*
*Skill: Knowledge*

6) Which of the following is the *most* common compound in the cell walls of gram-positive bacteria?

   A) cellulose

   B) lipopolysaccharide

   C) lignin

   D) peptidoglycan

   E) protein

Answer: D
*Topic: Concept 27.1*
*Skill: Knowledge*

7) If penicillin is an antibiotic that inhibits enzymes from catalyzing the synthesis of peptidoglycan, then which prokaryotes should be *most* vulnerable to inhibition by penicillin?

   A) mycoplasmas

   B) gram-positive bacteria

   C) archaea

   D) gram-negative bacteria

   E) spore-bearing bacteria

Answer: B
*Topic: Concept 27.1*
*Skill: Comprehension*

8) Which of the following is the correct order, from most external to most internal?
   1. cell wall
   2. plasma membrane
   3. capsule

   A) 1, 2, 3

   B) 1, 3, 2

   C) 2, 1, 3

   D) 3, 2, 1

   E) 3, 1, 2

Answer: E
*Topic: Concept 27.1*
*Skill: Knowledge*

9) Jams, jellies, preserves, honey, and other foodstuffs with a high sugar content hardly ever become contaminated by bacteria, even when the food containers are left open at room temperature. This is because bacteria that encounter such an environment

   A) undergo death by plasmolysis.

   B) are unable to metabolize the glucose or fructose, and thus starve to death.

   C) undergo death by lysis.

   D) are obligate anaerobes.

   E) are unable to swim through these thick and viscous materials.

Answer: A
*Topic: Concept 27.1*
*Skill: Application*

10) In a hypothetical situation, the genes for sex pilus construction and for tetracycline resistance are located together on the same plasmid within a particular bacterium. If this bacterium performs conjugation involving a copy of this plasmid, then the result should be

A) a transformed bacterium.

B) the rapid spread of tetracycline resistance to other bacteria in that habitat.

C) the subsequent loss of tetracycline resistance in this bacterium.

D) the production of endospores among the bacterium's progeny.

E) the temporary possession by this bacterium of a completely diploid genome.

Answer: B
*Topic: Concept 27.1*
*Skill: Application*

11) In a bacterium that possesses antibiotic resistance and the potential to persist through very adverse conditions, such as freezing, drying, or high temperatures, DNA should be located within, or be part of, which structures?
1. nucleoid region
2. flagellum
3. endospore
4. fimbriae
5. plasmids

A) 1 only

B) 1 and 4

C) 1 and 5

D) 1, 3, and 5

E) 2, 4, and 5

Answer: D
*Topic: Concept 27.1*
*Skill: Comprehension*

12) Which two structures play direct roles in permitting bacteria to adhere to each other, or to other surfaces?
1. capsules
2. endospores
3. fimbriae
4. plasmids
5. flagella

A) 1 and 2

B) 1 and 3

C) 2 and 3

D) 3 and 4

E) 3 and 5

Answer: B
*Topic: Concept 27.1*
*Skill: Knowledge*

13) The typical prokaryotic flagellum features

A) a 9 + 2 pattern of microtubules.

B) a covering provided by the plasma membrane.

C) a complex motor embedded in the cell wall and plasma membrane.

D) A and B

E) A and C

Answer: C
*Topic: Concept 27.1*
*Skill: Knowledge*

14) Prokaryotes have ribosomes different from those of eukaryotes. Because of this, which of the following is *true*?

A) Some selective antibiotics can block protein synthesis of bacteria without harming the eukaryotic host.

B) Eukaryotes did not evolve from prokaryotes.

C) Translation can occur at the same time as transcription in eukaryotes but not in prokaryotes.

D) Some antibiotics can block the formation of cross-links in the peptidoglycan walls of bacteria.

E) Prokaryotes are able to use a much greater variety of molecules as food sources than can eukaryotes.

Answer: A
*Topic: Concept 27.1*
*Skill: Knowledge*

15) Which of the following is a *correct* statement about the genomes of prokaryotes?

A) Prokaryotic genomes are diploid throughout most of the cell cycle.

B) Prokaryotic chromosomes are sometimes called "genochromes."

C) Prokaryotic cells have multiple chromosomes packaged with a relatively large amount of protein.

D) Prokaryotic chromosomes are not contained within a nucleus but, rather, are found at the nucleoid region.

E) Prokaryotic genomes are composed of linear DNA (that is, DNA existing in the form of a line with two ends).

Answer: D
*Topic: Concept 27.1*
*Skill: Knowledge*

16) If a bacterium regenerates from an endospore that does not have all of the plasmids contained in its parent cell, it will probably

A) lack "contingency" functions.

B) lack a cell wall.

C) lack a chromosome.

D) gain extra base pairs on its chromosome.

E) be unable to survive in its normal environment.

Answer: A
*Topic: Concept 27.1*
*Skill: Knowledge*

17) In regard to prokaryotic reproduction, which of the following is *true*?

A) Prokaryotes form gametes by meiosis.

B) Prokaryotes feature the union of haploid gametes, as do eukaryotes.

C) Prokaryotes exchange some of their genes by conjugation, the union of haploid gametes, and transduction.

D) Mutation is a primary source of variation in prokaryote populations.

E) Prokaryotes skip sexual life cycles because their life cycle is too short.

Answer: D
*Topic: Concept 27.1*
*Skill: Comprehension*

18) Which of the following statements about prokaryotes is *correct*?

   A) Bacterial cells conjugate to mutually exchange genetic material.

   B) Their genetic material is confined within a nuclear envelope.

   C) They divide by binary fission, without mitosis or meiosis.

   D) The persistence of bacteria throughout evolutionary time is due to genetic similarity.

   E) Genetic variation in bacteria is not known to occur, nor should it occur, because of their asexual mode of reproduction.

Answer: C
*Topic: Concept 27.1*
*Skill: Comprehension*

19) About half of all prokaryotes are capable of directional movement. The following statements are all *true* of such directional movement *except* that

   A) it may occur via flagellar action.

   B) it should not occur among the archaea.

   C) internal helical filaments with basal motors can drive this movement.

   D) it should occur in response to negative phototaxis in photosynthetic prokaryotes.

   E) it may occur via gliding along a thread of "slime" secreted by filamentous forms.

Answer: D
*Topic: Concept 27.1*
*Skill: Comprehension*

*The following questions refer to structures found in a gram-positive prokaryotic cell. Answers (A–E) may be used once, more than once, or not at all.*

   A.   endospore
   B.   sex pilus
   C.   flagellum
   D.   cell wall
   E.   capsule

20) composed almost entirely of peptidoglycan

Answer: D
*Topic: Concept 27.1*
*Skill: Knowledge*

21) requires ATP to function, and permits some species to respond to taxes.

Answer: C
*Topic: Concept 27.1*
*Skill: Knowledge*

22) Not present in all bacteria, this slimy material enables cells that possess it to resist the defenses of host organisms.

Answer: E
*Topic: Concept 27.1*
*Skill: Knowledge*

23) Not present in all bacteria, this structure enables those that possess it to germinate after exposure to harsh conditions, such as boiling.

Answer: A
*Topic: Concept 27.1*
*Skill: Knowledge*

24) structure that permits conjugation to occur

Answer: B
*Topic: Concept 27.1*
*Skill: Knowledge*

25) an important source of endotoxin in gram−negative species

Answer: D
*Topic: Concept 27.1*
*Skill: Knowledge*

26) If this structure connects the cytoplasm of two bacteria, one of these cells may gain new genetic material.

Answer: B
*Topic: Concept 27.1*
*Skill: Knowledge*

27) This structure contains a copy of the chromosome, along with a small amount of dehydrated cytoplasm, within a tough wall.

Answer: A
*Topic: Concept 27.1*
*Skill: Knowledge*

*Match the numbered terms to the descriptions that follow. Choose all appropriate terms, but* only *appropriate terms.*

1. autotroph
2. heterotroph
3. phototroph
4. chemotroph

28) an organism that obtains its energy from chemicals

A) 1 only
B) 2 only
C) 3 only
D) 4 only
E) 1 and 4

Answer: D
*Topic: Concept 27.2*
*Skill: Knowledge*

29) a prokaryote that obtains both energy and carbon as it decomposes dead organisms

A) 1 only
B) 4 only
C) 1 and 3
D) 2 and 4
E) 1, 3, and 4

Answer: D
*Topic: Concept 27.2*
*Skill: Knowledge*

30) an organism that obtains both carbon and energy by ingesting prey

A) 1 only
B) 4 only
C) 1 and 3
D) 2 and 4
E) 1, 3, and 4

Answer: D
*Topic: Concept 27.2*
*Skill: Knowledge*

31) an organism that relies on photons to excite electrons within its membranes

A) 1 only
B) 3 only
C) 1 and 3
D) 2 and 4
E) 1, 3, and 4

Answer: B
*Topic: Concept 27.2*
*Skill: Knowledge*

*For the following questions, use the list below of types of bacterial metabolism. Pick the term that best matches the statement. Responses may be used once, more than once, or not at all.*

    A. photoautotrophs
    B. photoheterotrophs
    C. chemoautotrophs
    D. chemoheterotrophs that perform decomposition
    E. parasitic chemoheterotrophs

32) responsible for many human diseases

Answer: E
*Topic: Concept 27.2*
*Skill: Knowledge*

33) cyanobacteria

Answer: A
*Topic: Concept 27.2*
*Skill: Knowledge*

34) use light energy to synthesize organic compounds from $CO_2$

Answer: A
*Topic: Concept 27.2*
*Skill: Knowledge*

35) obtain energy by oxidizing inorganic substances; energy that is used, in part, to fix $CO_2$

Answer: C
*Topic: Concept 27.2*
*Skill: Knowledge*

36) use light energy to generate ATP but do not release oxygen

Answer: B
*Topic: Concept 27.2*
*Skill: Knowledge*

37) responsible for high levels of $O_2$ in Earth's atmosphere

Answer: A
*Topic: Concept 27.2*
*Skill: Knowledge*

38) Modes of obtaining nutrition, used by at least some bacteria, include all of the following *except*

A) chemoautotrophy.

B) photoautotrophy.

C) heteroautotrophy.

D) chemoheterotrophy.

E) photoheterotrophy.

Answer: C
*Topic: Concept 27.2*
*Skill: Knowledge*

39) Modern mitochondria are the descendants of what were once free–living alpha proteobacteria. Insofar as mitochondria become inactive during periods of oxygen debt, what is probably true of their alpha proteobacterial ancestors?

A) They were obligate aerobes and heterotrophs.

B) They were obligate aerobes and autotrophs.

C) They were obligate anaerobes and heterotrophs.

D) They were obligate anaerobes and autotrophs.

E) They were facultative anaerobes and autotrophs.

Answer: A
*Topic: Concept 27.2*
*Skill: Comprehension*

40) Given that the enzymes that catalyze nitrogen fixation are poisoned by oxygen, what are two "strategies" that nitrogen-fixing prokaryotes might use to protect these enzymes from oxygen?
1. couple them with photosystem II
2. sequester them in gas-impermeable membranes
3. be obligate anaerobes
4. be strict aerobes
5. sequester these enzymes in specialized cells or compartments that inhibit oxygen entry

A) 1 and 4

B) 2 and 4

C) 2 and 5

D) 3 and 4

E) 3 and 5

Answer: E
*Topic: Concept 27.2*
*Skill: Comprehension*

41) "By studying modern prokaryotic organisms, we can be certain of how metabolic pathways evolved." This statement is

A) true, because all the fossil evidence indicates that ancient prokaryotes were much like modern prokaryotes.

B) false, because we have no evidence that ancient metabolic pathways even existed.

C) impossible to evaluate, because ancient prokaryotes are all dead.

D) false, because our understanding of early metabolic pathways must always be hypothetical.

E) true, because both ancient and modern prokaryotes have few enzymes.

Answer: D
*Topic: Concept 27.2*
*Skill: Application*

42) The termite gut protist, *Mixotricha paradoxa*, has at least two kinds of bacteria attached to its outer surface. One kind is a spirochete that propels its host through the termite gut. A second type of bacteria synthesizes ATP, some of which is used by the spirochetes. The locomotion provided by the spirochetes introduces the ATP-producing bacteria to new food sources. Which term(s) is (are) applicable to the relationship between the two kinds of bacteria?
1. mutualism
2. parasitism
3. symbiosis
4. metabolic cooperation

A) 1 only

B) 1 and 2

C) 2 and 3

D) 1, 3, and 4

E) all four terms

Answer: D
*Topic: Concept 27.2*
*Skill: Application*

43) Mitochondria are descendants of alpha proteobacteria. They are, however, no longer able to lead independent lives because most genes originally present on their chromosome are now located in the nuclear genome. What phenomenon most directly accounts for the movement of these genes?

A) horizontal gene transfer

B) binary fission

C) conjugation

D) meiosis

E) plasmolysis

Answer: A
*Topic: Concept 27.2*
*Skill: Comprehension*

44) Carl Woese of the University of Illinois and his collaborators identified two major branches of prokaryotic evolution. What was the basis for dividing prokaryotes into two domains?

A) microscopic examination of staining characteristics of the cell wall

B) metabolic characteristics such as the production of methane gas

C) metabolic characteristics such as chemoautotrophy and photosynthesis

D) molecular characteristics such as ribosomal RNA sequences

E) ecological characteristics such as the ability to survive in extreme environments

Answer: D
*Topic: Concept 27.3*
*Skill: Knowledge*

45) Prokaryotic organisms have recently been divided into two domains, Bacteria and Archaea. This division is based on characterstics such as

A) differences in cell wall composition.

B) differences in their initiator amino acid for start of protein synthesis.

C) presence or absence of histones.

D) B and C only

E) A, B, and C

Answer: E
*Topic: Concept 27.3*
*Skill: Knowledge*

46) Which of the following statements about the domain of Archaea is *false*?

A) Based on DNA analysis, archaea are probably more closely related to eukaryotes than they are to bacteria.

B) Some archaea can reduce $CO_2$ to methane.

C) Archaean cell walls are composed of peptidoglycan.

D) Some archaea can inhabit solutions that are nearly 30% salt.

E) Some archaea are adapted to waters with temperatures above the boiling point.

Answer: C
*Topic: Concept 27.3*
*Skill: Knowledge*

47) If archaea are more closely related to eukaryotes than to bacteria, then which of the following is a reasonable proposal?

A) Archaean DNA should have no introns.

B) Archaean chromosomes should have no protein bonded to them.

C) Archaean DNA should be single–stranded.

D) Archaean ribosomes should be larger than typical prokaryotic ribosomes.

E) Archaea should lack cell walls.

Answer: D
*Topic: Concept 27.3*
*Skill: Comprehension*

48) Which of the following traits do archaea and bacteria share?
1. composition of the cell wall
2. presence of plasma membrane
3. lack of a nuclear envelope
4. identical rRNA sequences

A) 1 only

B) 3 only

C) 1 and 3

D) 2 and 3

E) 2 and 4

Answer: D
*Topic: Concept 27.3*
*Skill: Knowledge*

49) In general, it should take the *least* amount of time to sequence the entire genome of a typical member of

A) Bacteria.

B) Crenarchaeota.

C) Euryarchaeota.

D) Korarchaeota.

E) Nanoarchaeota.

Answer: E
*Topic: Concept 27.3*
*Skill: Comprehension*

50) Which two groups of archaea should have SSU–rRNA sequences that are *most* similar to each other?
1. extreme halophiles
2. cyanobacteria
3. methanogens
4. alpha proteobacteria
5. Korarchaeota

A) 1 and 2

B) 1 and 3

C) 2 and 3

D) 2 and 5

E) 3 and 5

Answer: B
*Topic: Concept 27.3*
*Skill: Comprehension*

51) Which group should have had an ancestor whose SSU–rRNA sequences were *most* similar to those of the common ancestor of all archaea?

A) Euryarchaeota

B) Nanoarchaeota

C) Korarchaeota

D) Crenarchaeota

E) Archaeozoa

Answer: C
*Topic: Concept 27.3*
*Skill: Comprehension*

52) What do the archaea used in primary sewage treatment and the archaea that help cattle digest cellulose have in common?

A) They produce methane as a waste product.

B) They live only at extremely low pH levels.

C) They are nitrogen fixers.

D) They possess both photosystems I and II.

E) They require extremely high temperatures for reproduction.

Answer: A
*Topic: Concept 27.3*
*Skill: Comprehension*

53) Methane gas emitted by some cattle is produced by gut populations of _____ members of _____.

A) mutualistic; Euryarchaeota

B) parasitic; Euryarchaeota

C) mutualistic; Nanoarchaeota

D) parasitic; Nanoarchaeota

E) parasitic; Korarchaeota

Answer: A
*Topic: Concept 27.3*
*Skill: Knowledge*

54) Which prokaryotes should be expected to be most strongly resistant to plasmolysis in hypertonic environments?

A) extreme halophiles

B) extreme thermophiles

C) methanogens

D) cyanobacteria

E) nitrogen-fixing bacteria that live in root nodules

Answer: A
*Topic: Concept 27.3*
*Skill: Comprehension*

55) What two features do mycoplasmas and nanoarchaeotes have in common, despite belonging to different domains? They
1. lack peptidoglycan.
2. lack nucleoid regions.
3. have relatively small genomes.
4. lack plasma membranes.
5. are bacteria.

A) 1 and 2

B) 1 and 3

C) 2 and 3

D) 2 and 4

E) 3 and 5

Answer: B
*Topic: Concept 27.3*
*Skill: Knowledge*

56) What is the primary ecological role of prokaryotes?

A) parasitizing eukaryotes, thus causing diseases

B) breaking down organic matter

C) metabolizing materials in extreme environments

D) adding methane to the atmosphere

E) serving as primary producers in terrestrial environments

Answer: B
*Topic: Concept 27.4*
*Skill: Comprehension*

57) If all the bacteria on Earth suddenly disappeared, which of the following would be the most likely and most direct result?

A) The number of organisms on Earth would decrease by 10–20%.

B) Human populations would thrive in the absence of disease.

C) There would be little change in Earth's ecosystems.

D) The recycling of nutrients would be greatly reduced, at least initially.

E) There would be no more pathogens on Earth.

Answer: D
*Topic: Concept 27.4*
*Skill: Knowledge*

58) Which of the following would most likely occur if all prokaryotes were suddenly to perish?

A) All life would eventually perish due to disease.

B) Many organisms would perish as nutrient recycling underwent dramatic reduction.

C) All life would eventually perish because of increased global warming due to the greenhouse effect.

D) Only the organisms that feed directly on prokaryotes would perish.

E) Very little change would occur because prokaryotes are not of significant ecological importance.

Answer: B
*Topic: Concept 27.4*
*Skill: Comprehension*

59) In a hypothetical situation, a bacterium lives on the surface of a leaf, where it obtains nutrition from the leaf's nonliving, waxy covering, and where it inhibits the growth of other microbes that damage the plant. If this bacterium gains access to the inside of a leaf, it causes a fatal disease in the plant. Once the plant dies, the bacterium and its offspring decompose the plant. What is the correct sequence of ecological roles played by the bacterium in that situation? Use only those that apply.
1. nutrient recycler
2. mutualist
3. commensal
4. parasite
5. primary producer

A) 1, 3, 4

B) 2, 3, 4

C) 2, 4, 1

D) 1, 2, 5

E) 1, 2, 3

Answer: C
*Topic: Concept 27.4*
*Skill: Application*

60) Symbiosis is common among prokaryotes, and probably has been for billions of years. Which of the following does *not* represent a known prokaryotic symbiosis?

A) Some prokaryotes are pathogenic.

B) Bacteria on skin and mucous membranes can control the abundance of pathogenic microbes by outcompeting these microbes.

C) Bacteria are directly required for the pollination of some plants.

D) Bacteria in the human intestine produce essential vitamins.

E) Nitrogen–fixing bacteria inhabit root nodules of leguminous plants.

Answer: C
*Topic: Concept 27.4*
*Skill: Knowledge*

61) In a practice known as *crop rotation*, farmers alternate a crop of legumes (plants whose roots bear nodules containing *Rhizobium*) with a crop of nonlegumes. What is the benefit of this practice?

A) *Rhizobium* fixes nitrogen, and the fixed nitrogen will fertilize the soil.

B) It prevents the farmer from being exposed to the same crop pathogens year after year.

C) It keeps the plants from becoming tolerant of the bacteria in a particular variety of soil.

D) It keeps the plants from becoming pesticide resistant.

E) It keeps those bacteria that are plant pathogens from becoming pesticide resistant.

Answer: A
*Topic: Concept 27.4*
*Skill: Application*

62) In which of the following ways can prokaryotes be considered to be more successful on Earth than humans?

A) Prokaryotes are much more numerous and have more biomass.

B) Prokaryotes occupy more diverse habitats.

C) Prokaryotes are more diverse in metabolism.

D) Only B and C are correct.

E) A, B, and C are·correct.

Answer: E
*Topic: Concept 27.5*
*Skill: Comprehension*

63) Foods can be preserved in many ways by slowing or preventing bacterial growth. Which of the following methods would *not* substantially inhibit bacterial growth?

 A) Refrigeration: Slows bacterial metabolism and growth.

 B) Closing previously opened containers: Prevents more bacteria from entering.

 C) Pickling: Creates a pH at which bacterial enzymes cannot function.

 D) Canning in heavy sugar syrup: Creates osmotic conditions that remove water from bacterial cells.

 E) Irradiation: Kills bacteria by mutating their DNA.

Answer: B
*Topic: Concept 27.5*
*Skill: Application*

64) Many physicians administer antibiotics to patients at the first sign of any disease symptoms. Why can this practice cause more problems for these patients, and for others not yet infected?

 A) The antibiotic administered may kill viruses that had been keeping the bacteria in check.

 B) Antibiotics may cause other side effects in patients.

 C) Overuse of antibiotics can select for antibiotic-resistant strains of bacteria.

 D) Particular patients may be allergic to the antibiotic.

 E) Antibiotics may interfere with the ability to identify the bacteria present.

Answer: C
*Topic: Concept 27.5*
*Skill: Comprehension*

65) Broad–spectrum antibiotics inhibit the growth of most intestinal bacteria. Consequently, a hospital patient who is receiving broad–spectrum antibiotics is most likely to become _____, assuming that nothing is done to counter the reduction of intestinal bacteria.

 A) unable to fix carbon dioxide

 B) antibiotic resistant

 C) unable to fix nitrogen

 D) unable to synthesize peptidoglycan

 E) deficient in certain vitamins

Answer: E
*Topic: Concept 27.5*
*Skill: Application*

# Media Activity Questions

1) The _____ is the bacterial structure that acts as a selective barrier, allowing nutrients to enter the cell and wastes to leave the cell.

   A) plasma membrane

   B) ribosome

   C) cell wall

   D) nucleoid region

   E) pili

   Answer: A
   *Topic: Web/CD Activity: Prokaryotic Cell Structure*

2) Which structure is the outermost component of a bacterium?

   A) nucleoid region

   B) capsule

   C) cell wall

   D) ribosome

   E) plasma membrane

   Answer: B
   *Topic: Web/CD Activity: Prokaryotic Cell Structure*

3) What is the function of a bacterium's capsule?

   A) adhesion

   B) protection

   C) DNA containment

   D) protein synthesis

   E) propulsion

   Answer: B
   *Topic: Web/CD Activity: Prokaryotic Cell Structure*

4) The prokaryotic cells that built stromatolites are classified as _____.

   A) proteobacteria

   B) cyanobacteria

   C) chlamydias

   D) gram-positive bacteria

   E) spirochetes

   Answer: B
   *Topic: Web/CD Activity: Classification of Prokaryotes*

5) The chemoautotroph *Proteus vulgaris* is a rod-shaped bacterium classified with

   A) proteobacteria.

   B) gram-positive bacteria.

   C) chlamydias.

   D) spirochetes.

   E) cyanobacteria.

   Answer: A
   *Topic: Web/CD Activity: Classification of Prokaryotes*

# Self-Quiz Questions

1) Which of the following is *not* true of peptidoglycan?

    A) It is composed of modified-sugar polymers.

    B) It anchors other molecules on the surface of a bacterium.

    C) Gram-positive bacteria have a relatively large amount of it.

    D) It is found in the cell walls of all prokaryotes.

    E) It is located outside the plasma membrane of most bacteria.

    Answer: D

2) Photoautotrophs use

    A) light as an energy source and $CO_2$ as a carbon source.

    B) light as an energy source and methane as a carbon source.

    C) $N_2$ as an energy source and $CO_2$ as a carbon source.

    D) $CO_2$ as both an energy source and a carbon source.

    E) $H_2S$ as an energy source and $CO_2$ as a carbon source.

    Answer: A

3) Which of the following statements is *not* true?

    A) Archaea and bacteria have different membrane lipids.

    B) Both archaea and bacteria generally lack membrane-enclosed organelles.

    C) The cell walls of archaea lack peptidoglycan.

    D) Only bacteria have histones associated with DNA.

    E) Bacteria include the spirochetes.

    Answer: D

4) Which of the following features of prokaryotic biology involves metabolic cooperation among cells?

    A) binary fission

    B) endospore formation

    C) endotoxin release

    D) biofilms

    E) photoautotrophy

    Answer: D

5) Which of the following statements about archaea is *not* true?

    A) Archaea include euryarchaeotes and crenarchaeotes.

    B) Archaea include methanogens and extreme thermophiles.

    C) Archaea are not found in terrestrial habitats.

    D) Archaea share features with both bacteria and eukaryotes.

    E) Archaea are distinguished from bacteria based partly on molecular systematics.

    Answer: C

6) Which prokaryotic group is mismatched with its members?

    A) Proteobacteria—diverse gram-negative bacteria

    B) Chlamydias—intracellular parasites

    C) Spirochetes—helical heterotrophs

    D) Gram-positive bacteria—symbionts in legume root nodules

    E) Cyanobacteria—solitary and colonial photoautotrophs

    Answer: D

7) What kind of relationship exists between the Lyme disease-causing bacterium *B. burgdorferi* and humans?

   A) mutualism

   B) commensalism

   C) parasitism

   D) metabolic cooperation

   E) none

Answer: C

8) Erythromycin functions as an antibiotic mainly by inhibiting the ability of some prokaryotes to

   A) form spores.

   B) replicate DNA.

   C) synthesize normal cell walls.

   D) synthesize protein in ribosomes.

   E) synthesize ATP.

Answer: D

9) Plant–like photosynthesis that releases $O_2$ occurs in

   A) cyanobacteria.

   B) chlamydias.

   C) archaea.

   D) actinomycetes.

   E) chemoautotrophic bacteria.

Answer: A

10) An example of bioremediation is

   A) the use of prokaryotes to treat sewage or clean up oil spills.

   B) the production of antibiotics by cultured prokaryotes.

   C) the application of bacteria to produce transgenic plants.

   D) the introduction of parasitic bacteria to kill other bacteria.

   E) all of the above.

Answer: A

# Chapter 28  Protists

1) Protists are alike in that all are
    A) multicellular.
    B) photosynthetic.
    C) marine.
    D) nonparasitic.
    E) eukaryotic.

Answer: E
*Topic: Concept 28.1*
*Skill: Knowledge*

2) All of the following groups had taxonomic significance in the past, but only one is now considered to be a diverse clade. Which group is it?
    A) algae
    B) protist
    C) protozoa
    D) monera
    E) euglenozoa

Answer: E
*Topic: Concept 28.1*
*Skill: Knowledge*

3) Which of the following statements concerning living phytoplanktonic organisms are true?
    1.  They are important members of communities surrounding deep–sea hydrothermal vents.
    2.  They are important primary producers in most aquatic food webs.
    3.  They are important in maintaining oxygen in Earth's seas and atmosphere.
    4.  They are most often found growing in the sediments of seas and oceans.
    5.  They can be so concentrated that they affect the color of seawater.

    A) 1 and 4
    B) 1, 2, and 4
    C) 2, 3, and 4
    D) 2, 3, and 5
    E) 3, 4, and 5

Answer: D
*Topic: Concept 28.1*
*Skill: Comprehension*

4) Biologists have discovered the kingdom Protista to be paraphyletic. Which of the following statements is true, and consistent with this conclusion?
    A) Various combinations of prokaryotic ancestors gave rise to different lineages of protists.
    B) Animals, plants, and fungi arose from different protistan ancestors.
    C) Multicellularity has evolved only once among the protists.
    D) Chloroplasts among various protists are similar to those found in prokaryotes.
    E) The protists arose from a common ancestor that was a parabasalid.

Answer: A
*Topic: Concept 28.1*
*Skill: Comprehension*

5) The strongest evidence for the endosymbiotic origin of eukaryotic organelles is the similarity between extant prokaryotes and which of the following?

A) nuclei and chloroplasts

B) mitochondria and chloroplasts

C) cilia and mitochondria

D) mitochondria and nuclei

E) mitochondria and cilia

Answer: B
*Topic: Concept 28.1*
*Skill: Knowledge*

6) According to the endosymbiotic theory of the origin of eukaryotic cells, how did mitochondria originate?

A) from infoldings of the plasma membrane, coupled with mutations of genes for oxygen-using metabolism

B) from engulfed, originally free-living prokaryotes

C) by tertiary endosymbiosis

D) from the nuclear envelope folding outward and forming mitochondrial membranes

E) when a protoeukaryote engaged in a symbiotic relationship with a protobiont

Answer: B
*Topic: Concept 28.1*
*Skill: Knowledge*

7) Which of the following statements is consistent with the hypothesis that certain eukaryotic organelles originated as prokaryotic endosymbionts? Such organelles

A) are roughly the same size as bacteria.

B) can be cultured on agar since they make all their own proteins.

C) contain circular DNA molecules.

D) have ribosomes that are similar to those of bacteria.

E) A, C, and D

Answer: E
*Topic: Concept 28.1*
*Skill: Comprehension*

8) Which process allows nucleomorphs to be first reduced, and then lost altogether, without the loss of any genetic information from the host cell that ultimately surrounds the nucleomorph?

A) conjugation

B) horizontal gene transfer

C) binary fission

D) phagocytosis

E) meiosis

Answer: B
*Topic: Concept 28.1*
*Skill: Comprehension*

9) Which organisms represent the common ancestor of all photosynthetic plastids found in eukaryotes?

A) autotrophic euglenids

B) diatoms

C) dinoflagellates

D) red algae

E) cyanobacteria

Answer: E
*Topic: Concept 28.1*
*Skill: Knowledge*

10) The chloroplasts of modern plants are thought to have been derived according to which sequence?

  A) cyanobacteria → green algae → green plants

  B) cyanobacteria → green algae → fungi → green plants

  C) red algae → brown algae → green algae → green plants

  D) red algae → cyanobacteria → green plants

  E) cyanobacteria → red algae → green algae → green plants

Answer: A
*Topic: Concept 28.1*
*Skill: Knowledge*

11) The evolution of eukaryotes from prokaryotes probably

  A) occurred many times.

  B) involved endosymbiosis on multiple occasions.

  C) allowed for the formation of both complexity and multicellularity.

  D) B and C only

  E) A, B, and C

Answer: E
*Topic: Concept 28.1*
*Skill: Comprehension*

12) The goal in classifying organisms should be to create categories that reflect the evolutionary histories of organisms. What system would be best to use?

  A) a three-kingdom classification system

  B) a five-kingdom classification system

  C) an eight-kingdom classification system

  D) a system that uses as many kingdoms as necessary to be accurate

  E) a system that returns to that used by Linnaeus

Answer: D
*Topic: Concept 28.1*
*Skill: Comprehension*

13) The current state of the revision of "protistan" taxonomy is an example of which feature of good scientific practice?

  A) the need to suspend judgment until enough evidence is available to make an informed decision

  B) the need to base hypothetical phylogenies solely on fossil evidence

  C) the need to be willing to change or drop one's hypotheses when the data warrant it

  D) the need to avoid sampling techniques that can introduce bias

  E) both A and C

Answer: E
*Topic: Concept 28.1*
*Skill: Application*

14) A mixotroph loses its plastids yet continues to survive. Which of the following most likely accounts for its continued survival?

   A) It relies on photosystems that float freely in its cytosol.

   B) It must have gained extra mitochondria when it lost its plastids.

   C) It engulfs organic material by phagocytosis.

   D) It has an endospore.

   E) It is protected by a siliceous case.

   Answer: C
   *Topic: Concept 28.1*
   *Skill: Comprehension*

*For the following questions, refer to Figure 28.1, which represents a hypothetical eukaryotic cell that is the result of serial endosymbioses involving its mitochondria, one of which is pictured. Labeled arrows (A–E) indicate various membranes in this cell. Responses may be used once, more than once, or not at all.*

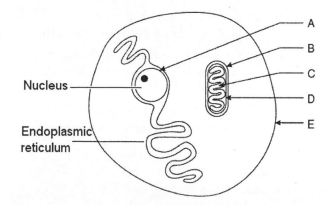

**Figure 28.1**

15) This membrane is homologous to the plasma membrane of the ancestral, gram–negative, aerobically respiring bacterium.

   Answer: C
   *Topic: Concept 28.1*
   *Skill: Application*

16) This membrane is homologous to an ancestral host plasma membrane and was derived from the primary (first) endosymbiotic event.

   Answer: B
   *Topic: Concept 28.1*
   *Skill: Application*

17) Which one of the mitochondrial membranes should bear the strongest similarity to the outer membrane of the cell wall of the ancestral, gram–negative, aerobically respiring bacterium?

   Answer: D
   *Topic: Concept 28.1*
   *Skill: Application*

18) If the genes for ATP synthase underwent horizontal gene transfer and are no longer within the mitochondrion, then which membrane most immediately surrounds the genes for ATP synthase?

   Answer: A
   *Topic: Concept 28.1*
   *Skill: Application*

19) A biologist discovers a new unicellullar organism that possesses more than two flagella and two small, but equal–sized, nuclei. The organism has reduced mitochondria and no chloroplasts. How would you classify this organism?

   A) apicomplexan

   B) diplomonad

   C) ciliate

   D) prokaryote

   E) *Chlamydomonas*

   Answer: B
   *Topic: Concept 28.2*
   *Skill: Knowledge*

20) Assuming that all of the flagella found among the various types of protists require the same amount of ATP per unit time to operate, and assuming that all of an individual protist's flagella are in use simultaneously, then which of these protists should use the greatest amount of ATP per unit time to move about?

A) *Chlamydomonas*

B) dinoflagellates

C) euglenids

D) diplomonads

E) golden algae

Answer: D
*Topic: Concept 28.2*
*Skill: Application*

21) Which of the following groups does *not* include many planktonic species?

A) kinetoplastids.

B) golden algae.

C) diatoms.

D) dinoflagellates.

E) radiolarians.

Answer: A
*Topic: Concept 28.3*
*Skill: Knowledge*

22) Organisms classified as Euglenozoa have previously been classified as protozoans, protista, plants, and animals. Why the confusion?

A) Like protozoans, they are unicellular.

B) Like animals, many are heterotrophic.

C) Like plants, many are photosynthetic.

D) A and B only

E) A, B, and C

Answer: E
*Topic: Concept 28.3*
*Skill: Comprehension*

23) When a protist possesses two flagella, both are generally used for propulsion. Assuming that a flagellum containing a crystalline rod cannot undulate back and forth, and assuming that two undulatory flagella can produce more effective locomotion than can a single flagellum, which of these organisms should have the *least* effective locomotion?

A) golden algae

B) dinoflagellates

C) euglenids

D) *Chlamydomonas*

E) oomycetes

Answer: C
*Topic: Concept 28.3*
*Skill: Application*

24) Which two genera have members that can evade the human immune system by frequently changing their surface proteins?
1. *Plasmodium*
2. *Trichomonas*
3. *Paramecium*
4. *Trypanosoma*
5. *Entamoeba*

A) 1 and 2

B) 1 and 4

C) 2 and 3

D) 2 and 4

E) 4 and 5

Answer: B
*Topic: Concepts 28.3, 28.4*
*Skill: Knowledge*

25) Which of the following marine organisms produce potent neurotoxins that cause extensive fish kills, contaminate shellfish, and create severe respiratory irritation to humans along the shore?

A) red algae

B) dinoflagellates

C) diplomonads

D) euglenids

E) golden algae

Answer: B
*Topic: Concept 28.4*
*Skill: Knowledge*

26) Which structure(s) consist(s), at least in part, of DNA?

A) *Trypanosoma* kinetoplast

B) diplomonad mitochondrion

C) chlorarachniophytes nucleomorph

D) A and C only

E) A, B, and C

Answer: D
*Topic: Concepts 28.1, 28.3*
*Skill: Knowledge*

27) Which of the following is mismatched?

A) apicomplexa—internal parasites

B) golden algae;—planktonic producers

C) euglenozoa—unicellular flagellates

D) ciliates—red tide organisms

E) entamoeba—ingestive heterotrophs

Answer: D
*Topic: Concept 28.4*
*Skill: Knowledge*

28) Which of the following statements about dinoflagellates is *false*?

A) They possess two flagella.

B) Some cause red tides.

C) their walls are composed of cellulose plates.

D) Many types contain chlorophyll.

E) Their fossil remains form limestone deposits.

Answer: E
*Topic: Concept 28.4*
*Skill: Knowledge*

29) Which group(s) within the Alveolata include(s) members that are important in ocean food webs, cause(s) red tides that kill many fish, and may even be carnivorous?

A) ciliates

B) apicomplexans

C) dinoflagellates

D) A and B only

E) A, B, and C

Answer: C
*Topic: Concept 28.4*
*Skill: Knowledge*

30) Which of the following *correctly* pairs a protist with one of its characteristics?

A) kinetoplastids;—slender pseudopodia

B) plasmodial slime molds—flagellated stages

C) apicomplexans—parasitic

D) gymnamoebas—calcium carbonate shell

E) foraminiferans—abundant in soils

Answer: C
*Topic: Concept 28.4*
*Skill: Knowledge*

31) Which of the following statements concerning protists is *false*?

A) All protists are eukaryotic organisms; many are unicellular or colonial.

B) The organism that causes malaria is transmitted to humans by the bite of the tsetse fly.

C) All apicomplexans are parasitic.

D) Cellular slime molds have an amoeboid stage that may be followed by a stage during which spores are produced.

E) The euglenozoans that are functionally mixotrophic contain chloroplasts.

Answer: B
*Topic: Concept 28.4*
*Skill: Knowledge*

32) You are given an unknown organism to identify. It is unicellular and heterotrophic. It is motile, using many short extensions of the cytoplasm, each featuring the 9+2 pattern. It has well-developed organelles and three nuclei, one large and two small. This organism is most likely to be a member of which group?

A) foraminiferans

B) radiolarians

C) ciliates

D) kinetoplastids

E) slime molds

Answer: C
*Topic: Concept 28.4*
*Skill: Application*

33) Which of the following is *not* characteristic of ciliates?

A) They use cilia as locomotory or feeding structures.

B) They are relatively complex cells.

C) They can exchange genetic material with other ciliates by the process of mitosis.

D) Most live as solitary cells in fresh water.

E) They have two or more nuclei.

Answer: C
*Topic: Concept 28.4*
*Skill: Knowledge*

34) If one speculates that it requires ten times as many ATP molecules to power a typical flagellum as to power a typical cilium for a given unit of time, and if one assumes that locomotion is the largest energy drain for protists, then which protist should have the largest number of ATP synthases per cell?

A) *Euglena*

B) *Chlamydomonas*

C) *Giardia*

D) *Plasmodium*

E) *Paramecium*

Answer: E
*Topic: Concept 28.4*
*Skill: Application*

35) Which process results in genetic recombination, but is separate from the process wherein the population size of paramecium increases?

A) budding

B) meiotic division

C) mitotic division

D) conjugation

E) binary fission

Answer: D
*Topic: Concept 28.4*
*Skill: Knowledge*

36) Which statement regarding resistance is *false*?

A) Many of the oomycetes that cause late potato blight have become resistant to pesticides.

B) Many of the mosquitoes that transmit malaria to humans have become resistant to pesticides.

C) Many of the malarial parasites have become resistant to antimalarial drugs.

D) Many humans have become resistant to antimalarial drugs.

E) *Trichomonas vaginalis* is resistant to the normal acidity of the human vagina.

Answer: D
*Topic: Concepts 28.4, 28.5*
*Skill: Comprehension*

37) Why is the filamentous morphology of the water molds considered a case of convergent evolution with the hyphae of fungi?

A) Fungi are closely related to the water molds.

B) Body shape reflects ancestor–descendant relationships among organisms.

C) Filamentous shape is an adaptation for a nutritional mode as a decomposer.

D) Hyphae and filaments are necessary for locomotion in both groups.

E) Filamentous body shape is evolutionarily primitive for all eukaryotes.

Answer: C
*Topic: Concept 28.5*
*Skill: Application*

38) The Irish potato famine was caused by an organism that belongs to which group?

A) bacterium

B) stramenopile

C) foraminiferan

D) apicomplexan

E) virus

Answer: B
*Topic: Concept 28.5*
*Skill: Knowledge*

39) If one were to apply the most recent technique used to fight late potato blight to the fight against the malarial infection of humans, then one would

A) increase the dosage of the least–expensive antimalarial drug administered to humans.

B) increase the dosage of the most common pesticide used to kill *Anopheles* mosquitoes.

C) introduce a predator of the malarial parasite into infected humans.

D) use a "cocktail" of at least three different pesticides against *Anopheles* mosquitoes.

E) insert genes from a *Plasmodium*-resistant strain of mosquito into *Anopheles* mosquitoes.

Answer: E
*Topic: Concept 28.5*
*Skill: Application*

40) Which of the following is correctly described as a primary producer?

A) oomycete

B) kinetoplastid

C) apicomplexan

D) diatom

E) radiolarian

Answer: D
*Topic: Concept 28.5*
*Skill: Comprehension*

41) A certain unicellular eukaryote has a siliceous (glasslike) shell and autotrophic nutrition. To which group does it belong?

A) dinoflagellate

B) diatom

C) gymnamoeba

D) foraminiferan

E) slime mold

Answer: B
*Topic: Concept 28.5*
*Skill: Knowledge*

42) Diatoms are members of the phytoplankton. Diatoms lack any organelles that might have the "9+2 pattern." They obtain their nutrition from functional chloroplasts, and each diatom is encased within two porous, glasslike valves. Which question would be most important for one interested in the day-to-day survival of individual diatoms?

A) How does carbon dioxide get into these protists?

B) How do diatoms move across the surfaces of bodies of water?

C) How do diatoms keep from sinking into poorly lit waters?

D) How do diatoms avoid being crushed by the action of waves?

E) How do diatom sperm cells locate diatom egg cells?

Answer: C
*Topic: Concept 28.5*
*Skill: Application*

43) Concerning diatoms' potential use as drug-delivery systems, which anatomical feature would seem to be *most* important?

A) their ability to withstand immense pressure

B) the chemical composition of their cell walls

C) the porous nature of their cell walls

D) the chemical composition of their food-storage material

E) the nuclear envelope

Answer: C
*Topic: Concept 28.5*
*Skill: Application*

44) The largest seaweeds belong to which group?

A) cyanobacteria

B) red algae

C) green algae

D) brown algae

E) golden algae

Answer: D
*Topic: Concept 28.5*
*Skill: Knowledge*

45) A large seaweed that floats freely on the surface of deep bodies of water would be expected to lack which of the following?

A) thalli

B) bladders

C) blades

D) holdfasts

E) gel-forming polysaccharides

Answer: D
*Topic: Concept 28.5*
*Skill: Comprehension*

46) The following are all characteristic of the water molds (Oomycota) *except*

A) the presence of filamentous feeding structures.

B) flagellated zoospores.

C) a nutritional mode that can result in the decomposition of dead organic matter.

D) a similarity to fungi that is the result of evolutionary convergence.

E) a feeding plasmodium.

Answer: E
*Topic: Concept 28.5*
*Skill: Comprehension*

47) Theoretically, which two of the following present the richest potential sources of silica?
1.  marine sediments consisting of foram tests
2.  diatomaceous earth
3.  marine sediments consisting of radiolarian tests
4.  marine sediments consisting of dinoflagellate plates

A) 1 and 2

B) 1 and 4

C) 2 and 3

D) 2 and 4

E) 3 and 4

Answer: C
*Topic: Concepts 28.5, 28.6*
*Skill: Knowledge*

48) Thread-like pseudopods that can perform phagocytosis are generally characteristic of which group?

A) cercozoans

B) gymnamoebas

C) entamoebas

D) amoeboid stage of cellular slime molds

E) oomycetes

Answer: A
*Topic: Concept 28.6*
*Skill: Knowledge*

49) Which two heterotrophic organisms most commonly derive nutrition from endosymbiotic relationships with photosynthetic protists?
1.  ciliates
2.  slime molds
3.  parabasalids
4.  reef-building coral animals
5.  foraminiferans

A) 1 and 2

B) 2 and 3

C) 2 and 4

D) 3 and 4

E) 4 and 5

Answer: E
*Topic: Concept 28.6*
*Skill: Knowledge*

50) Which of the following produce the dense glassy ooze of the deep-ocean floor?

A) forams

B) dinoflagellates

C) radiolarians

D) ciliates

E) apicomplexans

Answer: C
*Topic: Concept 28.6*
*Skill: Knowledge*

51) A snail–like, coiled, porous shell of calcium carbonate is characteristic of which group?

A) diatoms

B) foraminiferans

C) radiolarians

D) gymnamoebas

E) ciliates

Answer: B
*Topic: Concept 28.6*
*Skill: Knowledge*

52) What provides the best rationale for *not* classifying the slime molds as fungi? Their

A) SSU–rRNA sequences.

B) nutritional modes.

C) choice of habitats.

D) physical appearance.

E) reproductive methods.

Answer: A
*Topic: Concept 28.7*
*Skill: Comprehension*

53) Which dichotomous pair of alternatives is highlighted by the life cycle of the cellular slime molds?

A) prokaryotic versus eukaryotic

B) plant versus animal

C) unicellular versus multicellular

D) diploid versus haploid

E) autotroph versus heterotroph

Answer: C
*Topic: Concept 28.7*
*Skill: Comprehension*

54) What makes certain red algae appear red?

A) They live in warm coastal waters.

B) They possess pigments that reflect and transmit red light.

C) They use red light for photosynthesis.

D) They lack chlorophyll.

E) They contain the water–soluble pigment anthocyanin.

Answer: B
*Topic: Concept 28.8*
*Skill: Comprehension*

55) The structure and biochemistry of chloroplasts in red algae are most like the structure and biochemistry of chloroplasts in which of the following organisms?

A) golden algae

B) diatoms

C) dinoflagellates

D) green algae

E) brown algae

Answer: D
*Topic: Concept 28.8*
*Skill: Knowledge*

56) A biologist discovers an alga that is marine, multicellular, and lives at a depth reached only by blue light. This alga probably belongs to which group?

A) red algae

B) brown algae

C) green algae

D) dinoflagellates

E) golden algae

Answer: A
*Topic: Concept 28.8*
*Skill: Application*

57) If blue light is the component of the visible spectrum that can penetrate to the greatest depth in water, then what should be expected of photosynthetic protists that survive at great depths?

A) They should absorb green light preferentially.

B) They should absorb blue light preferentially.

C) They should absorb red light preferentially.

D) They should absorb white light preferentially.

E) They should reflect green light preferentially.

Answer: B
*Topic: Concept 28.8*
*Skill: Comprehension*

58) Members of the green algae often differ from members of the plant kingdom in that some green algae

A) are heterotrophs.

B) are unicellular.

C) have chlorophyll *a*.

D) store carbohydrates as starch.

E) have cell walls containing cellulose.

Answer: B
*Topic: Concept 28.8*
*Skill: Comprehension*

59) Which taxonomic group containing eukaryotic organisms is thought to be directly ancestral to the plant kingdom?

A) golden algae

B) radiolarians

C) foraminiferans

D) apicomplexans

E) green algae

Answer: E
*Topic: Concept 28.8*
*Skill: Knowledge*

60) Which of the following are actual mutualistic partnerships that involve a protist and a host organism?

A) green alga : fungal partner of lichen

B) dinoflagellate : reef–building coral animal

C) *Trichomonas* : human

D) alga : certain foraminiferans

E) A, B, and D

Answer: E
*Topic: Concept 28.8*
*Skill: Comprehension*

*Choose the organism from the list below that best fits each of the following descriptions.*

A. euglenozoans
B. *Chlamydomonas*
C. dinoflagellates
D. stramenopiles
E. diplomonads

61) possess more than two identical, functional flagella

Answer: E
*Topic: Concept 28.2*
*Skill: Knowledge*

62) have one normal and one crystalline–rod–containing flagellum

Answer: A
*Topic: Concept 28.3*
*Skill: Knowledge*

63) have one flagellum oriented at 90 degrees to the second flagellum

Answer: C
*Topic: Concept 28.4*
*Skill: Knowledge*

64) have one hairy and one smooth flagellum

Answer: D
*Topic: Concept 28.5*
*Skill: Knowledge*

65) have two identical, functional flagella, roughly parallel to each other and emerging from about the same site

Answer: B
*Topic: Concept 28.8*
*Skill: Knowledge*

*Choose the nutritional mode that is primarily employed by each of the protists listed below.*

   A.  autotrophic
   B.  mixotrophic
   C.  heterotrophic (by absorption)
   D.  heterotrophic (by ingestion)

66) diatoms

Answer: A
*Topic: Concept 28.5*
*Skill: Knowledge*

67) oomycetes

Answer: C
*Topic: Concept 28.5*
*Skill: Knowledge*

68) phagocytic euglenids that possess functional chloroplasts

Answer: B
*Topic: Concept 28.1*
*Skill: Knowledge*

69) amoebozoans that do not possess endosymbionts

Answer: D
*Topic: Concept 28.1*
*Skill: Knowledge*

You are given five test tubes, each containing an unknown protist, and your task is to read the description below and match these five protists to the correct test tube.

   A.  *Paramecium*
   B.  *Navicula* (diatom)
   C.  *Pfiesteria* (dinoflagellate)
   D.  *Entamoeba*
   E.  *Plasmodium*

In test tube 1, you observe an organism feeding. Your sketch of the organism looks very similar to Figure 28.2. When light, especially red and blue light, is shone on the tubes, oxygen bubbles accumulate on the inside of test tubes 2 and 3. Chemical analysis of test tube 3 indicates the presence of substantial amounts of silica. Chemical analysis of test tube 2 indicates the presence of a chemical that is toxic to fish and humans. Microscopic analysis of organisms in tubes 2, 4, and 5 reveals the presence of permanent, membrane-bounded sacs just under the plasma membrane. Microscopic analysis of organisms in tube 4 reveals the presence of an apicoplast in each. Microscopic analysis of the contents in tube 5 reveals the presence of one large nucleus and several small nuclei in each organism.

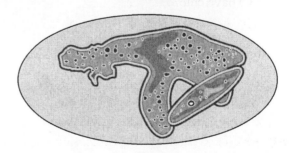

**Figure 28.2**

70) Test tube 2 contains

Answer: C
*Topic: Concept 28.4*
*Skill: Application*

71) Test tube 4 contains

Answer: E
*Topic: Concept 28.4*
*Skill: Application*

72) Test tube 5 contains

Answer: A
*Topic: Concept 28.4*
*Skill: Application*

73) Test tube 3 contains

Answer: B
*Topic: Concept 28.5*
*Skill: Application*

74) Test tube 1 contains

Answer: D
*Topic: Concept 28.7*
*Skill: Application*

# Media Activity Questions

1) Which of these groups consist of parasitic flagellated cells, such as *Trypanosoma*, the organism that causes sleeping sickness?

    A) metazoans

    B) kinetoplastids

    C) diatoms

    D) brown algae

    E) ciliates

Answer: B
*Topic: Activity: Tentative Phylogeny of Eukaryotes*

2) Stramenopiles include all of the following groups except

    A) golden algae.

    B) brown algae

    C) cellular  slime molds

    D) water molds

    E) diatoms

Answer: C
*Topic: Activity: Tentative Phylogeny of Eukaryotes*

3) A paramecium is a

    A) diatom.

    B) apicomplexan.

    C) ciliate.

    D) metazoan.

    E) dinoflagellate.

Answer: C
*Topic: Activity: Tentative Phylogeny of Eukaryotes*

4) Which of these groups includes multicellular organisms?

    A) choanoflagellates

    B) diatoms

    C) trichomonads

    D) diplomonads

    E) kinetoplastids

Answer: A
*Topic: Activity: Tentative Phylogeny of Eukaryotes*

5) Which group is characterized by cells with fine hairlike projections on their flagella?

    A) Alveolata

    B) Euglenoza

    C) Metozoa

    D) Stramenopila

    E) Rhodophyta

Answer: D
*Topic: Activity: Tentative Phylogeny of Eukaryotes*

# Self-Quiz Questions

1) Plastids that are surrounded by more than two membranes are evidence of

   A) evolution from mitochondria.

   B) fusion of plastids.

   C) origin of the plastids from archaea.

   D) secondary endosymbiosis.

   E) budding of the plastids from the nuclear envelope.

   Answer: D

2) Biologists suspect that endosymbiosis gave rise to mitochondria before plastids partly because

   A) the products of photosynthesis could not be metabolized without mitochondrial enzymes.

   B) almost all eukaryotes have mitochondria, while only autotrophic eukaryotes generally have plastids.

   C) mitochondrial DNA is less similar to prokaryotic DNA than is plastid DNA.

   D) without mitochondrial $CO_2$ production, photosynthesis could not occur.

   E) mitochondrial proteins are synthesized on cytosolic ribosomes, whereas plastids utilize their own ribosomes.

   Answer: B

3) Which of the following eukaryotes have mitochondria that lack an electron transport chain?

   A) golden algae

   B) diplomonads

   C) apicomplexans

   D) kinetoplastids

   E) diatoms

   Answer: B

4) Which organism is *incorrectly* paired with its description?

   A) cercozoans—amoebas with threadlike pseudopodia

   B) euglenids—protists that store paramylon

   C) forams—ciliated algae with numerous micronuclei

   D) apicomplexans—parasites with intricate life cycles

   E) diplomonads—protists with modified mitochondria

   Answer: C

5) Dinoflagellates, apicomplexans, and ciliates are placed in the clade Alveolata because they all

   A) have flagella or cilia.

   B) are parasites of animals.

   C) are found exclusively in freshwater or marine habitats.

   D) have mitochondria.

   E) have membrane-bounded sacs under their plasma membrane

   Answer: E

6) In ciliates, the process that produces genetic variation through the exchange of nuclei is

   A) mixotrophy.

   B) endosymbiosis.

   C) meiosis.

   D) conjugation.

   E) binary fission.

   Answer: D

7) The protist that contributed to the Irish potato famine was
   A) a foram.
   B) a ciliate.
   C) an oomycete.
   D) a plasmodial slime mold.
   E) a cellular slime mold.

   Answer: C

8) Which algal group is *mismatched* with its description?
   A) dinoflagellates—glassy, two-part shells
   B) green algae—closest relative of land plants
   C) red algae—no flagellated stages in life cycle
   D) brown algae—include the largest seaweeds
   E) diatoms—a major component of phytoplankton

   Answer: A

9) In life cycles with an alternation of generations, multicellular haploid forms alternate with
   A) unicellular haploid forms.
   B) unicellular diploid forms.
   C) multicellular haploid forms.
   D) multicellular diploid forms.
   E) multicellular polyploid forms.

   Answer: D

10) Which protists form colorful, multinucleate masses?
    A) euglenids
    B) plasmodial slime molds
    C) cellular slime molds
    D) forams
    E) water molds

    Answer: B

# Chapter 29  Plant Diversity I: How Plants Colonized Land

1) One of the major distinctions between plants and the green algae is that
   A) only green algae have flagellated, swimming sperm.
   B) embryos are not retained within parental tissues in green algae.
   C) meiosis proceeds at a faster pace in green algae than in plants.
   D) chlorophyll pigments in green algae are different from those in green plants.
   E) only plants form a cell plate during cytokinesis.

Answer: B
*Topic: Concept 29.1*
*Skill: Comprehension*

2) The most recent common ancestor of all land plants was most similar to modern-day members of which group?
   A) Cyanobacteria
   B) red algae
   C) Charophycea
   D) brown algae
   E) golden algae

Answer: C
*Topic: Concept 29.1*
*Skill: Knowledge*

3) Peptidoglycan is to the structural integrity of bacteria as _____ is to the structural integrity of plant spores.
   A) lignin
   B) cellulose
   C) terpene
   D) tannin
   E) sporopollenin

Answer: E
*Topic: Concept 29.1*
*Skill: Comprehension*

4) Which kind of plant tissue should lack phragmoplasts?
   A) bryophyte tissues of the gametophyte generation
   B) diploid tissues of charophyceans
   C) spore-producing tissues of all land plants
   D) tissues performing nuclear division without intervening cytokineses
   E) the meristematic tissues of fern gametophytes

Answer: D
*Topic: Concept 29.1*
*Skill: Comprehension*

5) The following are common to both charophyceans and land plants *except*
   A) sporopollenin.
   B) lignin.
   C) chlorophyll *a*.
   D) cellulose.
   E) chlorophyll *b*.

Answer: B
*Topic: Concept 29.1*
*Skill: Comprehension*

6) A number of characteristics are very similar between charophyceans and members of the kingdom Plantae. Of the following, which characteristic does *not* provide evidence for a close evolutionary relationship between these two groups?
   A) alternation of generations
   B) chloroplast structure
   C) cell plate formation during cytokinesis
   D) sperm cell structure
   E) ribosomal RNA nucleotide sequences

Answer: A
*Topic: Concept 29.1*
*Skill: Comprehension*

7) A researcher wants to develop an assay (test) that will distinguish charophyceans and land plants from chlorophyte green algae. Which of the following chemicals would be the best subject for such an assay?

   A) chlorophyll *b* —an accessory photosynthetic pigment

   B) carotenoids—a class of accessory photosynthetic pigments

   C) amylopectin—a starch-like food storage material

   D) glycolate oxidase—an enzyme of peroxisomes that is associated with photorespiration

   E) flavonoids—a class of phenolic compounds that is often associated with chemical signaling

Answer: D
*Topic: Concept 29.1*
*Skill: Application*

8) In animal cells and in the meristem cells of land plants, the nuclear envelope disintegrates during mitosis. This disintegration does not occur in the cells of most protists and fungi. According to our current knowledge of plant evolution, which group of organisms should feature a mitosis most similar to that of land plants?

   A) unicellular chlorophytes

   B) diatoms

   C) charophyceans

   D) red algae

   E) multicellular chlorophytes

Answer: C
*Topic: Concept 29.1*
*Skill: Application*

9) On a field trip, a student in a marine biology class collects an organism that has differentiated organs, cell walls of cellulose, and chloroplasts with chlorophyll *a*. Based on this description, the organism could be a brown alga, a red alga, a green alga, a charophycean recently washed into the ocean from a freshwater or brackish water source, or a land plant washed into the ocean. Which of the following features would definitively identify this organism as a land plant?

   A) presence of alternation of generations

   B) presence of sporopollenin

   C) presence of rosette cellulose–synthesizing complexes

   D) presence of flagellated sperm

   E) presence of embryos

Answer: E
*Topic: Concept 29.1*
*Skill: Application*

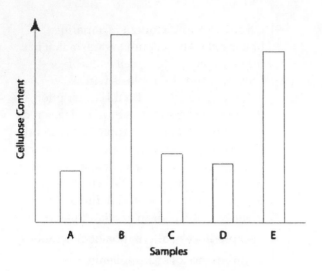

**Figure 29.1**

10) Figure 29.1 indicates varying cellulose contents among five different organisms. You are given five samples (A–E) of equal dry weights of a brown alga, a red alga, a marine green alga, a land plant, and a charophycean. Chemical analysis reveals the cellulose contents shown here. Which samples are probably from streptophytes?

   A) samples A and C

   B) samples C and D

   C) samples B and E

   D) samples, A, C, and D

   E) There is not enough information to tell.

Answer: C
*Topic: Concepts 29.1, 29.2*
*Skill: Application*

11) Which of the following is characteristic of alternation of generations in land plants?

   A) Haploid sporophytes make haploid spores.

   B) Gametophytes produce spores that develop into gametes.

   C) Sporophytes and gametophytes are typically similar in appearance.

   D) Meiosis in sporophytes produces haploid spores.

   E) Either the gametophyte or the sporophyte is unicellular.

Answer: D
*Topic: Concept 29.2*
*Skill: Comprehension*

12) Some green algae exhibit alternation of generations. All land plants exhibit alternation of generations. No charophyceans exhibit alternation of generations. Keeping in mind the recent evidence from molecular systematics, the correct interpretation of these observations is that

   A) charophyceans are not related to either green algae or land plants.

   B) plants evolved alternation of generations independently of green algae.

   C) alternation of generations cannot be beneficial to charophyceans.

   D) land plants evolved directly from the green algae that perform alternation of generations.

   E) scientists have no evidence to indicate whether or not land plants evolved from *any* kind of alga.

Answer: B
*Topic: Concept 29.2*
*Skill: Knowledge*

13) Bryophytes have all of the following characteristics *except*

 A) multicellularity.

 B) specialized cells and tissues.

 C) lignified vascular tissue.

 D) walled spores in sporangia.

 E) a reduced, dependent sporophyte.

Answer: C
*Topic: Concept 29.2*
*Skill: Knowledge*

14) Which of the following characteristics, if observed in an unidentified green organism, would make it *unlikely* to be a charophycean?

 A) phragmoplast

 B) peroxisome

 C) apical meristem

 D) chlorophylls *a* and *b*

 E) rosette cellulose–synthesizing complex

Answer: C
*Topic: Concept 29.2*
*Skill: Knowledge*

15) Whereas the zygotes of charophyceans may remain within maternal tissues during their initial development, one should *not* expect to observe

 A) any nutrients from maternal tissues being used by the zygotes.

 B) specialized placental transfer cells surrounding the zygotes.

 C) the zygotes undergoing nuclear division.

 D) mitochondria in the maternal tissues, or in the tissues of the zygotes.

 E) the zygotes digested by enzymes from maternal lysosomes.

Answer: B
*Topic: Concept 29.2*
*Skill: Comprehension*

16) Which putative taxon is essentially equivalent to the "embryophytes"?

 A) Viridiplantae

 B) Plantae

 C) Pterophyta

 D) Streptophyta

 E) Charophycea

Answer: B
*Topic: Concept 29.2*
*Skill: Comprehension*

*Choose the adaptation below that best meets each particular challenge for life on land. Choices may be used once, more than once, or not at all.*

 A. nonflagellated sperm
 B. tracheids and phloem
 C. secondary compounds
 D. cuticle
 E. alternation of generations

17) protection from predators

Answer: C
*Topic: Concept 29.2*
*Skill: Knowledge*

18) protection from desiccation

Answer: D
*Topic: Concept 29.2*
*Skill: Knowledge*

19) transport of water, minerals, and nutrients

Answer: B
*Topic: Concept 29.2*
*Skill: Knowledge*

20) reproduction away from water

Answer: A
*Topic: Concept 29.2*
*Skill: Knowledge*

21) Which of the following was *not* a challenge for survival of the first land plants?

A) sources of water

B) sperm transfer

C) desiccation

D) animal predation

E) absorbing enough light

Answer: D
*Topic: Concept 29.2*
*Skill: Comprehension*

22) The following are all adaptations to life on land *except*

A) rosette cellulose-synthesizing complexes.

B) cuticles.

C) tracheids.

D) reduced gametophyte generation.

E) seeds.

Answer: A
*Topic: Concept 29.2*
*Skill: Comprehension*

23) Mitotic activity by the apical meristem of a root makes all of the following more possible *except*

A) increased length of the above-ground stem.

B) increased absorption of mineral nutrients.

C) increased absorption of water.

D) increased number of chloroplasts in roots.

E) more effective anchoring of plant in substrate.

Answer: D
*Topic: Concept 29.2*
*Skill: Comprehension*

24) Which of the following is *not* a secondary compound of embryophytes?

A) adenosine triphosphate

B) alkaloids

C) terpenes

D) tannins

E) flavonoids

Answer: A
*Topic: Concept 29.2*
*Skill: Knowledge*

25) Which event during the evolution of land plants probably made the synthesis of secondary compounds most beneficial?

A) the greenhouse effect present throughout the Devonian period

B) the reverse-greenhouse effect during the Carboniferous period

C) the association of the roots of land plants with fungi

D) the rise of herbivory

E) the rise of wind pollination

Answer: D
*Topic: Concept 29.2*
*Skill: Comprehension*

26) If one were attempting to catalog the *largest* amount of genetic diversity among plant-like organisms, then which group of organisms should one choose?

A) Embryophyta

B) Viridiplantae

C) Plantae

D) Streptophyta

E) Tracheophyta

Answer: B
*Topic: Concept 29.2*
*Skill: Comprehension*

27) Which of these should have had gene sequences most similar to the charophycean that was the common ancestor of the land plants?

A) early angiosperms

B) early bryophytes

C) early gymnosperms

D) early lycophytes

E) early pterophytes

Answer: B
*Topic: Concept 29.2*
*Skill: Comprehension*

28) Plant spores give rise directly to

A) sporophytes.

B) gametes.

C) gametophytes.

D) sporophylls.

E) seeds.

Answer: C
*Topic: Concept 29.3*
*Skill: Knowledge*

29) Which of the following statements is true of archegonia?

A) They are the sites where male gametes are produced.

B) They may temporarily contain sporophyte embryos.

C) They are the same as sporangia.

D) They are the ancestral versions of animal gonads.

E) They are asexual reproductive structures.

Answer: B
*Topic: Concept 29.3*
*Skill: Comprehension*

30) Which of the following is a true statement about plant reproduction?

A) "Embryophytes" are small because they are in an early developmental stage.

B) Both male and female bryophytes produce gametangia.

C) Gametangia protect gametes from excess water.

D) Eggs and sperm of bryophytes swim toward one another.

E) Bryophytes are limited to asexual reproduction.

Answer: B
*Topic: Concept 29.3*
*Skill: Comprehension*

31) Assuming that they all belong to the same plant, arrange the following structures from smallest to largest.
1. antheridia
2. gametes
3. gametophytes
4. gametangia

A) 1, 4, 3, 2

B) 3, 1, 2, 4

C) 3, 4, 2, 1

D) 3, 4, 1, 2

E) 4, 3, 1, 2

Answer: D
*Topic: Concept 29.3*
*Skill: Comprehension*

32) The leaflike appendages of moss gametophytes may be one- to two-cell-layers thick. Consequently, which of these is *least* likely to be found associated with such appendages?

A) cuticle

B) rosette cellulose–synthesizing complexes

C) stomata

D) peroxisomes

E) phenolics

Answer: C
*Topic: Concept 29.3*
*Skill: Comprehension*

33) Each of the following is a general characteristic of bryophytes *except*

A) a cellulose cell wall.

B) vascular tissue.

C) chlorophylls *a* and *b*.

D) being photosynthetic autotrophs.

E) being eukaryotic.

Answer: B
*Topic: Concept 29.3*
*Skill: Comprehension*

34) The following are all true about the life cycle of mosses *except*

A) external water is required for fertilization.

B) flagellated sperm are produced.

C) antheridia and archegonia are produced by gametophytes.

D) gametes are directly produced by meiosis.

E) gametophytes germinate from spores.

Answer: D
*Topic: Concept 29.3*
*Skill: Comprehension*

35) Beginning with the germination of a moss spore, what is the sequence of structures that develop after germination?
1. embryo
2. gametes
3. sporophyte
4. protonema
5. gametophore

A) 4, 1, 3, 5, 2

B) 4, 3, 5, 2, 1

C) 4, 5, 2, 1, 3

D) 3, 4, 5, 2, 1

E) 3, 1, 4, 5, 2

Answer: C
*Topic: Concept 29.3*
*Skill: Comprehension*

36) Bryophytes may feature all of the following at some time during their existence *except*

A) microphylls.

B) rhizoids.

C) archegonia.

D) sporangia.

E) conducting tissues.

Answer: A
*Topic: Concept 29.3*
*Skill: Knowledge*

37) A fungal infection damages all calyptra, preventing them from performing their function. Which process will be directly hindered as a result?

A) growth of the sporophyte

B) ability of sperm to locate eggs

C) growth of the protonema

D) lengthening of rhizoids

E) broadcast of spores

Answer: E
*Topic: Concept 29.3*
*Skill: Application*

38) Two, small, poorly drained lakes lie close to each other in a northern forest. The basins of both lakes are composed of the same geologic substratum. One lake is surrounded by a dense *Sphagnum* mat; the other is not. Compared with the pond without *Sphagnum*, the pond surrounded by the moss should have

A) a lower pH.

B) lower numbers of bacteria.

C) reduced rates of decomposition.

D) A and C only

E) A, B, and C

Answer: E
*Topic: Concept 29.3*
*Skill: Application*

39) If you are looking for structures that transfer water and nutrients from a bryophyte gametophyte to a bryophyte sporophyte, then on which part of the sporophyte should you focus your efforts?

A) spores

B) seta

C) foot

D) calyptra

E) peristome

Answer: C
*Topic: Concept 29.3*
*Skill: Application*

40) Bryophytes never formed forests (mats maybe, but not forests) because

A) they possess flagellated sperms.

B) not all are heterosporous.

C) they lack lignified vascular tissue.

D) they have no adaptations to prevent desiccation.

E) the sporophyte is too weak.

Answer: C
*Topic: Concept 29.3*
*Skill: Comprehension*

41) In which of the following does the sporophyte depend on the gametophyte for nutrition?

A) fern

B) moss

C) horsetail (*Equisetum*)

D) both A and C

E) A, B, and C

Answer: B
*Topic: Concepts 29.3, 29.4*
*Skill: Knowledge*

42) All things being equal, *except* the number of sporangia initially present, which of the following land plants should be most able to continue producing spores following an episode of herbivory that leaves the plant alive?

A) club moss

B) horsetail

C) whisk fern

D) moss sporophyte

E) hornwort sporophyte

Answer: C
*Topic: Concepts 29.3, 29.4*
*Skill: Application*

43) Of the following list, flagellated (swimming) sperm are generally present in which groups?
1. Lycophyta
2. Bryophyta
3. Angiosperms
4. Chlorophyta
5. Pterophyta

A) 1, 2, 3

B) 1, 2, 4, 5

C) 1, 3, 4, 5

D) 2, 3, 5

E) 2, 3, 4, 5

Answer: B
*Topic: Concept 29.4*
*Skill: Knowledge*

44) The following characteristics all helped seedless plants become better-adapted to land *except*

A) a dominant gametophyte.

B) vascular tissue.

C) a waxy cuticle.

D) stomata.

E) a branched sporophyte.

Answer: A
*Topic: Concept 29.4*
*Skill: Comprehension*

45) A botanist discovers a new species of plant in a tropical rain forest. After observing its anatomy and life cycle, the following characteristics are noted: flagellated sperm, xylem with tracheids, separate gametophyte and sporophyte generations, and no seeds. This plant is probably most closely related to

A) mosses.

B) *Chara*.

C) ferns.

D) liverworts.

E) flowering plants.

Answer: C
*Topic: Concept 29.4*
*Skill: Application*

46) The sori of ferns are both homologous and analogous to which structures?

A) spores of bryophytes

B) capsules of moss sporophytes

C) gametangia of hornwort gametophytes

D) protonemata of moss gametophytes

E) cones (strobili) of gymnosperm sporophytes

Answer: E
*Topic: Concept 29.4*
*Skill: Comprehension*

47) A major change that occurred during the evolution of plants from their algal ancestors was the origin of a branched sporophyte. What advantage would branched sporophytes provide in this stage of the life cycle?

A) increased gamete production

B) increased spore production

C) increased potential for independence of the diploid stage from the haploid stage

D) increased fertilization rate

E) increased size of the diploid stage

Answer: B
*Topic: Concept 29.4*
*Skill: Knowledge*

48) Sporophylls can be found in which of the following?

A) mosses

B) liverworts

C) hornworts

D) pterophytes

E) charophyceans

Answer: D
*Topic: Concept 29.4*
*Skill: Knowledge*

49) Which of the following types of plants would *not* have been present in the forests that became coal deposits?

A) horsetails

B) lycophytes

C) pine trees

D) tree ferns

E) whisk ferns

Answer: C
*Topic: Concept 29.4*
*Skill: Comprehension*

50) If a fern gametophyte is a hermaphrodite (that is, has both male and female gametangia on the same plant), then it
   A) belongs to a species that is homosporous.
   B) must be diploid.
   C) has lost the need for a sporophyte generation.
   D) has antheridia and archegonia combined into a single sex organ.
   E) is a mutant, because fern gametophytes are always either male or female.

Answer: A
*Topic: Concept 29.4*
*Skill: Comprehension*

*The following questions are based on this description:*

A biology student hiking in a northern forest happens upon an erect, 15-cm-tall plant that bears a pinecone-like structure at its tallest point. When disturbed, the cone emits a cloud of brownish dust. A pocket magnifying glass reveals the dust to be composed of tiny spheres with a high oil content.

51) This student has probably found a(n)
   A) immature pine tree.
   B) moss sporophyte.
   C) fern sporophyte.
   D) horsetail gametophyte.
   E) club moss sporophyte.

Answer: E
*Topic: Concept 29.4*
*Skill: Application*

52) Besides oil, what other chemical should be detected in substantial amounts upon chemical analysis of these small spheres?
   A) sporopollenins
   B) phenolics
   C) waxes
   D) lignins
   E) terpenes

Answer: A
*Topic: Concept 29.4*
*Skill: Application*

53) Closer observation reveals that these small spheres are produced on tiny extensions of the stem, each of which helps compose the pinecone-like structure. Research would reveal that the cone-like structures are called _____, whereas the small, spore-producing extensions of the stem are called _____.
   A) pine cones; scales
   B) sori; sporangia
   C) strobili; sporophylls
   D) sporophylls; sporangia
   E) sporangia; strobili

Answer: C
*Topic: Concept 29.4*
*Skill: Application*

54) To which taxon does this organism seem to belong?
   A) Pterophyta
   B) Lycophyta
   C) Bryophyta
   D) angiosperms
   E) gymnosperms

Answer: B
*Topic: Concept 29.4*
*Skill: Application*

55) A dissection of the interior of the stem should reveal

A) lignified vascular tissues.

B) cuticle.

C) gametangia.

D) that it is composed of only a single, long cell.

E) a relatively high proportion of dead, water–filled cells.

Answer: A
*Topic: Concept 29.4*
*Skill: Application*

56) Assuming that they all belong to the same plant, arrange the following structures from largest to smallest (or from most inclusive to least inclusive).
1. spores
2. sporophylls
3. sporophytes
4. sporangia

A) 2, 4, 3, 1

B) 2, 3, 4, 1

C) 3, 1, 4, 2

D) 3, 4, 2, 1

E) 3, 2, 4, 1

Answer: E
*Topic: Concept 29.4*
*Skill: Comprehension*

57) If one were building a large, log structure during the Carboniferous period, which plant type(s) would be suitable sources of logs?

A) ferns and epiphytes

B) horsetails and bryophytes

C) lycophytes and bryophytes

D) horsetails and lycophytes

E) hornworts and gymnosperms

Answer: D
*Topic: Concept 29.4*
*Skill: Application*

58) Which of the following is true of seedless vascular plants?

A) Extant seedless vascular plants are larger than the extinct varieties.

B) Whole forests were once dominated by large, seedless vascular plants.

C) They produce many spores, which are really the same as seeds.

D) Seedless vascular plants are all homosporous.

E) *Sphagnum* is an economically and ecologically important example.

Answer: B
*Topic: Concept 29.4*
*Skill: Comprehension*

59) Working from deep geologic strata toward shallow geologic strata, what is the sequence in which fossils of these groups should make their first appearance?
1. charophyceans
2. single–celled green algae
3. hornworts
4. plants with a dominant sporophyte

A) 1, 3, 2, 4

B) 3, 1, 2, 4

C) 2, 1, 3, 4

D) 3, 2, 4, 1

E) 2, 4, 1, 3

Answer: C
*Topic: Concepts 29.1–29.4*
*Skill: Application*

# Media Activity Questions

1) Angiosperms are most closely related to

   A) green algae.

   B) charophyceans.

   C) bryophytes.

   D) seedless vascular plants.

   E) gymnosperms.

   Answer: E

   *Topic: Activity: Highlights of Plant Phylogeny*

2) Which of these was the dominant plant group at the time that dinosaurs were the dominant animals?

   A) seedless vascular plants

   B) charophyceans

   C) gymnosperms

   D) angiosperms

   E) bryophytes

   Answer: C

   *Topic: Activity: Highlights of Plant Phylogeny*

3) Which of these characteristics is shared by algae and seed plants?

   A) embryo development within gametangia

   B) roots and shoots

   C) vascular tissue

   D) pollen

   E) chloroplasts

   Answer: E

   *Topic: Activity: Terrestrial Adaptations of Plants*

4) In the moss life cycle _____ cells within a sporangium undergo _____ to produce _____ spores.

   A) diploid; meiosis; haploid

   B) haploid; mitosis; haploid

   C) diploid; mitosis; diploid

   D) diploid; mitosis; haploid

   E) haploid; meiosis; haploid

   Answer: A

   *Topic: Web/CD Activity: Moss Life Cycle*

5) Where do fern antheridia develop?

   A) on the underside of the gametophyte

   B) on the tip of the gametophyte

   C) on the tip of the sporophyte

   D) on the tip of protonema

   E) on the underside of the sporophyte

   Answer: A

   *Topic: Web/CD Activity: Fern Life Cycle*

# Self–Quiz Questions

1) Which of the following is *not* evidence that charophyceans are the closest algal relatives of plants?

A) similar sperm structure

B) similar cell wall structure

C) similarities in cell wall formation during cell division

D) genetic similarities in chloroplasts

E) similarities in proteins that synthesize cellulose

Answer: B

2) Which of the following characteristics of plants is absent in their closest relatives, the charophycean algae?

A) chlorophyll *b*

B) cellulose in cell walls

C) alternation of multicellular generations

D) sexual reproduction

E) formation of a cell plate during cytokinesis

Answer: C

3) Which of the following is a clade (monophyletic group)?

A) bryophytes and seedless vascular plants

B) lycophytes and pterophytes

C) liverworts, hornworts, and mosses

D) seedless vascular plants and seed plants

E) charophyceans and bryophytes

Answer: D

4) Which of the following characteristics do mosses, liverworts, and hornworts share?

A) reproductive cells in gametangia; embryos

B) branched sporophytes

C) vascular tissues, true leaves, and a waxy cuticle

D) seeds

E) lignified walls

Answer: A

5) Which of the following is *not* common to all phyla of vascular plants?

A) the development of seeds

B) alternation of generations

C) dominance of the diploid generation

D) xylem and phloem

E) the addition of lignin to cell walls

Answer: A

6) A heterosporous plant is one that

A) produces a gametophyte that bears both antheridia and archegonia.

B) produces microspores and megaspores, which give rise to male and female gametophytes.

C) produces spores all year long instead of during just one season.

D) produces two kinds of spores, one asexually by mitosis and the other sexually by meiosis.

E) reproduces only sexually.

Answer: B

7) Which of the following is diploid?

    A) the archegonia of a liverwort

    B) a non-reproductive cell in the gametangia of a moss

    C) a cell that is part of the stalk (seta) of a moss sporophyte

    D) a fern produced by a fern sporophyte

    E) a subterranean gametophyte of a lycophyte

Answer: C

8) Microphylls are characteristic of which types of plants?

    A) mosses

    B) liverworts

    C) lycophytes

    D) ferns

    E) hornworts

Answer: C

9) During the Carboniferous period, the dominant plants were

    A) giant lycophytes, horsetails, and ferns.

    B) conifers.

    C) angiosperms.

    D) charophyceans.

    E) early seed plants.

Answer: A

10) Which of the following is a land plant that produces flagellated sperm and has a sporophyte–dominant life cycle?

    A) fern

    B) moss

    C) liverwort

    D) charophycean

    E) hornwort

Answer: A

# Chapter 30   Plant Diversity II:  The Evolution of Seed Plants

1) The sporophytes of mosses depend on the gametophytes for water and nutrition.  In seed plants, the reverse is true.  From which seed plant sporophyte structure(s) do the immature (unfertilized) gametophytes directly gain water and nutrition?

   A) sporophylls

   B) embryos

   C) sporangia

   D) sporopollenin

   E) ovary

Answer: C
*Topic: Concept 30.1*
*Skill: Comprehension*

2) Which of the following is *not* true concerning the sporophyte or gametophyte generations of flowering plants?

   A) The flower is composed of gametophyte tissue only.

   B) The sporophyte generation is dominant.

   C) The sporophyte generation is what we see when looking at a large plant.

   D) The gametophyte generation is not photosynthetic.

   E) The gametophyte generation consists of relatively few cells within the flower.

Answer: A
*Topic: Concept 30.1*
*Skill: Comprehension*

3) Which of the following is an ongoing trend in the evolution of land plants?

   A) decrease in the size of the leaf

   B) reduction of the gametophyte phase of the life cycle

   C) elimination of sperm cells or sperm nuclei

   D) increasing reliance on water to bring sperm and egg together

   E) replacement of roots by rhizoids

Answer: B
*Topic: Concept 30.1*
*Skill: Comprehension*

4) All of the following cellular structures are found in cells of angiosperm and gymnosperm gametophytes *except*

   A) haploid nuclei.

   B) mitochondria.

   C) cell walls.

   D) chloroplasts.

   E) peroxisomes.

Answer: D
*Topic: Concept 30.1*
*Skill: Application*

5) Plants with a dominant sporophyte are successful on land partly because

   A) having no stomata, they lose less water.

   B) they all disperse by means of seeds.

   C) diploid plants experience fewer mutations than do haploid plants.

   D) their gametophytes are protected by, and obtain nutrition from, the sporophytes.

   E) eggs and sperm need not be produced.

Answer: D
*Topic: Concept 30.1*
*Skill: Knowledge*

6) Seeds commonly provide for each of the following *except*

    A) a choice of germination location.

    B) dispersal.

    C) dormancy.

    D) a nutrient supply for the embryo.

    E) desiccation resistance.

Answer: A
*Topic: Concept 30.1*
*Skill: Comprehension*

7) In addition to seeds, which of the following characteristics are unique to the seed–producing plants?

    A) a haploid gametophyte retained within tissues of the diploid sporophyte

    B) lignin present in cell walls

    C) pollen

    D) A and C only

    E) A, B, and C

Answer: D
*Topic: Concept 30.1*
*Skill: Knowledge*

8) Which of the following most closely represents the male gametophyte of seed–bearing plants?

    A) ovule

    B) microspore mother cell

    C) pollen grain

    D) embryo sac

    E) fertilized egg

Answer: C
*Topic: Concept 30.1*
*Skill: Knowledge*

9) Suppose that the cells of seed plants, like the skin cells of humans, produce a pigment upon increased exposure to UV radiation. Rank the cells below, from greatest to least, in terms of the likelihood of producing this pigment.
    1. cells of sporangium
    2. cells in the interior of a subterranean root
    3. epidermal cells of sporophyte megaphylls
    4. cells of a gametophyte

    A) 3, 4, 1, 2

    B) 3, 4, 2, 1

    C) 3, 1, 4, 2

    D) 3, 2, 1, 4

    E) 3, 1, 2, 4

Answer: C
*Topic: Concept 30.1*
*Skill: Application*

*The following questions refer to the generalized life cycle for land plants shown in Figure 30.1. Each number within a circle or square represents a specific plant or plant part, and each number over an arrow represents either meiosis, mitosis, or fertilization.*

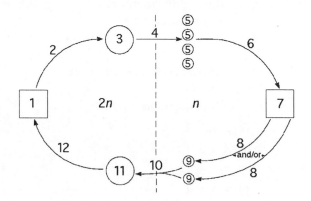

**Figure 30.1**

10) Which number represents the mature gametophyte?

    A) 1

    B) 3

    C) 5

    D) 7

    E) 11

Answer: D
*Topic: Concept 30.1*
*Skill: Comprehension*

11) Which number represents an embryo?

    A) 1

    B) 3

    C) 7

    D) 9

    E) 11

Answer: E
*Topic: Concept 30.1*
*Skill: Comprehension*

12) Meiosis is most likely to be represented by which number(s)?

    A) 2

    B) 4

    C) 2 and 8

    D) 4 and 8

    E) 10 and 12

Answer: B
*Topic: Concept 30.1*
*Skill: Comprehension*

13) Which number represents a megaspore mother cell?

    A) 1

    B) 3

    C) 5

    D) 7

    E) 11

Answer: B
*Topic: Concept 30.1*
*Skill: Comprehension*

14) Which numbers represent haploid cells or tissues?

    A) 1, 3, and 5

    B) 7, 9, and 11

    C) 1, 3, and 11

    D) 1, 5, and 7

    E) 5, 7, and 9

Answer: E
*Topic: Concept 30.1*
*Skill: Knowledge*

15) The process labeled "6" involves

    A) nuclear fission.

    B) mitosis.

    C) meiosis.

    D) fertilization.

    E) binary fission.

Answer: B
*Topic: Concept 30.1*
*Skill: Comprehension*

16) The embryo sac of an angiosperm flower is best represented by which number?

A) 1

B) 3

C) 7

D) 9

E) 11

Answer: C
*Topic: Concept 30.3*
*Skill: Comprehension*

17) In angiosperms, which number represents the event that initiates the formation of endosperm?

A) 4

B) 6

C) 8

D) 10

E) 12

Answer: D
*Topic: Concept 30.3*
*Skill: Comprehension*

18) In seed plants, which structure or material is considered part of a pollen grain?

A) sporophyll

B) male gametophyte

C) sporopollenin

D) stigma

E) both B and C

Answer: E
*Topic: Concept 30.1*
*Skill: Comprehension*

19) In terms of alternation of generations, the pollen grains of seed-producing plants are most similar to a

A) moss sporophyte.

B) moss gametophyte bearing both male and female gametangia.

C) fern sporophyte.

D) hermaphroditic fern gametophyte.

E) fern gametophyte that will bear only antheridia.

Answer: E
*Topic: Concept 30.1*
*Skill: Comprehension*

20) Which of these is most important in making the typical seed more resistant to adverse conditions than the typical spore?

A) a different type of sporopollenin

B) an internal reservoir of liquid water

C) integument(s)

D) ability to be dispersed

E) waxy cuticle

Answer: C
*Topic: Concept 30.1*
*Skill: Comprehension*

21) Gymnosperms differ from both extinct and extant ferns because they

A) are woody.

B) have macrophylls.

C) have pollen.

D) have sporophylls.

E) have spores.

Answer: C
*Topic: Concept 30.2*
*Skill: Knowledge*

22) The main way that pine trees disperse their offspring is by using
    A) fruits that are eaten by animals.
    B) spores.
    C) squirrels to bury cones.
    D) windblown seeds.
    E) flagellated sperm swimming through water.

Answer: D
*Topic: Concept 30.2*
*Skill: Knowledge*

23) Generally, wind pollination is most likely to be found in seed plants that grow
    A) close to the ground.
    B) in dense, single-species stands.
    C) in relative isolation from other members of the same species.
    D) along coastlines where prevailing winds blow from the land out to sea.
    E) in well-drained soils.

Answer: B
*Topic: Concept 30.2*
*Skill: Application*

24) Which of the following statements does *not* describe a portion of the pine life cycle?
    A) Female gametophytes use meiosis to produce eggs.
    B) Seeds are produced in ovulate (ovule-bearing) cones.
    C) Meiosis occurs in sporangia.
    D) Pollen grains contain male gametophytes.
    E) A pollen tube enters an ovule through a micropyle in the single integument.

Answer: A
*Topic: Concept 30.2*
*Skill: Comprehension*

25) Which of the following statement is *not* generally true of the pine life cycle?
    A) Cones are short stems with spore-bearing, leaflike structures.
    B) The pine tree is a sporophyte.
    C) Male and female gametophytes are in close proximity during fertilization.
    D) Pollen grains are very different from pine male gametophytes.
    E) Double fertilization is a relatively rare phenomenon.

Answer: D
*Topic: Concept 30.2*
*Skill: Comprehension*

26) Within a gymnosperm megasporangium, what is the correct sequence in which the following should appear during development, assuming that fertilization occurs?
    1.  sporophyte embryo
    2.  female gametophyte
    3.  egg cell
    4.  megaspore

    A) 4, 3, 2, 1
    B) 4, 2, 3, 1
    C) 4, 1, 2, 3
    D) 1, 4, 3, 2
    E) 1, 4, 2, 3

Answer: B
*Topic: Concept 30.2*
*Skill: Comprehension*

27) Arrange the following structures, which can be found on male pine trees, from the largest structure to the smallest structure (or from most inclusive to least inclusive).
1. sporophyte
2. microspores
3. microsporangia
4. pollen cone
5. pollen nuclei
   A) 1, 4, 3, 2, 5
   B) 1, 4, 2, 3, 5
   C) 1, 2, 3, 5, 4
   D) 4, 1, 2, 3, 5
   E) 4, 3, 2, 5, 1

Answer: A
*Topic: Concept 30.2*
*Skill: Comprehension*

28) Which of the following statements is *false*?
   A) A female pine cone is a short stem with spore–bearing appendages.
   B) A male pine cone is a short stem with spore–bearing appendages.
   C) A flower is a short stem with spore–bearing appendages.
   D) A strobilus is a short stem with spore–bearing appendages.
   E) A mature fruit is a short stem with spore–bearing appendages.

Answer: E
*Topic: Concepts 30.2, 30.3*
*Skill: Comprehension*

29) Before pollination occurs, what does an individual flower potentially have that an individual pine cone does *not* have?
   A) sporophylls
   B) both male and female gametophytes
   C) sporangia
   D) structures for dispersing seed or pollen grains
   E) spore mother cells

Answer: B
*Topic: Concepts 30.2, 30.3*
*Skill: Comprehension*

30) Which trait(s) is (are) shared by modern gymnosperms and angiosperms?
1. pollen transported by wind
2. tracheids
3. microscopic gametophytes
4. sterile sporophylls, modified to attract pollinators
5. endosperm
   A) 1
   B) 1 and 3
   C) 1, 2, and 3
   D) 1, 3, and 5
   E) 2, 4, and 5

Answer: C
*Topic: Concepts 30.2, 30.3*
*Skill: Comprehension*

31) Which structure is common to both gymnosperms and angiosperms?
   A) male strobilus
   B) carpel
   C) ovule
   D) ovary
   E) anthers

Answer: C
*Topic: Concepts 30.2, 30.3*
*Skill: Knowledge*

32) A botanist discovers a new species of land plant with a dominant sporophyte, chlorophylls *a* and *b*, and a cell wall made of cellulose. In assigning this plant to a phylum, all of the following would provide useful information *except* whether or not the plant has

A) endosperm.

B) seeds.

C) flagellated sperm.

D) flowers.

E) spores.

Answer: E
*Topic: Concepts 30.2, 30.3*
*Skill: Application*

33) What is true of stamens, sepals, petals, and pine cone scales?

A) They are female reproductive parts.

B) None are capable of photosynthesis.

C) They are modified leaves.

D) They are found on flowers.

E) They are found on angiosperms.

Answer: C
*Topic: Concepts 30.2, 30.3*
*Skill: Comprehension*

34) Reptilian embryos are protected from desiccation by a leathery shell. Similarly, sporophytes of both gymnosperms and angiosperms protect embryos within _____, and they also protect male gametophytes against desiccation using _____.

A) ovules; waxy cuticle

B) ovaries; filaments

C) fruits; stamens

D) pollen grains; waxy cuticle

E) integuments; sporopollenin

Answer: E
*Topic: Concepts 30.2, 30.3*
*Skill: Comprehension*

*For the following questions, match the various structures of seed plants with the proper sex and generation (A–D) that most directly produces them.*

A. male gametophyte
B. female gametophyte
C. male sporophyte
D. female sporophyte

35) scale of ovulate (ovule–bearing) pine cone

Answer: D
*Topic: Concept 30.2*
*Skill: Comprehension*

36) integument of pine nut

Answer: D
*Topic: Concepts 30.2, 30.3*
*Skill: Comprehension*

37) egg cell in the embryo sac

Answer: B
*Topic: Concepts 30.2, 30.3*
*Skill: Comprehension*

38) fruit

Answer: D
*Topic: Concept 30.3*
*Skill: Comprehension*

39) pollen tube

Answer: A
*Topic: Concepts 30.2, 30.3*
*Skill: Comprehension*

40) Which of these would have been the most likely dietary staple for a 20-foot-tall, bipedal, herbivorous dinosaur of about 100 million years ago?

A) moss gametophytes (*Bryophyta*)

B) corn plants (*Zea maize*)

C) cycads (*Cycadophyta*)

D) giant club mosses (*Lycophyta*)

E) watermelons (*Anthophyta*)

Answer: C
*Topic: Concept 30.3*
*Skill: Application*

41) All of the following are characteristic of angiosperms *except*

A) coevolution with animal pollinators.

B) double internal fertilization.

C) free-living gametophytes.

D) styles and stigmas.

E) fruit.

Answer: C
*Topic: Concept 30.3*
*Skill: Knowledge*

42) All of the following are sporophyte structures *except*

A) immature ovules.

B) pollen tubes.

C) ovaries.

D) stamens.

E) sepals.

Answer: B
*Topic: Concept 30.3*
*Skill: Knowledge*

43) Which of the following statements is *not* true of monocots?

A) They are currently thought to be polyphyletic.

B) The veins of their leaves are parallel to each other.

C) They, along with the eudicots and basal angiosperms, are currently placed in the phylum Anthophyta.

D) They possess a single cotyledon.

E) All of the statements are true.

Answer: A
*Topic: Concept 30.3*
*Skill: Knowledge*

44) Carpels and stamens are

A) sporophyte plants in their own right.

B) gametophyte plants in their own right.

C) gametes.

D) spores.

E) modified sporophylls.

Answer: E
*Topic: Concept 30.3*
*Skill: Comprehension*

45) All of the following statements are true of angiosperm carpels *except* that they

A) are features of the sporophyte generation.

B) consist of stigma, style, and ovary.

C) are structures that directly produce female gametes.

D) surround and nourish the female gametophyte.

E) consist of highly modified sporophylls.

Answer: C
*Topic: Concept 30.3*
*Skill: Comprehension*

46) A hypothetical angiosperm opens its flowers only at night. The flowers are brown and emit a putrid odor. The pollinator is most likely to be which organism?

A) nectar-eating hummingbird

B) nectar-eating bee

C) pollen-eating moth

D) fruit-eating bat

E) detritivorous (scavenging) animal

Answer: E
*Topic: Concept 30.3*
*Skill: Application*

47) How have fruits contributed to the success of angiosperms?

A) by nourishing the plants that make them

B) by facilitating dispersal of seeds

C) by attracting insects to the pollen inside

D) by producing sperm and eggs inside a protective coat

E) by producing triploid cells via double fertilization

Answer: B
*Topic: Concept 30.3*
*Skill: Comprehension*

48) In flowering plants, meiosis occurs specifically in the

A) spore mother cells.

B) gametophytes.

C) endosperm.

D) gametes.

E) embryos.

Answer: A
*Topic: Concept 30.3*
*Skill: Comprehension*

49) Arrange the following structures from largest to smallest, assuming that they belong to two generations of the same angiosperm.
1. ovary
2. ovule
3. egg
4. carpel
5. embryo sac

A) 4, 2, 1, 5, 3

B) 4, 5, 2, 1, 3

C) 5, 4, 3, 1, 2

D) 5, 1, 4, 2, 3

E) 4, 1, 2, 5, 3

Answer: E
*Topic: Concept 30.3*
*Skill: Comprehension*

50) Which structure(s) must pass through the micropyle for successful fertilization to occur in angiosperms?

A) one sperm nucleus

B) two sperm nuclei

C) the pollen tube

D) both A and C

E) both B and C

Answer: E
*Topic: Concept 30.3*
*Skill: Comprehension*

*In onions (Allium), cells of the sporophyte have 16 chromosomes within each nucleus. Match the number of chromosomes present in each of the onion tissues listed below.*

A. 4
B. 8
C. 16
D. 24
E. 32

51) How many chromosomes should be in a tube cell nucleus?

Answer: B
*Topic: Concept 30.3*
*Skill: Application*

52) How many chromosomes should be in an endosperm nucleus?

Answer: D
*Topic: Concept 30.3*
*Skill: Application*

53) How many chromosomes should be in a generative cell nucleus?

Answer: B
*Topic: Concept 30.3*
*Skill: Application*

54) How many chromosomes should be in an embryo sac nucleus?

Answer: B
*Topic: Concept 30.3*
*Skill: Application*

55) How many chromosomes should be in an embryo nucleus?

Answer: C
*Topic: Concept 30.3*
*Skill: Application*

56) Double fertilization means that angiosperms

A) are the only plants that can produce dizygotic twins.

B) have embryos that are triploid.

C) have two sperm nuclei, both of which unite with nuclei of the female gametophyte.

D) have two sperm nuclei, which simultaneously fertilize the single egg.

E) produce twice as many embryos per fertilization event as do gymnosperms.

Answer: C
*Topic: Concept 30.3*
*Skill: Comprehension*

57) Hypothetically, one of the major benefits of double fertilization in angiosperms is to

A) decrease the potential for mutation by insulating the embryo with other cells.

B) increase the number of fertilization events and offspring produced.

C) promote diversity in flower shape and color.

D) coordinate developmental timing between the embryo and its food stores.

E) emphasize embryonic survival by increasing embryo size.

Answer: D
*Topic: Concept 30.3*
*Skill: Knowledge*

58) Which of the following flower parts develops into a seed?

A) ovule

B) ovary

C) fruit

D) style

E) stamen

Answer: A
*Topic: Concept 30.3*
*Skill: Knowledge*

59) Which of the following flower parts develops into a fruit?

A) stigma

B) style

C) ovule

D) ovary

E) receptacle

Answer: D
*Topic: Concept 30.3*
*Skill: Knowledge*

60) All of the following are found in angiosperms *except*

A) tracheids.

B) triploid endosperm tissues.

C) fruits.

D) flagellated sperm.

E) carpels.

Answer: D
*Topic: Concept 30.3*
*Skill: Comprehension*

61) Angiosperms are the most successful terrestrial plants. This success is due to all of the following *except*

A) animal pollination.

B) reduced gametophytes.

C) fruits enclosing seeds.

D) highly efficient xylem.

E) sperm cells with flagella.

Answer: E
*Topic: Concept 30.3*
*Skill: Comprehension*

62) A plant whose reproductive parts produce nectar should be expected to

A) have brightly colored reproductive parts.

B) produce sweet-tasting fruit.

C) rely on wind pollination.

D) have no parts that can perform photosynthesis.

E) suffer significant seed loss to sugar-seeking insects.

Answer: A
*Topic: Concept 30.3*
*Skill: Comprehension*

63) If the "mostly male" hypothesis for the origin of flowers is correct, then the development of which gymnosperm structure below should be controlled by genes most similar to those that control the development of bisexual flowers?

A) microsporangium

B) megasporangium

C) ovule

D) scale of ovulate (ovule-bearing) pine cone

E) embryo

Answer: A
*Topic: Concept 30.3*
*Skill: Application*

64) Many mammals have skins and mucous membranes that are sensitive to phenolic secretions of plants like poison oak (*Rhus*). These secondary compounds are probably an adaptation that

A) promotes grazing.

B) favors pollination.

C) fosters seed dispersal.

D) decreases competition.

E) inhibits herbivory.

Answer: E
*Topic: Concept 30.3*
*Skill: Comprehension*

65) Which feature of honeybees probably arose under the mutual evolutionary influence of flowering plants that are *not* wind pollinated?

A) possessing three pairs of legs

B) possessing a metabolism whose rate is influenced by environmental temperature

C) possessing an exoskeleton made of chitin

D) possessing an abdomen that is densely covered with short bristles

E) possessing an ovipositor modified as a non-reusable stinger

Answer: D
*Topic: Concept 30.3*
*Skill: Comprehension*

66) The fruit of the mistletoe, a parasitic angiosperm, is a one-seeded berry. In members of the genus *Viscum*, the outside of the seed is viscous (sticky), which permits the seed to adhere to surfaces, such as the branches of host plants or the beaks of birds. What should be expected of the pericarp if the viscosity of *Viscum* seeds is primarily an adaptation for dispersal rather than an adaptation for infecting host plant tissues?

A) It should be drab in color.

B) It should be colored so as to provide it with camouflage.

C) It should be nutritious.

D) It should secrete enzymes that can digest bark.

E) It should contain chemicals that cause birds to fly to the ground and vomit.

Answer: C
*Topic: Concept 30.3*
*Skill: Application*

*For the following questions, match the adaptations of the various fruits below with the most likely means used by the fruit to disperse the seeds contained within the fruit (A–E).*

A. animal skin, fur, or feathers
B. animal digestive tract
C. water currents
D. gravity and terrain
E. air currents

67) The fruit is made of material high in calories.

Answer: B
*Topic: Concept 30.3*
*Skill: Application*

68) The fruit is covered with spines or hooks.

Answer: A
*Topic: Concept 30.3*
*Skill: Application*

69) The fruit contains an air bubble.

Answer: C
*Topic: Concept 30.3*
*Skill: Application*

70) The fruit has a heavy weight and spheroidal shape.

Answer: D
*Topic: Concept 30.3*
*Skill: Application*

71) The fruit has light, fibrous plumes or puffs.

Answer: E
*Topic: Concept 30.3*
*Skill: Application*

72) Over human history, which process has been most important in improving the features of plants that have long been used by humans as staple foods?
    A) genetic engineering
    B) artificial selection
    C) natural selection
    D) sexual selection
    E) pesticide and herbicide application

Answer: B
*Topic: Concept 30.4*
*Skill: Knowledge*

73) What is the greatest threat to plant diversity?
    A) insects
    B) grazing and browsing by animals
    C) pathogenic fungi
    D) competition with other plants
    E) human population growth

Answer: E
*Topic: Concept 30.4*
*Skill: Knowledge*

74) Which of the following is *not* a valid argument for preserving tropical forests?
    A) People in the tropics do not need to increase agricultural output.
    B) Many organisms are becoming extinct.
    C) Plants that are possible sources of medicines are being lost.
    D) Plants that could be developed into new crops are being lost.
    E) Clearing land for agriculture results in soil destruction.

Answer: A
*Topic: Concept 30.4*
*Skill: Knowledge*

75) Assume that a botanist was visiting a tropical region for the purpose of discovering plants with medicinal properties. All of the following might be ways of identifying potentially useful plants *except*
    A) observing which plants sick animals seek out.
    B) observing which plants are the most used food plants.
    C) observing which plants animals do not eat.
    D) collecting plants and subjecting them to chemical analysis.
    E) asking local people which plants they use as medicine.

Answer: B
*Topic: Concept 30.4*
*Skill: Application*

# Media Activity Questions

1) In pines, an embryo is a(n) _____.

    A) seed

    B) immature sporophyte

    C) food reserve for the immature sporophyte

    D) immature male gametophyte

    E) immature female gametophyte

Answer: A
*Topic: Web/CD Activity: Pine Life Cycle*

2) In pine trees, pollen grains get to the ovule via the

    A) micropyle.

    B) eggs.

    C) megaspore.

    D) pollen cone.

    E) integument.

Answer: A
*Topic: Web/CD Activity: Pine Life Cycle*

3) In pine trees, microsporangia form _____ microspores by _____.

    A) triploid; fertilization

    B) diploid; mitosis

    C) diploid; meiosis

    D) haploid; mitosis

    E) haploid; meiosis

Answer: E
*Topic: Web/CD Activity: Pine Life Cycle*

4) In flowering plants the integuments of the ovule develop into a(n)

    A) endosperm.

    B) cotyledon.

    C) fruit.

    D) sporophyte.

    E) seed coat.

Answer: B
*Topic: Web/CD Activity: Angiosperm Life Cycle*

5) A stamen consists of a(n)

    A) anther and filament.

    B) stigma and style.

    C) stigma and anther.

    D) stigma and filament.

    E) ovary and sepal.

Answer: A
*Topic: Web/CD Activity: Angiosperm Life Cycle*

# Self-Quiz Questions

1) Where in an angiosperm would you find a megasporangium?

   A) in the style of a flower

   B) producing a megaspore within the archegonium of the female gametophyte

   C) enclosed in the stigma of a flower

   D) within an ovule contained within an ovary of a flower

   E) packed into pollen sacs within the anthers found on a stamen

   Answer: D

2) A fruit is most commonly

   A) a mature ovary.

   B) a thickened style.

   C) an enlarged ovule.

   D) a modified root.

   E) a mature female gametophyte.

   Answer: A

3) With respect to angiosperms, which of the following is *incorrectly* paired with its chromosome count?

   A) egg cell—$n$

   B) megaspore—$2n$

   C) microspore—$n$

   D) zygote—$2n$

   E) sperm—$n$

   Answer: B

4) Which of the following is *not* a characteristic that distinguishes gymnosperms and angiosperms from other plants?

   A) alternation of generations

   B) ovules

   C) integuments

   D) pollen

   E) dependent gametophytes

   Answer: A

5) Which of the following traits is *not* shared by most angiosperms?

   A) two cotyledons

   B) vessel elements

   C) taproot

   D) pollen grain with three openings

   E) parallel leaf venation

   Answer: E

6) Gymnosperms and angiosperms have the following in common *except*

   A) seeds.

   B) pollen.

   C) vascular tissue.

   D) ovaries.

   E) ovules.

   Answer: D

*In the following diagram, match the derived characters with the correct branch points.*

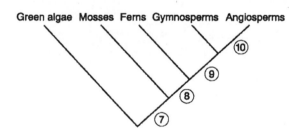

7) label 7

   A) flowers

   B) embryos

   C) seeds

   D) vascular tissues

   Answer: B

8) label 8

   A) flowers

   B) embryos

   C) seeds

   D) vascular tissues

   Answer: D

9) label 9

    A) flowers

    B) embryos

    C) seeds

    D) vascular tissues

   Answer: C

10) label 10

    A) flowers

    B) embryos

    C) seeds

    D) vascular tissues

   Answer: A

# Chapter 31  Fungi

1) Which of the following do all fungi have in common?

   A) meiosis in basidia

   B) coenocytic hyphae

   C) sexual life cycle

   D) absorption of nutrients

   E) symbioses with algae

   Answer: D
   *Topic: Concept 31.1*
   *Skill: Knowledge*

2) The hydrolytic digestion of which of the following should produce the monomer, an aminated molecule of β-glucose?

   A) insect exoskeleton

   B) plant cell walls

   C) fungal cell walls

   D) A and C only

   E) A, B and C

   Answer: D
   *Topic: Concept 31.1*
   *Skill: Knowledge*

3) If all saprobic fungi in an environment were to suddenly die, which group of organisms should benefit as a whole?

   A) plants

   B) protists

   C) prokaryotes

   D) animals

   E) mutualistic fungi

   Answer: C
   *Topic: Concept 31.1*
   *Skill: Comprehension*

4) When a mycelium infiltrates an unexploited source of dead organic matter, what are most likely to appear within the food source soon thereafter?

   A) haustoria

   B) soredia

   C) exoenzymes

   D) increased oxygen levels

   E) larger bacterial populations

   Answer: C
   *Topic: Concept 31.1*
   *Skill: Comprehension*

5) Which of the following is *not* a characteristic of hyphate fungi (fungi featuring hyphae)?

   A) They acquire their nutrients by absorption.

   B) Their body plan is a netlike mass of filaments called a mycelium.

   C) Their cell walls consist mainly of cellulose microfibrils.

   D) They may be saprobes, parasites, or mutualistic symbionts.

   E) The nuclei of the mycelia are typically haploid.

   Answer: C
   *Topic: Concept 31.1*
   *Skill: Knowledge*

6) The functional significance of porous septa in certain fungal hyphae is most similar to that represented by the _____ of certain animal cells, and by the _____ of certain plant cells.

   A) desmosomes; tonoplasts

   B) gap junctions; plasmodesmata

   C) tight junctions; plastids

   D) centrioles; plastids

   E) flagella; central vacuoles

Answer: B
*Topic: Concept 31.1*
*Skill: Comprehension*

7) What is the primary role of a mushroom's underground mycelium?

   A) absorbing nutrients

   B) anchoring

   C) sexual reproduction

   D) asexual reproduction

   E) protection

Answer: A
*Topic: Concept 31.1*
*Skill: Comprehension*

8) What do fungi and arthropods have in common?

   A) Both groups are commonly coenocytic.

   B) The haploid state is dominant in both groups.

   C) Both groups are predominantly saprobic in nutrition.

   D) The protective coats of both groups are made of chitin.

   E) Both groups have cell walls.

Answer: D
*Topic: Concept 31.1*
*Skill: Comprehension*

9) In septate fungi, what structures allow cytoplasmic streaming to distribute needed nutrients, synthesized compounds, and organelles throughout the hyphae?

   A) chitinous layers in cell walls

   B) pores in septal walls

   C) complex microtubular cytoskeletons

   D) two nuclei

   E) tight junctions that form in septal walls between cells

Answer: B
*Topic: Concept 31.1*
*Skill: Comprehension*

10) What best accounts for the extremely fast growth of a fungal mycelium?

   A) a rapid distribution of synthesized proteins by cytoplasmic streaming

   B) their lack of motility that requires rapid spread of hyphae

   C) a long tubular body shape

   D) the readily available nutrients from their predatory mode of nutrition

   E) a dikaryotic condition that supplies greater amounts of proteins and nutrients

Answer: A
*Topic: Concept 31.1*
*Skill: Knowledge*

11) The vegetative (nutritionally active) bodies of *most* fungi are

   A) composed of hyphae.

   B) referred to as a mycelium.

   C) usually underground.

   D) A and B only

   E) A, B, and C

Answer: E
*Topic: Concept 31.1*
*Skill: Comprehension*

12) Both fungus-farming ants and their fungi can synthesize the same structural polysaccharide from the β-glucose molecules that are derived from the digestion of plant leaves. What is the synthesized polysaccharide?

A) amylopectin

B) chitin

C) cellulose

D) lignin

E) glycogen

Answer: B
*Topic: Concept 31.1*
*Skill: Application*

13) Consider two hyphae having equal dimensions: one from a septate species and the other from a coenocytic species. Compared with the septate species, the coenocytic species should have

A) fewer nuclei.

B) more pores.

C) less chitin.

D) less cytoplasm.

E) reduced cytoplasmic streaming.

Answer: C
*Topic: Concept 31.1*
*Skill: Application*

14) Which of the following terms is *not* properly associated with the fungi as a kingdom?

A) decomposers

B) sexual and asexual spores

C) ecologically important

D) polyphyletic

E) absorptive nutrition

Answer: D
*Topic: Concept 31.1*
*Skill: Knowledge*

15) Which of the following cannot be assigned to any one kind of morphology (that is, unicellular or hyphate) or to any one fungal taxon?

A) yeasts

B) ascomycetes

C) club fungi

D) bread molds

E) ergot fungi

Answer: A
*Topic: Concept 31.2*
*Skill: Comprehension*

16) In fungi, karyogamy does not immediately follow plasmogamy, which

A) means that sexual reproduction can occur in specialized structures.

B) results in more genetic variation during sexual reproduction.

C) allows fungi to reproduce asexually most of the time.

D) results in heterokaryotic cells.

E) is strong support for the claim that fungi are not truly eukaryotic.

Answer: D
*Topic: Concept 31.2*
*Skill: Comprehension*

17) If all of their nuclei are equally active transcriptionally, then the cells of both dikaryotic and heterokaryotic fungi are essentially like _____ cells in terms of the gene products they can make.

A) haploid

B) diploid

C) alloploid

D) completely homozygous

E) completely hemizygous

Answer: B
*Topic: Concept 31.2*
*Skill: Comprehension*

18) What is a fungal process that has the *opposite* effect on chromosome number than the effect of meiosis?

A) mitosis

B) plasmogamy

C) crossing over

D) binary fission

E) karyogamy

Answer: E
*Topic: Concept 31.2*
*Skill: Comprehension*

Diploid nuclei of the ascomycete *Neurospora crassa* contain 14 chromosomes. A single diploid cell in an ascus will undergo one round of meiosis, followed in each of the daughter cells by one round of mitosis, producing a total of eight ascospores.

19) If a single, diploid $G_2$ nucleus in an ascus contains 400 nanograms (ng) of DNA, then a single mature ascospore of this species should contain _____ ng of DNA, carried on a total of _____ chromosomes.

A) 100; 7

B) 100; 14

C) 200; 7

D) 200; 14

E) 400; 14

Answer: A
*Topic: Concept 31.2*
*Skill: Application*

20) What is the ploidy of a single mature *Neurospora* ascospore?

A) haploid

B) diploid

C) triploid

D) tetraploid

E) polyploid

Answer: A
*Topic: Concept 31.2*
*Skill: Comprehension*

21) Each of the eight ascospores present at the end of mitosis has the same chromosome number and DNA content (ng) as each of the four cells at the end of meiosis. What must have occurred between the round of meiosis and the round of mitosis?

A) double fertilization

B) crossing over

C) nondisjunction

D) autopolyploidy

E) S phase

Answer: E
*Topic: Concept 31.2*
*Skill: Application*

22) Cytokinesis is to nuclear division as _____ is to karyogamy.

A) syngamy

B) plasmogamy

C) gametogenesis

D) endosymbiosis

E) parasitism

Answer: B
*Topic: Concept 31.2*
*Skill: Comprehension*

23) Which of the following statements is *true* of deuteromycetes?

A) They are the second of five fungal phyla to have evolved.

B) They represent the phylum in which all the fungal components of lichens are classified.

C) They are the group of fungi that have, at present, no known sexual stage.

D) They are the group that includes molds, yeasts, and lichens.

E) They include the imperfect fungi that lack hyphae.

Answer: C
*Topic: Concept 31.2*
*Skill: Knowledge*

24) A chemical secreted by female *Bombyx* moths helps the male of the species locate her, at which time sexual reproduction may occur. This chemical is most similar in function to which chemicals used by certain fungi?

A) chitin

B) exoenzymes

C) lysergic acids

D) aflatoxins

E) pheromones

Answer: E
*Topic: Concept 31.2*
*Skill: Comprehension*

25) Which of the following is characterized by the lack of an observed sexual phase in its members' life cycle?

A) Ascomycota

B) Basidiomycota

C) Chytridiomycota

D) Deuteromycota

E) Zygomycota

Answer: D
*Topic: Concept 31.2*
*Skill: Knowledge*

26) A biologist is trying to classify a new organism on the basis of the following characteristics: fungus–like in appearance, reproduces by conidia, has no apparent sexual phase, and parasitizes woody plants. If asked for advice, to which group would you assign this new species?

A) Deuteromycota

B) Zygomycota

C) Ascomycota

D) Basidiomycota

E) Glomeromycota

Answer: A
*Topic: Concept 31.2*
*Skill: Application*

27) Which of these structures are most likely to be a component of both chytrid zoospores and motile animal cells?

A) chloroplasts

B) 9 + 2 pattern of microtubules in flagella

C) cell walls composed of chitin

D) heterokaryons

E) haustoria

Answer: B
*Topic: Concept 31.3*
*Skill: Comprehension*

28) If the choanoflagellate protist from which animals are thought to have evolved were classified as an opisthokont, then what should be true of these choanoflagellates?

A) They should also have given rise to the chytrids.

B) They should be the common ancestor of the chytrids and the zygomycetes.

C) The end of the cell from which the flagellum emerges should be homologous to the posterior ends of animal sperm cells and chytrid zoospores.

D) They should perform heterotrophy by secretion of exoenzymes.

E) Like diplomonads and parabasalids, they should bear multiple flagella.

Answer: C
*Topic: Concept 31.3*
*Skill: Comprehension*

29) Considered at the taxonomic level of the kingdom, which of the following constitute a monophyletic clade?

A) mosses and zygomycetes

B) chytrids and fungi

C) algae and ascomycetes

D) chytrids and slime molds

E) mosses and fungi

Answer: B
*Topic: Concept 31.3*
*Skill: Comprehension*

30) Fossil fungi date back to the origin and early evolution of plants. What combination of environmental and morphological change is similar in the evolution of both fungi and plants?

A) presence of "coal forests" and change in mode of nutrition

B) periods of drought and presence of filamentous body shape

C) predominance in swamps and presence of cellulose in cell walls

D) colonization of land and loss of flagellated cells

E) continental drift and mode of spore dispersal

Answer: D
*Topic: Concept 31.3*
*Skill: Comprehension*

31) Which of the following characteristics is *not* shared by both chytrids and other kinds of fungi?

A) presence of hyphae

B) flagellated zoospores

C) absorptive mode of nutrition

D) chitinous cell walls

E) amino acid base sequences of some enzymes

Answer: B
*Topic: Concept 31.3*
*Skill: Knowledge*

32) If the multicellular condition is an adaptation, rather than an accident, then the multicellular condition of animals and fungi seems to have arisen

A) due to common ancestry.

B) by convergent evolution.

C) by inheritance of acquired traits.

D) by natural means, and is a homology.

E) More than one of these is correct.

Answer: B
*Topic: Concept 31.3*
*Skill: Comprehension*

33) Asexual reproduction in yeasts occurs by budding. Due to unequal cytokinesis, the "bud" cell receives less cytoplasm than the parent cell. Which of the following should be true of the smaller cell until it reaches the size of the larger cell?

A) It should produce fewer fermentation products per unit time.

B) It should produce ribosomal RNA at a slower rate.

C) It should be transcriptionally less active.

D) It should have reduced motility.

E) It should have a smaller nucleus.

Answer: A
*Topic: Concept 31.3*
*Skill: Application*

*Match the phyla below with the descriptions that follow.*
*Each term may be used once, more than once, or not at all.*

    A.  Zygomycota
    B.  Ascomycota
    C.  Basidiomycota
    D.  Glomeromycota
    E.  Chytridiomycota

34) This phylum contains organisms that most closely resemble the common ancestor of fungi and animals.

Answer: E
*Topic: Concept 31.4*
*Skill: Knowledge*

35) This phylum formerly included the members of the new phylum Glomeromycota, and may also contain the Microsporidia.

Answer: A
*Topic: Concept 31.4*
*Skill: Knowledge*

36) Members of this phylum produce two kinds of haploid spores, one kind being asexually produced conidia.

Answer: B
*Topic: Concept 31.4*
*Skill: Knowledge*

37) This phylum contains the mushrooms, shelf fungi, and puffballs.

Answer: C
*Topic: Concept 31.4*
*Skill: Knowledge*

38) Members of this phylum form arbuscular mycorrhizae.

Answer: D
*Topic: Concept 31.4*
*Skill: Knowledge*

39) You have been given the assignment of locating living members of the phylum Glomeromycota. Where is the best place to look for these fungi?
    A) between the toes of a person with "athlete's foot"
    B) in stagnant freshwater ponds
    C) the roots of vascular plants
    D) growing on rocks and tree bark
    E) the kidneys of cattle

Answer: C
*Topic: Concept 31.4*
*Skill: Application*

40) What are the sporangia of bread molds?
    A) asexual structures that produce haploid spores
    B) asexual structures that produce diploid spores
    C) sexual structures that produce haploid spores
    D) sexual structures that produce diploid spores
    E) vegetative structures with no role in reproduction

Answer: A
*Topic: Concept 31.4*
*Skill: Knowledge*

41) The gray-black filamentous mycelium growing on bread is most likely what kind of organism?
    A) chytrid
    B) ascomycete
    C) basidiomycete
    D) deuteromycete
    E) zygomycete

Answer: E
*Topic: Concept 31.4*
*Skill: Knowledge*

42) The ascomycetes get their name from which aspect of their life cycle?

A) vegetative growth form

B) asexual spore production

C) sexual structures

D) shape of the spore

E) type of vegetative mycelium

Answer: C
*Topic: Concept 31.4*
*Skill: Knowledge*

43) Which of these fungal structures are structurally and functionally most alike?

A) conidia and basidiocarps

B) sporangia and hyphae

C) soredia and gills

D) haustoria and arbuscles

E) zoospores and mycelia

Answer: D
*Topic: Concept 31.4*
*Skill: Comprehension*

44) You are given an organism to identify. It has a fruiting body that contains many structures with eight haploid spores lined up in a row. What kind of a fungus is this?

A) zygomycete

B) ascomycete

C) deuteromycete

D) chytrid

E) basidiomycete

Answer: B
*Topic: Concept 31.4*
*Skill: Application*

45) Which has the *least* affiliation with all of the others?

A) Glomeromycota

B) endomycorrhizae

C) lichens

D) arbuscular mycorrhizae

E) symbiotic fungi

Answer: C
*Topic: Concept 31.4*
*Skill: Comprehension*

46) Which of these fungal structures is associated with asexual reproduction?

A) zygospore

B) basidium

C) conidium

D) ascus

E) antheridium

Answer: C
*Topic: Concept 31.4*
*Skill: Knowledge*

47) How are mushrooms and toadstools classified?

A) basidiomycetes

B) ascomycetes

C) deuteromycetes

D) zygomycetes

E) chytrids

Answer: A
*Topic: Concept 31.4*
*Skill: Knowledge*

48) Arrange the following from largest to smallest, assuming that they all come from the same fungus.
1. basidiocarp
2. basidium
3. basidiospore
4. mycelium
5. gill

A) 4, 5, 1, 2, 3
B) 5, 1, 4, 2, 3
C) 5, 1, 4, 3, 2
D) 5, 1, 3, 2, 4
E) 4, 1, 5, 2, 3

Answer: E
*Topic: Concept 31.4*
*Skill: Comprehension*

49) Mushrooms with gills, typically available in supermarkets, have meiotically produced spores located in or on _____ and belong to the phylum _____.

A) asci; Basidiomycota
B) hyphae; Zygomycota
C) basidia; Basidiomycota
D) asci; Ascomycota
E) hyphae; Ascomycota

Answer: C
*Topic: Concept 31.4*
*Skill: Knowledge*

50) A fungal spore germinates, giving rise to a mycelium that grows outward into the soil surrounding the site where the spore originally landed. What process best accounts for the observation that, upon reaching sexual maturity, this fungus produces a nearly circular fairy ring despite the fact that organic nutrients are not evenly distributed in the soil?

A) karyogamy
B) plasmogamy
C) alternation of generations
D) fermentation
E) cytoplasmic streaming

Answer: E
*Topic: Concept 31.4*
*Skill: Application*

51) In what structures do both *Penicillium* and *Aspergillus* produce asexual spores?

A) asci
B) antheridia
C) rhizoids
D) gametangia
E) conidiophores

Answer: E
*Topic: Concept 31.4*
*Skill: Knowledge*

52) The nonpathogenic fungus that produces a fairy ring grows outward in concentric rings over the course of years. As a result, what should be *less* abundant in the soil within the ring soon after the fungal hyphae colonize it?

A) antibiotic molecules
B) living organic matter
C) living plant roots
D) dead organic matter
E) fungal exoenzymes

Answer: D
*Topic: Concept 31.4*
*Skill: Comprehension*

53) Chemicals, secreted by soil fungi, that inhibit the growth of bacteria are known as

A) antibodies.

B) aflatoxins.

C) hallucinogens.

D) antigens.

E) antibiotics.

Answer: E
*Topic: Concept 31.5*
*Skill: Knowledge*

54) Lichens are symbiotic associations of fungi and

A) mosses.

B) cyanobacteria.

C) green algae.

D) either A or B

E) either B or C

Answer: E
*Topic: Concept 31.5*
*Skill: Knowledge*

55) Lichens sometimes reproduce asexually using

A) aseptate fungal hyphae located within photosynthetic cells.

B) the fruiting bodies of fungi.

C) flagellated, conjoined spores of both the fungus and alga.

D) specialized conidiophores.

E) small clusters of fungal hyphae surrounding photosynthetic cells.

Answer: E
*Topic: Concept 31.5*
*Skill: Knowledge*

56) The symbiotic associations involving roots and soil fungi are considered

A) parasitic.

B) mutualistic.

C) commensal.

D) harmful to the plant partner.

E) the beginning stages of the formation of lichens.

Answer: B
*Topic: Concept 31.5*
*Skill: Knowledge*

57) If there were no mycorrhizae, then which of the following would be true?

A) There would be fewer infectious diseases.

B) We wouldn't have any antibiotics.

C) There would be no mushrooms for pizza.

D) Most vascular plants would be stunted in their growth.

E) Cheeses like blue cheese or Roquefort would not exist.

Answer: D
*Topic: Concept 31.5*
*Skill: Comprehension*

58) Which of the following *best* describes the physical relationship of the partners involved in lichens?

A) Fungal cells are enclosed within algal cells.

B) Lichen cells are enclosed within fungal cells.

C) Photosynthetic cells are surrounded by fungal hyphae.

D) The fungi grow on rocks and trees and are covered by algae.

E) Algal cells and fungal cells mix together without any apparent structure.

Answer: C
*Topic: Concept 31.5*
*Skill: Knowledge*

59) If haustoria were to appear within the photosynthetic partner of a lichen, and if the growth rate of the photosynthetic partner consequently slowed substantially, then this would support the claim that

A) algae and cyanobacteria are autotrophic.

B) lichens are not purely mutualistic relationships.

C) algae require maximal contact with the fungal partner in order to grow at optimal rates.

D) fungi get all of the nutrition they need via the "leakiness" of photosynthetic partners.

E) soredia are asexual reproductive structures combining both the fungal and photosynthetic partners.

Answer: B
*Topic: Concept 31.5*
*Skill: Application*

60) How are the vascular plants that are involved in mycorrhizae and the photosynthetic cells that are involved in lichens alike?

A) They provide organic nutrients to fungal partners.

B) They secrete acids that keep the fungal partner from growing too quickly.

C) They are in intimate associations with chytrids.

D) They are digested by fungal exoenzymes while still alive.

E) They contain endosymbiotic fungi.

Answer: A
*Topic: Concept 31.5*
*Skill: Comprehension*

61) When pathogenic fungi are found growing on the roots of grape vines, grape farmers sometimes respond by covering the ground around their vines with plastic sheeting and pumping a gaseous fungicide into the soil. The most important concern of viticulturists who engage in this practice should be that the

A) fungicide might also kill the native yeasts residing on the surfaces of the grapes.

B) fungicide isn't also harmful to insect pests.

C) lichens growing on the vines' branches are not harmed.

D) fungicide might also kill mycorrhizae.

E) sheeting is transparent so that photosynthesis can continue.

Answer: D
*Topic: Concept 31.5*
*Skill: Application*

62) The terms below all refer to symbiotic relationships that involve fungi *except*

A) pathogens.

B) mycoses.

C) spore production.

D) lichens.

E) mycorrhizae.

Answer: C
*Topic: Concept 31.5*
*Skill: Knowledge*

63) If *Penicillium* secreted penicillin while involved in a lichen relationship, what must have been true about its partner?

   A) It should have lacked peptidoglycan in its cell wall.

   B) It was probably a green alga.

   C) It was probably *not* a member of the domain Bacteria.

   D) It was probably *not* a heterotrophic prokaryote.

   E) All of these are true.

   Answer: E
   *Topic: Concept 31.5*
   *Skill: Application*

64) Sexual reproduction has never been observed among the fungi that produce the blue-green marbling of blue cheeses. What is true of these fungi and others that do not have a a sexual stage?

   A) They are currently classified among the deuteromycetes.

   B) They do *not* form heterokaryons.

   C) Their spores are produced by mitosis.

   D) Only A and B are correct.

   E) A, B, and C are correct.

   Answer: E
   *Topic: Concept 31.5*
   *Skill: Comprehension*

65) Both fungus-derived antibiotics and hallucinogens used by humans probably evolved in fungi as a means to

   A) reduce competition for nutrients.

   B) help humanity survive.

   C) promote their ingestion of foodstuffs.

   D) eliminate other fungi.

   E) discourage animal predators.

   Answer: A
   *Topic: Concept 31.5*
   *Skill: Comprehension*

66) A billionaire buys a sterile volcanic island that recently emerged from the sea. To speed the arrival of conditions necessary for plant growth, the billionaire might be advised to aerially sow _____ over the island.

   A) basiodiospores

   B) spores of ectomycorrhizae

   C) soredia

   D) yeasts

   E) leaves (as food for fungus-farming ants)

   Answer: C
   *Topic: Concept 31.5*
   *Skill: Application*

67) *Taxol* is a drug derived from a certain species of yew trees. In humans, the drug's cancer-fighting properties may counter the effects of

   A) antibiotics.

   B) immunosuppressants.

   C) aflatoxins.

   D) yeasts.

   E) hallucinogens.

   Answer: C
   *Topic: Concept 31.5*
   *Skill: Knowledge*

68) The following conditions are all caused by a fungus *except*

   A) AIDS.

   B) athlete's foot.

   C) ringworm.

   D) candidiasis (*Candida* yeast infection).

   E) coccidioidomycosis.

   Answer: A
   *Topic: Concept 31.5*
   *Skill: Knowledge*

# Media Activity Questions

1) Basidia produce spores by a process known as

   A) decomposition.

   B) mitosis.

   C) meiosis.

   D) hyphae.

   E) binary fission.

   Answer: C
   *Topic: Activity: Fungal Reproduction and Nutrition*

2) Karyogamy produces a

   A) diploid zygote.

   B) haploid zygote.

   C) spores.

   D) mycelium.

   E) hypha.

   Answer: A
   *Topic: Web/CD Activity: Fungal Life Cycles*

3) Which of these contain two haploid nuclei?

   A) the heterokaryotic stage of the fungal life cycle

   B) zygote

   C) spore-producing structures

   D) mycelium

   E) hypha

   Answer: A
   *Topic: Web/CD Activity: Fungal Life Cycles*

4) In sac fungi, karyogamy and meiosis occur in

   A) ascospores.

   B) antheridia.

   C) asci.

   D) ascogonia.

   E) basidia.

   Answer: C
   *Topic: Web/CD Activity: Fungal Life Cycles*

5) A nucleus with an ascus undergoes meiosis, producing four haploid spores, which then undergo mitosis, producing eight haploid ascospores. These haploid ascospores contain a maximum of _____ different genetic types.

   A) one

   B) two

   C) three

   D) four

   E) five

   Answer: D
   *Topic: Activity: Fungal Reproduction and Nutrition*

# Self–Quiz Questions

1) *All* fungi share which of the following characteristics?

   A) symbiotic

   B) heterotrophic

   C) flagellated

   D) pathogenic

   E) saprobic

   Answer: B

2) Which feature seen in chytrids supports the hypothesis that they represent the most primitive fungi?

   A) the absence of chitin within the cell wall

   B) coenocytic hyphae

   C) flagellated spores

   D) formation of resistant zygosporangia

   E) parasitic lifestyle

   Answer: C

3) Which of the following cells or structures are associated with *asexual* reproduction in fungi?

   A) ascospores

   B) basidiospores

   C) conidiophores

   D) zygosporangia

   E) ascocarps

   Answer: C

4) Which of the following is an example of an opportunistic pathogen that can cause a mycosis?

   A) *Claviceps purpurea*, which produces ergots on rye that can cause serious symptoms in humans if milled into flour

   B) *Ophiostoma ulmi*, which causes Dutch elm disease

   C) the ascomycetes that cause ringworm

   D) *Candida albicans*, which causes vaginal yeast infections

   E) *Penicillium*, which is grown in culture to produce antibiotics

   Answer: D

5) The adaptive advantage associated with the filamentous nature of the mycelium is primarily related to

   A) the ability to form haustoria and parasitize other organisms.

   B) avoiding sexual reproduction until the environment changes.

   C) the potential to inhabit almost all terrestrial habitats.

   D) the increased probability of contact between different mating types.

   E) an extensive surface area well suited for absorptive nutrition.

   Answer: E

6) Sporangia on erect hyphae that produce asexual spores are characteristic of

   A) ascomycetes.

   B) basidiomycetes.

   C) club fungi.

   D) zygomycetes.

   E) lichens.

   Answer: D

7) Basidiomycetes differ from other fungi in that they

    A) have no known sexual stage.

    B) have long–lived dikaryotic mycelia.

    C) produce resistant sporangia that are initially heterokaryotic before karyogamy and meiosis occur.

    D) have members that are symbionts with algae in lichens.

    E) form eight spores that line up in a sac in the order they were formed in meiosis.

Answer: B

8) Which of the following is the best description of a mold?

    A) a deuteromycete, which has no known sexual stage

    B) a coenocytic, rapidly growing mycelium

    C) a mycorrhiza that envelops plant roots and reproduces without forming spores

    D) a unicellular fungi that grow rapidly in moist habitats

    E) the fast–growing mycelia of any asexually reproducing fungus

Answer: E

9) The photosynthetic symbiont of a lichen is often a(n)

    A) moss.

    B) green alga.

    C) brown alga.

    D) ascomycete.

    E) small vascular plant.

Answer: B

10) The closest relatives of fungi are probably

    A) animals.

    B) vascular plants.

    C) mosses.

    D) brown algae.

    E) slime molds.

Answer: A

# Chapter 32  An Introduction to Animal Diversity

1) Most animals exhibit the following structures or functions *except*

   A) nervous and muscle tissue.

   B) unique types of intercellular junctions, such as tight junctions and gap junctions.

   C) autotrophic nutrition.

   D) sexual reproduction.

   E) multicellularity.

   Answer: C
   *Topic: Concept 32.1*
   *Skill: Knowledge*

2) Which of the following terms or structures is *not* associated with animals?

   A) eukaryotic

   B) cell wall

   C) desmosome

   D) zygote

   E) blastula

   Answer: B
   *Topic: Concept 32.1*
   *Skill: Knowledge*

3) A researcher is trying to construct a molecular-based phylogeny of the entire animal kingdom. Assuming that none of the following genes is absolutely conserved, which of the following would be the best choice on which to base the phylogeny?

   A) genes involved in chitin synthesis

   B) collagen genes

   C) crystallin genes

   D) myosin genes

   E) globin genes

   Answer: B
   *Topic: Concept 32.1*
   *Skill: Comprehension*

4) Both animals and fungi are heterotrophic. What distinguishes animal heterotrophy from fungal heterotrophy is that only animals derive their nutrition

   A) from organic matter.

   B) by preying on animals.

   C) by ingesting it.

   D) by consuming living, rather than dead, prey.

   E) by using enzymes to digest their food.

   Answer: C
   *Topic: Concept 32.1*
   *Skill: Comprehension*

5) The young of some insects are merely small versions of the adult, whereas the larvae of other insects look completely different from adults, eat different foods, and may live in different habitats. Which of the following most directly favors the evolution of the latter more radical kind of metamorphosis?

   A) natural selection of sexually immature forms of insects

   B) changes in the homeobox genes governing early development

   C) the evolution of meiosis

   D) B and C only

   E) A, B, and C

   Answer: B
   *Topic: Concept 32.1*
   *Skill: Application*

6) What is the correct sequence of the following four events during an animal's development?
1. gastrulation
2. metamorphosis
3. fertilization
4. cleavage

A) 4, 3, 2, 1

B) 4, 3, 1, 2

C) 3, 2, 4, 1

D) 3, 4, 2, 1

E) 3, 4, 1, 2

Answer: E
*Topic: Concept 32.1*
*Skill: Comprehension*

7) At which stage would one be able to first distinguish a diploblastic embryo from a triploblastic embryo?

A) fertilization

B) cleavage

C) gastrulation

D) organogenesis

E) metamorphosis

Answer: C
*Topic: Concept 32.1*
*Skill: Comprehension*

8) Which of the following is *not* unique to animals?

A) cells that have tight junctions, desmosomes, or gap junctions

B) the structural protein collagen

C) nervous conduction and muscular movement

D) regulatory genes called *Hox* genes

E) sexual reproduction

Answer: E
*Topic: Concept 32.1*
*Skill: Knowledge*

9) The number of legs an insect has, or the number of vertebrae in a vertebral column, or the number of joints in a digit (such as a finger) are all strongly influenced by _____ genes.

A) haploid

B) introns within

C) heterotic

D) heterogeneous

E) *Hox*

Answer: E
*Topic: Concept 32.1*
*Skill: Knowledge*

10) What should animals as diverse as corals and monkeys have in common?

A) body cavity between body wall and digestive system

B) number of embryonic tissue layers

C) type of body symmetry

D) presence of *Hox* genes

E) degree of cephalization

Answer: D
*Topic: Concept 32.1*
*Skill: Comprehension*

11) What may have occurred to prevent species that are of the same grade from also belonging to the same clade?

A) similar structures arising independently in different lineages

B) convergent evolution among different lineages

C) adaptation by different lineages to the same selective pressures

D) A and B only

E) A, B, and C

Answer: E
*Topic: Concept 32.1*
*Skill: Comprehension*

12) The *Hox* genes came to regulate each of the following in what sequence, from earliest to most recent?

1. identity and position of paired appendages in protostome embryos
2. formation of channels in sponges
3. anterior-posterior orientation of segments in protostome embryos
4. positioning of tentacles in cnidarians
5. anterior-posterior orientation of somites in vertebrate embryos

A) 4, 1, 3, 2, 5

B) 4, 2, 3, 1, 5

C) 4, 2, 5, 3, 1

D) 2, 4, 5, 3, 1

E) 2, 4, 3, 1, 5

Answer: E
*Topic: Concept 32.1*
*Skill: Application*

13) Almost all of the major animal body plans seen today appeared in the fossil record over 500 million years ago at the beginning of the

A) Cambrian period.

B) Ediacaran period.

C) Permian period.

D) Carboniferous period.

E) Cretaceous period.

Answer: A
*Topic: Concept 32.2*
*Skill: Knowledge*

14) Evidence of which structure or characteristic would be most surprising to find among fossils of the Ediacaran fauna?

A) true tissues

B) mineralized hard parts

C) bilateral symmetry

D) cephalization

E) embryos

Answer: B
*Topic: Concept 32.2*
*Skill: Comprehension*

15) Which statement is most consistent with the hypothesis that the Cambrian explosion was caused by the rise of predator-prey relationships?

A) increased incidence of worm burrows in the fossil record

B) increased incidence of larger animals in the fossil record

C) increased incidence of organic material in the fossil record

D) increased incidence of fern galls in the fossil record

E) increased incidence of hard parts in the fossil record

Answer: E
*Topic: Concept 32.2*
*Skill: Application*

16) Which of these genetic processes may be most helpful in accounting for the Cambrian explosion?

A) binary fission

B) mitosis

C) random segregation

D) gene duplication

E) chromosomal condensation

Answer: D
*Topic: Concept 32.2*
*Skill: Comprehension*

17) Whatever its ultimate cause(s), the Cambrian explosion is a prime example of

A) anagenesis (phyletic evolution).

B) evolutionary stasis.

C) adaptive radiation.

D) A and B only

E) A, B, and C

Answer: C
*Topic: Concept 32.2*
*Skill: Comprehension*

18) Fossil evidence indicates that the following events occurred in what sequence, from earliest to most recent?
1. Protostomes invade terrestrial environments.
2. Cambrian explosion occurs.
3. Deuterostomes invade terrestrial environments.
4. Vertebrates become top predators in the seas.

A) 2, 4, 3, 1

B) 2, 1, 4, 3

C) 2, 4, 1, 3

D) 2, 3, 1, 4

E) 2, 1, 3, 4

Answer: C
*Topic: Concept 32.2*
*Skill: Comprehension*

19) If one encounters the deepest stratum in which aquatic and flying reptiles can be found, then one has likely found a stratum that was laid during which era?

A) Mesozoic

B) Paleozoic

C) Cenozoic

D) Neoproterozoic

E) Precambrian

Answer: A
*Topic: Concept 32.2*
*Skill: Comprehension*

20) What is the probable sequence in which the following clades of animals originated, from earliest to most recent?
1. tetrapods
2. vertebrates
3. deuterostomes
4. amniotes
5. bilaterians

A) 5, 3, 2, 4, 1

B) 5, 3, 2, 1, 4

C) 5, 3, 4, 2, 1

D) 3, 5, 4, 2, 1

E) 3, 5, 2, 1,4

Answer: B
*Topic: Concept 32.2*
*Skill: Comprehension*

21) During which era did the greatest radiation of mammals occur?

A) Mesozoic

B) Paleozoic

C) Cenozoic

D) Neoproterozoic

E) Precambrian

Answer: C
*Topic: Concept 32.2*
*Skill: Knowledge*

22) The major branches of Eumetazoa are the Radiata and the Bilateria. These names refer to what characteristic of these animals?

A) size

B) body symmetry

C) embryonic cleavage

D) types of appendages

E) presence or absence of a nucleus in their cells

Answer: B
*Topic: Concept 32.3*
*Skill: Knowledge*

23) Organisms showing radial symmetry would likely

    A) be good swimmers.

    B) have rapid escape behavior.

    C) move from place to place relatively slowly, if at all.

    D) be able to fly.

    E) have many fins.

Answer: C
*Topic: Concept 32.3*
*Skill: Comprehension*

24) During metamorphosis, echinoderms undergo a transformation from motile larvae to a sedentary (and sometimes sessile) existence as adults. What is true of adults, but *not* of larvae? Adults should

    A) be diploblastic.

    B) have radial symmetry.

    C) lack mesodermally derived tissues.

    D) A and B only

    E) A, B, and C

Answer: B
*Topic: Concept 32.3*
*Skill: Comprehension*

25) Cephalization is primarily associated with

    A) adaptation to dark environments.

    B) method of reproduction.

    C) fate of the blastopore.

    D) type of digestive system.

    E) bilateral symmetry.

Answer: E
*Topic: Concept 32.3*
*Skill: Knowledge*

26) Cephalization is generally associated with all of the following *except*

    A) bilateral symmetry.

    B) concentration of sensory structures at the anterior end.

    C) a brain.

    D) a longitudinal nerve cord.

    E) a sessile existence.

Answer: E
*Topic: Concept 32.3*
*Skill: Comprehension*

27) Which of the following is an *incorrect* association of an animal germ layer with the tissues or organs to which it gives rise?

    A) ectoderm—outer covering

    B) endoderm—internal lining of digestive tract

    C) mesoderm—nervous system

    D) mesoderm—muscle

    E) endoderm—internal linings of liver and lungs

Answer: C
*Topic: Concept 32.3*
*Skill: Knowledge*

28) You are trying to identify an organism. It is an animal, but it does not have nerve or muscle tissue. It is *neither* diploblastic nor triploblastic. It is probably a

    A) flatworm.

    B) jelly.

    C) comb jelly.

    D) sponge.

    E) nematode.

Answer: D
*Topic: Concept 32.3*
*Skill: Application*

(See page 515 for Figure 32.1.)

*Figure 32.1 shows a chart of the animal kingdom set up as a modified phylogenetic tree. Use the diagram to answer the following questions.*

29) Which group contains diploblastic organisms?

A) I

B) II

C) III

D) IV

E) V

Answer: A
*Topic: Concept 32.3*
*Skill: Knowledge*

30) Which group consists of deuterostomes?

A) I

B) II

C) III

D) IV

E) V

Answer: B
*Topic: Concept 32.3*
*Skill: Knowledge*

31) Which group includes both ecdysozoans and lophotrochozoans?

A) I

B) II

C) III

D) IV

E) V

Answer: C
*Topic: Concept 32.4*
*Skill: Knowledge*

32) Which two groups are most clearly represented in the Ediacaran fauna?

A) I and II

B) I and III

C) II and IV

D) II and V

E) IV and V

Answer: B
*Topic: Concept 32.4*
*Skill: Knowledge*

33) Which of these is the basal group of the Eumetazoa?

A) I

B) II

C) III

D) IV

E) V

Answer: A
*Topic: Concept 32.4*
*Skill: Knowledge*

34) Which two groups have members that undergo ecdysis?

A) I  and II

B) II and III

C) III and IV

D) III and V

E) IV and V

Answer: C
*Topic: Concept 32.4*
*Skill: Knowledge*

35) Organisms that are neither coelomate nor pseudocoelomate should, apart from their digestive systems, have bodies that

    A) are solid with tissue.

    B) lack the ability to metabolize food.

    C) are incapable of muscular contraction.

    D) lack true tissues.

    E) lack mesodermally derived tissues.

Answer: A
*Topic: Concept 32.3*
*Skill: Comprehension*

36) What distinguishes a coelomate animal from a pseudocoelomate animal is that coelomates

    A) have a body cavity, whereas pseudocoelomates have a solid body.

    B) contain tissues derived from mesoderm, whereas pseudocoelomates have no such tissue.

    C) have a body cavity completely lined by mesodermal tissue, whereas pseudocoelomates do not.

    D) have a complete digestive system with mouth and anus, whereas pseudocoelomates have a digestive tract with only one opening.

    E) have a gut that lacks suspension within the body cavity, whereas pseudocoelomates have mesenteries that hold the digestive system in place.

Answer: C
*Topic: Concept 32.3*
*Skill: Knowledge*

37) Which of the following functions is an advantage of a fluid-filled body cavity?

    A) Internal organs are cushioned and protected from injury.

    B) Organs can grow and move independently of the outer body wall.

    C) The cavity acts as a hydrostatic skeleton.

    D) A and C only

    E) A, B, and C

Answer: E
*Topic: Concept 32.3*
*Skill: Comprehension*

38) You have before you a living organism, which you examine carefully. Which of the following should convince you that the organism is an acoelomate?

    A) It responds to food by moving toward it.

    B) It is triploblastic.

    C) It has bilateral symmetry.

    D) It possesses sensory structures at its anterior end.

    E) Muscular activity of its digestive system distorts the body wall.

Answer: E
*Topic: Concept 32.3*
*Skill: Application*

39) An animal that swims rapidly in search of prey that it captures using visual senses concentrated at its anterior end is likely to be all of the following *except*

    A) bilaterally symmetrical.

    B) coelomate.

    C) eumetazoan.

    D) diploblastic.

    E) cephalized.

Answer: D
*Topic: Concept 32.3*
*Skill: Comprehension*

40) The blastopore is a structure that is evident in the

    A) zygote.

    B) blastula.

    C) eight-cell embryo.

    D) gastrula.

    E) egg and sperm.

Answer: D
*Topic: Concept 32.3*
*Skill: Knowledge*

41) The blastopore denotes the presence of an endoderm-lined cavity in the developing embryo, a cavity that is known as the

    A) archenteron.

    B) blastula.

    C) coelom.

    D) germ layer.

    E) blastocoel.

Answer: A
*Topic: Concept 32.3*
*Skill: Comprehension*

42) Which of the following is descriptive of protostomes?

    A) spiral and indeterminate cleavage, blastopore becomes mouth, schizocoelous development

    B) spiral and determinate cleavage, blastopore becomes mouth, schizocoelous development

    C) spiral and determinate cleavage, blastopore becomes anus, enterocoelous development

    D) radial and determinate cleavage, blastopore becomes anus, enterocoelous development

    E) radial and determinate cleavage, blastopore becomes mouth, schizocoelous development

Answer: B
*Topic: Concept 32.3*
*Skill: Knowledge*

43) Which of the following characteristics generally applies to protostome development?

    A) radial cleavage

    B) determinate cleavage

    C) enterocoelous

    D) blastopore becomes the anus

    E) archenteron absent

Answer: B
*Topic: Concept 32.3*
*Skill: Knowledge*

44) Protostome characteristics include all of the following *except*

    A) a mouth that develops from the blastopore.

    B) schizocoelous development.

    C) spiral cleavage.

    D) indeterminate cleavage.

    E) solid masses of mesodermal tissue that split and form the body cavity.

Answer: D
*Topic: Concept 32.3*
*Skill: Comprehension*

A student encounters an animal embryo at the eight-cell stage. The four smaller cells that comprise one hemisphere of the embryo seem to be rotated 45 degrees and lie in the grooves between larger, underlying cells (spiral cleavage). Use this information to answer the questions that follow.

45) This embryo may potentially develop into any one of these organisms *except*

    A) a turtle.

    B) an earthworm.

    C) a fruit fly.

    D) a crab.

    E) a mollusc.

Answer: A
*Topic: Concept 32.3*
*Skill: Comprehension*

46) If one were to separate these eight cells and attempt to culture them individually, then what is most likely to happen?

A) All eight cells will die immediately.

B) Each cell will survive but will experience immediate cessation of further growth and cell division.

C) Each cell will continue development, but only into an inviable embryo that lacks many parts.

D) Each cell will develop into a full-sized, normal embryo.

E) Each cell will develop into a smaller-than-average, but otherwise normal, embryo.

Answer: C
*Topic: Concept 32.3*
*Skill: Comprehension*

47) If an undisturbed embryo is allowed to develop further, then one should expect that

A) the first opening of the gastrula will ultimately serve as the mouth.

B) upon metamorphosis, the resulting trochophore larva will gain a notochord.

C) upon gastrulation, a solid ball of cells will be produced.

D) both A and B

E) both B and C

Answer: A
*Topic: Concept 32.3*
*Skill: Comprehension*

48) The most ancient branch point in animal phylogeny is that between having

A) radial or bilateral symmetry.

B) a well-defined head or no head.

C) diploblastic or triploblastic embryos.

D) true tissues or no tissues.

E) a body cavity or no body cavity.

Answer: D
*Topic: Concept 32.3*
*Skill: Comprehension*

49) With the current molecular-based phylogeny in mind, rank the following from most inclusive to least inclusive.
1. ecdysozoan
2. protostome
3. eumetazoan
4. triploblastic

A) 4, 2, 3, 1

B) 4, 3, 1, 2

C) 3, 4, 1, 2

D) 3, 4, 2, 1

E) 4, 3, 2, 1

Answer: D
*Topic: Concept 32.4*
*Skill: Comprehension*

50) What does recent evidence from molecular systematics reveal about the relationship between grades and clades?

A) They are one and the same.

B) There is no relationship.

C) Some, but not all, grades reflect evolutionary relatedness.

D) Grades have their basis in, and flow from, clades.

E) Each branch point on a cladogram is associated with the evolution of a new grade.

Answer: C
*Topic: Concept 32.4*
*Skill: Comprehension*

51) What is characteristic of all ecdysozoans?

A) the deuterostome condition

B) some kind of exoskeleton, or hard outer covering

C) a pseudocoelom

D) agile, speedy, and powerful locomotion

E) the diploblastic condition

Answer: B
*Topic: Concept 32.4*
*Skill: Knowledge*

52) What kind of data should probably have the greatest impact on animal taxonomy in the coming decades?

A) fossil evidence

B) comparative morphology of living species

C) nucleotide sequences of homologous genes

D) similarities in metabolic pathways

E) the number and size of chromosomes within nuclei

Answer: C
*Topic: Concept 32.4*
*Skill: Comprehension*

53) Phylogenetic trees are best described as

A) true and inerrant statements about evolutionary relationships.

B) hypothetical portrayals of evolutionary relationships.

C) the most accurate representations possible of genetic relationships among taxa.

D) theories of evolution.

E) the closest things to absolute certainty that modern systematics can produce.

Answer: B
*Topic: Concept 32.4*
*Skill: Comprehension*

54) According to the evidence collected so far, the animal kingdom is

A) monophyletic.

B) paraphyletic.

C) polyphyletic.

D) euphyletic.

E) multiphyletic.

Answer: A
*Topic: Concept 32.4*
*Skill: Knowledge*

55) The common ancestor of all animals was probably a

A) bacterium.

B) prokaryote.

C) plant.

D) fungus.

E) protist.

Answer: E
*Topic: Concept 32.4*
*Skill: Knowledge*

56) If a multicellular animal lacks true tissues, then it can be classified among the

A) eumetazoans.

B) metazoans.

C) protozoans.

D) lophotrochozoans.

E) hydrozoans.

Answer: B
*Topic: Concept 32.4*
*Skill: Knowledge*

57) According to both the molecular- and morphology-based animal phylogenies, the following are all protostomes *except*

A) molluscs.

B) echinoderms.

C) segmented worms.

D) insects.

E) spiders.

Answer: B
*Topic: Concept 32.4*
*Skill: Knowledge*

58) Which of the following organisms are deuterostomes?

A) molluscs

B) annelids

C) echinoderms

D) chordates

E) both C and D

Answer: E
*Topic: Concept 32.4*
*Skill: Knowledge*

59) Which of the following statements concerning animal taxonomy is (are) *true*?
1.   Animals are more closely related to plants than to fungi.
2.   All animal clades based on body plan have been found to be incorrect.
3.   Kingdom Animalia is monophyletic.
4.   Only animals reproduce by sexual means.
5.   Animals are thought to have evolved from flagellated protists similar to modern choanoflagellates.

A) 5

B) 1, 3

C) 2, 4

D) 3, 5

E) 3, 4, 5

Answer: D
*Topic: Concept 32.4*
*Skill: Knowledge*

60) If the current molecular evidence regarding animal origins is well substantiated in the future, then what will be true of any contrary evidence regarding the origin of animals derived from the fossil record?

A) The contrary fossil evidence will be seen as a hoax.

B) The fossil evidence will be understood to have been incorrect because it is incomplete.

C) The fossil record will be ignored.

D) Phylogenies involving even the smallest bit of fossil evidence will need to be discarded.

E) Only phylogenies based solely on fossil evidence will need to be discarded.

Answer: B
*Topic: Concept 32.4*
*Skill: Application*

*The following questions refer to Figure 32.2a (morphological) and Figure 32.2b (molecular) phylogenetic trees of the animal kingdom.*

*(See pages 516 and 517 for Figures 32.2a and 32.2b.)*

61) According to the molecular phylogeny, which of these phyla is *not* monophyletic?

A) Porifera

B) Cnidaria

C) Chordata

D) Phoronida

E) Rotifera

Answer: A
*Topic: Concept 32.4*
*Skill: Comprehension*

62) Within the morphological phylogeny, which shared derived character is emphasized to the point of causing several phyla to be placed in an entirely different branch of the bilaterian clade, relative to their position on the molecular phylogeny?

A) calcareous spicules

B) bilateral symmetry

C) deuterostomy

D) pseudocoelom

E) cnidocytes

Answer: C
*Topic: Concept 32.4*
*Skill: Comprehension*

63) Which distinction is given more emphasis by the morphological phylogeny than by the molecular phylogeny?

A) metazoan and eumetazoan

B) radial and bilateral

C) true coelom and pseudocoelom

D) protostome and deuterostome

E) molting and lack of molting

Answer: D
*Topic: Concept 32.4*
*Skill: Comprehension*

64) According to the molecular phylogeny, but *not* according to the morphological phylogeny, _____ are more derived than _____.

A) rotifers; phoronids

B) ctenophores; cnidarians

C) ectoprocta; brachiopods

D) arthropods; annelids

E) calcareous sponges; siliceous sponges

Answer: E
*Topic: Concept 32.4*
*Skill: Comprehension*

65) Which two phyla below are most closely related to each other in *both* phylogenies?

A) Annelida and Arthropoda

B) Echinodermata and Chordata

C) Arthropoda and Nematoda

D) Mollusca and Platyhelminthes

E) Ectoprocta and Brachiopoda

Answer: B
*Topic: Concept 32.4*
*Skill: Comprehension*

66) Which of these pairs of phyla have more apparent molecular similarity to each other than they have morphological similarity?

A) Arthropoda and Annelida

B) Cnidaria and Ctenophora

C) Chordata and Ectoprocta

D) Arthropoda and Nematoda

E) Mollusca and Nemertea

Answer: D
*Topic: Concept 32.4*
*Skill: Comprehension*

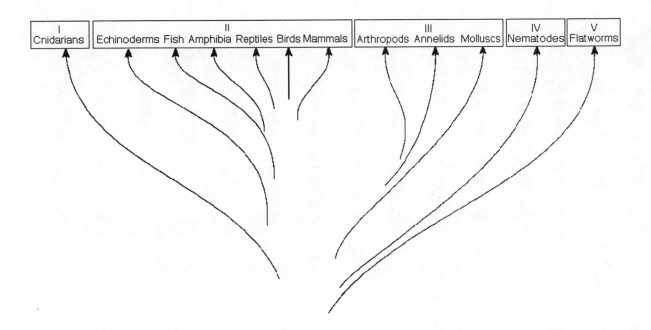

**Figure 32.1**

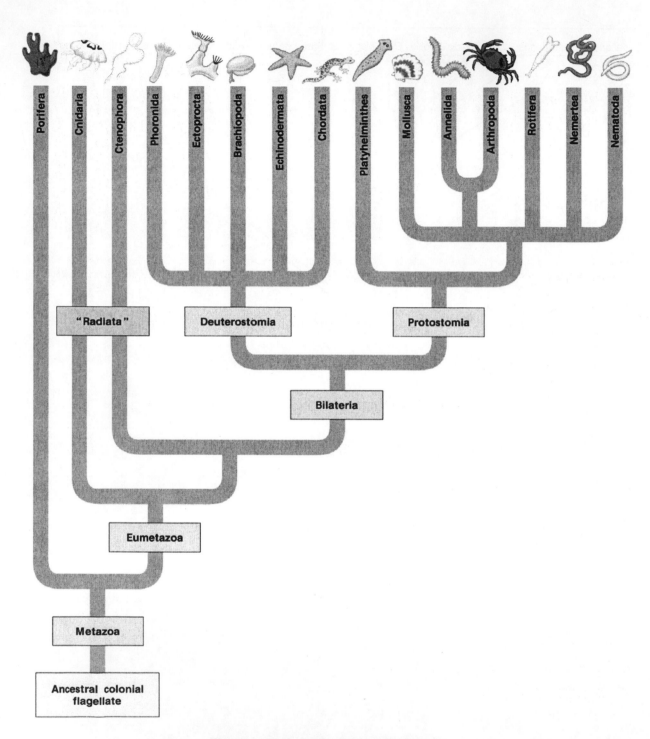

Figure 32.2a  Morphological Phylogeny

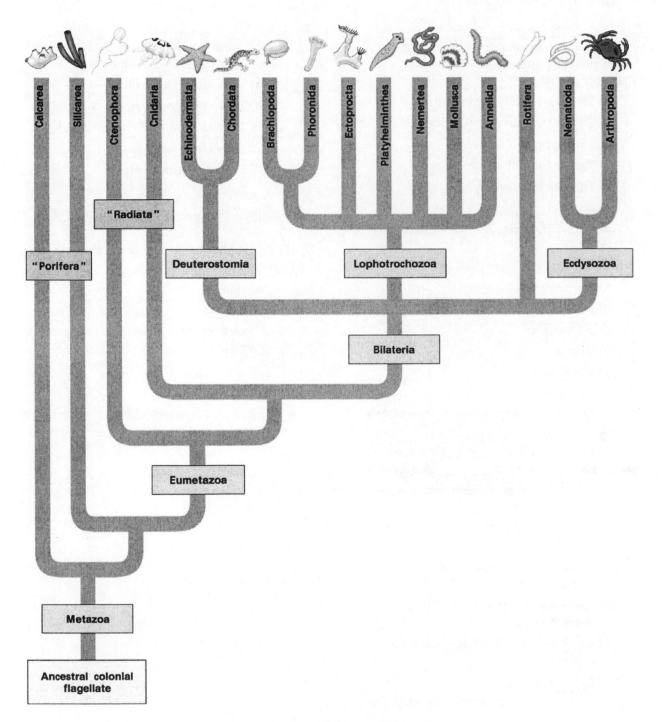

Figure 32.2b  Molecular Phylogeny

# Media Activity Questions

1) As a group, how do poriferans, cnidarians, and platyhelminthes differ from other animal phyla?

   A) They are radially symmetrical.

   B) They do not have a body cavity.

   C) They are triploblastic.

   D) They are diploblastic.

   E) The lack true tissues.

   Answer: B
   *Topic: Web/CD Activity: Animal Phylogenetic Tree*

2) Echinoderms are

   A) deuterstomes.

   B) parazoans.

   C) protostomes.

   D) radiata.

   E) acoelomates.

   Answer: A
   *Topic: Web/CD Activity: Animal Phylogenetic Tree*

3) Protostomes exhibit _____ cleavage; deuterostomes exhibit _____ cleavage.

   A) radial and spiral; determinate and indeterminate

   B) radial and indeterminate; spiral and determinate

   C) radial and determinate; spiral and indeterminate

   D) spiral and determinate; radial and indeterminate

   E) spiral and indeterminate; radial and determinate

   Answer: D
   *Topic: Web/CD Activity: Animal Phylogenetic Tree*

4) Why are annelids, arthropods, and molluscs placed in the same clade?

   A) They are triploblastic.

   B) They are protostomes.

   C) They are bilaterally symmetrical.

   D) They are coelomates.

   E) They are deuterostomes.

   Answer: B
   *Topic: Web/CD Activity: Animal Phylogenetic Tree*

5) At the phylum level, you are most closely related to a(n)

   A) clam.

   B) sea star.

   C) earthworm.

   D) jelly.

   E) planarian.

   Answer: B
   *Topic: Web/CD Activity: Animal Phylogenetic Tree*

# Self-Quiz Questions

1) Among the characteristics unique to animals is
   A) gastrulation.
   B) multicellularity.
   C) sexual reproduction.
   D) flagellated sperm.
   E) heterotrophic nutrition.

   Answer: A

2) Which of the following was the *least* likely factor causing the Cambrian explosion?
   A) the emergence of predator-prey relationships between animals
   B) the accumulation of diverse adaptations, such as shells and different modes of locomotion
   C) the movement of animals onto land
   D) the evolution of *Hox* genes that controlled development
   E) the accumulation of sufficient atmospheric oxygen to support the more active metabolism of mobile animals

   Answer: C

3) Bilateral symmetry in the animal kingdom is best correlated with
   A) an ability to sense equally in all directions.
   B) the presence of a skeleton.
   C) motility and active predation and escape.
   D) development of a true coelom.
   E) adaptation to terrestrial environments.

   Answer: C

4) Acoelomates are characterized by
   A) the absence of a brain.
   B) the absence of mesoderm.
   C) deuterostome development.
   D) a coelom that is not completely lined with mesoderm.
   E) a solid body without a cavity surrounding internal organs.

   Answer: E

5) A direct consequence of indeterminate cleavage is
   A) formation of the archenteron.
   B) the ability of cells isolated from the early embryo to develop into viable individuals.
   C) the arrangement of cleavage planes perpendicular to the egg's vertical axis.
   D) the unpredictable formation of either a schizocoelous or enterocoelous body cavity.
   E) a mouth that forms in association with the blastopore.

   Answer: B

6) The distinction between the sponges and other animal phyla is based mainly on the absence versus the presence of
   A) a body cavity.
   B) a complete digestive tract.
   C) true tissues.
   D) a circulatory system.
   E) mesoderm.

   Answer: C

7) Which of these is a point of conflict between the phylogenetic analyses presented in Figures 32.10 and 32.11 in your text?

A) the monophyly of the animal kingdom

B) the existence of the bilaterian clades Lophotrochozoa and Ecdysozoa

C) that sponges are basal animals

D) that chordates are deuterostomes

E) the monophyly of bilaterians

Answer: B

8) What is the main basis for placing the arthropods and nematodes in the Ecdysozoa in one hypothesis of animal phylogeny?

A) Animals in both groups are segmented.

B) Animals in both groups undergo ecdysis.

C) They both have radial, determinate cleavage, and their embryonic development is similar.

D) The fossil record has revealed a common ancestor to these two phyla.

E) Analysis of genes shows that their sequences are quite similar, and these sequences differ from those of the lophotrochozoans and deuterostomes.

Answer: E

9) Which of the following combinations of phylum and description is *incorrect*?

A) Echinodermata—branch of Bilateria, coelom forms from archenteron

B) Nematoda—roundworms, pseudocoelomate

C) Cnidaria—radial symmetry, diploblastic

D) Platyhelminthes—flatworms, acoelomates

E) Porifera—coelomates, mouth from blastopore

Answer: E

10) Which of the following subdivisions of the animal kingdom encompasses all the others in the list?

A) Protostomia

B) Bilateria

C) Radiata

D) Eumetazoa

E) Deuterostomia

Answer: D

# Chapter 33  Invertebrates

1) What are the cells in a sponge that are primarily responsible for trapping food particles from circulating water?

A) amoebocytes

B) choanocytes

C) mesohyl cells

D) pore cells (porocytes)

E) epidermal cells

Answer: B
*Topic: Concept 33.1*
*Skill: Knowledge*

2) Which of the following are *not* associated with sponges?

A) oscula

B) spongocoels

C) cnidocytes

D) spicules

E) amoebocytes

Answer: C
*Topic: Concept 33.1*
*Skill: Knowledge*

3) A structurally complex sponge would be expected to have

A) a multi-branched spongocoel.

B) wandering amoebocytes.

C) multiple oscula.

D) A and B only

E) A, B, and C

Answer: E
*Topic: Concept 33.1*
*Skill: Comprehension*

4) A sponge's skeletal materials (spicules, spongin) are manufactured by the

A) pore cells.

B) epidermal cells.

C) choanocytes.

D) zygotes.

E) amoebocytes.

Answer: E
*Topic: Concept 33.1*
*Skill: Knowledge*

5) In the mesohyl of various undisturbed sponges, one is likely to observe (at one time or another) all of the following *except*

A) amoebocytes.

B) spicules.

C) spongin.

D) zygotes.

E) choanocytes.

Answer: E
*Topic: Concept 33.1*
*Skill: Comprehension*

6) Which chemical is *not* normally found in any sponges?

A) chitin

B) spongin

C) calcium carbonate

D) silica

E) cribrostatin

Answer: A
*Topic: Concept 33.1*
*Skill: Knowledge*

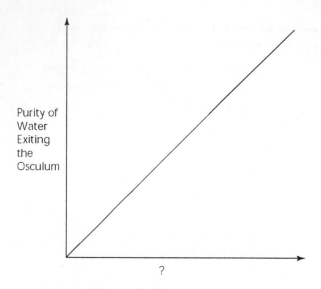

**Figure 33.1**

7) Which of these factors, when used to label the horizontal axis of the graph in Figure 33.1, would account most directly for the shape of the plot?

  A) spongin concentration (gm/unit volume)

  B) rate of cribrostatin synthesis (molecules/ unit time)

  C) number of amoebocytes per sponge

  D) number of spicules per sponge

  E) number of choanocytes per sponge

Answer: E
*Topic: Concept 33.1*
*Skill: Application*

8) In terms of food capture, which sponge cell is most similar to the cnidocyte?

  A) amoebocyte

  B) choanocyte

  C) gamete

  D) epidermal cell

  E) pore cell

Answer: B
*Topic: Concepts 33.1–33.2*
*Skill: Comprehension*

9) A radially symmetrical animal that has two embryonic tissue layers belongs to which phylum?

  A) Porifera

  B) Cnidaria

  C) Platyhelminthes

  D) Nematoda

  E) Echinodermata

Answer: B
*Topic: Concept 33.2*
*Skill: Knowledge*

10) All of the following are characteristics of the phylum Cnidaria *except*

  A) a gastrovascular cavity.

  B) a polyp stage.

  C) a medusa stage.

  D) cnidocytes.

  E) a pseudocoelom.

Answer: E
*Topic: Concept 33.2*
*Skill: Knowledge*

11) What is the best way to describe the brain of a sea anemone?

  A) a thick ring around the mouth

  B) a series of ganglia at the base of the tentacles

  C) a pair of ganglia at the anterior end

  D) a single ganglion in the body wall

  E) nonexistent

Answer: E
*Topic: Concept 33.2*
*Skill: Comprehension*

12) Which of the following is a *correct* statement about members of the phylum Cnidaria? They
   A) are not capable of locomotion because they lack true muscle tissue.
   B) are primarily filter feeders.
   C) have either or both of two body forms: mobile polyps and sessile medusae.
   D) may use a gastrovascular cavity as a hydrostatic skeleton.
   E) are the simplest organisms with a complete alimentary canal (two openings).

Answer: D
*Topic: Concept 33.2*
*Skill: Comprehension*

13) The members of which class of the phylum Cnidaria occur *only* as polyps?
   A) Hydrozoa
   B) Scyphozoa
   C) Anthozoa
   D) Cubozoa
   E) both B and D

Answer: C
*Topic: Concept 33.2*
*Skill: Knowledge*

14) Which class of the phylum Cnidaria includes "jellies" with rounded (as opposed to box-like) medusae?
   A) Hydrozoa
   B) Scyphozoa
   C) Anthozoa
   D) Cubozoa
   E) Both A and C are referred to as "jellies."

Answer: B
*Topic: Concept 33.2*
*Skill: Knowledge*

15) Corals are most closely related to which group?
   A) jellies
   B) freshwater hydras
   C) sea anemones
   D) sponges
   E) barnacles

Answer: C
*Topic: Concept 33.2*
*Skill: Comprehension*

16) Which characteristic is shared by both cnidarians and flatworms?
   A) dorsoventrally flattened bodies
   B) flame cells
   C) radial symmetry
   D) a digestive system with a single opening
   E) both A and D

Answer: D
*Topic: Concepts 33.2, 33.3*
*Skill: Knowledge*

17) Generally, members of which flatworm class are nonparasitic?
   A) Turbellaria
   B) Trematoda
   C) Cestoda
   D) Monogenea
   E) A, C, and D

Answer: A
*Topic: Concept 33.3*
*Skill: Knowledge*

18) In a small stream, you pick up a rock and observe many small, flattened worms crawling on its undersurface. You decide that they belong to the phylum Platyhelminthes. To which *class* do they probably belong?

A) Cestoda

B) Monogenea

C) Turbellaria

D) Trematoda

E) Hirudinea

Answer: C
*Topic: Concept 33.3*
*Skill: Application*

19) What would be the most effective method of reducing the incidence of blood flukes in a human population?

A) Reduce the mosquito population.

B) Reduce the freshwater snail population.

C) Purify all drinking water.

D) Avoid contact with rodent droppings.

E) Carefully wash all raw fruits and vegetables.

Answer: B
*Topic: Concept 33.3*
*Skill: Application*

20) The larvae of many common tapeworms affecting humans are usually found

A) encysted in human muscle.

B) encysted in the muscle of an animal such as a cow or pig.

C) in the abdominal blood vessels of humans.

D) in the human brain.

E) in the intestines of cows and pigs.

Answer: B
*Topic: Concept 33.3*
*Skill: Knowledge*

21) While vacationing in a country that lacks adequate meat inspection, a student ate undercooked ground beef. Sometime later the student became easily fatigued, and lost body weight. At about the same time, whitish, flattened, rectangular objects full of small white spheres started appearing in his feces. Administration of niclosamide cured the problem. The student had probably been infected by a

A) pinworm.

B) hookworm.

C) nematode.

D) tapeworm.

E) proboscis worm.

Answer: D
*Topic: Concept 33.3*
*Skill: Application*

22) Which of the following statements about Cestoda feeding methods is *false*?

A) They lack a digestive tract.

B) They use a degenerate mouth to ingest some of their food.

C) As adults, they live in a digestive tract.

D) They are parasites.

E) They absorb nutrients through the walls of their body.

Answer: B
*Topic: Concept 33.3*
*Skill: Comprehension*

23) All of the following characterize the phylum Rotifera *except*

A) a complete digestive tract.

B) a crown of cilia at the anterior end that resembles a wheel.

C) parthenogenic reproduction.

D) a life cycle stage that is resistant to desiccation.

E) a relatively large size.

Answer: E
*Topic: Concept 33.3*
*Skill: Knowledge*

24) A lophophore is used by ectoprocts, phoronids, and brachiopods

A) for locomotion.

B) at a larval stage.

C) for feeding.

D) for sensory reception.

E) as a skeletal system.

Answer: C
*Topic: Concept 33.3*
*Skill: Knowledge*

25) A brachiopod can be distinguished from a bivalve by the presence of

A) two hinged shells.

B) a digestive system with separate mouth and anus.

C) a lophophore.

D) suspension feeding.

E) a distinct head.

Answer: C
*Topic: Concept 33.3*
*Skill: Knowledge*

26) While sampling marine plankton in a lab, a student encounters large numbers of fertilized eggs. She rears some of the eggs in the laboratory for further study and finds that the blastopore becomes the mouth. The embryo develops into a trochophore larva and eventually has a coelom. These eggs probably belonged to a(n)

A) annelid.

B) echinoderm.

C) mollusc.

D) nematode.

E) arthropod.

Answer: C
*Topic: Concept 33.4*
*Skill: Application*

27) Which molluscan class includes members that undergo embryonic torsion?

A) Polyplacophora

B) Bivalvia

C) Cephalopoda

D) Gastropoda

E) All molluscan classes have this characteristic.

Answer: D
*Topic: Concept 33.4*
*Skill: Knowledge*

28) If a lung were to be found in a mollusc, where would it be located?

A) mantle cavity

B) coelom

C) foot

D) visceral mass

E) excurrent siphon

Answer: A
*Topic: Concept 33.4*
*Skill: Knowledge*

29) A terrestrial mollusc without a shell belongs to which class?

A) Gastropoda

B) Polyplacophora

C) Bivalvia

D) Cephalopoda

E) Arthropoda

Answer: A
*Topic: Concept 33.4*
*Skill: Application*

30) Which molluscan class includes chitons?

A) Polyplacophora

B) Bivalvia

C) Cephalopoda

D) Gastropoda

E) both C and D

Answer: A
*Topic: Concept 33.4*
*Skill: Knowledge*

31) A radula is present in members of which class(es)?

A) Gastropoda

B) Polyplacophora

C) Bivalvia

D) A and B only

E) A, B, and C

Answer: D
*Topic: Concept 33.4*
*Skill: Knowledge*

32) While snorkeling, a student observes an active marine animal that has a series of muscular tentacles bearing suckers associated with its head. Segmentation is not observed, but a pair of large, well-developed eyes is evident. The student is observing an animal belonging to which class?

A) Gastropoda

B) Cephalopoda

C) Polyplacophora

D) Polychaeta

E) Bivalvia

Answer: B
*Topic: Concept 33.4*
*Skill: Application*

33) Which of the following is *not* found in annelids?

A) a hydrostatic skeleton

B) segmentation

C) a digestive system with separate mouth and anus

D) a closed circulatory system

E) a cuticle made of chitin

Answer: E
*Topic: Concept 33.5*
*Skill: Knowledge*

*Match the descriptions to the correct annelid class(es) from the list below. Each choice may be used once, more than once, or not at all.*

A. Oligochaeta
B. Polychaeta
C. Hirudinea
D. two of the above
E. all of the above

34) have parapodia

Answer: B
*Topic: Concept 33.5*
*Skill: Knowledge*

35) many are parasites

Answer: C
*Topic: Concept 33.5*
*Skill: Knowledge*

36) have segmented bodies

Answer: E
*Topic: Concept 33.5*
*Skill: Knowledge*

37) make castings that are agriculturally important

Answer: A
*Topic: Concept 33.5*
*Skill: Knowledge*

38) name indicates the relative number of bristles its members have

Answer: D
*Topic: Concept 33.5*
*Skill: Knowledge*

39) some members release an anticoagulate that is of medical significance

Answer: C
*Topic: Concept 33.5*
*Skill: Knowledge*

40) Which of the following is *not* characteristic of nematodes?
   A) They play an important role in decomposition.
   B) They have both circular and longitudinal muscles.
   C) They have a pseudocoelom.
   D) They have an alimentary canal.
   E) Many species are parasitic.

Answer: B
*Topic: Concept 33.6*
*Skill: Knowledge*

41) Humans most frequently acquire trichinosis by
   A) having sexual contact with an infected partner.
   B) eating undercooked pork.
   C) inhaling the eggs of worms.
   D) eating undercooked beef.
   E) being bitten by tsetse flies.

Answer: B
*Topic: Concept 33.6*
*Skill: Knowledge*

42) All of the following can be used to distinguish a nematode worm from an annelid worm *except*
   A) type of body cavity.
   B) number of muscle layers in the body wall.
   C) presence of segmentation.
   D) number of embryonic tissue layers.
   E) presence of an alimentary canal.

Answer: D
*Topic: Concept 33.6*
*Skill: Comprehension*

43) Nematode worms and annelid worms share all of the following features *except*
   A) use of fluid in the body cavity as a hydrostatic skeleton.
   B) use of the outer covering as a respiratory surface.
   C) presence of a closed circulatory system.
   D) presence of an alimentary canal.
   E) parasitic lifestyles in some species.

Answer: C
*Topic: Concept 33.6*
*Skill: Comprehension*

44) A student observes a worm–like organism crawling about on dead organic matter. Later, the organism sheds its outer covering. One possibility is that the organism is a larval insect (like a maggot). On the other hand, it might be a member of the phylum _____. One way to distinguish between the two possibilities is by looking for the presence of

A) Platyhelminthes; a cuticle of chitin.

B) Nematoda; an alimentary canal.

C) Annelida; a body cavity.

D) Nematoda; a circulatory system.

E) Annelida; muscle in the body wall.

Answer: D
*Topic: Concept 33.6*
*Skill: Application*

45) The heartworms that can accumulate within the heart of dogs and other mammals have a pseudocoelom, an alimentary canal, and an outer covering that is occasionally shed. To which phylum does the heartworm belong?

A) Platyhelminthes

B) Arthropoda

C) Nematoda

D) Phoronida

E) Annelida

Answer: C
*Topic: Concept 33.6*
*Skill: Application*

46) Infection with which parasite would cause elasticity in human skeletal muscles?

A) trichinella worms

B) tapeworms

C) copepods

D) blood flukes

E) rotifers

Answer: A
*Topic: Concept 33.6*
*Skill: Application*

47) Skeletal structures that are entirely or partly composed of calcium carbonate can be found in some members of the following *except*

A) sponges.

B) coral animals.

C) molluscs.

D) arthropods.

E) nematodes.

Answer: E
*Topic: Concepts 33.1–33.7*
*Skill: Comprehension*

48) An arthropod has all the following characteristics *except*

A) protostome development.

B) bilateral symmetry.

C) a pseudocoelom.

D) three embryonic germ layers.

E) an open circulatory system.

Answer: C
*Topic: Concept 33.7*
*Skill: Knowledge*

49) All of the following are characteristics of adult arthropods *except*

A) an exoskeleton.

B) hemolymph.

C) jointed appendages.

D) a heart.

E) a coelom.

Answer: E
*Topic: Concept 33.7*
*Skill: Knowledge*

50) Among the invertebrates, arthropods are unique in possessing

A) a cuticle.

B) a ventral nerve cord.

C) open circulation.

D) wings.

E) segmented bodies.

Answer: D
*Topic: Concept 33.7*
*Skill: Knowledge*

51) The presence or absence of mandibles can be used to distinguish between

A) insects and centipedes.

B) insects and crustaceans.

C) insects and millipedes.

D) insects and spiders.

E) centipedes and millipedes.

Answer: D
*Topic: Concept 33.7*
*Skill: Comprehension*

52) A shared derived characteristic for members of the arthropod subgroup that includes spiders would be the presence of

A) chelicerae.

B) an open circulatory system.

C) an exoskeleton.

D) a cuticle.

E) a cephalothorax.

Answer: A
*Topic: Concept 33.7*
*Skill: Comprehension*

53) You find a small animal with eight legs crawling up your bedroom wall. Closer examination will probably reveal that this animal has

A) antennae.

B) no antennae.

C) chelicerae.

D) A and C

E) B and C

Answer: E
*Topic: Concept 33.7*
*Skill: Comprehension*

54) While working in your garden, you discover a worm–like, segmented animal with two pairs of jointed legs per segment. The animal is probably a

A) millipede.

B) caterpillar.

C) centipede.

D) polychaete worm.

E) sow bug.

Answer: A
*Topic: Concept 33.7*
*Skill: Application*

55) Which of the following characteristics most likely explains why insects are so successful at dispersing to distant environments?

A) hemocoel

B) wings

C) jointed appendages

D) chewing mandibles

E) internal fertilization

Answer: B
*Topic: Concept 33.7*
*Skill: Knowledge*

56) What distinguishes complete metamorphosis from incomplete metamorphosis in insects?

A) presence of wings in the adult, but not in earlier life stages

B) presence of sex organs in the adult, but not in earlier life stages

C) radically different appearance between adults and earlier life stages

D) only A and B

E) A, B, and C

Answer: C
*Topic: Concept 33.7*
*Skill: Comprehension*

57) A terrestrial animal species is discovered with the following larval characteristics: exoskeleton, tracheal system for gas exchange, and modified segmentation. A knowledgeable zoologist would predict that its adults probably also would have

A) eight legs.

B) two pairs of antennae.

C) a sessile lifestyle.

D) an open circulatory system.

E) parapodia.

Answer: D
*Topic: Concept 33.7*
*Skill: Application*

58) The possession of two pairs of antennae is a characteristic of

A) spiders.

B) insects.

C) centipedes.

D) millipedes.

E) crustaceans.

Answer: E
*Topic: Concept 33.7*
*Skill: Knowledge*

59) One should expect to find the 9 + 2 pattern of microtubules in association with the feeding apparatus of each of the following *except*

A) bivalves.

B) rotifers.

C) lophophorates.

D) sponges.

E) terrestrial insects.

Answer: E
*Topic: Concepts 33.1–33.7*
*Skill: Application*

60) Which of the following is a characteristic of adult echinoderms?

A) secondary radial symmetry

B) spiral cleavage during early embryonic development

C) gastrovascular cavity

D) exoskeleton

E) a lophophore

Answer: A
*Topic: Concept 33.8*
*Skill: Knowledge*

*Match the descriptions with the correct echinoderm class from the list below. Each choice may be used once, more than once, or not at all.*

A. class Crinoidea (sea lilies and feather stars)
B. class Asteroidea (sea stars)
C. class Ophiuroidea (brittle stars)
D. class Echinoidea (sea urchins and sand dollars)
E. class Holothuroidea (sea cucumbers)

61) They can extend the stomach through their mouth to feed.

Answer: B
*Topic: Concept 33.8*
*Skill: Knowledge*

62) They have distinct central disks and long, flexible arms.

Answer: C
*Topic: Concept 33.8*
*Skill: Knowledge*

63) They are elongated in the oral–aboral axis.

Answer: E
*Topic: Concept 33.8*
*Skill: Knowledge*

64) Their mouth is directed upward.

Answer: A
*Topic: Concept 33.8*
*Skill: Knowledge*

65) They can have long, movable spines.

Answer: D
*Topic: Concept 33.8*
*Skill: Knowledge*

66) What is true of echinoderms?
   A) They have an endoskeleton of hard calcareous plates.
   B) Tube feet provide motility in most species.
   C) They have a pseudocoelom.
   D) Only A and B are true.
   E) A, B, and C are true.

Answer: D
*Topic: Concept 33.8*
*Skill: Knowledge*

67) A stalked, sessile marine organism has several feathery feeding structures surrounding an opening through which food enters. The organism could potentially be a cnidarian, a lophophorate, a tube-dwelling worm, a crustacean, or an echinoderm. Finding which of the following in this organism would allow the greatest certainty of identification?
   A) the presence of what seems to be radial symmetry
   B) a hard covering made partly of calcium carbonate
   C) a digestive system with mouth and anus separate from each other
   D) a water vascular system
   E) a nervous system

Answer: D
*Topic: Concept 33.8*
*Skill: Application*

68) All of the following animal groups include terrestrial life forms *except*
   A) Mollusca.
   B) Crustacea.
   C) Echinodermata.
   D) Arthropoda.
   E) Annelida.

Answer: C
*Topic: Concept 33.8*
*Skill: Knowledge*

69) In a tide pool, a student encounters an organism with a hard outer covering that contains much calcium carbonate, an open circulatory system, and gills. The organism could potentially be a crab, a shrimp, a barnacle, or a bivalve. Which structure below would allow for the most certain identification?

   A) a mantle

   B) a heart

   C) a body cavity

   D) a lophophore

   E) eyes

   Answer: A
   *Topic: Concepts 33.2–33.8*
   *Skill: Application*

*For the following questions, match the descriptions with the correct phylum below. Each choice may be used once, more than once, or not at all.*

   A.  Cnidaria
   B.  Annelida
   C.  Mollusca
   D.  Arthropoda
   E.  Echinodermata

70) protostomes that have an open circulatory system and an exoskeleton of chitin

   Answer: D
   *Topic: Concept 33.7*
   *Skill: Knowledge*

71) protostomes with a unique drape of tissue that may secrete a shell

   Answer: C
   *Topic: Concept 33.4*
   *Skill: Knowledge*

72) a diploblastic phylum of aquatic predators

   Answer: A
   *Topic: Concept 33.2*
   *Skill: Knowledge*

73) deuterostomes that have an endoskeleton

   Answer: E
   *Topic: Concept 33.8*
   *Skill: Knowledge*

74) protostomes that have a closed circulatory system and obvious segmentation

   Answer: B
   *Topic: Concept 33.5*
   *Skill: Knowledge*

75) An organism is able to extend its feeding structure(s) through a hole in an exoskeleton. If the organism were an ectoproct, it would extend a _____; if a coral animal, it would extend _____; if a bivalve, it would extend _____; and if a barnacle, it would extend _____.

   A) stomach; a pharynx; a radula; mandibles

   B) lophophore; trophi; a radula; jointed appendages

   C) pharynx; a proboscis; trophi; mandibles

   D) lophophore; tentacles; gill(s); jointed appendages

   E) tentacle; a proboscis; gill(s); a pharynx

   Answer: D
   *Topic: Concepts 33.1–33.8*
   *Skill: Knowledge*

76) Which of the following is *not* the primary dispersal form of its group?

   A) the adults of bivalves

   B) the medusae of hydrozoans

   C) the larvae of echinoderms

   D) the adults of insects

   E) the larvae of sponges

   Answer: A
   *Topic: Concepts 33.1–33.8*
   *Skill: Comprehension*

# Media Activity Questions

1) Which one of these chordate groups lacks a post–anal tail and a notochord as adults?

   A) lancelets

   B) tunicates

   C) amphibians

   D) mammals

   E) reptiles

   Answer: B
   *Topic: Web/CD Activity: Characteristics of Chordates*

2) The common ancestor of all these chordate groups *except* the _____ probably had paired appendages.

   A) mammals

   B) amphibians

   C) lampreys

   D) ray-finned fishes

   E) reptiles

   Answer: C
   *Topic: Web/CD Activity: Characteristics of Chordates*

3) _____ are the oldest known primate group.

   A) Apes

   B) Prosimians

   C) Anthropoids

   D) Hominids

   E) Monkeys

   Answer: B
   *Topic: Web/CD Activity: Primate Diversity*

4) Which of these primate groups lives in trees in Central and South America and have nostrils that are wide open and far apart?

   A) hominids

   B) apes

   C) New World monkeys

   D) anthropoids

   E) Old World monkeys

   Answer: C
   *Topic: Web/CD Activity: Primate Diversity*

5) Evidence indicates that _____ was the first hominid to use fire.

   A) *Australopithecus*

   B) *Homo erectus*

   C) *Ardipithecus*

   D) *Homo habilis*

   E) *Homo sapiens*

   Answer: B
   *Topic: Web/CD Activity: Human Evolution*

# Self–Quiz Questions

1) Which two main clades branch from the earliest Eumetazoan ancestor?

   A) Porifera and Bilateria

   B) Porifera and Radiata

   C) Cnidaria and Bilateria

   D) Rotifera and Deuterostomia

   E) Deuterostomia and Ecdysozoa

   Answer: C

2) Water movement through a sponge would follow what path?

   A) porocyte → spongocoel → osculum

   B) blastopore → gastrovascular cavity → protostome

   C) choanocyte → mesohyl → spongocoel

   D) porocyte → choanocyte → mesohyl

   E) collar cell → coelom → porocyte

   Answer: A

3) Although a diverse group, all cnidarians are characterized by

   A) a gastrovascular cavity.

   B) an alternation between a medusa and a polyp stage.

   C) some degree of cephalization.

   D) muscle tissue of mesodermal origin.

   E) the complete absence of asexual reproduction.

   Answer: A

4) A land snail, a clam, and an octopus all share

   A) a mantle.

   B) a radula.

   C) gills.

   D) embryonic torsion.

   E) distinct cephalization.

   Answer: A

5) Which of the following is *not* a characteristic of most members of the phylum Annelida?

   A) hydrostatic skeleton

   B) segmentation

   C) metanephridia

   D) pseudocoelom

   E) closed circulatory system

   Answer: D

6) Which phylum is characterized by animals that have a segmented body?

   A) Cnidaria

   B) Platyhelminthes

   C) Porifera

   D) Arthropoda

   E) Mollusca

   Answer: D

7) Which of the following is *not* true of the cheliceriforms?

   A) They have antennae.

   B) Their body is divided into a cephalothorax and an abdomen.

   C) Horseshoe crabs are surviving marine members.

   D) They include ticks, scorpions, and spiders.

   E) Their anterior appendages are modified as pincers or fangs.

   Answer: A

8) Which of the following characteristics is probably *most* responsible for the incredible diversification of insects on land?

    A) segmentation

    B) antennae

    C) tracheal system

    D) bilateral symmetry

    E) flight

Answer: E

9) The water vascular system of echinoderms

    A) functions as a circulatory system that distributes nutrients to body cells.

    B) functions in locomotion, feeding, and gas exchange.

    C) is bilateral in organization, even though the adult animal has radial anatomy.

    D) moves water through the animal's body during suspension feeding.

    E) is analogous to the gastrovascular cavity of flatworms.

Answer: B

10) Which of the following combinations of phylum and description is *incorrect*?

    A) Echinodermata—bilateral and radial symmetry, coelom from archenteron

    B) Nematoda—roundworms, pseudocoelomate

    C) Cnidaria—radial symmetry, polyp and medusa body forms

    D) Platyhelminthes—flatworms, gastrovascular cavity, acoelomate

    E) Porifera—gastrovascular cavity, coelom present

Answer: E

# Chapter 34  Vertebrates

1) Which of the following is *not* a shared characteristic of all chordates?

   A) pharyngeal clefts

   B) post-anal tail

   C) notochord

   D) dorsal, hollow nerve cord

   E) four-chambered heart

   Answer: E
   *Topic: Concept 34.1*
   *Skill: Knowledge*

2) What is one characteristic that separates chordates from all other animals?

   A) true coelom

   B) dorsal, hollow nerve cord

   C) blastopore, which becomes the anus

   D) bilateral symmetry

   E) segmentation

   Answer: B
   *Topic: Concept 34.1*
   *Skill: Knowledge*

3) Which of these are characteristics of all chordates during at least a portion of their development?

   A) a dorsal, hollow nerve cord

   B) pharyngeal clefts

   C) post-anal tail

   D) A and B only

   E) A, B, and C

   Answer: E
   *Topic: Concept 34.1*
   *Skill: Knowledge*

4) Pharyngeal slits appear to have functioned first as

   A) the digestive system's opening.

   B) suspension-feeding devices.

   C) components of the jaw.

   D) gill slits for respiration.

   E) portions of the inner ear.

   Answer: B
   *Topic: Concept 34.1*
   *Skill: Knowledge*

5) Which of the following statements would be *least* acceptable to most zoologists?

   A) The extant cephalochordates are contemporaries, not ancestors, of vertebrates.

   B) The first fossils resembling cephalochordates appeared in the fossil record around 550 million years ago.

   C) Recent work in molecular systematics supports the hypothesis that cephalochordates are the most recent common ancestor of all vertebrates.

   D) The extant cephalochordates are the immediate ancestors of the fishes.

   E) Cephalochordates display the same method of swimming as do fishes.

   Answer: D
   *Topic: Concept 34.1*
   *Skill: Comprehension*

6) Which extant chordate group is postulated to be *most* like the earliest chordates in appearance?

A) Cephalochordata

B) adult Urochordata

C) Amphibia

D) Reptilia

E) Chondrichthyes

Answer: A
*Topic: Concept 34.1*
*Skill: Knowledge*

7) Which are extinct organisms that may represent a transition between cephalochordates and vertebrates?

A) *Haikouella* and *Haikouichthys*

B) *Archaeopteryx*

C) *Acanthostega*

D) conodonts

E) acanthodians

Answer: A
*Topic: Concept 34.2*
*Skill: Knowledge*

8) A new species of aquatic chordate is discovered that closely resembles an ancient form. It has the following characteristics: external armor of bony plates, no paired fins, and a suspension–feeding mode of nutrition. In addition to these, it will probably have which of the following characteristics?

A) legs

B) no jaws

C) an amniotic egg

D) metamorphosis

E) endothermy

Answer: B
*Topic: Concept 34.2*
*Skill: Application*

9) Lampreys *differ* from hagfishes in

A) lacking jaws.

B) having a cranium.

C) having pharyngeal clefts that develop into pharyngeal slits.

D) having a notochord throughout life.

E) having a notochord that is surrounded by a tube of cartilage.

Answer: E
*Topic: Concepts 34.2, 34.3*
*Skill: Knowledge*

10) Parasitism is to most species of lampreys as _____ seems to have been to the extinct conodonts.

A) herbivory

B) suspension feeding

C) predation

D) filter feeding

E) absorptive feeding

Answer: C
*Topic: Concept 34.3*
*Skill: Knowledge*

11) What do hagfishes and lampreys have in common with the extinct conodonts?

A) lungs

B) the jawless condition

C) bony vertebrae

D) their mode of feeding

E) swim bladders

Answer: B
*Topic: Concept 34.3*
*Skill: Comprehension*

12) The earliest known mineralized structures in vertebrates are associated with which function?

   A) reproduction

   B) feeding

   C) locomotion

   D) defense

   E) respiration

Answer: B
*Topic: Concept 34.3*
*Skill: Knowledge*

13) The exoskeletons of marine arthropods are made of calcified _____, and the endoskeletons of vertebrates are mostly composed of calcified _____.

   A) cartilage; cartilage

   B) silica; bone

   C) chitin; silica

   D) dentin; enamel

   E) chitin; cartilage

Answer: E
*Topic: Concept 34.3*
*Skill: Knowledge*

14) A team of researchers has developed a poison that has proven effective against lamprey larvae in freshwater cultures. The poison is ingested and causes paralysis by detaching myomeres from the skeletal elements. The team wants to test the poison's effectiveness in streams feeding Lake Michigan, but one critic worries about potential effects on lancelets, which are similar to lampreys in many ways. Why is this concern misplaced?

   A) A chemical poisonous to lampreys could not also be toxic to organisms as ancestral as lancelets.

   B) Lamprey larvae and lancelets have very different feeding mechanisms.

   C) Lancelets do not have myomeres.

   D) Lancelets live only in salt-water environments.

   E) Lancelets and lamprey larvae eat different kinds of food.

Answer: D
*Topic: Concept 34.3*
*Skill: Application*

15) The lamprey species whose larvae live in freshwater streams, but whose adults live most of their lives in seawater, are similar in this respect to certain species of

   A) chondrichthyans.

   B) actinopterygians.

   C) lungfishes.

   D) coelacanths.

   E) hagfishes.

Answer: B
*Topic: Concept 34.4*
*Skill: Comprehension*

16) In which extant class did jaws occur earliest?

A) Cephalaspidomorphi

B) Chondrichthyes

C) Actinopterygii

D) Dipnoi

E) Placodermi

Answer: B
*Topic: Concept 34.4*
*Skill: Knowledge*

17) According to one hypothesis, the jaws of vertebrates were derived by the modification of

A) scales of the lower lip.

B) skeletal rods that had supported pharyngeal (gill) slits.

C) one or more gill slits.

D) one or more of the bones of the cranium.

E) one or more of the vertebrae.

Answer: B
*Topic: Concept 34.4*
*Skill: Knowledge*

18) All of these might have been observed in the common ancestor of chondrichthyans and osteichthyans, *except*

A) a mineralized, bony skeleton.

B) scales.

C) lungs.

D) gills.

E) a swim bladder.

Answer: E
*Topic: Concept 34.4*
*Skill: Comprehension*

19) What is a distinctive feature of the chondrichthyans?

A) an amniotic egg

B) unpaired fins

C) an acute sense of vision that includes the ability to distinguish colors

D) a cartilaginous endoskeleton

E) lack of jaws

Answer: D
*Topic: Concept 34.4*
*Skill: Knowledge*

20) To which of these are the scales of chondrichthyans most closely related in a structural sense?

A) osteichthyan scales

B) reptilian scales

C) mammalian scales

D) bird scales

E) chondrichthyan teeth

Answer: E
*Topic: Concept 34.4*
*Skill: Knowledge*

21) Which of these statements accurately describes a similarity between sharks and fishes?

A) The skin is typically covered by flattened bony scales.

B) They are equally able to exchange gases with the environment while stationary.

C) They are highly maneuverable due to their flexibility.

D) They have a lateral line that is sensitive to changes in water pressure.

E) A swim bladder helps control buoyancy.

Answer: D
*Topic: Concept 34.4*
*Skill: Comprehension*

22) Which group's members had (have) both lungs and gills during their adult lives?

    A) sharks, skates, and rays

    B) lungfishes

    C) cephalochordates

    D) paramphibians

    E) ichthyosaurs and plesiosaurs

Answer: B
*Topic: Concept 34.4*
*Skill: Comprehension*

23) There is evidence that bony fishes (osteichthyans) originally evolved

    A) in response to a crisis that wiped out the chondrichthyans.

    B) directly from lampreys and hagfish.

    C) early in the Cambrian period.

    D) directly from cephalochordates.

    E) in freshwater environments.

Answer: E
*Topic: Concept 34.4*
*Skill: Knowledge*

24) Which are the most abundant and diverse of the extant vertebrates?

    A) bony fishes

    B) avian reptiles

    C) amphibians

    D) non-avian reptiles

    E) mammals

Answer: A
*Topic: Concept 34.4*
*Skill: Knowledge*

25) The bony fishes are characterized by

    A) a bony endoskeleton, operculum, and usually a swim bladder.

    B) a cartilaginous endoskeleton.

    C) an amniotic egg.

    D) teeth that are replaced regularly.

    E) a lateral line system and ears with three semicircular canals.

Answer: A
*Topic: Concept 34.4*
*Skill: Knowledge*

26) The swim bladder of bony fishes

    A) was probably modified from simple lungs of freshwater fishes.

    B) developed into lungs in saltwater fishes.

    C) first appeared in sharks.

    D) provides buoyancy, but at a high energy cost.

    E) both C and D

Answer: A
*Topic: Concept 34.4*
*Skill: Knowledge*

27) All of the following belong to the lobe-fin clade, *except*

    A) chondrichthyans.

    B) Australian lungfishes.

    C) African lungfishes.

    D) coelacanths.

    E) tetrapods.

Answer: A
*Topic: Concept 34.4*
*Skill: Comprehension*

28) Arrange these taxonomic terms from most inclusive (*i.e.* most general) to least inclusive (*i.e.* most specific).

1. lobe-fins
2. amphibians
3. gnathostomes
4. osteichthyans
5. tetrapods

A) 4, 3, 1, 5, 2

B) 4, 3, 2, 5, 1

C) 4, 2, 3, 5, 1

D) 3, 4, 1, 5, 2

E) 3, 4, 5, 1, 2

Answer: D
*Topic: Concepts 34.4, 34.5*
*Skill: Comprehension*

29) An extinct transitional form linking aquatic and terrestrial lobe-fins is

A) the coelacanth.

B) *Archaeopteryx.*

C) *Haikouichthys.*

D) *Acanthostega.*

E) *Ardipithecus.*

Answer: D
*Topic: Concept 34.5*
*Skill: Knowledge*

30) A trend in the evolution of the earliest tetrapods was

A) the appearance of jaws.

B) the appearance of bony vertebrae.

C) feet with digits.

D) the mineralization of the endoskeleton.

E) the ability to move in a fish-like manner.

Answer: C
*Topic: Concept 34.5*
*Skill: Comprehension*

31) What should be true of fossils of the earliest tetrapods?

A) They should show evidence of internal fertilization.

B) They should show evidence of having produced shelled eggs.

C) They should indicate limited adaptation to life on land.

D) They should be transitional forms with the fossils of chondrichthyans that lived at the same time.

E) They should feature the earliest indications of the appearance of jaws.

Answer: C
*Topic: Concept 34.5*
*Skill: Comprehension*

32) What permits reptiles to thrive in arid environments?

A) Their bright coloration reflects the intense UV radiation.

B) A large number of prey and a limited number of predators are available in the desert.

C) A cartilaginous endoskeleton provides needed flexibility for locomotion on sand.

D) Their scales contain the protein keratin, which helps prevent dehydration.

E) They have an acute sense of sight, especially in bright sunlight.

Answer: D
*Topic: Concept 34.6*
*Skill: Comprehension*

33) Which of these is *not* considered an amniote?

   A) amphibians

   B) non-avian reptiles

   C) avian reptiles

   D) egg-laying mammals

   E) placental mammals

Answer: A
*Topic: Concept 34.6*
*Skill: Knowledge*

34) Why is the amniotic egg considered an important evolutionary breakthrough? It

   A) has a shell that increases gas exchange.

   B) allows incubation of eggs in a terrestrial environment.

   C) prolongs embryonic development.

   D) provides insulation to conserve heat.

   E) permits internal fertilization to be replaced by external fertilization.

Answer: B
*Topic: Concept 34.6*
*Skill: Comprehension*

35) Which era is known as the "age of reptiles"?

   A) Cenozoic

   B) Mesozoic

   C) Paleozoic

   D) Precambrian

   E) Cambrian

Answer: B
*Topic: Concept 34.6*
*Skill: Knowledge*

36) Which of these characteristics added most to vertebrate success in relatively dry environments?

   A) the amniotic egg

   B) the ability to maintain a constant body temperature

   C) two pairs of appendages

   D) claws

   E) a four-chambered heart

Answer: A
*Topic: Concept 34.6*
*Skill: Knowledge*

37) From which of the following groups are snakes most likely descended?

   A) dinosaurs

   B) plesiosaurs

   C) lizards

   D) crocodiles

   E) synapsids

Answer: C
*Topic: Concept 34.6*
*Skill: Knowledge*

38) All of the following are characteristics of most extant non-avian reptiles, *except*

   A) ectothermy.

   B) brachiation.

   C) the amniotic egg.

   D) keratinized skin.

   E) conical teeth that are relatively uniform in size.

Answer: B
*Topic: Concept 34.6*
*Skill: Knowledge*

39) When did dinosaurs and pterosaurs become extinct?

A) Cretaceous "crisis"

B) Permian extinctions

C) Devonian "disaster"

D) Phanerozoic eon

E) Hadean eon

Answer: A
*Topic: Concept 34.6*
*Skill: Knowledge*

40) Which of the following are the only extant animals that descended directly from dinosaurs?

A) lizards

B) crocodiles

C) snakes

D) birds

E) mammals

Answer: D
*Topic: Concept 34.6*
*Skill: Knowledge*

41) Examination of the fossils of *Archaeopteryx* reveals that, in common with extant birds, it had

A) a long tail containing vertebrae.

B) feathers.

C) teeth.

D) both A and B

E) A, B, and C

Answer: B
*Topic: Concept 34.6*
*Skill: Knowledge*

42) Why is the discovery of the fossil *Archaeopteryx* significant? It supports the

A) phylogenetic relatedness of birds and reptiles.

B) contention that birds are much older than we originally thought.

C) claim that mammals and dinosaurs coexisted.

D) idea that the first birds were ratites.

E) hypothesis that some extinct reptiles were endothermic.

Answer: A
*Topic: Concept 34.6*
*Skill: Comprehension*

43) What is the single unique characteristic that distinguishes extant birds from other extant animals?

A) a hinged jaw

B) feathers

C) an amniotic egg

D) flight

E) a gizzard

Answer: B
*Topic: Concept 34.6*
*Skill: Knowledge*

44) Which of the following structures are possessed only by birds?

A) enlarged pectoral muscles and heavy bones

B) a four-chambered heart

C) feathers and keeled sternum

D) a short tail and mammary glands

E) a large brain and endothermy

Answer: C
*Topic: Concept 34.6*
*Skill: Knowledge*

The following questions refer to the phylogenetic tree shown in Figure 34.1.

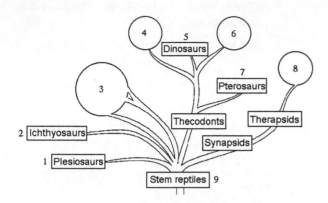

**Figure 34.1**

45) The organisms represented by 8 most likely are

A) avian reptiles.

B) mammals.

C) non-avian, terrestrial reptiles.

D) aquatic reptiles.

E) all mammals except humans.

Answer: B
*Topic: Concept 34.6*
*Skill: Comprehension*

46) Which organisms are represented by 6?

A) avian reptiles

B) mammals

C) non-avian, terrestrial reptiles

D) aquatic reptiles

E) all mammals except humans

Answer: A
*Topic: Concept 34.6*
*Skill: Comprehension*

47) Which pair of numbers represents extinct reptiles that had returned to an aquatic life?

A) 1 and 2

B) 3 and 4

C) 5 and 7

D) 6 and 8

E) 7 and 9

Answer: A
*Topic: Concept 34.6*
*Skill: Comprehension*

48) Which pair of numbers most likely represents extant, non-avian reptiles?

A) 1 and 2

B) 3 and 4

C) 5 and 7

D) 6 and 8

E) 7 and 9

Answer: B
*Topic: Concept 34.6*
*Skill: Comprehension*

49) Whose forelimbs are most analogous to those of keeled birds and bats?

A) 1

B) 2

C) 3

D) 7

E) 9

Answer: D
*Topic: Concept 34.6*
*Skill: Comprehension*

50) Whose DNA would have had the most sequence homologies with amphibian DNA?

   A) 5

   B) 6

   C) 7

   D) 8

   E) 9

Answer: E
*Topic: Concept 34.6*
*Skill: Comprehension*

51) Which pair of numbers includes extant endotherms?

   A) 3 and 4

   B) 4 and 5

   C) 6 and 8

   D) 3 and 8

   E) 6 and 7

Answer: C
*Topic: Concept 34.6*
*Skill: Comprehension*

52) According to modern systematics, which of these terms is now more narrowly applied than it has been in the past?

   A) lobe-fins

   B) osteichthyans

   C) fishes

   D) reptiles

   E) gnathostomes

Answer: C
*Topic: Concepts 34.4–34.6*
*Skill: Comprehension*

53) During chordate evolution, what is the sequence (from earliest to most recent) in which the following structures arose?

1. amniotic egg
2. paired fins
3. jaws
4. swim bladder
5. four-chambered heart

   A) 2, 3, 4, 1, 5

   B) 3, 2, 4, 1, 5

   C) 3, 2, 1, 4, 5

   D) 2, 1, 4, 3, 5

   E) 2, 4, 3, 1, 5

Answer: A
*Topic: Concepts 34.3–34.6*
*Skill: Comprehension*

54) Structures that are made of keratin include which of the following?

   A) avian feathers

   B) reptilian scales

   C) mammalian hair

   D) A and C only

   E) A, B, and C

Answer: E
*Topic: Concepts 34.6, 34.7*
*Skill: Knowledge*

55) A sheet of muscle called the diaphragm is found in extant

   A) birds.

   B) mammals.

   C) non-avian reptiles.

   D) both A and B

   E) A, B, and C

Answer: B
*Topic: Concept 34.7*
*Skill: Knowledge*

56) Differentiation of teeth is greatest in

A) sharks.

B) bony fishes.

C) amphibians.

D) reptiles.

E) mammals.

Answer: E
*Topic: Concept 34.7*
*Skill: Knowledge*

57) Which is *not* characteristic of all mammals?

A) a four-chambered heart that prevents mixing of oxygenated and deoxygenated blood

B) giving birth to live young (viviparous)

C) having hair during at least some period of life

D) having glands to produce nourishing milk for offspring

E) having a diaphragm to assist in ventilating the lungs

Answer: B
*Topic: Concept 34.7*
*Skill: Knowledge*

58) Which of these would a paleontologist be most likely to do in order to determine whether a fossil represents a reptile or a mammal?

A) Look for the presence of milk-producing glands.

B) Look for the mammalian characteristics of a four-chambered heart and a diaphragm.

C) Because mammals are eutherians, look for evidence of a placenta.

D) Use molecular analysis to look for the protein keratin.

E) Examine the teeth.

Answer: E
*Topic: Concept 34.7*
*Skill: Comprehension*

59) Which of the following classifications do *not* apply to both dogs and humans?

A) class Mammalia

B) order Primates

C) phylum Chordata

D) kingdom Animalia

E) subphylum Vertebrata

Answer: B
*Topic: Concept 34.7*
*Skill: Comprehension*

60) Which of these is *not* a trend in primate evolution?

A) enhanced depth perception

B) well-developed claws for clinging to trees

C) a shoulder joint adapted to brachiation

D) increased brain to body ratio

E) a long period of parental care of offspring

Answer: B
*Topic: Concept 34.7*
*Skill: Knowledge*

61) How are primates different from all other mammals?

A) placental embryonic development

B) hairy bodies

C) arboreal lifestyles

D) ability to produce milk

E) opposable thumbs in many species

Answer: E
*Topic: Concept 34.7*
*Skill: Comprehension*

62) In which vertebrates is fertilization exclusively internal?

A) chondrichthyans, osteichthyans, and mammals

B) amphibians, mammals, and reptiles

C) chondrichthyans, osteichthyans, and reptiles

D) reptiles and mammals

E) reptiles and amphibians

Answer: D
*Topic: Concepts 34.5–34.7*
*Skill: Knowledge*

*For the following items, match the vertebrate groups below with the descriptions that follow. Each choice may be used once, more than once, or not at all.*

A.  amphibians
B.  non-avian reptiles
C.  chondrichthyans
D.  mammals
E.  avian reptiles

63) their scales closely resemble teeth in both structure and origin

Answer: C
*Topic: Concept 34.4*
*Skill: Knowledge*

64) internal fertilization, amniotic egg, skin that resists drying, heavy bones

Answer: B
*Topic: Concept 34.6*
*Skill: Knowledge*

65) three major groups: egg–laying, pouched, and placental

Answer: D
*Topic: Concept 34.7*
*Skill: Knowledge*

66) may have lungs, or gills, and may use skin as a respiratory surface

Answer: A
*Topic: Concept 34.5*
*Skill: Knowledge*

67) honeycombed bones, females with one ovary, no teeth

Answer: E
*Topic: Concept 34.6*
*Skill: Knowledge*

68) Arrange the following taxonomic terms from most inclusive (i.e. most general) to least inclusive (i.e. most specific):
1.  hominoids
2.  hominids
3.  *Homo*
4   anthropoids
5.  primates

A) 5, 1, 4, 2, 3

B) 5, 4, 1, 2, 3

C) 5, 4, 2, 1, 3

D) 5, 2, 1, 4, 3

E) 5, 2, 4, 1, 3

Answer: B
*Topic: Concept 34.8*
*Skill: Comprehension*

69) The adaptation to arboreal life by early human ancestors can explain, at least in part, all of the following human characteristics *except*

A) limber shoulder joints.

B) dexterous hands with opposable thumbs.

C) excellent eye–hand coordination.

D) enhanced depth perception.

E) reduced body hair.

Answer: E
*Topic: Concept 34.8*
*Skill: Comprehension*

70) Which of these hominid traits seems to have occurred before the others?

A) tool use

B) increased brain size

C) symbolic thought

D) language

E) bipedalism

Answer: E
*Topic: Concept 34.8*
*Skill: Knowledge*

71) Which of these traits is *not* directly associated with the adoption of bipedalism?

A) shortening of jaw

B) shortening of limbs

C) straightening and shortening of digits

D) loss of ability to oppose big toe

E) repositioning of foramen magnum

Answer: A
*Topic: Concept 34.8*
*Skill: Comprehension*

72) Which of the following statements about human evolution is *correct*?

A) Modern humans are the only human species to have evolved on Earth.

B) Human ancestors were virtually identical to chimpanzees.

C) Human evolution occurred by anagenetic change within an unbranched lineage.

D) The upright posture and enlarged brain of humans evolved simultaneously.

E) Fossil evidence indicates that early anthropoids were arboreal, and cat-sized.

Answer: E
*Topic: Concept 34.8*
*Skill: Comprehension*

73) Humans and apes are presently classified in the same category as all of the following levels *except*

A) class.

B) genus.

C) kingdom.

D) order.

E) phylum.

Answer: B
*Topic: Concept 34.8*
*Skill: Comprehension*

74) Which of the following are *not* considered hominoids?

A) gibbons

B) gorillas

C) rhesus monkeys

D) orangutans

E) chimpanzees

Answer: C
*Topic: Concept 34.8*
*Skill: Knowledge*

75) The most primitive hominid discovered to date

A) may have hunted dinosaurs.

B) lived 1.2 million years ago.

C) closely resembled a chimpanzee.

D) walked on two legs.

E) had a relatively large brain.

Answer: D
*Topic: Concept 34.8*
*Skill: Comprehension*

*Match the taxonomic terms below with the descriptions that follow. Options may be used once, more than once, or not at all.*

A) *H. heidelbergensis*
B) *H. erectus*
C) *H. ergaster*
D) *H. habilis*
E) *H. sapiens*

76) the first of these species to have been adapted for long-distance bipedalism

Answer: C
*Topic: Concept 34.8*
*Skill: Knowledge*

77) the first of these species to craft stone tools

Answer: D
*Topic: Concept 34.8*
*Skill: Knowledge*

78) the first of these species to show a trend toward reduced sexual dimorphism

Answer: C
*Topic: Concept 34.8*
*Skill: Knowledge*

79) the first of these species to have some members migrate out of Africa

Answer: B
*Topic: Concept 34.8*
*Skill: Knowledge*

80) the species currently thought to be the direct ancestor of *H. neanderthalensis*

Answer: A
*Topic: Concept 34.8*
*Skill: Knowledge*

81) the species that demonstrates symbolic thought, art, and full–blown language

Answer: E
*Topic: Concept 34.8*
*Skill: Knowledge*

82) With which of the following statements would a biologist be *most* inclined to agree?
    A) Humans and apes represent divergent lines of evolution from a common ancestor.
    B) Humans evolved from New World monkeys.
    C) Humans have stopped evolving and now represent the pinnacle of evolution.
    D) Apes evolved from humans.
    E) Humans and apes are the result of disruptive selection in a species of gorilla.

Answer: A
*Topic: Concept 34.8*
*Skill: Knowledge*

83) Which of these statements about human evolution is *true*?
    A) The ancestors of *Homo sapiens* were chimpanzees and other apes.
    B) Human evolution has proceeded in an orderly fashion from an ancestral anthropoid to *Homo sapiens*.
    C) The evolution of upright posture and enlarged brain occurred simultaneously.
    D) Different features have evolved at different rates.
    E) Mitochondrial DNA analysis indicates that modern humans are genetically very similar to Neanderthals.

Answer: D
*Topic: Concept 34.8*
*Skill: Comprehension*

84) Rank the following in terms of body–size differences that are attributed to sexual dimorphism, from most dimorphic to least dimorphic.
1. *Homo sapiens*
2. Chimpanzees and bonobos
3. *Australopithecus afarensis*
4. *Homo habilis*

A) 1, 2, 3, 4

B) 1, 3, 2, 4

C) 3, 2, 4, 1

D) 2, 3, 4, 1

E) 4, 3, 2, 1

Answer: D
*Topic: Concept 34.8*
*Skill: Comprehension*

85) Based on current evidence, which of the following statements *best* describes the evolution of humans?

A) Humans evolved from the chimpanzee.

B) Humans evolved in a single, orderly series of stages in which each stage became more advanced than the predecessor.

C) The various characteristics that we associate with humans evolved in unison over long periods of time.

D) Humans and apes diverged from a common ancestor about 5–10 million years ago.

E) Humans are more closely related to gorillas than to chimpanzees.

Answer: D
*Topic: Concept 34.8*
*Skill: Knowledge*

86) The oldest fossil remains of *Homo sapiens* found so far date from about

A) 6 million years ago.

B) 1.6 million years ago.

C) 160,000 years ago.

D) 60,000 years ago.

E) 16,000 years ago.

Answer: C
*Topic: Concept 34.8*
*Skill: Knowledge*

87) The common ancestors of all humans alive today lived in Africa until about

A) 5 million years ago.

B) 500,000 years ago.

C) 50,000 years ago.

D) 5,000 years ago.

E) There is no evidence available that could answer this question.

Answer: C
*Topic: Concept 34.8*
*Skill: Knowledge*

88) Which of the following statements is *false* in regards to *Homo erectus*?

A) Their fossils are limited to Africa.

B) On average, *H. erectus* had a larger brain than *H. habilis*.

C) *H. erectus* had a level of sexual dimorphism similar to that of modern humans.

D) *H. erectus* was able to use tools.

E) *H. erectus* evolved after the rise of *H. habilis*.

Answer: A
*Topic: Concept 34.8*
*Skill: Knowledge*

89) Why is it thought that the Neanderthals contributed little to the gene pool of modern humanity?

    A) Recent studies of human and Neanderthal DNA show significant differences in base sequences.

    B) The fossils found in the Neander Valley were a hoax and the "Neanderthals" never really existed.

    C) Neanderthals had degenerated brain capacity and thus could not have contributed to human ancestry.

    D) There is no evidence that Neanderthals were capable of walking upright or using tools.

    E) Humans, the "naked apes," have nothing in common with the Neanderthals, the "hairy apes."

Answer: A
*Topic: Concept 34.8*
*Skill: Comprehension*

*Match the taxonomic terms below with the descriptions that follow. Each option may be used once, more than once, or not at all.*

    A) hominoids
    B) *Homo*
    C) anthropoids
    D) hominids
    E) primates

90) Which is the most inclusive (most general) group, all of whose members have foramina magna centrally positioned in the base of the cranium?

Answer: D
*Topic: Concept 34.8*
*Skill: Comprehension*

91) Which term is most nearly synonymous with "apes"?

Answer: A
*Topic: Concept 34.8*
*Skill: Comprehension*

92) Which is a genus that has only one extant species?

Answer: B
*Topic: Concept 34.8*
*Skill: Knowledge*

93) Which is the most inclusive (most general) group, all of whose members have fingernails instead of claws?

Answer: E
*Topic: Concept 34.8*
*Skill: Comprehension*

94) Which is the most inclusive (most general) group, all of whose members have fully opposable thumbs?

Answer: C
*Topic: Concept 34.8*
*Skill: Comprehension*

95) Which is the most specific group in which prosimians can be included?

Answer: E
*Topic: Concept 34.8*
*Skill: Comprehension*

96) Which is the most specific group that includes both the Old World monkeys and the New World monkeys?

Answer: C
*Topic: Concept 34.8*
*Skill: Comprehension*

*Match the genes below with the descriptions that follow.*

    A) *Hox*
    B) *Dlx*
    C) *Otx*
    D) *FOXP2*
    E) more than one of these

97) At least one of these has been found in all species of animals studied thus far.

Answer: A
*Topic: Concept 34.1*
*Skill: Knowledge*

98) This is a code for transcription factors involved in the evolution of innovations in early vertebrate nervous systems and vertebrae.

Answer: B
*Topic: Concept 34.3*
*Skill: Knowledge*

99) This is a gene linked to the development of speech in hominids.

Answer: D
*Topic: Concept 34.8*
*Skill: Knowledge*

# Media Activity Questions

1) Which one of these chordate groups lacks a post–anal tail and a notochord as adults?

   A) lancelets

   B) tunicates

   C) amphibians

   D) mammals

   E) reptiles

   Answer: B
   *Topic: Web/CD Activity: Characteristics of Chordates*

2) The common ancestor of all these chordate groups *except* the _____ probably had paired appendages.

   A) mammals

   B) amphibians

   C) lampreys

   D) ray-finned fishes

   E) reptiles

   Answer: C
   *Topic: Web/CD Activity: Characteristics of Chordates*

3) _____ are the oldest known primate group.

   A) Apes

   B) Prosimians

   C) Anthropoids

   D) Hominids

   E) Monkeys

   Answer: B
   *Topic: Web/CD Activity: Primate Diversity*

4) Which of these primate groups lives in trees in Central and South America and have nostrils that are wide open and far apart?

   A) hominids

   B) apes

   C) New World monkeys

   D) anthropoids

   E) Old World monkeys

   Answer: C
   *Topic: Web/CD Activity: Primate Diversity*

5) Evidence indicates that _____ was the first hominid to use fire.

   A) *Australopithecus*

   B) *Homo erectus*

   C) *Ardipithecus*

   D) *Homo habilis*

   E) *Homo sapiens*

   Answer: B
   *Topic: Web/CD Activity: Human Evolution*

# Self-Quiz Questions

1) Vertebrates and tunicates share

   A) jaws adapted for feeding.

   B) a high degree of cephalization.

   C) the formation of structures from the neural crest.

   D) an endoskeleton that includes a skull.

   E) a notochord and a dorsal, hollow nerve cord.

   Answer: E

2) Some animals that lived 530 million years ago resembled lancelets but had a brain and a skull. These animals may represent

   A) the first chordates.

   B) a "missing link" between urochordates and cephalochordates.

   C) early craniates.

   D) marsupials.

   E) non-tetrapod gnathostomes.

   Answer: C

3) Chondrichthyans can be distinguished from osteichthyans by the

   A) presence in osteichthyans of a skull.

   B) presence in osteichthyans of a lateral line system.

   C) presence in condrichthyans of unpaired fins.

   D) absence in chondrichthyans of a swim bladder and lungs.

   E) absence in chondrichthyans of paired sensory organs.

   Answer: D

4) Which of the following could be considered the most recent common ancestor of living tetrapods?

   A) a sturdy-finned, shallow-water lobe-fin whose appendages had skeletal supports similar to those of terrestrial vertebrates

   B) an armored, jawed placoderm that had two sets of paired appendages

   C) an early ray-finned fish that developed bony skeletal supports in its paired fins

   D) a salamander that had legs supported by a bony skeleton but moved with the side-to-side bending typical of fishes

   E) an early terrestrial caecilian whose legless condition had evolved secondarily

   Answer: A

5) Mammals and living birds share all of the following characteristics *except*

   A) endothermy.

   B) descent from a common amniotic ancestor.

   C) a dorsal, hollow nerve cord.

   D) teeth specialized for diverse diets.

   E) the ability of some species to fly.

   Answer: D

6) Unlike eutherians, both monotremes and marsupials

   A) lack nipples.

   B) have some embryonic development outside the mother's uterus.

   C) lay eggs.

   D) are found in Australia and Africa.

   E) include only insectivores and herbivores.

   Answer: B

7) Which of the following characteristics of monkeys is specific to New World monkeys?

   A) distinct "seat pads"

   B) eyes close together on the front of the skull

   C) use of the tail to hang from a tree limb

   D) occasional bipedal walking

   E) downward orientation of the nostrils

Answer: C

8) Which clade does *not* include humans?

   A) synapsids

   B) lobe–fins

   C) diapsids

   D) craniates

   E) osteichthyans

Answer: C

9) As humans diverged from other primates, which of the following appeared first?

   A) the development of technology

   B) language

   C) a partial erect stance

   D) tool–making

   E) an enlarged brain

Answer: C

10) Studies on DNA indicate which of the following?

   A) *Homo erectus* had an Asian origin.

   B) *Homo sapiens* originated in Africa.

   C) Neanderthals are the ancestors of modern humans in Europe.

   D) Australopiths migrated out of Africa.

   E) North America had the first population of modern humans.

Answer: B

# Chapter 35  Plant Structure, Growth, and Development

1) You are studying a plant from the arid southwestern United States. Which of the following adaptations is *least* likely to have evolved in response to water shortages?
   A) closing the stomata during the hottest time of the day
   B) development of large leaf surfaces to absorb water
   C) formation of a fibrous root system spread over a large area
   D) mycorrhizae associated with the root system
   E) a thick waxy cuticle on the epidermis

Answer: B
*Topic: Overview*
*Skill: Application*

2) Which part of a plant absorbs most of the water and minerals taken up from the soil?
   A) taproots
   B) root hairs
   C) the thick parts of the roots near the base of the stem
   D) storage roots
   E) sections of the root that have secondary xylem

Answer: B
*Topic: Concept 35.1 (6)*
*Skill: Knowledge*

3) An evolutionary adaptation that increases exposure of a plant to light in a dense forest is
   A) closing of the stomata.
   B) lateral buds.
   C) apical dominance.
   D) absence of petioles.
   E) intercalary meristems.

Answer: C
*Topic: Concept 35.1*
*Skill: Knowledge*

4) A person working with plants may remove apical dominance by doing which of the following?
   A) pruning
   B) deep watering of the roots
   C) fertilizing
   D) transplanting
   E) feeding the plants nutrients

Answer: A
*Topic: Concept 35.1*
*Skill: Comprehension*

5) What effect does "pinching back" have on a houseplant?
   A) increases apical dominance
   B) inhibits the growth of lateral buds
   C) produces a plant that will grow taller
   D) produces a plant that will grow fuller
   E) increases the flow of auxin down the shoot

Answer: D
*Topic: Concept 35.1*
*Skill: Comprehension*

6) Land plants are composed of all the following tissue types *except*

A) mesodermal.

B) epidermal.

C) meristematic.

D) vascular.

E) ground tissue.

Answer: A
*Topic: Concept 35.1*
*Skill: Knowledge*

7) Vascular plant tissue includes all of the following cell types *except*

A) vessel elements.

B) sieve cells.

C) tracheids.

D) companion cells.

E) cambium cells.

Answer: E
*Topic: Concept 35.1*
*Skill: Knowledge*

8) Which functional plant cells lack a nucleus?

A) xylem only

B) sieve cells only

C) companion cells only

D) both companion and parenchyma cells

E) both xylem and sieve–tube cells

Answer: E
*Topic: Concept 35.1*
*Skill: Knowledge*

*The questions below use the following answers. Each answer may be used once, more than once, or not at all.*

A. parenchyma
B. collenchyma
C. sclerenchyma
D. tracheids
E. sieve cells

9) long, thin tapered cells with lignified cell walls that function in support and permit water to flow through pits

Answer: D
*Topic: Concept 35.1*
*Skill: Knowledge*

10) living cells that lack nuclei and ribosomes; they transport sugars and other organic nutrients

Answer: E
*Topic: Concept 35.1*
*Skill: Knowledge*

11) the least specialized plant cells, which serve general metabolic, synthetic, and storage functions

Answer: A
*Topic: Concept 35.1*
*Skill: Knowledge*

12) cells with unevenly thickened primary walls that support still–elongating parts of the plant

Answer: B
*Topic: Concept 35.1*
*Skill: Knowledge*

13) mature cells without protoplasts with thick, lignified secondary walls that may or may not function in transport

Answer: C
*Topic: Concept 35.1*
*Skill: Knowledge*

14) Which of the following is *not* a characteristic of parenchyma cells?

   A) thin primary walls

   B) flexible primary walls

   C) lack of specialization

   D) lack of secondary walls

   E) little metabolism and synthesis

Answer: E
*Topic: Concept 35.1*
*Skill: Knowledge*

15) Which of the following tissues is *incorrectly* matched with its characteristics?

   A) collenchyma—uniformly thick-walled supportive tissue

   B) epidermis—protective outer covering of plant body

   C) sclerenchyma—heavily lignified secondary walls

   D) meristematic tissue—undifferentiated tissue capable of cell division

   E) parenchyma—thin-walled, loosely packed, unspecialized cells

Answer: A
*Topic: Concept 35.1*
*Skill: Knowledge*

16) The fiber cells of plants are a type of

   A) parenchyma.

   B) sclerenchyma.

   C) collenchyma.

   D) meristematic cell.

   E) phloem

Answer: B
*Topic: Concept 35.1*
*Skill: Knowledge*

17) The vascular bundle in the shape of a single central cylinder in a root is called the

   A) cortex.

   B) stele.

   C) endodermis.

   D) periderm.

   E) pith.

Answer: B
*Topic: Concept 35.1*
*Skill: Knowledge*

18) One important difference between the anatomy of roots and the anatomy of leaves is that

   A) only leaves have phloem and only roots have xylem.

   B) the cells of roots have cell walls and leaf cells do not.

   C) a waxy cuticle covers leaves but is absent in roots.

   D) vascular tissue is found in roots but is absent from leaves.

   E) leaves have epidermal tissue but roots do not.

Answer: C
*Topic: Concept 35.1*
*Skill: Comprehension*

19) The photosynthetic cells in the interior of a leaf are what kind of cells?

   A) parenchyma

   B) collenchyma

   C) sclerenchyma

   D) phloem

   E) endodermis

Answer: A
*Topic: Concept 35.1*
*Skill: Knowledge*

20) A student examining leaf cross sections under a microscope finds many loosely packed cells with relatively thin cell walls. The cells have numerous chloroplasts. What type of cells are these?

A) parenchyma

B) xylem

C) endodermis

D) collenchyma

E) sclerenchyma

Answer: A
*Topic: Concept 35.1*
*Skill: Application*

21) The best word to describe the growth of plants in general is

A) perennial.

B) weedy.

C) indeterminate.

D) derivative.

E) primary.

Answer: C
*Topic: Concept 35.2*
*Skill: Comprehension*

22) Which of the following is *true* about secondary growth in plants?

A) Flowers may have secondary growth.

B) Secondary growth is a common feature of eudicot leaves.

C) Secondary growth is produced by both the vascular cambium and the cork cambium.

D) Primary growth and secondary growth alternate in the life cycle of a plant.

E) Plants with secondary growth are typically the smallest ones in an ecosystem.

Answer: C
*Topic: Concept 35.2*
*Skill: Knowledge*

23) A friend has discovered a new plant and brings it to you to classify. The plant has the following characteristics: a taproot system with growth rings evident in cross section and a layer of bark around the outside. Which of the following best describes the new plant?

A) herbaceous eudicot

B) woody eudicot

C) woody monocot

D) herbaceous monocot

E) woody annual

Answer: B
*Topic: Concept 35.3*
*Skill: Application*

24) The driving force that pushes the root tip through the soil is due primarily to

A) continuous cell division in the root cap at the tip of the root.

B) continuous cell division just behind the root cap in the center of the apical meristem.

C) elongation of cells behind the root apical meristem.

D) A and B only.

E) A, B, and C.

Answer: C
*Topic: Concept 35.3*
*Skill: Comprehension*

25) Shoot elongation in a growing bud is due primarily to

A) cell division at the shoot apical meristem.

B) cell elongation directly behind the shoot apical meristem.

C) cell division localized in each internode.

D) cell elongation localized in each internode.

E) A and B only.

Answer: D
*Topic: Concept 35.3*
*Skill: Knowledge*

26) Axillary buds

A) are initiated by the cork cambium.

B) develop from meristematic cells left by the apical meristem.

C) are composed of a series of internodes lacking nodes.

D) grow immediately into shoot branches.

E) do not form a vascular connection with the primary shoot.

Answer: B
*Topic: Concept 35.3*
*Skill: Knowledge*

27) Gas exchange, necessary for photosynthesis, can occur most easily in which leaf tissue?

A) epidermis

B) palisade mesophyll

C) spongy mesophyll

D) vascular tissue

E) bundle sheath

Answer: C
*Topic: Concept 35.3*
*Skill: Knowledge*

*The following question is based on parts of a growing primary root.*

I.   root cap
II.  zone of elongation
III. zone of cell division
IV.  zone of cell maturation
V.   apical meristem

28) Which of the following is the *correct* sequence from the growing tips of the root upward?

A) I, II, V, III, IV

B) III, V, I, II, IV

C) II, IV, I, V, III

D) IV, II, III, I, V

E) I, V, III, II, IV

Answer: E
*Topic: Concept 35.3*
*Skill: Knowledge*

29) Which of the following is *incorrectly* paired with its structure and function?

A) sclerenchyma—supporting cells with thick secondary walls

B) periderm—protective coat of woody stems and roots

C) pericycle—waterproof ring of cells surrounding the central stele in roots

D) mesophyll—parenchyma cells functioning in photosynthesis in leaves

E) ground meristem—primary meristem that produces the ground tissue system

Answer: C
*Topic: Concept 35.3*
*Skill: Knowledge*

30) Which of the following illustrates the idea that the fate of a cell is a direct result of its position?

    A) Some root epidermal cells form hairs; others do not.

    B) Floating leaves of *Cabomba* have a different shape than submerged leaves.

    C) Some shoot epidermal cells form stomata; others do not.

    D) A and C only

    E) A, B, and C

Answer: E
*Topic: Concept 35.3*
*Skill: Knowledge*

31) Which of the following root tissues gives rise to lateral roots?

    A) endodermis

    B) phloem

    C) cortex

    D) epidermis

    E) pericycle

Answer: E
*Topic: Concept 35.3*
*Skill: Knowledge*

*The following questions are based on the drawing of root or stem cross sections shown in Figure 35.1.*

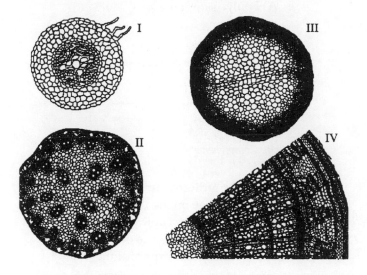

**Figure 35.1**

32) A woody eudicot is represented by

    A) I only.

    B) II only.

    C) III only.

    D) IV only.

    E) both I and III.

Answer: D
*Topic: Concept 35.4*
*Skill: Comprehension*

33) A monocot stem is represented by

    A) I only.

    B) II only.

    C) III only.

    D) IV only.

    E) both I and III.

Answer: B
*Topic: Concept 35.3*
*Skill: Comprehension*

34) A plant that is at least three years old is represented by

A) I only.

B) II only.

C) III only.

D) IV only.

E) both I and III.

Answer: D
*Topic: Concept 35.3*
*Skill: Comprehension*

35) A leaf primordium is initiated as a small mound of tissue on the flank of a dome-shaped shoot apical meristem. The earliest physical evidence of the site of a newly forming leaf primordium would be

A) development of chloroplasts in a surface cell of the shoot apical meristem.

B) cell division in the shoot apical meristem with the newly forming walls perpendicular to the surface of the meristem.

C) pre-prophase bands parallel to the surface of the meristem in subsurface cells of the shoot apical meristem.

D) elongation of epidermal cells perpendicular to the surface of the shoot apical meristem.

E) formation of stomata in the epidermal layer of the shoot apical meristem.

Answer: C
*Topic: Concept 35.3*
*Skill: Comprehension*

36) Pores on the leaf surface that function in gas exchange are called

A) hairs.

B) xylem cells.

C) phloem cells.

D) stomata.

E) sclereids.

Answer: D
*Topic: Concept 35.3*
*Skill: Knowledge*

37) Which of the following is a *true* statement about growth in plants?

A) Only primary growth is localized at meristems.

B) Some plants lack secondary growth.

C) Only stems have secondary growth.

D) Only secondary growth produces reproductive structures.

E) Monocots have only primary growth, and eudicots have only secondary growth.

Answer: B
*Topic: Concept 35.3*
*Skill: Comprehension*

38) All of the following cell types are correctly matched with their functions *except*

A) mesophyll—photosynthesis

B) guard cell—regulation of transpiration

C) sieve-tube member—translocation

D) vessel element—water transport

E) companion cell—formation of secondary xylem and phloem

Answer: E
*Topic: Concept 35.3*
*Skill: Comprehension*

39) As a youngster, you drive a nail in the trunk of a young tree that is 3 meters tall. The nail is about 1.5 meters from the ground. Fifteen years later, you return and discover the tree has grown to a height of 30 meters. The nail is now _____ meters above the ground.

A) 0.5

B) 1.5

C) 3.0

D) 15.0

E) 28.5

Answer: B
*Topic: Concept 35.3*
*Skill: Application*

40) A short branch was cut into three segments as shown in Figure 35.2 to root some cuttings. Roots will form at which position(s)?

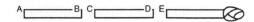

**Figure 35.2**

A) A only

B) A and B

C) A, B, and C

D) A, C, and E

E) A, B, C, D, and E

Answer: D
*Topic: Concept 35.3*
*Skill: Application*

41) What tissue makes up most of the wood of a tree?

A) primary xylem

B) secondary xylem

C) secondary phloem

D) mesophyll cells

E) vascular cambium

Answer: B
*Topic: Concept 35.4*
*Skill: Knowledge*

42) The vascular system of a three–year–old eudicot stem consists of

A) 3 rings of xylem and 3 of phloem.

B) 2 rings of xylem and 2 of phloem.

C) 2 rings of xylem and 1 of phloem.

D) 2 rings of xylem and 3 of phloem.

E) 3 rings of xylem and 1 of phloem.

Answer: E
*Topic: Concept 35.4*
*Skill: Comprehension*

43) If you were able to walk into an opening cut into the center of a large redwood tree, when you exit from the middle of the trunk (stem) outward, you would cross, in order,

A) the annual rings, phloem, and bark.

B) the newest xylem, oldest phloem, and periderm.

C) the vascular cambium, oldest xylem, and newest xylem.

D) the secondary xylem, secondary phloem, and vascular cambium.

E) the summer wood, bark, and phloem.

Answer: A
*Topic: Concept 35.4*
*Skill: Application*

44) Which of the following is *true* of bark?

A) It is composed of phloem plus periderm.

B) It is associated with annuals but not perennials.

C) It is formed by the apical meristems.

D) It has no identifiable function in trees.

E) It forms annual rings in deciduous trees.

Answer: A
*Topic: Concept 35.4*
*Skill: Knowledge*

45) Bark becomes scaly because

    A) the cork cambium stops dividing in certain places.

    B) some cork cells die and slough off while others remain alive.

    C) ray parenchyma supplies only the "ridges" of bark.

    D) cork cambium divides only parallel to the surface, and thus does not increase in circumference.

    E) cork cambium has both ray and fusiform initials.

Answer: D
*Topic: Concept 35.4*
*Skill: Comprehension*

46) Suppose George Washington completely removed the bark from around the base of a cherry tree but was stopped by his father before cutting the tree down. The leaves retained their normal appearance for several weeks, but the tree eventually died. The tissue(s) that George left functional was (were) the

    A) phloem.

    B) xylem.

    C) cork cambium.

    D) cortex.

    E) companion and sieve–tube members.

Answer: B
*Topic: Concept 35.4*
*Skill: Application*

47) Additional vascular tissue produced as secondary growth in a root originates from which cells?

    A) vascular cambium

    B) apical meristem

    C) endodermis

    D) phloem

    E) xylem

Answer: A
*Topic: Concept 35.4*
*Skill: Comprehension*

48) While studying the plant *Arabidopsis*, a botanist finds that an RNA probe produces colored spots in the sepals of the plant. From this information, what information can be inferred?

    A) The differently colored plants will attract different pollinating insects.

    B) The RNA probe is transported only to certain tissues.

    C) The colored regions were caused by mutations that occurred in the sepals.

    D) The RNA probe is specific to a gene active in sepals.

    E) More research needs to be done on the sepals of *Arabidopsis*.

Answer: D
*Topic: Concept 35.5*
*Skill: Application*

49) Before differentiation can begin during the processes of plant cell and tissue culture, parenchyma cells from the source tissue must

    A) differentiate into procambium.

    B) undergo dedifferentiation.

    C) increase the number of chromosomes in their nuclei.

    D) enzymatically digest their primary cell walls.

    E) establish a new polarity in their cytoplasm.

Answer: B
*Topic: Concept 35.5*
*Skill: Comprehension*

50) The polarity of a plant is established when
    A) the zygote divides.
    B) cotyledons form at the shoot end of the embryo.
    C) the shoot–root axis is established in the embryo.
    D) the primary root breaks through the seed coat.
    E) the shoot first breaks through the soil into the light as the seed germinates.

Answer: A
*Topic: Concept 35.5*
*Skill: Comprehension*

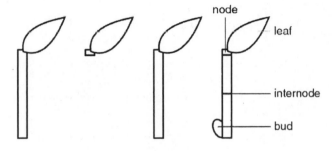

**Figure 35.3
Sectors of corn plants**

51) Each of the patterns indicated in Figure 35.3 above occurred as a sector during clonal analysis of several corn plants. Based on this data, a growth module in corn must consist of
    A) a leaf only.
    B) a leaf and its associated node.
    C) a leaf, its associated node, and the internode below.
    D) a leaf, its associated node, the internode below, and the bud below the leaf.
    E) a leaf and its associated node and axillary bud, and the internode below the leaf.

Answer: D
*Topic: Concept 35.5*
*Skill: Comprehension*

52) "Totipotency" is a term used to describe the ability of a cell to give rise to a complete new organism. In plants, this means that
    A) plant development is *not* under genetic control.
    B) the cells of shoots and the cells of roots have different genes.
    C) cell differentiation depends largely on the control of gene expression.
    D) a cell's environment has no effect on its differentiation.
    E) sexual reproduction is *not* necessary in plants.

Answer: C
*Topic: Concept 35.5*
*Skill: Application*

53) According to the ABC model of floral development, a showy ornamental flower with multiple sepals and petals but no stamens or carpels would express
    A) *A* genes only.
    B) *B* genes only.
    C) *C* genes only.
    D) *A* and *B* genes only.
    E) *A* and *C* genes only.

Answer: D
*Topic: Concept 35.5*
*Skill: Knowledge*

54) Suppose a feeding insect destroys only the very central portion of a developing flower bud. Which of the following statements is most likely to be true?

  A) None of the *A*, *B*, or *C* floral organ identifying genes will "turn on" as floral development proceeds.

  B) Petals formed subsequent to the insect attack will be disfigured.

  C) Stamens formed subsequent to the insect attack will be sterile.

  D) Carpels will not form in the developing flower.

  E) Only the *A* floral organ identifying gene will be affected.

Answer: D
*Topic: Concept 35.5*
*Skill: Comprehension*

# Media Activity Questions

1) In leaves, chloroplasts are found in
   A) xylem.
   B) cuticle.
   C) phloem
   D) guard cells.
   E) palisade mesophyll.

   Answer: E
   *Topic: Activity: Roots, Stems, and Leaves*

2) _____ provides cells for secondary growth.
   A) Apical meristem
   B) Secondary xylem
   C) Vascular cambium
   D) Secondary phloem
   E) The root

   Answer: C
   *Topic: Web/CD Activity: Growth*

3) Secondary growth *never* occurs in
   A) stems.
   B) roots.
   C) leaves.
   D) stems and leaves.
   E) roots and leaves.

   Answer: C
   *Topic: Web/CD Activity: Growth*

4) How is the supply of vascular cambium maintained?
   A) by the differentiation of the secondary xylem
   B) by the differentiation of the secondary phloem
   C) by the differentiation of cork
   D) by the division of cells
   E) by the differentiation of apical meristem

   Answer: D
   *Topic: Web/CD Activity: Growth*

5) _____ provides cells for primary growth.
   A) Lateral meristems
   B) Apical meristems
   C) Vascular cambium
   D) Cork cambium
   E) Xylem

   Answer: B
   *Topic: Web/CD Activity: Growth*

# Self–Quiz Questions

1) Which structure is *incorrectly* paired with its tissue system?

    A) root hair—dermal tissue

    B) palisade parenchyma—ground tissue

    C) guard cell—dermal tissue

    D) companion cell—ground tissue

    E) tracheid—vascular tissue

Answer: D

2) A vessel cell would likely lose its protoplast in which zone of growth in a root?

    A) zone of cell division

    B) zone of elongation

    C) zone of maturation

    D) root cap

    E) apical meristem

Answer: C

3) Wood consists of

    A) bark.

    B) periderm.

    C) secondary xylem.

    D) secondary phloem.

    E) cork.

Answer: C

4) Which of the following is *not* part of an older tree's bark?

    A) cork

    B) cork cambium

    C) lenticels

    D) secondary xylem

    E) secondary phloem

Answer: D

5) The phase change of an apical meristem from the juvenile to mature vegetative phase is often signaled by

    A) a change in the morphology of the leaves that are produced.

    B) the initiation of secondary growth.

    C) the formation of lateral roots.

    D) a change in the orientation of the preprophase bands and cytoplasmic microtubules in lateral meristems.

    E) the activation of floral meristem identity genes.

Answer: A

6) Which of the following arise from meristematic activity?

    A) secondary xylem

    B) leaves

    C) trichomes

    D) tubers

    E) all of the above

Answer: E

7) "Pinching off" the tops of snapdragons causes the plants to make many more flowers than they would if left alone. Why does removal of the snapdragon's top cause more flowers to form?

    A) Removal of an apical meristem causes a phase transition from vegetative to floral development.

    B) Removal of an apical meristem causes cell division to become disorganized, much like in the *fass* mutant of *Arabidopsis*.

    C) Removal of an apical meristem allows more nutrients to be delivered to floral meristems.

    D) Removal of an apical meristem causes outgrowth of lateral buds that produce extra branches, which ultimately produce flowers.

    E) Removal of an apical meristem allows the periderm to produce new lateral branches.

Answer: D

8) _____ is to xylem as _____ is to phloem.

    A) Sclerenchyma cell; parenchyma cell

    B) Apical meristem; vascular cambium

    C) Vessel element; sieve–tube member

    D) Cortex; pith

    E) Vascular cambium; cork cambium

Answer: C

9) The type of mature cell that a particular embryonic plant cell will become appears to be determined mainly by

    A) the selective loss of genes.

    B) the cell's final position in a developing organ.

    C) the cell's pattern of migration.

    D) the cell's age.

    E) the cell's particular meristematic lineage.

Answer: B

10) Based on the hypothesis presented in Figure 35.31 in your textbook, predict floral morphology of a mutant lacking activity of *B* genes.

    A) carpel-petal-petal-carpel

    B) petal-petal-petal-petal

    C) sepal-sepal-carpel-carpel

    D) sepal-carpel-carpel-sepal

    E) carpel-carpel-carpel-carpel

Answer: C

# Chapter 36   Transport in Vascular Plants

1) Which of the following would be *least* likely to affect osmosis in plants?
   A) proton pumps in the membrane
   B) a difference in solute concentrations
   C) receptor proteins in the membrane
   D) aquaporins
   E) a difference in water potential

   Answer: C
   *Topic: Concept 36.1*
   *Skill: Comprehension*

2) Active transport involves all of the following *except* the
   A) slow movement through the lipid bilayer of a membrane.
   B) pumping of solutes across the membrane.
   C) hydrolysis of ATP.
   D) transport of solute against a concentration gradient.
   E) a specific transport protein in the membrane.

   Answer: A
   *Topic: Concept 36.1*
   *Skill: Comprehension*

3) Like many plant processes, transport of various materials in plants at the cellular level requires all of the following *except*
   A) a proton gradient.
   B) ATP.
   C) specific membrane proteins.
   D) active transport.
   E) xylem membranes.

   Answer: E
   *Topic: Concept 36.1*
   *Skill: Comprehension*

4) Which of the following is *not* a function of the plasma membrane proton pump?
   A) hydrolyzes ATP
   B) produces a proton gradient
   C) generates a membrane potential
   D) equalizes the charge on each side of a membrane
   E) stores potential energy on one side of a membrane

   Answer: D
   *Topic: Concept 36.1*
   *Skill: Comprehension*

5) A unifying principle of cellular energetics that links energy-releasing processes to energy-consuming processes is
   A) active transport.
   B) chemiosmosis.
   C) ATP hydrolysis.
   D) water potential.
   E) source–sink relationships.

   Answer: B
   *Topic: Concept 36.1*
   *Skill: Knowledge*

6) Which of the following is an example of osmosis?
   A) flow of water out of a cell
   B) pumping of water into a cell
   C) flow of water between cells
   D) both A and B
   E) both A and C

   Answer: E
   *Topic: Concept 36.1*
   *Skill: Comprehension*

7) The amount and direction of movement of water in plants can *always* be predicted by measuring which of the following?

   A) air pressure

   B) rainfall

   C) proton gradients

   D) dissolved solutes

   E) water potential ($\Psi$)

Answer: E
*Topic: Concept 36.1*
*Skill: Comprehension*

8) Which of the following is *true* concerning the water potential of a plant cell?

   A) It is higher than that of air.

   B) It is equal to zero when the cell is in pure water and is turgid.

   C) It is equal to 0.23 MPa.

   D) It becomes higher when $K^+$ is actively moved into the cell.

   E) It becomes lower after the uptake of water by osmosis.

Answer: B
*Topic: Concept 36.1*
*Skill: Knowledge*

9) Your laboratory partner has an open beaker of pure water. By definition, the water potential ($\Psi$) of this water is

   A) not meaningful, because it is an open beaker and not plant tissue.

   B) a negative number set by the volume of the beaker.

   C) a positive number set by the volume of the beaker.

   D) equal to the atmospheric pressure.

   E) zero.

Answer: E
*Topic: Concept 36.1*
*Skill: Comprehension*

10) Which of the following has an effect on water potential ($\Psi$) in plants?

   A) air pressure

   B) water–attracting matrices

   C) dissolved solutes

   D) A and C only

   E) A, B, and C

Answer: E
*Topic: Concept 36.1*
*Skill: Comprehension*

11) If $\Psi_P = 0.3$ MPa and $\Psi_S = -0.45$ MPa, the resulting $\Psi$ is

   A) +0.75 MPa.

   B) –0.75 MPa.

   C) –0.15 MPa.

   D) +0.15 MPa.

   E) impossible to calculate with this information.

Answer: C
*Topic: Concept 36.1*
*Skill: Application*

12) The value for $\Psi$ in root tissue was found to be –0.15 MPa. If you take the root tissue and place it in a 0.1 $M$ solution of sucrose ($\Psi = -0.23$), net water flow would

   A) be from the tissue into the sucrose solution.

   B) be from the sucrose solution into the tissue.

   C) be in both directions and the concentrations would remain equal.

   D) occur only as ATP was hydrolyzed in the tissue.

   E) be impossible to determine from the values given here.

Answer: A
*Topic: Concept 36.1*
*Skill: Application*

13) Compared to a cell with few aquaporins in its membrane, a cell containing many aquaporins will

A) have a faster rate of osmosis.

B) have a lower water potential.

C) have a higher water potential.

D) have a faster rate of active transport.

E) be flaccid.

Answer: A
*Topic: Concept 36.1*
*Skill: Application*

14) Some botanists argue that the entire plant should be considered as a single unit rather than a composite of many individual cells. Which of the following cellular structures *cannot* be used to support this view?

A) cell wall

B) cell membrane

C) cytosol

D) tonoplast

E) symplast

Answer: D
*Topic: Concept 36.1*
*Skill: Comprehension*

15) Which of the following statements is *false* about bulk flow?

A) It is driven primarily by pressure potential.

B) It is more effective than diffusion over distances greater than 100 μm.

C) It depends on a difference in pressure potential at the source and sink.

D) It depends on the force of gravity on a column of water.

E) It may be the result of either positive or negative pressure potential.

Answer: D
*Topic: Concept 36.1*
*Skill: Comprehension*

16) Which of the following statements about xylem is *incorrect*?

A) It conducts material upward.

B) It conducts materials within dead cells.

C) It transports mainly sugars and amino acids.

D) It has a lower water potential than soil does.

E) No energy input from the plant is required for xylem transport.

Answer: C
*Topic: Concept 36.2*
*Skill: Knowledge*

17) Which of the following would likely *not* contribute to the surface area available for water absorption from the soil by a plant root system?

A) root hairs

B) endodermis

C) mycorrhizae

D) fungi associated with the roots

E) fibrous arrangement of the roots

Answer: B
*Topic: Concept 36.2*
*Skill: Comprehension*

18) Root hairs are most important to a plant because they

A) anchor a plant in the soil.

B) store starches.

C) increase the surface area for absorption.

D) provide a habitat for nitrogen–fixing bacteria.

E) contain xylem tissue.

Answer: C
*Topic: Concept 36.2*
*Skill: Knowledge*

19) What is the role of proton pumps in root hair cells?

   A) establish ATP gradients

   B) acquire minerals from the soil

   C) pressurize xylem transport

   D) eliminate excess electrons

   E) A and D only

Answer: B
*Topic: Concept 36.2*
*Skill: Comprehension*

20) In plant roots, the Casparian strip is *correctly* described by which of the following?

   A) It is located in the walls between endodermal cells and cortex cells.

   B) It provides energy for the active transport of minerals into the stele from the cortex.

   C) It ensures that all minerals are absorbed from the soil in equal amounts.

   D) It ensures that all water and dissolved substances must pass through a cell before entering the stele.

   E) It provides increased surface area for the absorption of mineral nutrients.

Answer: D
*Topic: Concept 36.2*
*Skill: Comprehension*

21) All of the following describe an important component of the long-distance transport process in plants *except*

   A) cohesion-tension-transpiration.

   B) osmosis.

   C) endodermis Casparian strip.

   D) active transport.

   E) bulk flow from source to sink.

Answer: C
*Topic: Concept 36.2*
*Skill: Comprehension*

22) Pine seedlings grown in sterile potting soil grow much slower than seedlings grown in soil from the area where the seeds were collected. This is most likely because

   A) the sterilization process kills the root hairs as they emerge from the seedling.

   B) the normal symbiotic fungi are not present in the sterilized soil.

   C) sterilization removes essential nutrients from the soil.

   D) water and mineral uptake is faster when mycorrhizae are present.

   E) both B and D

Answer: E
*Topic: Concept 36.2*
*Skill: Comprehension*

23) A water molecule could move all the way through a plant from soil to root to leaf to air and pass through a living cell only once. This living cell would be a part of which structure?

   A) the Casparian strip

   B) a guard cell

   C) the root epidermis

   D) the endodermis

   E) the root cortex

Answer: D
*Topic: Concept 36.2*
*Skill: Comprehension*

24) The following factors may sometimes play a role in the movement of sap through xylem. Which one depends on the direct expenditure of ATP by the plant?

A) capillarity of water within the xylem

B) evaporation of water from leaves

C) cohesion among water molecules

D) concentration of ions in the symplast

E) bulk flow of water in the root apoplast

Answer: D
*Topic: Concept 36.2*
*Skill: Knowledge*

25) The soil solution is usually very dilute. After fertilizing a lawn, the concentration of salts in the soil builds up. What would be a response of grass roots to this increase?

A) Water absorption would increase because of the higher solute potential in the soil.

B) $K^+$ will be actively transported into the root cells.

C) Root cells will immediately dehydrate and die.

D) Nutrient salts will diffuse into the root faster.

E) There will be no noticeable effect.

Answer: B
*Topic: Concept 36.2*
*Skill: Application*

26) What is the main cause of guttation in plants?

A) root pressure

B) transpiration

C) pressure flow in phloem

D) plant injury

E) condensation of atmospheric water

Answer: A
*Topic: Concept 36.2*
*Skill: Knowledge*

27) One is most likely to see guttation in small plants when the

A) transpiration rates are high.

B) root pressure exceeds transpiration pull.

C) preceding evening was hot, windy, and dry.

D) water potential in the stele of the root is high.

E) roots are not absorbing minerals from the soil.

Answer: B
*Topic: Concept 36.2*
*Skill: Knowledge*

28) What is the main force by which most of the water within xylem vessels moves toward the top of a tree?

A) active transport of ions into the stele

B) atmospheric pressure on roots

C) evaporation of water through stoma

D) the force of root pressure

E) osmosis in the root

Answer: C
*Topic: Concept 36.3*
*Skill: Knowledge*

29) In which plant cell or tissue would the *pressure* component of water potential most often be negative?

A) leaf mesophyll cell

B) stem xylem

C) stem phloem

D) root cortex cell

E) root epidermis

Answer: B
*Topic: Concept 36.3*
*Skill: Comprehension*

30) Water potential is generally most negative in which of the following parts of a plant?

A) mesophyll cells of the leaf

B) xylem vessels in leaves

C) xylem vessels in roots

D) cells of the root cortex

E) root hairs

Answer: A
*Topic: Concept 36.3*
*Skill: Comprehension*

31) Which of the following has the *lowest* (most negative) water potential?

A) soil

B) root xylem

C) trunk xylem

D) leaf cell walls

E) leaf air spaces

Answer: E
*Topic: Concept 36.3*
*Skill: Comprehension*

32) Which of the following is responsible for the cohesion of water molecules?

A) hydrogen bonds between the oxygen atoms of a water molecule and cellulose in a vessel cell

B) covalent bonds between the hydrogen atoms of two adjacent water molecules

C) hydrogen bonds between the oxygen atom of one water molecule and a hydrogen atom of another water molecule

D) covalent bonds between the oxygen atom of one water molecule and a hydrogen atom of another water molecule

E) Cohesion has nothing to do with the bonding but is the result of the tight packing of the water molecules in the xylem column.

Answer: C
*Topic: Concept 36.3*
*Skill: Comprehension*

33) Transpiration in plants requires all of the following *except*

A) adhesion of water molecules to cellulose.

B) cohesion between water molecules.

C) evaporation of water molecules.

D) active transport through xylem cells.

E) transport through tracheids.

Answer: D
*Topic: Concept 36.3*
*Skill: Comprehension*

34) Which of the following statements about transport in plants is *false*?

A) Weak bonding between water molecules and the walls of xylem vessels or tracheids helps support the columns of water in the xylem.

B) Hydrogen bonding between water molecules, which results in the high cohesion of the water, is essential for the rise of water in tall trees.

C) Although some angiosperm plants develop considerable root pressure, this is not sufficient to raise water to the tops of tall trees.

D) Most plant physiologists now agree that the pull from the top of the plant resulting from transpiration is sufficient, when combined with the cohesion of water, to explain the rise of water in the xylem in even the tallest trees.

E) Gymnosperms can sometimes develop especially high root pressure, which may account for the rise of water in tall pine trees without transpiration pull.

Answer: E
*Topic: Concept 36.3*
*Skill: Comprehension*

35) Active transport would be *least* important in the normal functioning of which of the following plant tissue types?

A) leaf transfer cells

B) stem xylem

C) root endodermis

D) leaf mesophyll

E) root phloem

Answer: B
*Topic: Concept 36.3*
*Skill: Comprehension*

36) Which of the following statements is *false* concerning the xylem?

A) Xylem tracheids and vessels fulfill their vital function only after their death.

B) The cell walls of the tracheids are greatly strengthened with cellulose fibrils forming thickened rings or spirals.

C) Water molecules are transpired from the cells of the leaves, and replaced by water molecules in the xylem pulled up from the roots due to the cohesion of water molecules.

D) Movement of materials is by mass flow; materials move owing to a turgor pressure gradient from "source" to "sink."

E) In the morning, sap in the xylem begins to move first in the twigs of the upper portion of the tree, and later in the lower trunk.

Answer: D
*Topic: Concept 36.3*
*Skill: Comprehension*

37) Xylem vessels, found in angiosperms, have a much greater internal diameter than tracheids, the only xylem conducting cells found in gymnosperms. The tallest living trees, redwoods, are gymnosperms. Which of the following is an advantage of tracheids over vessels for long–distance transport to great heights?

A) Adhesive forces are proportionally greater in narrower cylinders than in wider cylinders.

B) The smaller the diameter of the xylem, the more likely cavitation will occur.

C) Cohesive forces are greater in narrow tubes than in wide tubes of the same height.

D) Only A and C are correct.

E) A, B, and C are correct.

Answer: D
*Topic: Concept 36.3*
*Skill: Comprehension*

38) Water rises in plants primarily by the cohesion–tension model. Which of the following is *not* true about this model?

A) Water loss (transpiration) is the driving force for water movement.

B) The "tension" of this model represents the excitability of the xylem cells.

C) Cohesion represents the tendency for water molecules to stick together by hydrogen bonds.

D) The physical forces in the capillary-sized xylem cells make it easier to overcome gravity.

E) The water potential of the air is more negative than the xylem.

Answer: B
*Topic: Concept 36.3*
*Skill: Comprehension*

39) Assume that a particular chemical interferes with the establishment and maintenance of proton gradients across the membranes of plant cells. All of the following processes would be directly affected by this chemical *except*

A) photosynthesis.

B) phloem loading.

C) xylem transport.

D) cellular respiration.

E) stomatal opening.

Answer: C
*Topic: Concept 36.3*
*Skill: Application*

40) Guard cells do which of the following?

A) protect the endodermis

B) accumulate $K^+$ and close the stomata

C) contain chloroplasts that import $K^+$ directly into the cells

D) guard against mineral loss through the stomata

E) help balance the photosynthesis–transpiration compromise

Answer: E
*Topic: Concept 36.4*
*Skill: Knowledge*

41) All of the following normally enter the plant through the roots *except*

A) carbon dioxide.

B) nitrogen.

C) potassium.

D) water.

E) calcium.

Answer: A
*Topic: Concept 36.4*
*Skill: Comprehension*

42) Photosynthesis begins to decline when leaves wilt because

A) flaccid cells are incapable of photosynthesis.

B) $CO_2$ accumulates in the leaves and inhibits photosynthesis.

C) there is insufficient water for photolysis during light reactions.

D) stomata close, preventing $CO_2$ entry into the leaf.

E) the chlorophyll of flaccid cells cannot absorb light.

Answer: D
*Topic: Concept 36.4*
*Skill: Application*

43) The water lost during transpiration is an unfortunate side effect of the plant's exchange of gases. However, the plant derives some benefit from this water loss in the form of

A) evaporative cooling.

B) mineral transport.

C) increased turgor.

D) A and B only

E) A, B, and C

Answer: D
*Topic: Concept 36.4*
*Skill: Knowledge*

44) Ignoring all other factors, what kind of day would result in the fastest delivery of water and minerals to the leaves of a tree?

A) cool, dry day

B) warm, dry day

C) warm, humid day

D) cool, humid day

E) very hot, dry, windy day

Answer: B
*Topic: Concept 36.4*
*Skill: Comprehension*

45) If the guard cells and surrounding epidermal cells in a plant are deficient in potassium ions, all of the following would occur *except*

A) photosynthesis would decrease.

B) roots would take up less water.

C) phloem transport rates would decrease.

D) leaf temperatures would decrease.

E) stomata would be closed.

Answer: D
*Topic: Concept 36.4*
*Skill: Application*

46) The opening of stomata is thought to involve

A) an increase in the osmotic concentration of the guard cells.

B) a decrease in the osmotic concentration of the stoma.

C) active transport of water out of the guard cells.

D) decreased turgor pressure in guard cells.

E) movement of $K^+$ from guard cells.

Answer: A
*Topic: Concept 36.4*
*Skill: Knowledge*

47) Which of the following experimental procedures would most likely reduce transpiration while allowing the normal growth of a plant?

A) subjecting the leaves of the plant to a partial vacuum

B) increasing the level of carbon dioxide around the plant

C) putting the plant in drier soil

D) decreasing the relative humidity around the plant

E) injecting potassium ions into the guard cells of the plant

Answer: B
*Topic: Concept 36.4*
*Skill: Application*

48) Guard cells are the only cells in the epidermis that contain chloroplasts and can undergo photosynthesis. This is important because

A) chloroplasts sense when light is available so that guard cells will open.

B) photosynthesis provides the energy necessary for contractile proteins to flex and open the guard cells.

C) guard cells will produce the $O_2$ necessary to power active transport.

D) ATP is required to power proton pumps in the guard cell membranes.

E) both A and C

Answer: D
*Topic: Concept 36.4*
*Skill: Comprehension*

49) All of the following are adaptations that help reduce water loss from a plant *except*

A) transpiration.

B) sunken stomata.

C) $C_4$ photosynthesis.

D) small, thick leaves.

E) crassulacean acid metabolism.

Answer: A
*Topic: Concept 36.4*
*Skill: Knowledge*

50) Which of the following best explains why CAM plants are not tall?

A) They would be unable to move water and minerals to the top of the plant during the day.

B) They would be unable to supply sufficient sucrose for active transport of minerals into the roots during the day or night.

C) Transpiration occurs only at night, and this would cause a highly negative $\Psi$ in the roots of a tall plant during the day.

D) Since the stomata are closed in the leaves, the Casparian strip is closed in the endodermis of the root.

E) With the stomata open at night, the transpiration rate would limit plant height.

Answer: A
*Topic: Concept 36.4*
*Skill: Application*

51) As a biologist, it is your job to look for plants that have evolved structures with a selective advantage in dry, hot conditions. Which of the following adaptations wouldbe *least* likely to meet your objective?

    A) CAM plants that grow rapidly

    B) small, thick leaves with stomata on the lower surface

    C) a thick cuticle on fleshy leaves

    D) large, fleshy stems with the ability to carry out photosynthesis

    E) plants that do not produce abscisic acid and have a short, thick tap root

Answer: E
*Topic: Concept 36.4*
*Skill: Application*

52) Phloem transport of sucrose can be described as going from "source to sink." Which of the following would *not* normally function as a sink?

    A) growing leaf

    B) growing root

    C) storage organ in summer

    D) mature leaf

    E) shoot tip

Answer: D
*Topic: Concept 36.5*
*Skill: Comprehension*

53) Which of the following is a *correct* statement about sugar movement in phloem?

    A) Diffusion can account for the observed rates of transport.

    B) Movement can occur both upward and downward in the plant.

    C) Sugar is translocated from sinks to sources.

    D) Only phloem cells with nuclei can perform sugar movement.

    E) Sugar transport does not require energy.

Answer: B
*Topic: Concept 36.5*
*Skill: Knowledge*

54) Phloem transport is described as being from source to sink. Which of the following would most accurately complete this statement about phloem transport as applied to most plants in the late spring? Phloem transports _____ from the _____ source to the _____ sink.

    A) amino acids; root; mycorrhizae

    B) sugars; leaf; apical meristem

    C) nucleic acids; flower; root

    D) proteins; root; leaf

    E) sugars; stem; root

Answer: B
*Topic: Concept 36.5*
*Skill: Comprehension*

55) Arrange the following five events in an order that explains the mass flow of materials in the phloem.
   1. Water diffuses into the sieve tubes.
   2. Leaf cells produce sugar by photosynthesis.
   3. Solutes are actively transported into sieve tubes.
   4. Sugar is transported from cell to cell in the leaf.
   5. Sugar moves down the stem.

   A) 2, 1, 4, 3, 5
   B) 1, 2, 3, 4, 5
   C) 2, 4, 3, 1, 5
   D) 4, 2, 1, 3, 5
   E) 2, 4, 1, 3, 5

   Answer: C
   *Topic: Concept 36.5*
   *Skill: Comprehension*

56) Water flows into the source end of a sieve tube because
   A) sucrose has diffused into the sieve tube, making it hypertonic.
   B) sucrose has been actively transported into the sieve tube, making it hypertonic.
   C) water pressure outside the sieve tube forces in water.
   D) the companion cell of a sieve tube actively pumps in water.
   E) sucrose has been dumped from the sieve tube by active transport.

   Answer: B
   *Topic: Concept 36.5*
   *Skill: Comprehension*

57) Which one of the following statements about transport of nutrients in phloem is *false*?
   A) Solute particles can be actively transported into phloem at the source.
   B) Companion cells control the rate and direction of movement of phloem sap.
   C) Differences in osmotic concentration at the source and sink cause a hydrostatic pressure gradient to be formed.
   D) A sink is that part of the plant where a particular solute is consumed or stored.
   E) A sink may be located anywhere in the plant.

   Answer: B
   *Topic: Concept 36.5*
   *Skill: Knowledge*

58) According to the pressure flow hypothesis of phloem transport,
   A) solute moves from a high concentration in the "source" to a lower concentration in the "sink."
   B) water is actively transported into the "source" region of the phloem to create the turgor pressure needed.
   C) the combination of a high turgor pressure in the "source" and transpiration water loss from the "sink" moves solutes through phloem conduits.
   D) the formation of starch from sugar in the "sink" increases the osmotic concentration.
   E) the pressure in the phloem of a root is normally greater than the pressure in the phloem of a leaf.

   Answer: A
   *Topic: Concept 36.5*
   *Skill: Application*

59) As predicted by the pressure flow hypothesis of translocation in plants, phloem exudates from the severed stylets of aphids near photosynthetic cells are sites of

   A) relatively high hydrostatic pressure.

   B) relatively low hydrostatic pressure.

   C) relatively high concentrations of organic nutrients.

   D) active pumping of sucrose out of the sieve tube.

   E) A and C only

Answer: E
*Topic: Concept 36.5*
*Skill: Comprehension*

60) Plants do not have a circulatory system like that of some animals. If a given water molecule did "circulate" (that is, go from one point in a plant to another and back), it would require the activity of

   A) only the xylem.

   B) only the phloem.

   C) only the endodermis.

   D) both the xylem and the endodermis.

   E) both the xylem and the phloem.

Answer: E
*Topic: Concept 36.5*
*Skill: Application*

61) In the pressure flow hypothesis of translocation, what causes the pressure?

   A) root pressure

   B) the osmotic uptake of water by sieve tubes at the source

   C) the accumulation of minerals and water by the stele in the root

   D) the osmotic uptake of water by the sieve tubes of the sink

   E) hydrostatic pressure in xylem vessels

Answer: B
*Topic: Concept 36.5*
*Skill: Comprehension*

# Media Activity Questions

1) Which of these involves a symbiotic relationship?

   A) root hairs

   B) apoplasts

   C) Casparian strips

   D) mycorrhizae

   E) symplasts

   Answer: D
   *Topic: Web/CD Activity: Transport of Xylem Sap*

2) _____ increase the surface area of roots.

   A) Symplasts

   B) Apoplasts

   C) Mycorrhizae

   D) Root hairs

   E) Root hairs and mycorrhizae

   Answer: E
   *Topic: Web/CD Activity: Transport of Xylem Sap*

3) In roots the _____ forces water and solutes to pass through the plasma membranes of _____ cells before entering the _____.

   A) Casparian strip; ectoderm; xylem

   B) Casparian strip; endodermis; xylem

   C) Casparian strip; endodermis; phloem

   D) xylem; endodermis; Casparian strip

   E) transpiration; endodermis; xylem

   Answer: B
   *Topic: Web/CD Activity: Transport of Xylem Sap*

4) Sugar moves from leaves into the _____ of _____ by _____.

   A) sieve-tube members; phloem; active transport

   B) sieve-tube members; xylem; active transport

   C) sieve-tube members; phloem; diffusion

   D) tracheids; phloem; active transport

   E) tracheids; phloem; diffusion

   Answer: A
   *Topic: Activity: Translocation of Phloem Sap*

5) The water pressure that pulses water and sugar from sugar source to sugar sink is referred to as _____.

   A) translocation

   B) bulk flow

   C) transpiration

   D) root pressure

   E) solute pressure

   Answer: B
   *Topic: Activity: Translocation of Phloem Sap*

# Self-Quiz Questions

1) Which of the following would *not* contribute to water uptake by a plant cell?

   A) an increase in the water potential ($\Psi$) of the surrounding solution

   B) a decrease in pressure on the cell exerted by the wall

   C) the uptake of solutes by the cell

   D) a decrease in $\Psi$ of the cytoplasm

   E) an increase in tension on the solution that surrounds the cell

   Answer: E

2) Stomata open when guard cells

   A) sense an increase in $CO_2$ in the air spaces of the leaf.

   B) flop open because of a decrease in turgor pressure.

   C) become more turgid because of an influx of $K^+$, followed by the osmotic entry of water.

   D) close aquaporins, preventing uptake of water.

   E) accumulate water by active transport.

   Answer: C

3) Which of the following is *not* part of the transpiration–cohesion–tension mechanism for the ascent of xylem sap?

   A) the loss of water from the mesophyll cells, which initiates a pull of water molecules from neighboring cells

   B) the transfer of transpirational pull from one water molecule to the next, owing to the cohesion caused by hydrogen bonds

   C) the hydrophilic walls of the narrow tracheids and xylem vessels that help maintain the column of water against the force of gravity

   D) the active pumping of water into the xylem of roots

   E) the lowering of water potential in the surface film of mesophyll cells due to transpiration

   Answer: D

4) Which of the following does *not* appear to involve active transport across membranes?

   A) the movement of mineral nutrients from the apoplast to the symplast

   B) the movement of sugar from mesophyll cells into sieve-tube members in maize

   C) the movement of sugar from one sieve-tube member to the next

   D) $K^+$ uptake by guard cells during stomatal opening

   E) the movement of mineral nutrients into cells of the root cortex

   Answer: C

5) Movement of phloem sap from a sugar source to sugar sink

    A) occurs through the apoplast of sieve-tube members.

    B) may translocate sugars from the breakdown of stored starch in a root up to developing shoots.

    C) is similar to the flow of xylem sap in depending on tension, or negative pressure.

    D) depends on the active pumping of water into sieve tubes at the source end.

    E) results mainly from diffusion.

Answer: B

6) The productivity of a crop declines when leaves begin to wilt mainly because

    A) the chlorophyll of wilting leaves decomposes.

    B) flaccid mesophyll cells are incapable of photosynthesis.

    C) stomata close, preventing $CO_2$ from entering the leaf.

    D) photolysis, the water–splitting step of photosynthesis, cannot occur when there is a water deficiency.

    E) an accumulation of $CO_2$ in the leaf inhibits the enzymes required for photosynthesis.

Answer: C

7) Imagine cutting a live twig from a tree and examining the cut surface of the twig with a magnifying glass. You locate the vascular tissue and observe a growing droplet of fluid exuding from the cut surface. This fluid is probably

    A) phloem sap.

    B) xylem sap.

    C) guttation fluid.

    D) fluid of the transpiration stream.

    E) make up entirely of vascular sap from nonvascular cells.

Answer: A

8) Which structure or compartment is *not* part of the plant's apoplast?

    A) the lumen of a xylem vessel

    B) the lumen of a sieve tube

    C) the cell wall of a mesophyll cell

    D) the cell wall of a transfer cell

    E) the cell wall of a root hair

Answer: B

9) Which of the following is *not* an adaptation that enhances the uptake of water and minerals by roots?

    A) mycorrhizae, the symbiotic associations of roots and fungi

    B) root hairs, which increase surface area near root tips

    C) selective uptake of minerals by xylem vessels

    D) selective uptake of minerals by cortical cells

    E) plasmodesmata, which facilitate symplastic transport from root hairs to the endodermis

Answer: C

10) A plant cell with a solute potential of –0.65 MPa maintains a constant volume when bathed in a solution that has a solute potential of –0.30 MPa and is in an open container. What do we know about the cell?

    A) The cell has a pressure potential of +0.65 MPa.

    B) The cell has a water potential of –0.65 MPa.

    C) The cell has a pressure potential of +0.35 MPa.

    D) The cell has a pressure potential of +0.30 MPa.

    E) The cell has a water potential of 0 MPa.

Answer: C

# Chapter 37   Plant Nutrition

1) Which of the following describes the fate of most of the water taken up by a plant?
   - A) It is used as a solvent.
   - B) It is used as a hydrogen source in photosynthesis.
   - C) It is lost during transpiration.
   - D) It makes cell elongation possible.
   - E) It is used to keep cells turgid.

   Answer: C
   *Topic: Concept 37.1*
   *Skill: Knowledge*

2) Most of the dry weight of a plant is the result of uptake of
   - A) water and minerals through root hairs.
   - B) water and minerals through mycorrhizae.
   - C) $CO_2$ through stomata in leaves.
   - D) $CO_2$ and $O_2$ through stomata in leaves.
   - E) both A and B

   Answer: C
   *Topic: Concept 37.1*
   *Skill: Comprehension*

3) Organic molecules make up what percentage of the dry weight of a plant?
   - A) 6%
   - B) 17%
   - C) 67%
   - D) 81%
   - E) 96%

   Answer: E
   *Topic: Concept 37.1*
   *Skill: Knowledge*

4) You are conducting an experiment on plant growth. You take a plant fresh from the soil that weighs 5 kg. Then you dry the plant overnight and determine the dry weight to be 1 kg. Of this dry weight, how much would you expect to be made up of inorganic minerals?
   - A) 1 gram
   - B) 5 grams
   - C) 50 grams
   - D) 75 grams
   - E) 1 kg

   Answer: C
   *Topic: Concept 37.1*
   *Skill: Application*

5) In hydroponic culture, what is the purpose of bubbling air into the solute?
   - A) to keep dissolved nutrients evenly distributed
   - B) to provide oxygen to root cells
   - C) to inhibit the growth of aerobic algae
   - D) to inhibit the growth of anaerobic bacteria
   - E) both C and D

   Answer: B
   *Topic: Concept 37.1*
   *Skill: Application*

6) When performing a mineral nutrition experiment, researchers use water from a glass still. Why is it *not* a good idea to use regular distilled water from a stainless steel still?

A) With a steel still, lime deposits from hard water will build up too quickly.

B) Salts in the water corrode steel more quickly than glass.

C) Metal ions dissolving off the steel may serve as micronutrients.

D) A glass still allows the distillation process to be observed.

E) There is no difference; both kinds of stills produce distilled water.

Answer: C
*Topic: Concept 37.1*
*Skill: Application*

7) Which of the following essential nutrients does *not* have a role in photosynthesis, either as a structural component or in the synthesis of a component?

A) Fe

B) Bo

C) Mg

D) H

E) K

Answer: E
*Topic: Concept 37.1*
*Skill: Comprehension*

8) Which of the following is of *least* concern to a researcher in a mineral nutrition experiment?

A) purity of the chemicals used to make the nutrient solutions

B) purity of the water used to make the nutrient solutions

C) chemical inertness of the container used to make and store the nutrient solutions

D) ability of a laboratory balance to weigh very small quantities of chemicals

E) medium in which the test seedlings were grown

Answer: D
*Topic: Concept 37.1*
*Skill: Application*

9) Which two elements make up more than 90% of the dry weight of plants?

A) carbon and nitrogen

B) oxygen and hydrogen

C) nitrogen and oxygen

D) oxygen and carbon

E) carbon and potassium

Answer: D
*Topic: Concept 37.1*
*Skill: Comprehension*

10) The bulk of a plant's dry weight is derived from

A) soil minerals.

B) $CO_2$.

C) the hydrogen from $H_2O$.

D) the oxygen from $H_2O$.

E) the uptake of organic nutrients from the soil.

Answer: B
*Topic: Concept 37.1*
*Skill: Comprehension*

11) What are the three main elements on which plant growth and development depend?

   A) nitrogen; carbon; oxygen

   B) potassium; carbon; oxygen

   C) oxygen; carbon; hydrogen

   D) phosphorus; nitrogen; oxygen

   E) sulfur; nitrogen; phosphorus

   Answer: C
   *Topic: Concept 37.1*
   *Skill: Application*

12) A growing plant exhibits chlorosis of the leaves of the entire plant. The chlorosis is probably due to a deficiency of which of the following macronutrients?

   A) carbon

   B) oxygen

   C) nitrogen

   D) calcium

   E) hydrogen

   Answer: C
   *Topic: Concept 37.1*
   *Skill: Comprehension*

13) Which of the following elements is *incorrectly* paired with its function in a plant?

   A) nitrogen—component of nucleic acids, proteins, hormones, coenzymes

   B) magnesium—component of chlorophyll; activates many enzymes

   C) phosphorus—component of nucleic acids, phospholipids, ATP, several coenzymes

   D) potassium—cofactor functional in protein synthesis; osmosis; operation of stomata

   E) sulfur—component of DNA; activates some enzymes

   Answer: E
   *Topic: Concept 37.1*
   *Skill: Application*

14) In the nutrition of a plant, which element is classified as a macronutrient?

   A) zinc

   B) chlorine

   C) calcium

   D) molybdenum

   E) manganese

   Answer: C
   *Topic: Concept 37.1*
   *Skill: Knowledge*

*For the following questions, match the element to its major function in plants. Choices may be used more than once.*

   Function
   A. component of lignin-biosynthetic enzymes
   B. component of DNA and RNA
   C. active in chlorophyll formation
   D. active in amino acid formation
   E. formation and stability of cell walls

15) zinc

   Answer: C
   *Topic: Concept 37.1*
   *Skill: Knowledge*

16) nitrogen

   Answer: B
   *Topic: Concept 37.1*
   *Skill: Knowledge*

17) copper

   Answer: A
   *Topic: Concept 37.1*
   *Skill: Knowledge*

18) Reddish–purple coloring of leaves, especially along the margins of young leaves, is a typical symptom of deficiency of which element?

A) C

B) $M^{++}$

C) N

D) P

E) $K^+$

Answer: D
*Topic: Concept 37.1*
*Skill: Knowledge*

19) Which of the following best describes the general role of micronutrients in plants?

A) They are cofactors in enzymatic reactions.

B) They are necessary for essential regulatory functions.

C) They prevent chlorosis.

D) They are components of nucleic acids.

E) They are necessary for the formation of cell walls.

Answer: A
*Topic: Concept 37.1*
*Skill: Knowledge*

20) Which of the following is *not* true of micronutrients in plants?

A) They are the elements required in relatively small amounts.

B) They are required for a plant to grow from a seed and complete its life cycle.

C) They generally help in catalytic functions in the plant.

D) They are the essential elements of small size and molecular weight.

E) Overdoses of them can be toxic.

Answer: D
*Topic: Concept 37.1*
*Skill: Application*

21) What is meant by the term *chlorosis*?

A) the uptake of the micronutrient chlorine by a plant

B) the formation of chlorophyll within the thylakoid membranes of a plant

C) the yellowing of leaves due to decreased chlorophyll production

D) a contamination of glassware in hydroponic culture

E) release of negatively charged minerals such as chloride from clay particles in soil

Answer: C
*Topic: Concept 37.1*
*Skill: Knowledge*

22) If an African violet has chlorosis, which of the following elements might be a useful addition to the soil?

A) chlorine

B) molybdenum

C) copper

D) iodine

E) magnesium

Answer: E
*Topic: Concept 37.1*
*Skill: Application*

23) Iron deficiency is often indicated by chlorosis in newly formed leaves. This suggests that

A) iron is an immobile nutrient in plants.

B) iron is tied up in formed chlorophyll molecules.

C) the concentration of iron in the xylem sap decreases the further it is transported from the source in the soil.

D) A and B only

E) A, B, and C

Answer: A
*Topic: Concept 37.1*
*Skill: Comprehension*

24) There are several properties of a soil in which typical plants would grow well. Of the following, which would be the *least* conducive to plant growth?

   A) abundant humus

   B) numerous soil organisms

   C) high clay content

   D) high porosity

   E) high cation exchange capacity

Answer: C
*Topic: Concept 37.2*
*Skill: Knowledge*

25) A soil well suited for the growth of most plants would have all of the following properties *except*

   A) abundant humus.

   B) air spaces.

   C) good drainage.

   D) high cation exchange capacity.

   E) a high pH.

Answer: E
*Topic: Concept 37.2*
*Skill: Knowledge*

26) What soil(s) is(are) the most fertile?

   A) humus only

   B) loam only

   C) silt only

   D) clay only

   E) both humus and loam

Answer: E
*Topic: Concept 37.2*
*Skill: Knowledge*

*Figure 37.1 shows the results of a study to determine the effect of soil air spaces on plant growth. Use these data to answer the following questions.*

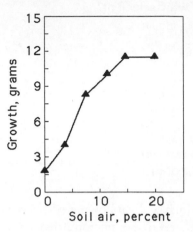

**Figure 37.1**

27) The best conclusion from the data in Figure 37.1 is that the plant

   A) grows best without air in the soil.

   B) grows fastest in 5 to 10% air.

   C) grows best in air levels above 15%.

   D) does not respond differently to different levels of air in the soil.

   E) would grow to 24 grams in 40% soil air.

Answer: B
*Topic: Concept 37.2*
*Skill: Application*

28) The best explanation for the shape of this growth response curve is that

   A) the plant requires air in the soil for photosynthesis.

   B) the roots are able to absorb more nitrogen ($N_2$) in high levels of air.

   C) most of the decrease in weight at low air levels is due to transpiration from the leaves.

   D) increased soil air produces more root mass in the soil but does not affect the top stems and leaves.

   E) the roots require oxygen for respiration and growth.

Answer: E
*Topic: Concept 37.2*
*Skill: Comprehension*

29) Why does overwatering a plant kill it?

   A) Water does not have all the necessary minerals a plant needs to grow.

   B) Water neutralizes the pH of the soil.

   C) The roots cannot get air.

   D) Water will attract parasites.

   E) Water will form hydrogen bonds with the root of the cell wall.

Answer: C
*Topic: Concept 37.2*
*Skill: Comprehension*

30) What should be added to soil to prevent minerals from leaching away?

   A) humus

   B) sand

   C) mycorrhizae

   D) nitrogen

   E) silt

Answer: A
*Topic: Concept 37.2*
*Skill: Knowledge*

31) Which soil mineral is most likely leached away during a hard rain?

   A) $Na^+$

   B) $K^+$

   C) $CA^{++}$

   D) $NO_3^-$

   E) $H^+$

Answer: D
*Topic: Concept 37.2*
*Skill: Comprehension*

32) All of the following contributed to the dust bowl in the American southwest during the 1930s *except*

   A) overgrazing by cattle.

   B) cutting of mature trees.

   C) plowing of native grasses.

   D) planting of field crops.

   E) lack of soil moisture.

Answer: B
*Topic: Concept 37.2*
*Skill: Knowledge*

33) The N–P–K percentages on a package of fertilizer refer to the

   A) total protein content of the three major ingredients of the fertilizer.

   B) percentages of manure collected from different types of animals.

   C) relative percentages of organic and inorganic nutrients in the fertilizer.

   D) percentages of three important mineral nutrients.

   E) proportions of three different nitrogen sources.

Answer: D
*Topic: Concept 37.2*
*Skill: Knowledge*

In west Texas, cotton has become an important crop in the last several decades. However, in this hot, dry part of the country there is little rainfall, so farmers irrigate their cotton fields. They must also regularly fertilize the cotton fields because the soil is very sandy. Figure 37.2 shows the record of annual productivity (measured in kilograms of cotton per hectare of land) since 1960 in a west Texas cotton field. Use these data to answer the following questions.

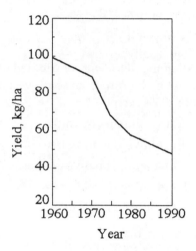

**Figure 37.2**

34) Based on the information provided above, what is the most likely cause of the decline in productivity?
   A) The farmer used the wrong kind of fertilizer.
   B) The cotton is developing a resistance to the fertilizer and to irrigation water.
   C) Water has accumulated in the soil due to irrigation.
   D) The soil has become hyperosmotic to the roots due to salination.
   E) The rate of photosynthesis has declined due to irrigation.

Answer: D
*Topic: Concept 37.2*
*Skill: Application*

35) If you were the county agriculture agent, what would be the best advice you could give the farmer who owns the field under study in Figure 37.2?
   A) Plant a variety of cotton that requires less water and can tolerate salinity.
   B) Continue to fertilize, but stop irrigating and rely on rainfall.
   C) Continue to irrigate, but stop fertilizing and rely on organic nutrients in the soil.
   D) Continue to fertilize and irrigate, but add the nitrogen–fixing bacteria *Rhizobium* to the irrigation water until the productivity increases.
   E) Add acid to the soil and increase its cation exchange capabilities so more nutrients are retained in the soil.

Answer: A
*Topic: Concept 37.2*
*Skill: Application*

36) A young farmer purchases some land in a relatively arid area and is interested in earning a reasonable profit for many years. Which of the following strategies would best allow such a goal to be achieved?
   A) establishing an extensive irrigation system
   B) using plenty of the best fertilizers
   C) finding a way to sell all parts of crop plants
   D) selecting crops adapted to arid areas
   E) converting hillsides into fields

Answer: D
*Topic: Concept 37.2*
*Skill: Application*

37) A farming commitment that embraces a variety of methods that are conservation-minded, environmentally safe, and profitable is called

A) hydroponics.

B) nitrogen fixation.

C) responsible irrigation.

D) genetic engineering.

E) sustainable agriculture.

Answer: E
*Topic: Concept 37.2*
*Skill: Knowledge*

38) An early use of indicator plants (plants that tolerate high levels of heavy metals in the soil) was to locate potential profitable areas to mine for those minerals. A current use for such plants is

A) to help locate suitable sites for toxic waste storage.

B) bioremediation to help clean up mine spoils.

C) to minimize soil erosion in arid lands.

D) nitrogen fixation by symbiotic bacteria in root nodules.

E) all of the above

Answer: B
*Topic: Concept 37.2*
*Skill: Knowledge*

39) Nitrogen fixation is a process that

A) recycles nitrogen compounds from dead and decaying materials.

B) converts ammonia to nitrate.

C) releases nitrate from the rock substrate.

D) converts nitrogen gas into ammonia.

E) both A and B

Answer: D
*Topic: Concept 37.3*
*Skill: Comprehension*

40) Why is nitrogen fixation such an important process?

A) Nitrogen fixation can only be done by certain prokaryotes.

B) Fixed nitrogen is most often the limiting factor in plant growth.

C) Nitrogen fixation is very expensive in terms of metabolic energy.

D) Nitrogen fixers are sometimes symbiotic with legumes.

E) Nitrogen-fixing capacity can be genetically engineered.

Answer: B
*Topic: Concept 37.3*
*Skill: Comprehension*

41) In what way do nitrogen compounds differ from other minerals needed by plants?

A) Only nitrogen can be lost from the soil.

B) Only nitrogen requires the action of bacteria to be made available to plants.

C) Only nitrogen is needed for protein synthesis.

D) Only nitrogen is held by cation exchange capacity in the soil.

E) Only nitrogen can be absorbed by root hairs.

Answer: B
*Topic: Concept 37.3*
*Skill: Knowledge*

42) Most crop plants acquire their nitrogen mainly in the form of
   A) $NH_3$.
   B) $N_2$.
   C) $CN_2H_2$.
   D) $NO_3^-$.
   E) amino acids absorbed from the soil.

Answer: D
*Topic: Concept 37.3*
*Skill: Comprehension*

43) The enzyme complex nitrogenase catalyzes the reaction that reduces atmospheric nitrogen to
   A) $N_2$.
   B) $NH_3$.
   C) $NO_2$.
   D) $NO^+$.
   E) $NH^-$.

Answer: B
*Topic: Concept 37.3*
*Skill: Comprehension*

44) In a root nodule, the gene coding for nitrogenase
   A) is inactivated by leghemoglobin.
   B) is absent in active bacteroids.
   C) is found in the cells of the pericycle.
   D) protects the nodule from nitrogen.
   E) is part of the *Rhizobium* chromosome.

Answer: E
*Topic: Concept 37.3*
*Skill: Knowledge*

45) The most efficient way to increase essential amino acids in crop plants for human consumption is to
   A) breed for higher yield of deficient amino acids.
   B) increase the amount of fertilizer used on fields.
   C) use 20–20–20 fertilizer instead of 20–5–5 fertilizer.
   D) engineer nitrogen-fixing nodules into crop plants lacking them.
   E) increase irrigation of nitrogen-fixing crops.

Answer: A
*Topic: Concept 37.3*
*Skill: Knowledge*

46) Among important crop plants, nitrogen-fixing root nodules are most commonly an attribute of
   A) corn.
   B) legumes.
   C) wheat.
   D) members of the potato family.
   E) cabbage and other members of the brassica family.

Answer: B
*Topic: Concept 37.4*
*Skill: Knowledge*

47) If a legume is infected with *Rhizobium*, what is the probable effect on the plant?
   A) It gets chlorosis.
   B) It dies.
   C) It desiccates.
   D) It obtains nitrogen from nitrogen fixation.
   E) It contributes water to the soil.

Answer: D
*Topic: Concept 37.4*
*Skill: Comprehension*

48) You are weeding your garden when you accidentally expose some roots. You notice swellings (root nodules) on the roots. Most likely your plant

A) suffers from a mineral deficiency.

B) is infected with a parasite.

C) is benefiting from a mutualistic bacterium.

D) is developing offshoots from the root.

E) contains developing insect pupa.

Answer: C
*Topic: Concept 37.4*
*Skill: Comprehension*

49) Which of the following is a *true* statement about nitrogen fixation in root nodules?

A) The plant contributes the nitrogenase enzyme.

B) The process is relatively inexpensive in terms of ATP costs.

C) Leghemoglobin helps maintain a low $O_2$ concentration within the nodule.

D) The process tends to deplete nitrogen compounds in the soil.

E) The bacteria of the nodule are autotrophic.

Answer: C
*Topic: Concept 37.4*
*Skill: Comprehension*

50) The function of a root nodule's leghemoglobin is to

A) extract macronutrients from the soil.

B) regulate the supply of oxygen to *Rhizobium*.

C) promote ion exchange in the soil.

D) form a mutualistic relationship with insects.

E) supply the legume with fixed nitrogen.

Answer: B
*Topic: Concept 37.4*
*Skill: Comprehension*

51) How do legume plant roots communicate with *Rhizobium* bacteria?

A) Flavonoids from *Rhizobium* create "nods."

B) Plants activate early nodulin genes.

C) *Rhizobium* secretes infection threads.

D) Flavonoids trigger gene-regulating proteins in bacterium.

E) Both A and C are correct.

Answer: D
*Topic: Concept 37.4*
*Skill: Knowledge*

52) A woodlot was sprayed with a fungicide. What would be the most serious effect of such spraying?

A) a decrease in food for animals that eat mushrooms

B) an increase in rates of wood decay

C) a decrease in tree growth due to the death of mycorrhizae

D) an increase in the number of decomposing bacteria

E) both A and B

Answer: C
*Topic: Concept 37.4*
*Skill: Application*

53) What is the mutualistic association between roots and fungi called?

A) nitrogen fixation

B) *Rhizobium* infection

C) mycorrhizae

D) parasitism

E) root hair enhancement

Answer: C
*Topic: Concept 37.4*
*Skill: Knowledge*

54) Hyphae form a covering over roots. Altogether, these hyphae create a large surface area that helps to do which of the following?

A) aid in absorbing minerals and ions

B) maintain cell shape

C) increase cellular respiration

D) anchor a plant

E) protect the roots from ultraviolet light

Answer: A
*Topic: Concept 37.4*
*Skill: Application*

55) Which of the following is a primary difference between ectomycorrhizae and endomycorrhizae?

A) Endomycorrhizae have thicker, shorter hyphae than ectomycorrhizae.

B) Endomycorrhizae, but not ectomycorrhizae, form a dense sheath over the surface of the root.

C) Ectomycorrhizae do not penetrate root cells, whereas endomycorrhizae grow into invaginations of the root cell membranes.

D) Ectomycorrhizae are found in woody plant species; about 85% of plant families form ectomycorrhizae.

E) There are no significant differences between ectomycorrhizae and endomycorrhizae.

Answer: C
*Topic: Concept 37.4*
*Skill: Knowledge*

56) The earliest vascular plants on land had underground stems (rhizomes) but no roots. Water and mineral nutrients were most likely obtained by

A) absorption by hairs and trichomes.

B) diffusion through stomata.

C) absorption by symbiotic fungi.

D) osmosis through root hairs.

E) diffusion across the cuticle of the rhizome.

Answer: C
*Topic: Concept 37.4*
*Skill: Comprehension*

57) Dwarf mistletoe grows on many pine trees in the Rockies. Although the mistletoe is green, it is probably not sufficiently active in photosynthesis to produce all the sugar it needs. The mistletoe also produces haustoria. Thus, dwarf mistletoe growing on pine trees is best classified as

A) an epiphyte.

B) a nitrogen–fixing legume.

C) a carnivorous plant.

D) a symbiotic plant.

E) a parasite.

Answer: E
*Topic: Concept 37.4*
*Skill: Application*

58) What are epiphytes?

A) aerial vines common in tropical regions

B) haustoria used for anchoring to host plants and obtaining xylem sap

C) plants that live in poor soil and digest insects to obtain nitrogen

D) plants that grow on other plants but do not obtain nutrients from their hosts

E) plants that have a symbiotic relationship with fungi

Answer: D
*Topic: Concept 37.4*
*Skill: Knowledge*

59) Carnivorous plants have evolved mechanisms that trap and digest small animals. The products of this digestion are used to supplement the plant's supply of

A) energy.

B) carbohydrates.

C) lipids and steroids.

D) minerals.

E) water.

Answer: D
*Topic: Concept 37.4*
*Skill: Knowledge*

# Media Activity Questions

1) What process is the source of the $CO_2$ that root hairs release into the soil?

    A) photosynthesis

    B) cellular respiration

    C) photolysis

    D) nitrogen fixation

    E) mycorrhizae

    Answer: B
    *Topic: Activity: How Plants Obtain Minerals from Soi*

2) Roots expend ATP to pump _____ ions from the root to the soil and by doing so displace mineral ions bound to soil particles.

    A) $CO_3^{2-}$

    B) $H^+$

    C) He

    D) $Mg^{2+}$

    E) $Ca^{2+}$

    Answer: B
    *Topic: Activity: How Plants Obtain Minerals from Soi*

3) Acid precipitation

    A) promotes the attachment of anions to soil particles.

    B) enhances the diffusion of cations into root hairs.

    C) has no effect on soil fertility.

    D) increases soil fertility.

    E) decreases soil fertility.

    Answer: E
    *Topic: Activity: How Plants Obtain Minerals from Soi*

4) Denitrifying bacteria convert _____ to _____.

    A) ammonium; nitrogen gas

    B) nitrates; nitrogen gas

    C) nitrogen gas; ammonium

    D) nitrogen gas; nitrates

    E) nitrogen gas; nitrites

    Answer: E
    *Topic: Web/CD Activity: The Nitrogen Cycle*

5) Which one of these is a nitrite?

    A) $NO_2^-$

    B) $NH_4^-$

    C) $NH_2$

    D) $PO_4^-$

    E) $NO_3^-$

    Answer: A
    *Topic: Web/CD Activity: The Nitrogen Cycle*

# Self–Quiz Questions

1) Most of the mass of organic material of a plant comes from
   - A) water.
   - B) carbon dioxide.
   - C) soil minerals.
   - D) atmospheric oxygen.
   - E) nitrogen.

   Answer: B

2) Micronutrients are needed in very small amounts because
   - A) most of them are mobile in the plant.
   - B) most function as cofactors of enzymes.
   - C) most micronutrients are supplied in large enough quantities in seeds.
   - D) they play only a minor role in the growth and health of the plant.
   - E) only the growing regions of the plants require micronutrients.

   Answer: B

3) It is valid to consider water a plant nutrient because
   - A) plants die without a water source.
   - B) cell elongation depends mainly on the osmotic absorption of water by cells.
   - C) hydrogen and oxygen atoms from water molecules are incorporated into organic molecules.
   - D) transpiration depends on a continuous supply of water to leaves.
   - E) most of a plant's mass of organic compounds is derived from water.

   Answer: C

4) Based on our retrospective view, the most reasonable conclusion to draw from van Helmont's famous experiment on the growth of a willow is that
   - A) the tree increased in mass mainly by photosynthesis.
   - B) the increase in the mass of the tree could not be accounted for by the consumption of soil.
   - C) most of the increase in the mass of the tree was due to the uptake of $O_2$.
   - D) soil simply provides physical support for the tree without providing nutrients.
   - E) trees do not require water to grow.

   Answer: B

5) A mineral deficiency is likely to affect older leaves more than younger leaves if
   - A) the mineral is a micronutrient.
   - B) the mineral is very mobile within the plant.
   - C) the mineral is required for chlorophyll synthesis.
   - D) the mineral is a macronutrient.
   - E) the older leaves are in direct sunlight.

   Answer: B

6) Two groups of tomatoes were grown under laboratory conditions, one with humus added to the soil and one a control without the humus. The leaves of the plants grown without humus were yellowish (less green) than those of the plants growing in humus-enriched soil. The best explanation for this difference is that

A) the healthy plants used the food in the decomposing leaves of the humus for energy to make chlorophyll.

B) the humus made the soil more loosely packed, so water penetrated more easily to the roots.

C) the humus contained minerals such as magnesium and iron, needed for the synthesis of chlorophyll.

D) the heat released by the decomposing leaves of the humus caused more rapid growth and chlorophyll synthesis.

E) the healthy plants absorbed chlorophyll from the humus.

Answer: C

7) The specific relationship between a legume and its symbiotic *Rhizobium* strain probably depends on

A) each legume having a specific set of early nodulin genes.

B) each *Rhizobium* strain having a form of nitrogenase that only works in the appropriate legume host.

C) each legume being found where the soil has only the *Rhizobium* specific to that legume.

D) specific recognition between the chemical signals and signal receptors of the *Rhizobium* strain and legume species.

E) destruction of all incompatible *Rhizobium* strains by enzymes secreted from the legume's roots.

Answer: D

8) Mycorrhizae enhance plant nutrition mainly by

A) absorbing water and minerals through the fungal hyphae.

B) providing sugar to the root cells, which have no chloroplasts of their own.

C) converting atmospheric nitrogen to ammonia.

D) enabling the roots to parasitize neighboring plants.

E) stimulating the development of root hairs.

Answer: A

9) We would expect the greatest difference in size and general appearance between two groups of plants of the same species, one group with mycorrhizae and one without, in an environment

A) where nitrogen-fixing bacteria are abundant.

B) that has soil with poor drainage.

C) that has hot summers and cold winters.

D) in which the soil is relatively deficient in mineral nutrients.

E) that is near a body of water, such as a pond or river.

Answer: D

10) Carnivorous adaptations of plants mainly compensate for soil that has a relatively low content of

A) potassium.

B) nitrogen.

C) calcium.

D) water.

E) phosphate.

Answer: B

# Chapter 38  Angiosperm Reproduction and Biotechnology

1) The products of meiosis in plants are always which of the following?
   A) spores
   B) eggs
   C) sperm
   D) seeds
   E) both B and C

Answer: A
*Topic: Concept 38.1*
*Skill: Knowledge*

2) Which of the following is the *correct* sequence during alternation of generations in a flowering plant?
   A) sporophyte–meiosis–gametophyte–gametes–fertilization–diploid zygote
   B) sporophyte–mitosis–gametophyte–meiosis–sporophyte
   C) haploid gametophyte–gametes–meiosis–fertilization–diploid sporophyte
   D) sporophyte–spores–meiosis–gametophyte–gametes
   E) haploid sporophyte–spores–fertilization–diploid gametophyte

Answer: A
*Topic: Concept 38.1*
*Skill: Comprehension*

3) Which of the following is *true* in plants?
   A) Meiosis occurs in gametophytes to produce gametes.
   B) Meiosis occurs in sporophytes to produce spores.
   C) The gametophyte is the dominant generation in flowering plants.
   D) Plants exist continually as either sporophytes or gametophytes.
   E) Male gametophytes and female gametophytes have the same structure.

Answer: B
*Topic: Concept 38.1*
*Skill: Knowledge*

4) All of the following are features of angiosperms *except*
   A) a triploid endosperm.
   B) an ovary that becomes a fruit.
   C) animal pollination.
   D) a small (reduced) sporophyte.
   E) double fertilization.

Answer: D
*Topic: Concept 38.1*
*Skill: Knowledge*

5) Based on studies of plant evolution, which flower part is *not* a modified leaf?
   A) stamen
   B) carpel
   C) petal
   D) sepal
   E) receptacle

Answer: E
*Topic: Concept 38.1*
*Skill: Knowledge*

6) All of the following floral parts are directly involved in pollination or fertilization *except* the

A) stigma.

B) anther.

C) sepal.

D) carpel.

E) style.

Answer: C
*Topic: Concept 38.1*
*Skill: Knowledge*

7) A mutation in which of the following floral parts would have the greatest impact on pollination?

A) sepal

B) petal

C) stamen

D) carpel

E) either C or D

Answer: E
*Topic: Concept 38.1*
*Skill: Comprehension*

8) A mutation in which of the following floral parts would have the greatest potential impact on fertilization?

A) sepal

B) petal

C) stamen

D) carpel

E) either C or D

Answer: E
*Topic: Concept 38.1*
*Skill: Comprehension*

9) Which of the following is the *correct* order of floral organs from the outside to the inside of a complete flower?

A) petals-sepals-stamens-carpels

B) sepals-stamens-petals-carpels

C) spores-gametes-zygote-embryo

D) sepals-petals-stamens-carpels

E) male gametophyte-female gametophyte-sepals-petals

Answer: D
*Topic: Concept 38.1*
*Skill: Comprehension*

10) All of the following are primary functions of flowers *except*

A) pollen production.

B) photosynthesis.

C) meiosis.

D) egg production.

E) sexual reproduction.

Answer: B
*Topic: Concept 38.1*
*Skill: Knowledge*

11) Meiosis occurs within all of the following flower parts *except* the

A) ovule.

B) style.

C) megasporangium.

D) anther.

E) ovary.

Answer: B
*Topic: Concept 38.1*
*Skill: Comprehension*

12) A perfect flower is fertile, but may be either complete or incomplete. Which of the following correctly describes a perfect flower?

    A) It has no sepals.

    B) It has fused carpels.

    C) It is on a dioecious plant.

    D) It has no endosperm.

    E) It has both stamens and carpels.

Answer: E
*Topic: Concept 38.1*
*Skill: Comprehension*

13) Carpellate flowers

    A) are perfect.

    B) are complete.

    C) produce pollen.

    D) are found only on dioecious plants.

    E) develop into fruits.

Answer: E
*Topic: Concept 38.1*
*Skill: Comprehension*

14) Which of the following types of plants is *not* able to self-pollinate?

    A) dioecious

    B) monoecious

    C) complete

    D) wind-pollinated

    E) insect-pollinated

Answer: A
*Topic: Concept 38.1*
*Skill: Knowledge*

15) In flowering plants, pollen is released from the

    A) anther.

    B) stigma.

    C) carpel.

    D) filament.

    E) pollen tube.

Answer: A
*Topic: Concept 38.1*
*Skill: Knowledge*

16) In the life cycle of an angiosperm, which of the following stages is diploid?

    A) megaspore

    B) generative nucleus of a pollen grain

    C) polar nuclei of the embryo sac

    D) microsporocyte

    E) both megaspore and polar nuclei

Answer: D
*Topic: Concept 38.1*
*Skill: Comprehension*

17) Where does meiosis occur in flowering plants?

    A) megasporocyte

    B) microsporocyte

    C) endosperm

    D) pollen tube

    E) megasporocyte and microsporocyte

Answer: E
*Topic: Concept 38.1*
*Skill: Comprehension*

18) Which of the following is a *correct* sequence of processes that takes place when a flowering plant reproduces?

  A) meiosis-fertilization-ovulation-germination

  B) fertilization-meiosis-nuclear fusion-formation of embryo and endosperm

  C) meiosis-pollination-nuclear fusion-formation of embryo and endosperm

  D) growth of pollen tube-pollination-germination-fertilization

  E) meiosis-mitosis-nuclear fusion-pollen

Answer: C
*Topic: Concept 38.1*
*Skill: Application*

19) Which of these is *incorrectly* paired with its life-cycle generation?

  A) anther—gametophyte

  B) pollen—gametophyte

  C) embryo sac—gametophyte

  D) stamen—sporophyte

  E) embryo—sporophyte

Answer: A
*Topic: Concept 38.1*
*Skill: Knowledge*

20) Which of the following is the *correct* sequence of events in a pollen sac?

  A) sporangia-meiosis-two haploid cells-meiosis-two pollen grains per cell

  B) pollen grain-meiosis-two generative cells-two tube cells per pollen grain

  C) two haploid cells-meiosis-generative cell-tube cell-fertilization-pollen grain

  D) pollen grain-mitosis-microspores-meiosis-generative cell plus tube cell

  E) microsporocyte-meiosis-microspores-mitosis-two haploid cells per pollen grain

Answer: E
*Topic: Concept 38.1*
*Skill: Comprehension*

21) Which of the following occurs in an angiosperm ovule?

  A) An antheridium forms from the megasporophyte.

  B) A megaspore mother cell undergoes meiosis.

  C) The egg nucleus is usually diploid.

  D) A pollen tube emerges to accept pollen after pollination.

  E) The endosperm surrounds the megaspore mother cell.

Answer: B
*Topic: Concept 38.1*
*Skill: Knowledge*

22) Where and by which process are sperm produced in plants?

  A) meiosis in pollen grains

  B) meiosis in anthers

  C) mitosis in male gametophytes

  D) mitosis in the micropyle

  E) mitosis in the embryo sac

Answer: C
*Topic: Concept 38.1*
*Skill: Knowledge*

23) In which of the following pairs are the two terms equivalent?

   A) ovule—egg

   B) embryo sac—female gametophyte

   C) endosperm—male gametophyte

   D) seed—zygote

   E) microspore—pollen grain

Answer: B
*Topic: Concept 38.1*
*Skill: Comprehension*

24) Which of the following is the male gametophyte of a flowering plant?

   A) ovule

   B) microsporocyte

   C) pollen grain

   D) embryo sac

   E) stamen

Answer: C
*Topic: Concept 38.1*
*Skill: Knowledge*

25) In flowering plants, a mature male gametophyte contains

   A) two haploid gametes and a diploid pollen grain.

   B) a generative cell and a tube cell.

   C) two sperm nuclei and one tube cell nucleus.

   D) two haploid microspores.

   E) a haploid nucleus and a diploid pollen wall.

Answer: C
*Topic: Concept 38.1*
*Skill: Knowledge*

26) Within the female gametophyte, three mitotic divisions of the megaspore produce

   A) three antipodal cells, two polar nuclei, one egg, and two synergids.

   B) the triple fusion nucleus.

   C) three pollen grains.

   D) two antipodal cells, two polar nuclei, two eggs, and two synergids.

   E) a tube nucleus, a generative cell, and a sperm cell.

Answer: A
*Topic: Concept 38.1*
*Skill: Knowledge*

27) The largest cell(s) of the typical angiosperm embryo sac is (are) the

   A) egg cell.

   B) antipodals.

   C) synergids.

   D) central cell.

   E) microsporocyte.

Answer: D
*Topic: Concept 38.1*
*Skill: Comprehension*

*The following questions refer to the diagram of an embryo sac of an angiosperm.*

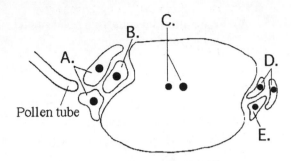

**Figure 38.1**

28) Which cell(s), after fertilization, give(s) rise to the embryo plant?

Answer: B
*Topic: Concept 38.1*
*Skill: Knowledge*

29) Which cell(s) become(s) the triploid endosperm?

Answer: C
*Topic: Concept 38.1*
*Skill: Knowledge*

30) Which cell(s) guide(s) the pollen tube to the egg cell?

Answer: A
*Topic: Concept 38.1*
*Skill: Knowledge*

31) What is the relationship between pollination and fertilization in flowering plants?

A) Fertilization precedes pollination.

B) Pollination easily occurs between plants of different species.

C) Pollen is formed within megasporangia so that male and female gametes are near each other.

D) Pollination brings gametophytes together so that fertilization can occur.

E) If fertilization occurs, pollination is unnecessary.

Answer: D
*Topic: Concept 38.1*
*Skill: Comprehension*

32) Recent research has shown that pollination requires that carpels recognize pollen grains as "self or nonself." For self-incompatibility, the system requires

A) rejection of nonself cells.

B) the rejection of self cells.

C) carpel incompatibility with the egg cells.

D) that the flowers be incomplete.

E) the union of genetically identical sperm and egg cells.

Answer: B
*Topic: Concept 38.1*
*Skill: Comprehension*

33) Genetic incompatibility does *not* affect the

A) attraction of a suitable insect pollinator.

B) germination of the pollen on the stigma.

C) growth of the pollen tube in the style.

D) membrane permeability of cells.

E) different individuals of the same species.

Answer: A
*Topic: Concept 38.1*
*Skill: Comprehension*

34) You are studying a plant from the Amazon that shows strong self-incompatibility. To characterize this reproductive mechanism, you would look for

A) ribonuclease (RNAase) activity in stigma cells.

B) RNA in the plants.

C) pollen grains with very thick walls.

D) carpels that cannot produce eggs by meiosis.

E) systems of wind, but not insect, pollination.

Answer: A
*Topic: Concept 38.1*
*Skill: Application*

35) As flowers develop, which transition does not occur?

A) The microspores become pollen grains.

B) The ovary becomes a fruit.

C) The petals are discarded.

D) The tube nucleus becomes a sperm nucleus.

E) The ovules become seeds.

Answer: D
*Topic: Concept 38.2*
*Skill: Comprehension*

36) The integuments of an ovule function to do what?

A) protect against animal predation

B) ensure double fertilization

C) form a seed coat

D) both A and B

E) both A and C

Answer: C
*Topic: Concept 38.2*
*Skill: Comprehension*

37) Which of the following events suggests there is a change in the egg cell membrane after penetration by a sperm?

A) The pollen tube grows away from the egg toward the polar nuclei.

B) $Ca^{2+}$ builds up in the cytoplasm of the egg.

C) The egg cell plasmolyzes.

D) Double fertilization occurs.

E) All of the above are correct.

Answer: B
*Topic: Concept 38.2*
*Skill: Comprehension*

38) A fruit includes

A) one or more seeds.

B) the ovary wall.

C) fleshy cells rich in sugars.

D) brightly colored pigments to attract animal dispersers.

E) both A and B

Answer: E
*Topic: Concept 38.2*
*Skill: Comprehension*

39) Which of the following is *not* an advantage of an extended gametophyte generation in plants?

A) Male gametophytes can travel more easily within spore walls.

B) The protection of female gametophytes within ovules keeps them from drying out.

C) The lack of need for swimming sperm makes life on land easier.

D) Female gametophytes develop egg cells, which are fertilized within an ovule that will become a seed.

E) Endosperm forms a protective seed coat.

Answer: E
*Topic: Concept 38.2*
*Skill: Comprehension*

40) What is typically the result of double fertilization in angiosperms?

A) The endosperm develops into a diploid nutrient tissue.

B) A triploid zygote is formed.

C) Both a diploid embryo and triploid endosperm are formed.

D) Two embryos develop in every seed.

E) The fertilized antipodal cells develop into the seed coat.

Answer: C
*Topic: Concept 38.2*
*Skill: Comprehension*

41) Which of the following statements regarding the endosperm is *false*?

A) Its nutrients may be absorbed by the cotyledons in the seeds of eudicots.

B) It develops from a triploid cell.

C) Its nutrients are digested by enzymes in monocot seeds following hydration.

D) It develops from the fertilized egg.

E) It is rich in nutrients, which it provides to the embryo.

Answer: D
*Topic: Concept 38.2*
*Skill: Comprehension*

42) In angiosperms, products of the terminal cell become the

A) suspensor.

B) proembryo.

C) cotyledons.

D) suspensor and the proembryo.

E) proembryo and the cotyledons.

Answer: E
*Topic: Concept 38.2*
*Skill: Comprehension*

43) Which of the following statements is *correct* about the basal cell in a zygote?

A) It develops into the root of the embryo.

B) It forms the suspensor that anchors the embryo.

C) It results directly from the fertilization of the polar nuclei by a sperm nucleus.

D) It divides and initiates the two cotyledons.

E) It forms the proembryo.

Answer: B
*Topic: Concept 38.2*
*Skill: Knowledge*

44) What is the embryonic root called?

A) plumule

B) hypocotyl

C) epicotyl

D) radicle

E) shoot

Answer: D
*Topic: Concept 38.2*
*Skill: Knowledge*

45) Which of the following "vegetables" is botanically a fruit?

A) potato

B) lettuce

C) radish

D) celery

E) green beans

Answer: E
*Topic: Concept 38.2*
*Skill: Comprehension*

46) Which of these structures is unique to the seed of a monocot?

A) cotyledon

B) endosperm

C) coleoptile

D) radicle

E) seed coat

Answer: C
*Topic: Concept 38.2*
*Skill: Knowledge*

47) Which of the following statements about fruits is *false*?

A) Fruits form from microsporangia and integuments.

B) All normal fruits have seeds inside them.

C) Green beans, corn, tomatoes, and wheat are all fruits.

D) Fruits aid in the dispersal of seeds.

E) During fruit development, the wall of the ovary becomes the pericarp.

Answer: A
*Topic: Concept 38.2*
*Skill: Knowledge*

48) Fruits develop from

A) microsporangia.

B) receptacles.

C) fertilized eggs.

D) ovaries.

E) ovules.

Answer: D
*Topic: Concept 38.2*
*Skill: Knowledge*

49) The first step in the germination of a seed is usually

A) pollination.

B) fertilization.

C) imbibition of water.

D) hydrolysis of starch and other food reserves.

E) emergence of the radicle.

Answer: C
*Topic: Concept 38.2*
*Skill: Knowledge*

50) When seeds germinate, the radicle emerges before the shoot. This allows the seedling to quickly

   A) obtain a dependable water supply.

   B) mobilize stored carbohydrates.

   C) protect the emerging coleoptile.

   D) avoid etiolation.

   E) initiate photosynthesis.

   Answer: A
   *Topic: Concept 38.2*
   *Skill: Comprehension*

51) Which of the following is *not* true of the hypocotyl hook?

   A) It is the first structure to emerge from a eudicot seed.

   B) It pulls the cotyledons up through the soil.

   C) It straightens when exposed to light.

   D) It becomes very long in an etiolated seedling.

   E) It is the region just below the cotyledons.

   Answer: A
   *Topic: Concept 38.2*
   *Skill: Knowledge*

52) In plants, which of the following could be an advantage of sexual reproduction as opposed to asexual reproduction?

   A) genetic variation

   B) mitosis

   C) stable populations

   D) rapid population increase

   E) greater longevity

   Answer: A
   *Topic: Concept 38.3*
   *Skill: Comprehension*

53) A disadvantage of monoculture is that

   A) the whole crop ripens at one time.

   B) genetic uniformity makes a crop vulnerable to a new pest or disease.

   C) it predominantly uses vegetative propagation.

   D) most grain crops self–pollinate.

   E) it allows for the cultivation of large areas of land.

   Answer: B
   *Topic: Concept 38.3*
   *Skill: Comprehension*

54) Which of the following is *true* about vegetative reproduction?

   A) It involves both meiosis and mitosis to produce haploid and diploid cells.

   B) It produces vegetables.

   C) It involves meiosis only.

   D) It can lead to genetically altered forms of the species.

   E) It produces clones.

   Answer: E
   *Topic: Concept 38.3*
   *Skill: Knowledge*

55) Which of the following is a *true* statement about clonal reproduction in plants?

   A) Clones of plants do *not* occur naturally.

   B) Cloning, although achieved in animals, has not been demonstrated in plants.

   C) Making cuttings of ornamental plants is a form of fragmentation.

   D) Reproduction of plants by cloning may be either sexual or asexual.

   E) Viable seeds can result from sexual reproduction only.

   Answer: C
   *Topic: Concept 38.3*
   *Skill: Application*

56) Which of the following statements about a seed produced by apomixis is *incorrect*?

A) The seed coat is made of diploid cells derived from the ovule of a flower.

B) The embryo consists of diploid cells derived from fertilization of a haploid egg by a haploid sperm.

C) Cotyledons are the primary food storage tissue of the embryo.

D) A diploid embryo is contained within the seed.

E) The embryo of the seed is a clone.

Answer: B
*Topic: Concept 38.3*
*Skill: Comprehension*

57) All of the following could be considered advantages of asexual reproduction in plants *except*

A) success in a stable environment.

B) increased agricultural productivity.

C) cloning an exceptional plant.

D) production of artificial seeds.

E) adaptation to change.

Answer: E
*Topic: Concept 38.3*
*Skill: Comprehension*

58) Regardless of where in the world a vineyard is located, in order for the winery to produce a Burgundy, it must use varietal grapes that originated in Burgundy, France. The most effective way for a new California grower to plant a vineyard to produce Burgundy is to

A) plant seeds obtained from French varietal Burgundy grapes.

B) transplant varietal Burgundy plants from France.

C) root cuttings of varietal Burgundy grapes from France.

D) cross French Burgundy grapes with native American grapes.

E) graft varietal Burgundy grape scions onto native (Californian) root stocks.

Answer: E
*Topic: Concept 38.3*
*Skill: Application*

59) Under which conditions would asexual plants have the greatest advantage over sexual plants?

A) an environment that varies on a regular, predictable basis

B) an environment with irregular fluctuations of conditions

C) a relatively constant environment with infrequent disturbances

D) a fire–maintained ecosystem

E) an environment with many seed predators

Answer: C
*Topic: Concept 38.3*
*Skill: Knowledge*

60) Which of the following statements is *true* of protoplast fusion?

A) It occurs when the second sperm nucleus fuses with the polar nuclei in the embryo sac.

B) It can be used to form new plant varieties by combining genomes from two plants.

C) It is used to develop gene banks to preserve genetic variability.

D) It is the method of test-tube cloning that produces whole plants from explants.

E) It occurs within a callus that is developing in tissue culture.

Answer: B
*Topic: Concept 38.3*
*Skill: Knowledge*

61) Which of the following statements is *correct* about protoplast fusion?

A) It is used to develop gene banks to maintain genetic variability.

B) It is the method of test-tube cloning thousands of copies.

C) It can be used to form new plant species.

D) It occurs within a callus.

E) It requires that the cell wall remain intact during the fusion process.

Answer: C
*Topic: Concept 38.3*
*Skill: Knowledge*

62) Typical cultivated maize is homozygous for the dominant alleles of the *opaque-2* gene and deficient in lysine. Conventional breeding required almost 20 years to introduce the recessive *opaque-2* genes into maize. Which of the following statements is *false*?

A) All of the characteristics found in the original *opaque-2* mutant plant were desirable.

B) Modern maize varieties containing *opaque-2* are genetically modified.

C) None of the $F_1$ progeny from a cross of an *opaque-2* mutant and a normal maize plant will express the *opaque-2* character.

D) It takes three growing seasons to determine which $F_1$ progeny have a recessive parental trait when one parent is the recessive mutant and the other is wild-type.

E) Both C and D are false.

Answer: A
*Topic: Concept 38.4*
*Skill: Comprehension*

63) Which of the following statements is *true* about transgenic plants?

A) They can be produced only by genetic engineering.

B) They contain genes from more than one species.

C) Intermediate species are required for transgenic plants to be produced.

D) They require many years to be produced.

E) A and D are correct statements.

Answer: B
*Topic: Concept 38.4*
*Skill: Comprehension*

64) The most immediate potential benefits of introducing genetically modified crops include

A) increasing the amount of land suitable for agriculture.

B) overcoming genetic incompatibility.

C) increasing the frequency of self-pollination.

D) increasing crop yield.

E) both B and C

Answer: D
*Topic: Concept 38.4*
*Skill: Knowledge*

65) Which of the following is *not* a scientific concern relating to creating genetically modified crops?

A) Herbicide resistance may spread to weedy species.

B) Insect pests may evolve resistance to toxins more rapidly.

C) Nontarget species may be affected.

D) The monetary costs of growing genetically modified plants are significantly greater than traditional breeding techniques.

E) Genetically modified plants may lead to unknown risks to human health.

Answer: D
*Topic: Concept 38.4*
*Skill: Comprehension*

66) Which of the following statements about genetic engineering is (are) *true*?

A) Genes can only be transferred between closely related species.

B) Intermediate species are necessary to transfer genes between unrelated species.

C) Cell and protoplast culture techniques simplify the process of inserting modified genes into a plant species.

D) Only A and B are correct.

E) A, B, and C are correct.

Answer: C
*Topic: Concept 38.4*
*Skill: Comprehension*

67) Currently available transgenic plants have been modified for all of the following traits *except*

A) insect resistance.

B) nitrogen fixation.

C) herbicide resistance.

D) improved nutritional quality.

E) virus resistance.

Answer: B
*Topic: Concept 38.4*
*Skill: Knowledge*

68) In modern agriculture, what does "terminator technology" refer to?

A) introduction of bacterial genes that release insect toxins into plants

B) introduction of male sterility genes into plants to prevent selfing

C) introduction of genes into a plant that prevent its seeds from maturing

D) *Bt* genes produced in maize pollen

E) selection of resistant clones following mutator treatment of seeds

Answer: C
*Topic: Concept 38.4*
*Skill: Knowledge*

# Media Activity Questions

1) Flowers are made of modified
   A) roots.
   B) stems.
   C) leaves.
   D) ovules.
   E) shoots.

   Answer: C
   *Topic: Web/CD Activity: Angiosperm Life Cycle*

2) Which of these is unique to flowering plants?
   A) a dominant sporophyte generation
   B) an embryo surrounded by nutritive tissue
   C) haploid gametophytes
   D) double fertilization
   E) pollen production

   Answer: D
   *Topic: Web/CD Activity: Angiosperm Life Cycle*

3) What is endosperm?
   A) the male portion of a flowering plant
   B) a food-storing tissue of the seed
   C) the leaves that are part of the embryo
   D) the female portion of a flowering plant
   E) tissue that develops into a protective seed coat surrounding the embryo

   Answer: B
   *Topic: Activity: Seed and Fruit Development*

4) _____ is the first event in seed formation.
   A) Formation of a zygote
   B) Pollination
   C) Formation of endosperm
   D) Fertilization
   E) Growth of the pollen tube

   Answer: B
   *Topic: Activity: Seed and Fruit Development*

5) Which of these is a symptom of vitamin A deficiency?
   A) osteoporosis
   B) impaired taste perception
   C) overstimulation of the immune system
   D) blindness
   E) impaired blood clotting

   Answer: D
   *Topic: Web/CD Activity: Golden Rice*

# Self-Quiz Questions

1) A plant that has small, green petals is most likely to be

   A) bee-pollinated.

   B) bird-pollinated.

   C) bat-pollinated.

   D) wind-pollinated

   Answer: D

2) Pollen grain is to _____ as _____ is to female gametophyte.

   A) male gametophyte; embryo sac

   B) embryo sac; ovule

   C) ovule; sporophyte

   D) anther; seed

   E) petal; sepal

   Answer: A

3) A seed develops from

   A) an ovum.

   B) a pollen grain.

   C) an ovule.

   D) an ovary.

   E) an embryo.

   Answer: C

4) A fruit is a (an)

   A) mature ovary.

   B) mature ovule.

   C) seed plus its integuments.

   D) fused carpel.

   E) enlarged embryo sac.

   Answer: A

5) Which of the following conditions is needed by almost all seeds to break dormancy?

   A) exposure to light

   B) imbibition

   C) abrasion of the seed coat

   D) exposure to cold

   E) covering of fertile soil

   Answer: B

6) Sources of genetic variability in an asexually propagated species may involve all of the following processes *except*

   A) protoplast fusion.

   B) mutation.

   C) hybridization.

   D) genetic engineering.

   Answer: C

7) Plant biotechnologists use protoplast fusion mainly to

   A) culture plant cells *in vitro*.

   B) asexually propagate desirable plant varieties.

   C) introduce bacterial genes into a plant genome.

   D) study the early events following fertilization.

   E) produce new hybrid species.

   Answer: E

8) The basal cell formed from the first division of a plant zygote will eventually develop into

   A) the suspensor that anchors the embryo and transfers nutrients.

   B) the proembryo.

   C) the endosperm that nourishes the developing embryo.

   D) the root apex of the embryo.

   E) two cotyledons in eudicots, but one in monocots.

   Answer: A

9) The development of *Bt* crops continues to cause concern because

   A) *Bt* crops have been shown to be toxic to humans.

   B) pollen from these crops is harmful to monarch butterfly larvae in the field.

   C) if genes for *Bt* toxin "escape" to related weed species, the hybrid weeds could have harmful ecological effects.

   D) *Bacillus thuringiensis* is a pathogen of humans.

   E) *Bt* toxin reduces the nutritional quality of crops.

   Answer: C

10) "Golden Rice" is a transgenic variety that

   A) is resistant to various herbicides, making it practical to weed rice fields with those herbicides.

   B) is resistant to a virus that commonly attacks rice fields.

   C) includes bacterial genes that produce a toxin that reduces damage from insect pests.

   D) produces much larger, golden grains that increase crop yields.

   E) contains daffodil genes that increase the vitamin A content.

   Answer: E

# Chapter 39  Plant Responses to Internal and External Signals

1) The step(s) between a plant's perception of a change in the environment and the plant's response to that change is (are) best called

   A) a mutation.

   B) hormone production.

   C) pH change.

   D) signal transduction.

   E) an "all-or-none" response.

Answer: D
*Topic: Concept 39.1*
*Skill: Knowledge*

2) All of the following may function in signal transduction in plants *except*

   A) calcium ions.

   B) nonrandom mutations.

   C) receptor proteins.

   D) phytochrome.

   E) second messengers.

Answer: B
*Topic: Concept 39.1*
*Skill: Knowledge*

3) Which of the following statements is (are) true of plants?

   A) Unlike animals, plants cannot respond to stimuli.

   B) Plants are stationary and are incapable of movement.

   C) Plants adjust their growth and development in response to environmental cues.

   D) Only A and B are true.

   E) A, B, and C are true.

Answer: C
*Topic: Concept 39.1*
*Skill: Comprehension*

4) External stimuli would be received most quickly by a plant cell if the receptors for signal transduction were located in the

   A) cell membrane.

   B) cytoplasmic matrix.

   C) endoplasmic reticulum.

   D) nuclear membrane.

   E) nucleoplasm.

Answer: A
*Topic: Concept 39.1*
*Skill: Comprehension*

5) Secondary messengers are associated with which of the following?

   A) reception

   B) transduction

   C) response

   D) both A and B

   E) both B and C

Answer: B
*Topic: Concept 39.1*
*Skill: Knowledge*

6) In a signal  transduction pathway, the transduction stage amplifies the original signal by

   A) involving more than one receptor molecule to receive the stimulus.

   B) having each receptor molecule produce multiple secondary messengers.

   C) having each secondary messenger activate numerous specific enzymes.

   D) B and C only

   E) A, B, and C

Answer: D
*Topic: Concept 39.1*
*Skill: Comprehension*

7) What would happen if the secondary messenger cGMP was blocked in the de-etiolation pathway?

   A) Specific protein kinase 1 would be activated, and greening would occur.

   B) $Ca^{2+}$ channels would not open, and no greening would occur.

   C) $Ca^{2+}$ channels could open, and specific protein kinase 2 could still be produced.

   D) No transcription of genes that function in de-etiolation would occur.

   E) Transcription of de-etiolation genes in the nucleus would not be affected.

Answer: C
*Topic: Concept 39.1*
*Skill: Application*

8) If protein synthesis was blocked in etiolated cells, what would be necessary for any de-etiolation to occur?

   A) reception of light by phytochrome

   B) activation of protein kinase 1 by cAMP

   C) activation of protein kinase 2 by $Ca^{2+}$

   D) post-translational modification of existing proteins

   E) A, B, and C

Answer: D
*Topic: Concept 39.1*
*Skill: Application*

9) Which of the following have accelerated recent discoveries about the function of plant hormones?

   A) the frequent use of brassinosteroids

   B) our increased knowledge of development using *Arabidopsis*

   C) better analysis of signal transduction pathways using mutant plants

   D) more precise use of molecular biology techniques

   E) B, C, and D

Answer: E
*Topic: Concept 39.2*
*Skill: Comprehension*

10) Charles and Francis Darwin concluded from their experiments on phototropism by grass seedlings that the part of the seedling that detects the direction of light is the

   A) tip of the coleoptile.

   B) part of the coleoptile that bends during the response.

   C) root tip.

   D) cotyledon.

   E) phytochrome.

Answer: A
*Topic: Concept 39.2*
*Skill: Knowledge*

11) Plants growing in a partially dark environment will grow toward light in a response called phototropism. Choose the *incorrect* statement regarding phototropism.

A) It is caused by a chemical signal.

B) One chemical involved is auxin.

C) Auxin causes a growth increase on one side of the stem.

D) Auxin causes a decrease in growth on the side of the stem exposed to light.

E) Removing the apical meristem prevents phototropism.

Answer: D
*Topic: Concept 39.2*
*Skill: Comprehension*

12) Which of these conclusions is supported by the research of both Went and Charles and Frances Darwin on shoot responses to light?

A) When shoots are exposed to light, a chemical substance migrates toward the light.

B) Agar contains a chemical substance that mimics a plant hormone.

C) A chemical substance involved in shoot bending is produced in shoot tips.

D) Once shoot tips have been cut, normal growth cannot be induced.

E) Light stimulates the synthesis of a plant hormone that responds to light.

Answer: C
*Topic: Concept 39.2*
*Skill: Comprehension*

13) We know from the experiments of the past that plants bend toward light because

A) they need sunlight energy for photosynthesis.

B) the sun stimulates stem growth.

C) cell expansion is greater on the dark side of the stem.

D) auxin is inactive on the dark side of the stem.

E) phytochrome stimulates florigen production.

Answer: C
*Topic: Concept 39.2*
*Skill: Comprehension*

14) Which of the following is *not* presently considered a major mechanism whereby hormones control plant development?

A) affecting cell respiration via regulation of the citric acid cycle

B) affecting cell division via the cell cycle

C) affecting cell elongation through acid growth

D) affecting cell differentiation through altered gene activity

E) mediating short-term physiological responses to environmental stimuli

Answer: A
*Topic: Concept 39.2*
*Skill: Knowledge*

15) Evidence for phototropism due to the asymmetric distribution of auxin moving down the stem

    A) has not been found in eudicots such as sunflower and radish.

    B) has been found in all monocots and most eudicots.

    C) has been shown to involve only IAA stimulation of cell elongation on the dark side of the stem.

    D) can be demonstrated with unilateral red light, but not blue light.

    E) is now thought by most plant scientists *not* to involve the shoot tip.

Answer: A
*Topic: Concept 39.2*
*Skill: Knowledge*

16) Vines in tropical rain forests must grow toward large trees before being able to grow toward the sun. To reach a large tree, the most useful kind of growth movement for a tropical vine presumably would be the *opposite* of

    A) positive thigmotropism.

    B) positive phototropism.

    C) positive gravitropism.

    D) sleep movements.

    E) circadian rhythms.

Answer: B
*Topic: Concept 39.2*
*Skill: Application*

17) Plant hormones can be characterized by all of the following *except* that they

    A) may act by altering gene expression.

    B) have a multiplicity of effects.

    C) function independently of other hormones.

    D) control plant growth and development.

    E) affect division, elongation, and differentiation of cells.

Answer: C
*Topic: Concept 39.2*
*Skill: Knowledge*

18) Plant hormones produce their effects by

    A) altering the expression of genes.

    B) modifying the permeability of the plasma membrane.

    C) modifying the structure of the nuclear envelope membrane.

    D) both A and B.

    E) both B and C only

Answer: D
*Topic: Concept 39.2*
*Skill: Comprehension*

19) Why might animal hormones function differently from plant hormones?

    A) Animals move rapidly away from negative stimuli, and most plants don't.

    B) Plant cells have a cell wall that blocks passage of many hormones.

    C) Plants must have more precise timing of their reproductive activities.

    D) Plants are much more variable in their morphology and development than animals.

    E) Both A and D are correct.

Answer: E
*Topic: Concept 39.2*
*Skill: Comprehension*

20) Why is it so difficult to study the actions of plant hormones?

   A) Their effects are often the result of an interaction of hormones.

   B) They are found in small quantities in the plant.

   C) We probably have not discovered all of them.

   D) They sometimes cause different responses in different plants.

   E) All of the above make the study of plant hormones difficult.

Answer: E
*Topic: Concept 39.2*
*Skill: Comprehension*

21) Plant hormones can have different effects at different concentrations. This explains how

   A) some plants are long-day plants and others are short-day plants.

   B) signal transduction pathways in plants are different from those in animals.

   C) plant genes recognize pathogen genes.

   D) auxin can stimulate cell elongation in apical meristems, yet will inhibit the growth of axillary buds.

   E) they really don't fit the definition of "hormone."

Answer: D
*Topic: Concept 39.2*
*Skill: Knowledge*

22) Which plant hormones might be used to enhance stem elongation and fruit growth?

   A) brassinosteroids and oligosaccharides

   B) auxins and gibberellins

   C) abscisic acid and phytochrome

   D) ethylene and cytokinins

   E) phytochrome and flowering hormone

Answer: B
*Topic: Concept 39.2*
*Skill: Knowledge*

23) Which of the following has *not* been established as an aspect of auxin's role in cell elongation?

   A) Auxin instigates a loosening of cell wall fibers.

   B) Auxin increases the quantity of cytoplasm in the cell.

   C) Through auxin activity, vacuoles increase in size.

   D) Auxin activity permits an increase in turgor pressure.

   E) Auxin stimulates proton pumps.

Answer: B
*Topic: Concept 39.2*
*Skill: Comprehension*

24) According to the acid growth hypothesis, auxin works by

    A) dissolving sieve plates, permitting more rapid transport of nutrients.

    B) dissolving the cell membranes temporarily, permitting cells that were on the verge of dividing to divide more rapidly.

    C) changing the pH within the cell, which would permit the electron transport chain to operate more efficiently.

    D) increasing wall plasticity and allowing the affected cell walls to elongate.

    E) greatly increasing the rate of deposition of cell wall material.

Answer: D
*Topic: Concept 39.2*
*Skill: Comprehension*

25) Which of the following hormones would be most useful in promoting the rooting of plant cuttings?

    A) oligosaccharins

    B) abscisic acid

    C) cytokinins

    D) gibberellins

    E) auxins

Answer: E
*Topic: Concept 39.2*
*Skill: Application*

26) Which plant hormone(s) is (are) most closely associated with cell division?

    A) ethylene

    B) cytokinin

    C) abscisic acid

    D) phytochrome

    E) brassinosteroids

Answer: B
*Topic: Concept 39.2*
*Skill: Knowledge*

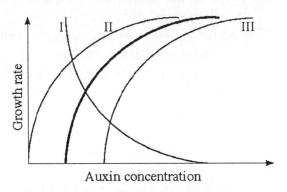

**Figure 39.1**

27) The heavy line in Figure 39.1 illustrates the relationship between auxin concentration and cell growth in stem tissues. If the same range of concentrations were applied to lateral buds, what curve would probably be produced?

    A) I

    B) II

    C) III

    D) II and III

    E) either I or III

Answer: A
*Topic: Concept 39.2*
*Skill: Application*

28) The application of which of the following hormones would be a logical first choice in an attempt to produce normal growth in mutant dwarf plants?

    A) indoleacetic acid

    B) cytokinin

    C) gibberellin

    D) abscisic acid

    E) ethylene

Answer: C
*Topic: Concept 39.2*
*Skill: Knowledge*

*Refer to Figure 39.2 to answer the following questions.*

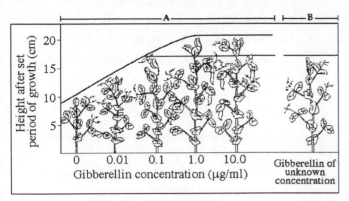

**Figure 39.2**

29) The results of this experiment, shown on the left of the graph (area A), may be used to

A) show that these plants can live without gibberellin.

B) show that gibberellin is necessary in positive gravitropism.

C) show that taller plants with more gibberellin produce fruit (pods).

D) show a correlation between plant height and gibberellin concentration.

E) study phytoalexins in plants.

Answer: D
*Topic: Concept 39.2*
*Skill: Comprehension*

30) This experiment suggests that the unknown amount of gibberellin in the experimental plant (B) is approximately

A) zero.

B) 0.01 µg/mL.

C) 0.1 µg/mL.

D) 1.0 µg/mL.

E) equal to the amount of gibberellin in the shortest plant.

Answer: C
*Topic: Concept 39.2*
*Skill: Application*

31) One effect of gibberellins is to stimulate cereal seeds to produce

A) RuBP carboxylase.

B) lipids.

C) abscisic acid.

D) starch.

E) amylase.

Answer: E
*Topic: Concept 39.2*
*Skill: Knowledge*

32) In attempting to make a seed break dormancy, one logically could treat it with

A) IAA.

B) 2, 4–D.

C) $CO_2$.

D) gibberellins.

E) abscisic acid.

Answer: D
*Topic: Concept 39.2*
*Skill: Knowledge*

33) Ethylene, as an example of a plant hormone, may have multiple effects on a plant, depending on all of the following *except* the

A) site of action within the plant.

B) developmental stage of the plant.

C) concentration of ethylene.

D) altered chemical structure of ethylene from a gas to a liquid.

E) readiness of cell membrane receptors for the ethylene.

Answer: D
*Topic: Concept 39.2*
*Skill: Comprehension*

34) If you were shipping green bananas to a supermarket thousands of miles away, which of the following chemicals would you want to eliminate from the plants' environment?

A) $CO_2$

B) cytokinins

C) ethylene

D) auxin

E) gibberellic acids

Answer: C
*Topic: Concept 39.2*
*Skill: Application*

35) Which of the following is currently the most powerful method of research on plant hormones?

A) comparing of photoperiodic responses

B) comparing tropisms with turgor movements

C) subjecting plants to unusual stresses

D) studying phytochromes

E) analyzing mutant plants

Answer: E
*Topic: Concept 39.2*
*Skill: Knowledge*

36) We tend to think of plants as immobile when, in fact, they can move in many ways. All of the following are movements plants can accomplish *except*

A) growth movements up or down in response to gravity.

B) folding and unfolding of leaves using muscle–like tissues.

C) growth movements toward or away from light.

D) changes in plant growth form in response to wind or touch.

E) rapid responses using action potentials similar to those found in the nervous tissue of animals.

Answer: B
*Topic: Concept 39.2*
*Skill: Comprehension*

37) Auxin is responsible for all of the following plant growth responses *except*

A) phototropism.

B) formation of adventitious roots.

C) apical dominance.

D) the detection of photoperiod.

E) cell elongation.

Answer: D
*Topic: Concept 39.2*
*Skill: Knowledge*

38) Incandescent light bulbs, which have high output of red light, are *least* effective in promoting

A) photosynthesis.

B) seed germination.

C) phototropism.

D) flowering.

E) entrainment of circadian rhythms.

Answer: C
*Topic: Concept 39.3*
*Skill: Application*

39) Both red and blue light are involved in

    A) stem elongation.

    B) photoperiodism.

    C) positive phototropism.

    D) tracking seasons.

    E) all of the above

Answer: A
*Topic: Concept 39.3*
*Skill: Knowledge*

40) Seed packets give a recommended planting depth for the enclosed seeds. The most likely reason some seeds are to be covered with only 1/4 inch of soil is that the

    A) seedlings do not produce a hypocotyl.

    B) seedlings do not have an etiolation response.

    C) seeds require light to germinate.

    D) seeds require a higher temperature to germinate.

    E) seeds are very sensitive to waterlogging.

Answer: C
*Topic: Concept 39.3*
*Skill: Application*

41) Most plants close their stomata at night. What color of light would be most effective in promoting stomatal opening in the middle of the night?

    A) red

    B) far-red

    C) blue

    D) red followed by far-red

    E) far-red followed by blue

Answer: C
*Topic: Concept 39.3*
*Skill: Knowledge*

42) The houseplants in a windowless room with only fluorescent lights begin to grow tall and leggy. Which of the following treatments would promote more normal growth?

    A) Leave the lights on at night as well as during the day.

    B) Add additional fluorescent tubes to increase the light output.

    C) Add some incandescent bulbs to increase the amount of red light.

    D) Set a timer to turn on the lights for 5 minutes during the night.

    E) Turn off the lights for 5 minutes during the day.

Answer: C
*Topic: Concept 39.3*
*Skill: Application*

43) In legumes, it has been shown that "sleep" movements are correlated with

    A) positive thigmotropisms.

    B) rhythmic opening and closing of $K^+$ channels in motor cell membranes.

    C) senescence (the aging process in plants).

    D) flowering and fruit development.

    E) ABA-stimulated closing of guard cells caused by loss of $K^+$.

Answer: B
*Topic: Concept 39.3*
*Skill: Knowledge*

44) Biological clocks cause organisms to perform daily activities on a regular basis. Which of the following is a *false* statement about this kind of "circadian rhythm"?

   A) It may have the same signal transduction pathway in all organisms.

   B) It must be reset on a daily basis.

   C) It may help to cause photoperiodic responses.

   D) Once set, it is independent of external signals.

   E) The exact mechanism of biological clocks remains unknown.

Answer: D
*Topic: Concept 39.3*
*Skill: Knowledge*

45) The biological clock controlling circadian rhythms must ultimately

   A) depend on environmental cues.

   B) affect gene transcription.

   C) stabilize on a 24-hour cycle.

   D) speed up or slow down with increasing or decreasing temperature.

   E) do all of the above.

Answer: B
*Topic: Concept 39.3*
*Skill: Comprehension*

46) Plants often use changes in day length (photoperiod) to trigger events such as dormancy and flowering. It is logical that plants have evolved this mechanism because photoperiod changes

   A) are more predictable than air temperature changes.

   B) alter the amount of energy available to the plant.

   C) are modified by soil temperature changes.

   D) can reset the biological clock.

   E) are correlated with moisture availability.

Answer: A
*Topic: Concept 39.3*
*Skill: Application*

47) If the range of a species of plants expands to a higher latitude, which of the following processes is the most *likely* to be modified by natural selection?

   A) circadian rhythm

   B) photoperiodic response

   C) phototropic response

   D) biological clock

   E) thigmomorphogenesis

Answer: B
*Topic: Concept 39.3*
*Skill: Application*

48) In nature, poinsettias bloom in early March. Research has shown that the flowering process is triggered three months before blooming occurs. In order to make poinsettias bloom in December, florists change the length of the light-dark cycle in September. Given the information and clues above, which of the following is a *false* statement about poinsettias?

A) They are short-day plants.

B) They require a light period shorter than some set maximum.

C) They require a longer dark period than is available in September.

D) The dark period can be interrupted without affecting flowering.

E) They will flower even if there are brief periods of dark during the daytime.

Answer: D
*Topic: Concept 39.3*
*Skill: Application*

49) A botanist exposed two groups of the same plant species to two photoperiods—one with 14 hours of light and 10 hours of dark and the other with 10 hours of light and 14 hours of dark. Under the first set of conditions, the plants flowered, but they failed to flower under the second set of conditions. Which of the following conclusions would be consistent with these results?

A) The critical night length is 14 hours.

B) The plants are short-day plants.

C) The critical day length is 10 hours.

D) The plants can convert phytochrome to florigen.

E) The plants flower in the spring.

Answer: E
*Topic: Concept 39.3*
*Skill: Application*

50) In order to flower, a short-day plant needs a

A) burst of red light in the middle of the night.

B) burst of far-red light in the middle of the night.

C) day that is longer than a certain length.

D) night that is longer than a certain length.

E) higher ratio of $P_r$ to $P_{fr}$.

Answer: D
*Topic: Concept 39.3*
*Skill: Comprehension*

51) If a short-day plant has a critical night length of 15 hours, then which of the following 24-hour cycles will prevent flowering?

A) 8 hours light / 16 hours dark

B) 4 hours light / 20 hours dark

C) 6 hours light / 2 hours dark / light flash / 16 hours dark

D) 8 hours light / 8 hours dark / light flash / 8 hours dark

E) 2 hours light / 20 hours dark / 2 hours light

Answer: D
*Topic: Concept 39.3*
*Skill: Comprehension*

52) A long-day plant will flower if

A) the duration of continuous light exceeds a critical length.

B) the duration of continuous light is less than a critical length.

C) the duration of continuous darkness exceeds a critical length.

D) the duration of continuous darkness is less than a critical length.

E) it is kept in continuous far-red light.

Answer: D
*Topic: Concept 39.3*
*Skill: Knowledge*

53) Plants that have their flowering inhibited by being exposed to bright lights at night are

A) day-neutral plants.

B) short-night plants.

C) devoid of phytochrome.

D) short-day plants.

E) long-day plants.

Answer: D
*Topic: Concept 39.3*
*Skill: Comprehension*

54) Suppose there is a large deciduous ornamental tree on your campus and the city places a very bright street light right next to it on a tall pole. A botanist on the faculty complains to the city council and asks them to remove the light. Most likely the botanist is concerned because the light

A) will alter the photosynthetic rate of the tree and keep it growing at night.

B) may cause the stomata to close because of increased ABA synthesis. This could starve the tree for $CO_2$ and it could die.

C) may change the photoperiod and cause the tree to retain its leaves during the winter. This could cause dehydration and loss of the tree.

D) will cause the tree to bend toward the light on the pole, and the tree could fall.

E) will stimulate ethylene production, premature senescence, and early death of the tree.

Answer: C
*Topic: Concept 39.3*
*Skill: Application*

55) If you take a short-day plant and put it in a lab under conditions where it will flower (long nights and short days), but interrupt its day period with a few minutes of darkness, what will happen?

A) It will flower.

B) It will not flower.

C) It will die.

D) It will lose its ability to photosynthesize.

E) It will form new shoots from the axillary buds.

Answer: A
*Topic: Concept 39.3*
*Skill: Comprehension*

56) Florigen is a flowering signal, not yet chemically identified, found in

A) flowers.

B) leaves.

C) roots.

D) seeds.

E) floral buds.

Answer: B
*Topic: Concept 39.3*
*Skill: Knowledge*

57) What do results of research on gravitropic responses of roots and stems show?

A) Different tissues have the same response to auxin.

B) The effect of a plant hormone can depend on the tissue.

C) Some responses of plants require no hormones at all.

D) Light is required for the gravitropic response.

E) Cytokinin can only function in the presence of auxin.

Answer: B
*Topic: Concept 39.4*
*Skill: Comprehension*

58) A botanist discovers a plant that lacks the ability to form starch grains in root cells, yet the roots still grow downward. This evidence refutes the long-standing hypothesis that

A) falling statoliths trigger gravitropism.

B) starch accumulation triggers the negative phototropic response of roots.

C) starch grains block the acid growth response in roots.

D) starch is converted to auxin, which causes the downward bending in roots.

E) starch and downward movement are necessary for thigmotropism.

Answer: A
*Topic: Concept 39.4*
*Skill: Application*

59) If a plant is mechanically stimulated, it will grow shorter, thicker stems. This response is

A) the result of ethylene production.

B) caused by an increase in turgor.

C) an adaptation to windy environments.

D) A and C only

E) A, B, and C

Answer: D
*Topic: Concept 39.4*
*Skill: Knowledge*

60) When transplanting a tree, it is recommended to loosely attach three or four guylines. The purpose of leaving these supports loose is to

A) prevent constriction of secondary growth.

B) permit moderate bending to stimulate thickness growth.

C) allow room for expansion as the tree grows taller.

D) B and C only

E) A, B, and C

Answer: B
*Topic: Concept 39.4*
*Skill: Application*

61) Which of the following watering regimens will be most effective at keeping a lawn green during the hot, dry summer months?

A) daily sprinkling to soak the soil to 0.5 inch

B) sprinkling every other day to soak the soil to 1.0 inch

C) sprinkling every third day to soak the soil to 2.0 inches

D) A or B would be equally effective.

E) A, B or C would be equally effective.

Answer: C
*Topic: Concept 39.4*
*Skill: Application*

62) You are part of a desert plant research team trying to discover crops that will be productive in arid climates. You discover a plant that produces a guard cell hormone under water-deficit conditions. Most likely the hormone is

A) ABA.

B) GA.

C) IAA.

D) 2, 4-D.

E) salicylic acid.

Answer: A
*Topic: Concept 39.4*
*Skill: Knowledge*

63) If you wanted to genetically engineer a plant to be more resistant to drought, increasing amounts of which of the following hormones might be a good first attempt?

A) abscisic acid

B) brassinosteroids

C) gibberellins

D) cytokinins

E) auxin

Answer: A
*Topic: Concept 39.4*
*Skill: Application*

64) Plant cells begin synthesizing large quantities of heat-shock proteins

A) after the induction of chaperone proteins.

B) in response to the lack of $CO_2$ following the closing of stomata by ethylene.

C) when desert plants are quickly removed from high temperatures.

D) when they are subjected to moist heat (steam) followed by electric shock.

E) when the air around species from temperate regions is above 40°C.

Answer: E
*Topic: Concept 39.4*
*Skill: Knowledge*

65) Most scientists agree that global warming is underway; thus it is important to know how plants respond to heat stress. Which of the following is an immediate short-term response of plants to heat stress?

A) the production of heat-shock carbohydrates unique to each plant

B) the production of heat-shock proteins like those of other organisms

C) the opening of stomata to increase evaporational heat loss

D) their evolution into more xerophytic plants

E) all of the above

Answer: B
*Topic: Concept 39.4*
*Skill: Knowledge*

66) In extremely cold regions, woody species may survive freezing temperatures by
    A) emptying water from the vacuoles to prevent freezing.
    B) decreasing the numbers of phospholipids in cell membranes.
    C) decreasing the fluidity of all cellular membranes.
    D) producing canavanine as a natural antifreeze.
    E) increasing cytoplasmic levels of specific solute concentrations, such as sugars.

Answer: E
*Topic: Concept 39.4*
*Skill: Knowledge*

67) All of the following are responses of plants to cold stress *except*
    A) the production of a specific solute "plant antifreeze" that reduces water loss.
    B) excluding ice crystals from the interior walls.
    C) conversion of the fluid mosaic cell membrane to a solid mosaic one.
    D) an alteration of membrane lipids so that the membranes remain flexible.
    E) increasing the proportion of unsaturated fatty acids in the membranes.

Answer: C
*Topic: Concept 39.4*
*Skill: Comprehension*

68) Bald cypress and Loblolly pine are both gymnosperm trees native to the southern United States. The cypress grows in swamps; the pine grows in sandy soil. How do you think their anatomies differ?
    A) There are larger intercellular spaces in the roots of the cypress than in the roots of the pine.
    B) Water-conducting cells are larger in the stems of the cypress than in the stems of the pine.
    C) The springwood and summerwood are more distinct in the cypress.
    D) There is less parenchyma in the roots of the cypress than in the pine roots.
    E) There are no major anatomical differences between these species because they're both gymnosperms.

Answer: A
*Topic: Concept 39.4*
*Skill: Application*

69) The initial response of the root cells of a tomato plant watered with seawater would be to
    A) rapidly produce organic solutes in the cytoplasm.
    B) rapidly expand until the cells burst.
    C) begin to plasmolyze as water is lost.
    D) actively transport water from the cytoplasm into the vacuole.
    E) actively absorb salts from the seawater.

Answer: C
*Topic: Concept 39.4*
*Skill: Application*

70) In general, which of the following is *not* a plant response to herbivores?

    A) domestication, so that humans can protect the plant

    B) attracting predatory animals, such as parasitoid wasps

    C) chemical defenses, such as toxic compounds

    D) physical defenses, such as thorns

    E) production of volatile molecules

Answer: A
*Topic: Concept 39.5*
*Skill: Knowledge*

71) In order for a plant to initiate chemical responses to herbivory,

    A) the plant must be directly attacked by an herbivore.

    B) volatile "signal" compounds must be perceived.

    C) gene-for-gene recognition must occur.

    D) phytoalexins must be released.

    E) all of the above must happen.

Answer: B
*Topic: Concept 39.5*
*Skill: Comprehension*

72) Plants are affected by an array of pathogens. Which of the following is *not* a plant defense against disease?

    A) cells near the point of infection destroying themselves to prevent the spread of the infection

    B) production of chemicals that kill pathogens

    C) acquiring gene-for-gene recognition that allows specific proteins to interact so that the plant can produce defenses against the pathogen

    D) a waxy cuticle that pathogens have trouble penetrating

    E) All of the above are plant defenses against disease.

Answer: E
*Topic: Concept 39.5*
*Skill: Comprehension*

73) A pathogenic fungus invades a plant. What does the infected plant produce in response to the attack?

    A) antisense RNA

    B) phytoalexins

    C) phytochrome

    D) statoliths

    E) thickened cellulose microfibrils in the cell wall

Answer: B
*Topic: Concept 39.5*
*Skill: Knowledge*

74) Which of the following are defenses that some plants use against herbivory?

   A) production of the unusual amino acid canavanine

   B) release of volatile compounds that attract parasitoid wasps

   C) association of plant tissues with mycorrhizae

   D) A and B only

   E) A, B, and C

Answer: D
*Topic: Concept 39.5*
*Skill: Comprehension*

75) The transduction pathway that activates systemic acquired resistance in plants is initially signaled by

   A) antisense RNA.

   B) $P_{fr}$ phytochrome.

   C) salicylic acid.

   D) abscisic acid.

   E) red, but not far-red, light.

Answer: C
*Topic: Concept 39.5*
*Skill: Knowledge*

76) Which of the following are examples or parts of plants' systemic acquired resistance against infection?

   A) phytoalexins

   B) salicylic acid

   C) alarm hormones

   D) A and B only

   E) A, B, and C

Answer: E
*Topic: Concept 39.5*
*Skill: Knowledge*

77) A plant will recognize a pathogenic invader

   A) if it has many specific plant disease resistance (R) genes.

   B) when the pathogen has an *R* gene complimentary to the plant's antivirulence (*Avr*) gene.

   C) only if the pathogen and the plant have the same *R* genes.

   D) if it has the specific *R* gene that corresponds to the pathogen molecule encoded by an *Avr* gene.

   E) when the pathogen secretes Avr protein.

Answer: D
*Topic: Concept 39.5*
*Skill: Application*

78) When an arborist prunes a limb off a valuable tree, he or she usually paints the cut surface. The primary purpose of the paint is to

   A) minimize water loss by evaporation from the cut surface.

   B) improve the appearance of the cut surface.

   C) stimulate growth of the cork cambium to "heal" the wound.

   D) block entry of pathogens through the wound.

   E) induce the production of phytoalexins.

Answer: D
*Topic: Concept 39.5*
*Skill: Application*

# Media Activity Questions

1) The breakdown of chlorophyll reveals the _____ pigments of a leaf.

   A) carotenoid

   B) xanthophyll

   C) anthocyanin

   D) melanin

   E) phycoerythrin

   Answer: A
   *Topic: Web/CD Activity: Leaf Abscission*

2) The protective layer that forms between the abscission layer and the stem consists of

   A) a layer of green palisade cells.

   B) weak, colorless, thin-walled cells.

   C) mycorrhizae.

   D) irregularly shaped cells with very thick-lignified secondary walls.

   E) densely colored cells filled with a waxy layer

   Answer: B
   *Topic: Web/CD Activity: Leaf Abscission*

3) After leaf abscission, growth will resume from the

   A) petiole.

   B) protective layer.

   C) palisade layer.

   D) axillary bud.

   E) abscission layer.

   Answer: A
   *Topic: Web/CD Activity: Leaf Abscission*

4) What is the specific term that refers to seasonal changes in the relative lengths of night and day?

   A) photoperiod

   B) circadian rhythm

   C) chemotaxis

   D) gravitropism

   E) phototaxis

   Answer: A
   *Topic: Web/CD Activity: Flowering Lab*

5) Day-neutral plants flower regardless of

   A) night length.

   B) day length.

   C) photoperiod.

   D) day length or night length.

   E) day length, night length, or photoperiod.

   Answer: E
   *Topic: Web/CD Activity: Flowering Lab*

# Self–Quiz Questions

1) Which hormone is *incorrectly* paired with its function?

   A) auxin—promotes stem growth through cell elongation

   B) cytokinins—initiate programmed cell death

   C) gibberellins—stimulate seed germination

   D) abscisic acid—promotes seed dormancy

   E) ethylene—inhibits cell elongation

   Answer: B

2) Which of the following is *not* a typical component of a signal transduction pathway?

   A) production of more signal

   B) production of second messengers such as cGMP

   C) expression of specific proteins

   D) activation of protein kinases

   E) phosphorylation of transcription factors

   Answer: A

3) Buds and sprouts often form on tree stumps. Which of the following hormones would you expect to stimulate their formation?

   A) auxin

   B) cytokinins

   C) abscisic acid

   D) ethylene

   E) gibberellins

   Answer: B

4) Which of the following is *not* part of the acid growth hypothesis?

   A) Auxin stimulates proton pumps in cell membranes.

   B) Lowered pH results in the breakage of cross-links between cellulose microfibrils.

   C) The wall fabric becomes looser (more plastic).

   D) Auxin-activated proton pumps stimulate cell division in meristems.

   E) The turgor pressure of the cell exceeds the restraining pressure of the loosened cell wall, and the cell takes up water and elongates.

   Answer: D

5) The signal for flowering could be released earlier than normal in a long-day plant experimentally exposed to flashes of

   A) far-red light during the night.

   B) red light during the night.

   C) red light followed by far-red light during the night.

   D) far-red light during the day.

   E) red light during the day.

   Answer: B

6) How might a plant respond to *severe* heat stress?

    A) by orienting leaves toward the sun to increase evaporative cooling

    B) by producing ethylene, which kills some cortex cells and creates air tubes for ventilation

    C) by producing salicylic acid, which initiates a systemic acquired resistance response

    D) by increasing the proportion of unsaturated fatty acids in cell membranes to reduce their fluidity

    E) by producing heat-shock proteins, which may protect the plant's proteins from denaturing

Answer: E

7) If a long-day plant has a critical night length of 9 hours, which of the following 24-hour cycles would prevent flowering?

    A) 16 hours light/8 hours dark

    B) 14 hours light/10 hours dark

    C) 15.5 hours light/8.5 hours dark

    D) 4 hours light/8 hours dark/4 hours light/8 hours dark

    E) 8 hours light/8 hours dark/light flash/8 hours dark

Answer: B

8) The probable role of salicylic acid in systemic acquired resistance of plants is to

    A) destroy pathogens directly.

    B) activate plant defenses throughout the plant before infection spreads.

    C) close stomata, thus preventing the entry of pathogens.

    D) activate heat-shock proteins.

    E) sacrifice infected tissues by hydrolyzing cells.

Answer: B

9) Auxin triggers the acidification of cell walls that results in rapid growth, but also stimulates sustained, long-term cell elongation. What best explains how auxin brings about this dual growth response?

    A) Auxin binds to different receptors in different cells.

    B) Different concentrations of auxin have different effects.

    C) Auxin causes second messengers to activate both proton pumps and certain genes.

    D) The dual effects are due to two different auxins.

    E) Other antagonistic hormones modify auxin's effects.

Answer: C

10) If a scientist discovered an *Arabidopsis* mutant that did not store starch in its plastids but underwent normal gravitropic bending, what aspect of our current understanding of root gravitropism would have to be reevaluated?

    A) the role of auxin in gravitropism

    B) the role of calcium in gravitropism

    C) the role of statoliths in gravitropism

    D) the role of light in gravitropism

    E) the role of differential growth in gravitropic bending

Answer: C

# Chapter 40 Basic Principles of Animal Form and Function

1) How do animal structures well suited to specific functions come about?
   A) Natural selection favors the most functional structures for a particular environment.
   B) Mutations arise to provide required structures for survival in a particular environment.
   C) An animal that needs a new function will develop a new structure to provide it.
   D) Animals invent structural designs that enhance their functions.
   E) Animals continually improve their structures in order to improve their functions.

   Answer: A
   *Topic: Concept 40.1*
   *Skill: Comprehension*

2) Which represent adaptations to the same environmental challenge?
   A) gastrovascular activity, two-layered body, and torpedo shape
   B) large volume, long tubular body, wings
   C) external respiratory surface, small size, two-layered body
   D) complex internal structures, small size, large surface area
   E) branched internal surfaces, small size, moist outer covering

   Answer: C
   *Topic: Concept 40.1*
   *Skill: Application*

3) Why do sharks, penguins, and aquatic mammals have the same fusiform body shape?
   A) Natural selection shapes similar adaptations when diverse organisms face the same environmental challenge.
   B) Respiration through gills is enhanced by having a fusiform shape.
   C) The laws of hydrodynamics constrain the shapes that are possible for aquatic animals that swim very fast.
   D) A and C only
   E) A, B, and C

   Answer: D
   *Topic: Concept 40.1*
   *Skill: Knowledge*

4) Which of the following ideas is *not* consistent with our understanding of animal structure?
   A) The environment imposes similar problems on all animals.
   B) The evolution of structure in an animal is influenced by its environment.
   C) All but the simplest animals demonstrate the same hierarchical levels of organization.
   D) Different animals contain fundamentally different categories of tissues.
   E) Short-term adjustments to environmental changes are mediated by physiological organ systems.

   Answer: D
   *Topic: Concept 40.1*
   *Skill: Comprehension*

5) Regardless of their size, the one thing that is common to all animals is

A) an external body surface that is dry.

B) a basic body plan that resembles a two-layered sac.

C) the use of homeostatic mechanisms to control their internal environment.

D) the use of positive and negative feedback cycles to regulate body water content.

E) having cells surrounded by an aqueous medium.

Answer: E
*Topic: Concept 40.1*
*Skill: Application*

6) Which of the following is a problem faced by animals as they increase in size?

A) decreasing surface-to-volume ratio

B) reproducing in aqueous environments

C) the tendency for larger bodies to be more variable in metabolic rate

D) A and B only

E) A, B, and C

Answer: A
*Topic: Concept 40.1*
*Skill: Comprehension*

7) An increase in which of the following parameters is most important in the evolution of specialized exchange surfaces such as the linings of the lungs or intestines?

A) surface area

B) body thickness

C) number of cell layers

D) metabolic rate of component cells

E) volume of component cells

Answer: A
*Topic: Concept 40.1*
*Skill: Comprehension*

8) What is the common functional significance of the extended number of cells making up such seemingly different human structures as the lining of the air sacs in the lungs and the wavy lining of the intestine?

A) increased oxygen demand from their metabolic activity

B) increased exchange surface provided by their membranes

C) greater numbers of cell organelles contained within their cytoplasm

D) greater protection due to increased cellular mass

E) lowered basal metabolic rate due to cooperation between cells

Answer: B
*Topic: Concept 40.1*
*Skill: Comprehension*

9) Which of the following is true of interstitial fluid?

A) It forms the extracellular matrix of connective tissue.

B) It is the internal environment found in animal cells.

C) It is composed of blood.

D) It provides for the exchange of materials between blood and body cells.

E) It is found inside the small intestine.

Answer: D
*Topic: Concept 40.1*
*Skill: Knowledge*

10) Why must multicellular organisms keep their cells awash in an "internal pond"?

    A) Negative feedback will only operate in interstitial fluids.

    B) Cells need an aqueous medium for the exchange of nutrients, gases, and wastes.

    C) Cells of multicellular organisms tend to lose water because of osmosis.

    D) Cells of multicellular organisms tend to accumulate wastes, a consequence of diffusion.

    E) This phenomenon occurs only in aquatic organisms because terrestrial organisms have adapted to life in dry environments.

Answer: B
*Topic: Concept 40.1*
*Skill: Comprehension*

11) Cells are to tissues as tissues are to

    A) organs.

    B) membranes.

    C) organ systems.

    D) organelles.

    E) organisms.

Answer: A
*Topic: Concept 40.2*
*Skill: Knowledge*

12) In a typical multicellular animal, the circulatory system interacts with various specialized surfaces in order to exchange materials with the exterior environment. Which of the following is *not* an example of such an exchange surface?

    A) lung

    B) muscle

    C) skin

    D) intestine

    E) kidney

Answer: B
*Topic: Concept 40.2*
*Skill: Comprehension*

13) The epithelium best adapted for a body surface subject to abrasion is

    A) simple squamous.

    B) simple cuboidal.

    C) simple columnar.

    D) stratified columnar.

    E) stratified squamous.

Answer: E
*Topic: Concept 40.2*
*Skill: Knowledge*

14) Which of the following tissues lines the kidney tubules?

    A) connective

    B) smooth muscle

    C) nervous

    D) epithelial

    E) adipose

Answer: D
*Topic: Concept 40.2*
*Skill: Knowledge*

15) Collagenous fibers are primarily found in what type of animal tissue?

    A) connective

    B) striated muscle

    C) nerve

    D) epithelial

    E) bone

Answer: A
*Topic: Concept 40.2*
*Skill: Knowledge*

16) What is stratified cuboidal epithelium composed of?

A) several layers of box–like cells

B) a hierarchical arrangement of flat cells

C) a tight layer of square cells attached to a basement membrane

D) an irregularly arranged layer of pillar–like cells

E) a layer of ciliated, mucus–secreting cells

Answer: A
*Topic: Concept 40.2*
*Skill: Comprehension*

17) Which statement best links the group of tissues known as connective tissue? A connective tissue will have

A) an extracellular matrix containing fibers.

B) a supporting material such as chondroitin sulfate.

C) an epithelial origin.

D) relatively few cells and a large amount of extracellular matrix.

E) both A and B

Answer: D
*Topic: Concept 40.2*
*Skill: Application*

18) Which of the following fibers are responsible for the resistant property of tendons?

A) elastin fibers

B) fibrin fibers

C) collagenous fibers

D) reticular fibers

E) spindle fibers

Answer: C
*Topic: Concept 40.2*
*Skill: Comprehension*

19) If you gently twist your ear lobe it does not remain distorted because it contains

A) collagenous fibers.

B) elastin fibers.

C) reticular fibers.

D) adipose tissue.

E) loose connective tissue.

Answer: B
*Topic: Concept 40.2*
*Skill: Application*

20) What do fibroblasts secrete?

A) fats

B) chondroitin sulfate

C) interstitial fluids

D) calcium phosphate for bone

E) proteins for connective fibers

Answer: E
*Topic: Concept 40.2*
*Skill: Knowledge*

21) Which of the following characteristics of blood best explains its classification as connective tissue?

A) Its cells are widely dispersed and surrounded by a fluid.

B) It contains more than one type of cell.

C) It is contained in vessels that "connect" different parts of an organism's body.

D) Its cells can move from place to place.

E) It is found within all the organs of the body.

Answer: A
*Topic: Concept 40.2*
*Skill: Knowledge*

22) What joins muscles to bones?

 A) ligaments

 B) tendons

 C) loose connective tissue

 D) Haversian systems

 E) spindle fibers

Answer: B
*Topic: Concept 40.2*
*Skill: Knowledge*

23) Cartilage is an example of which of the following types of tissue?

 A) connective

 B) reproductive

 C) nervous

 D) epithelial

 E) adipose

Answer: A
*Topic: Concept 40.2*
*Skill: Knowledge*

24) What holds bones together at joints?

 A) cartilage

 B) Haversian systems

 C) loose connective tissue

 D) tendons

 E) ligaments

Answer: E
*Topic: Concept 40.2*
*Skill: Knowledge*

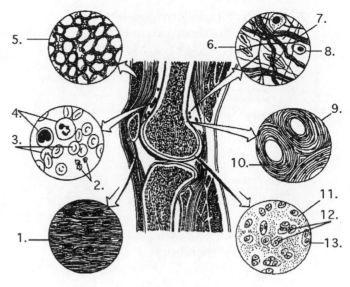

**Figure 40.1**

25) Which of the following numbers represents a tissue found in tendons?

 A) 1

 B) 5

 C) 6

 D) 9

 E) 13

Answer: A
*Topic: Concept 40.2*
*Skill: Comprehension*

26) Which of the following numbers represents a tissue rich in hydroxyapatite?

 A) 1

 B) 5

 C) 6

 D) 9

 E) 13

Answer: D
*Topic: Concept 40.2*
*Skill: Comprehension*

27) Which of the following numbers represents a tissue rich in fat?

  A) 1

  B) 5

  C) 6

  D) 9

  E) 13

Answer: B
*Topic: Concept 40.2*
*Skill: Comprehension*

28) Which of the following numbers represents chondrocytes?

  A) 3

  B) 4

  C) 8

  D) 10

  E) 12

Answer: E
*Topic: Concept 40.2*
*Skill: Comprehension*

29) Which of the following numbers represents the location of osteocytes?

  A) 2

  B) 3

  C) 8

  D) 10

  E) 12

Answer: D
*Topic: Concept 40.2*
*Skill: Comprehension*

30) Matrices of connective tissue include all of the following except

  A) chondroitin sulfate of cartilage.

  B) actin and myosin of muscle.

  C) plasma of blood.

  D) hydroxyapatite of bone.

  E) more than one of the above

Answer: B
*Topic: Concept 40.2*
*Skill: Knowledge*

31) What is the functional unit of nervous tissue?

  A) cell body

  B) neuron

  C) axon

  D) dendrite

  E) brain

Answer: B
*Topic: Concept 40.2*
*Skill: Knowledge*

32) Which of the following traits is characteristic of *all* types of muscle tissue?

  A) intercalated discs that allow cells to communicate

  B) striated banding pattern seen under the microscope

  C) cells that lengthen when appropriately stimulated

  D) a response that can be consciously controlled

  E) cells that contain actin and myosin

Answer: E
*Topic: Concept 40.2*
*Skill: Knowledge*

33) Which of the following describes skeletal muscle?

   A) smooth and involuntary

   B) smooth and unbranched

   C) striated and voluntary

   D) smooth and voluntary

   E) striated and branched

   Answer: C
   *Topic: Concept 40.2*
   *Skill: Knowledge*

34) Which of the following describes cardiac muscle?

   A) striated and branched

   B) striated and unbranched

   C) smooth and voluntary

   D) striated and voluntary

   E) smooth and involuntary

   Answer: A
   *Topic: Concept 40.2*
   *Skill: Knowledge*

35) What type of muscle tissue is associated with internal organs, other than the heart?

   A) skeletal

   B) cardiac

   C) striated

   D) intercalated

   E) smooth

   Answer: E
   *Topic: Concept 40.2*
   *Skill: Knowledge*

36) Which type of muscle is responsible for moving food along the digestive tract?

   A) cardiac

   B) smooth

   C) voluntary

   D) striated

   E) skeletal

   Answer: B
   *Topic: Concept 40.2*
   *Skill: Comprehension*

37) Which of the following layers of the stomach is best described as being composed primarily of epithelial tissue?

   A) mucosa

   B) submucosa

   C) muscularis

   D) serosa

   E) lumen

   Answer: A
   *Topic: Concept 40.2*
   *Skill: Knowledge*

38) Which choice offers the best time to measure basal metabolic rate?

   A) at rest prior to the first meal of the day

   B) at rest just after the first meal of the day

   C) immediately after having eaten a sugar-free meal

   D) one hour after having drinking a diet soda

   E) one hour after exercising for 30 minutes

   Answer: A
   *Topic: Concept 40.3*
   *Skill: Application*

39) Which statement about standard metabolic rate (SMR) and basal metabolic rate (BMR) is correct?

 A) SMR measures energy use during exercise, and BMR is measured at rest.

 B) SMR is a measure of metabolic rate in endotherms, and BMR is a measure of metabolic rate in ectotherms.

 C) The measurement of both SMR and BMR is temperature dependent.

 D) Human females have a higher BMR and a lower SMR than males.

 E) Both SMR and BMR are measured in a resting, fasting, nonstressed state.

Answer: E
*Topic: Concept 40.3*
*Skill: Application*

40) Which of the following is an important distinction between the measurement of basal metabolic rate (BMR) and standard metabolic rate (SMR)?

 A) An animal must be fasting for the measurement of SMR.

 B) BMRs are performed only on ectothermic animals.

 C) An organism must be actively exercising for the measurement of BMR.

 D) SMRs must be determined at a specific temperature.

 E) The BMR for a particular animal is usually lower than that animal's SMR.

Answer: D
*Topic: Concept 40.3*
*Skill: Comprehension*

41) An extended low-fat diet will have the most significant effect on which of the following?

 A) muscle mass

 B) glucose utilization

 C) basal metabolic rate (BMR)

 D) standard metabolic rate (SMR)

 E) energy reserves

Answer: E
*Topic: Concept 40.3*
*Skill: Application*

42) The *least* reliable indicator of an animal's metabolic rate would be the amount of

 A) ATP produced within its cells.

 B) heat it generates.

 C) oxygen it inspires.

 D) carbon dioxide it expires.

 E) water it drinks.

Answer: E
*Topic: Concept 40.3*
*Skill: Comprehension*

43) The most significant single factor in preventing you from being able to run for a full 24 hours without stopping is the

 A) changes in blood pressure that accompany extended periods of exercise.

 B) circadian rhythm of the sleep-wake cycle.

 C) basal metabolic rate exceeding the amount of ATP available.

 D) lack of sustainable levels of cellular respiration.

 E) type of muscle fibers.

Answer: D
*Topic: Concept 40.3*
*Skill: Application*

44) Which common event most closely resembles negative feedback?

A) The water shuts off when the float rises in the tank of a toilet.

B) The chlorine level of a swimming pool decreases when the chlorinator is turned off.

C) The flame size on a gas stove changes when the gas is turned off.

D) There is a continual buildup of moisture in a basement with a dehumidifier running.

E) There is a decrease in water pressure when the faucet is slowly turned off.

Answer: A
*Topic: Concept 40.4*
*Skill: Application*

45) The body's automatic tendency to maintain a constant internal environment is termed

A) negative feedback.

B) physiologic control.

C) homeostasis.

D) static equilibrium.

E) organ system function.

Answer: C
*Topic: Concept 40.4*
*Skill: Knowledge*

46) Which example best describes a homeostatic control system?

A) The core body temperature of a runner is allowed to gradually rise from 37°C to 45°C.

B) The kidneys excrete salt into the urine when dietary salt levels rise.

C) A blood cell shrinks when placed in a solution of salt and water.

D) The blood pressure increases in response to an increase in blood volume.

E) Motility in the digestive tract increases following a meal.

Answer: B
*Topic: Concept 40.4*
*Skill: Application*

47) Which of the following is the best example of an effector's response in negative feedback?

A) an increase in body temperature resulting from shivering

B) an increase in body temperature resulting from exercise

C) an increase in body temperature resulting from exposure to the sun

D) an increase in body temperature resulting from fever

E) a decrease in body temperature resulting from shock

Answer: A
*Topic: Concept 40.4*
*Skill: Application*

48) Which of the following is an example of positive feedback?

A) An increase in blood sugar concentration increases the amount of the hormone that stores sugar as glycogen.

B) A decrease in blood sugar concentration increases the amount of the hormone that converts glycogen to glucose.

C) An infant's suckling at the mother's breast increases the amount of the hormone that induces the release of milk from the mammary glands.

D) An increase in calcium concentration increases the amount of the hormone that stores calcium in bone.

E) A decrease in calcium concentration increases the amount of the hormone that releases calcium from bone.

Answer: C
*Topic: Concept 40.4*
*Skill: Application*

49) How does positive feedback differ from negative feedback?

A) Positive feedback benefits the organism, whereas negative feedback is detrimental.

B) In positive feedback, the effector's response is in the same direction as the initiating stimulus rather than opposite to it.

C) In positive feedback, the effector increases some parameter (such as temperature), whereas in negative feedback it decreases.

D) Positive feedback systems have effectors, whereas negative feedback systems utilize receptors.

E) Positive feedback systems have control centers that are lacking in negative feedback systems.

Answer: B
*Topic: Concept 40.4*
*Skill: Comprehension*

50) Consider a husband and wife sharing a bed, with each one having an electric blanket. Their controls become switched. When the husband feels cold, he turns up the control. This warms up his spouse, who turns down her control. This chills the husband, who turns up his control even more. The process continues. For both the wife and the husband, this would be an example of

A) negative feedback.

B) positive feedback.

C) homeostasis.

D) regulated change.

E) integrated control.

Answer: B
*Topic: Concept 40.4*
*Skill: Comprehension*

51) Consider an ectotherm and an endotherm of equal body size. The ectotherm is more likely to survive an extended period of food deprivation than the endotherm because

A) the ectotherm is sustained by a higher basal metabolic rate.

B) the ectotherm will expend less energy/kg body weight than the endotherm.

C) the ectotherm will invest little to no energy in temperature regulation.

D) actually, assuming equal size, the ectotherm and the endotherm will have the same energy expenditures.

E) both B and C

Answer: E
*Topic: Concept 40.5*
*Skill: Application*

52) Terrestrial animals mainly exchange heat with the environment by all of the following physical processes *except*

A) conduction.

B) convection.

C) evaporation.

D) illumination.

E) radiation.

Answer: D
*Topic: Concept 40.5*
*Skill: Knowledge*

53) Of the mechanisms by which organisms exchange heat with their surroundings, which one results *only* in loss of heat from the organism?

A) conduction

B) convection

C) radiation

D) evaporation

E) metabolism

Answer: D
*Topic: Concept 40.5*
*Skill: Comprehension*

54) Which of the following is true about the activity levels of a snake?

A) A snake is less active in winter because the food supply is decreased.

B) A snake is less active in winter because it does not need to avoid predators.

C) A snake is more active in summer because that is the period for mating.

D) A snake is more active in summer because it can gain body heat by conduction.

E) A snake is more active in summer as a result of being disturbed by other animals.

Answer: D
*Topic: Concept 40.5*
*Skill: Comprehension*

55) Which organism is ectothermic and has little behavioral ability to adjust its body temperature?

A) lizard

B) sea star

C) bluefin tuna

D) hummingbird

E) winter moth

Answer: B
*Topic: Concept 40.5*
*Skill: Application*

56) All of the following are mechanisms of thermoregulation in terrestrial mammals *except*

A) changing the rate of evaporative heat loss.

B) changing the rate of metabolic heat production.

C) changing the rate of heat exchange by conforming to environmental temperatures.

D) changing the rate of heat loss by vasodilation and vasoconstriction.

E) relocating to cool areas when too hot, or to warm areas when too cold.

Answer: C
*Topic: Concept 40.5*
*Skill: Comprehension*

57) Which of the following assertions about regulation of body temperature is *true*?

A) Most animals are endotherms.

B) Endothermy involves production of heat through metabolism.

C) Ectothermic animals are cold-blooded.

D) Mammals are always ectothermic.

E) Insects are always ectothermic.

Answer: B
*Topic: Concept 40.5*
*Skill: Comprehension*

58) Most terrestrial animals dissipate excess heat by

A) countercurrent exchange.

B) acclimation.

C) vasoconstriction.

D) hibernation.

E) evaporation.

Answer: E
*Topic: Concept 40.5*
*Skill: Knowledge*

59) Which of the following organisms controls its body temperature by behavior *only*?

A) green frog

B) penguin

C) bluefin tuna

D) house sparrow

E) gray wolf

Answer: A
*Topic: Concept 40.5*
*Skill: Knowledge*

60) Most amphibians and land–dwelling invertebrates have what in common?

A) They are ectothermic organisms.

B) They use behavioral adaptations to maintain body temperature.

C) When on land, most have a net loss of heat across a moist body surface.

D) When in water, they are mainly thermoconformers.

E) Invertebrates have nothing in common with amphibians when it comes to regulating body temperatures.

Answer: A
*Topic: Concept 40.5*
*Skill: Comprehension*

61) Where is the thermostat of vertebrates located?

A) medulla oblongata

B) thyroid gland

C) hypothalamus

D) subcutaneous layer of the skin

E) liver

Answer: C
*Topic: Concept 40.5*
*Skill: Knowledge*

62) Which of the following is *not* an aspect of temperature acclimation?

A) The increase in production of certain enzymes by cells.

B) Cells may produce enzymes with different temperature optima.

C) Organisms may adjust some of the mechanisms that control internal temperature.

D) The proportion of saturated and unsaturated fats may change in cell membranes.

E) Allowing denaturation of proteins that cannot withstand extreme temperature.

Answer: E
*Topic: Concept 40.5*
*Skill: Comprehension*

*Match the terms to the following questions. Each term may be used once, more than once, or not at all*

A. ectothermy
B. endothermy
C. evaporation
D. torpor
E. thermogenesis

63) hibernation

Answer: D
*Topic: Concept 40.5*
*Skill: Knowledge*

64) estivation

Answer: D
*Topic: Concept 40.5*
*Skill: Knowledge*

65) absorption of heat from the surroundings

Answer: A
*Topic: Concept 40.5*
*Skill: Knowledge*

66) process that occurs in the brown fat of some mammals

Answer: E
*Topic: Concept 40.5*
*Skill: Knowledge*

67) panting in dogs

Answer: C
*Topic: Concept 40.5*
*Skill: Knowledge*

68) fur and feathers

Answer: B
*Topic: Concept 40.5*
*Skill: Knowledge*

*The following questions refer to Figure 40.2*

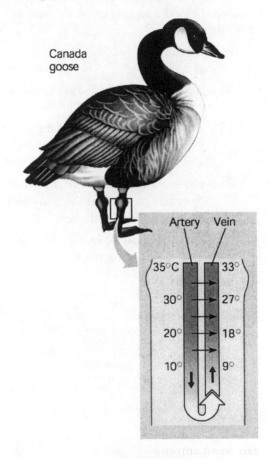

Canada goose

Artery    Vein

35°C    33°

30°    27°

20°    18°

10°    9°

**Figure 40.2**

69) What does the difference in temperature between arteries and veins in the goose's legs indicate?

A) The legs need to be kept cool so that muscles will function well.

B) The feet need to be kept very warm so they do not freeze in water.

C) Heat loss is proportional to the difference in temperature inside and outside, so minimizing the difference means the goose will lose less heat.

D) Arterial blood helps return heat to the core of the goose.

E) Warm venous blood is necessary to keep the goose's feet from freezing.

Answer: C
*Topic: Concept 40.5*
*Skill: Comprehension*

70) The temperature difference between arterial blood and venous blood near the goose's body

A) is minimized by countercurrent exchange.

B) is maximized because the blood has run through very cold feet.

C) is minimized by dilation of the capillaries in the feet of the goose, allowing heat to be lost.

D) is more than the difference between the venous blood near the body and the venous blood at the feet.

E) allows the goose to lose maximum heat to the environment.

Answer: A
*Topic: Concept 40.5*
*Skill: Comprehension*

# Media Activity Questions

1) Which type of epithelial tissue, found in the intestines, absorbs nutrients?

   A) stratified cuboidal epithelium

   B) simple cuboidal cells

   C) simple columnar epithelium

   D) stratified columnar epithelium

   E) stratified squamous epithelium

   Answer: C
   *Topic: Web/CD Activity: Epithelial Tissue*

2) A neuron consists of

   A) a cell body.

   B) dendrites.

   C) axons.

   D) dendrites, a cell body, and axons.

   E) striations.

   Answer: D
   *Topic: Web/CD Activity: Nervous Tissue*

3) Cardiac muscle is the only muscle composed of _____ fibers.

   A) branched

   B) unstriated

   C) unbranched and cylindrical

   D) spindle shaped

   E) striated

   Answer: A
   *Topic: Web/CD Activity: Muscle Tissue*

4) Which muscle tissue is responsible for voluntary movement?

   A) cardiac muscle only

   B) skeletal muscle only

   C) smooth muscle only

   D) cardiac and smooth muscle

   E) skeletal and smooth muscle

   Answer: B
   *Topic: Web/CD Activity: Muscle Tissue*

5) Which of these is an example of positive feedback?

   A) sweating when hot

   B) labor pains increasing in frequency and intensity

   C) drinking when thirsty

   D) shivering when cold

   E) eating when hungry

   Answer: B
   *Topic: Activity: Negative and Positive Feedback*

# Self–Quiz Questions

1) Consider the energy budgets for a human, an elephant, a penguin, a mouse, and a python. The _____ would have the highest total annual energy expenditure, and the _____ would have the highest energy expenditure per unit mass.

A) elephant; mouse

B) elephant; human

C) human; penguin

D) mouse; python

E) penguin; mouse

Answer: A

2) Which of the following structures or substances is *incorrectly* paired with a tissue?

A) osteon—bone

B) fibroblasts—skeletal muscle

C) platelets—blood

D) chondroitin sulfate—cartilage

E) basement membrane—epithelium

Answer: B

3) For which of the following animals would the percent of its energy budget spent for homeostatic regulation be the largest?

A) an amoeba in fresh water

B) a marine jellyfish

C) a snake in a temperate forest

D) a desert insect

E) a desert bird

Answer: E

4) The involuntary muscles that cause the wavelike contractions pushing food along our intestines are

A) striated muscles.

B) cardiac muscles.

C) skeletal muscles.

D) smooth muscles.

E) intercalated muscles.

Answer: D

5) Which of the following statements about bioenergetics is true?

A) An animal's metabolic rate never changes.

B) BMR can be determined only at a specific temperature.

C) Endotherms are warmed by metabolic heat.

D) SMR is best measured just after an ectotherm eats.

E) Ectotherms and endotherms use the same basic energy "strategy."

Answer: C

6) Compared to a smaller cell, a larger cell of the same shape has

A) less surface area.

B) less surface area per unit of volume.

C) the same surface-to-volume ratio.

D) a smaller average distance between its mitochondria and the external source of oxygen.

E) a smaller cytoplasm-to-nucleus ratio.

Answer: B

7) Which of the following is *not* an adaptation for reducing the rate of heat exchange between an animal and its environment?

 A) feathers or fur

 B) vasoconstriction

 C) nonshivering thermogenesis

 D) countercurrent heat exchanger

 E) blubber or fat layer

Answer: C

8) Which of the following physiological responses is an example of *positive* feedback?

 A) An increase in the concentration of glucose in the blood stimulates the pancreas to secrete insulin, a hormone that lowers blood glucose concentration.

 B) A high concentration of $CO_2$ in the blood causes deeper, more rapid breathing, which expels $CO_2$.

 C) Stimulation of a nerve cell causes sodium ions to leak into the cell, and the sodium influx triggers the inward leaking of even more sodium.

 D) The body's production of red blood cells, which transport oxygen from the lungs to other organs, is stimulated by a low concentration of oxygen.

 E) The pituitary gland secretes a hormone called TSH, which stimulates the thyroid gland to secrete another hormone called thyroxine; a high concentration of thyroxine suppresses the pituitary's secretion of TSH.

Answer: C

9) An animal's inputs of energy and materials would exceed its outputs

 A) if the animal is an endotherm, which must always take in more energy because of its high metabolic rate.

 B) if it is actively foraging for food.

 C) if it is hibernating.

 D) if it is growing and increasing its biomass.

 E) never—homeostasis makes these energy and material budgets always balance.

Answer: D

10) You are studying a large tropical reptile that has a high and relatively stable body temperature. How would you determine whether this animal is an endotherm or an ectotherm?

 A) You know from its high and stable body temperature that it must be an endotherm.

 B) You know that it is an ectotherm because it is not a bird or mammal.

 C) You subject this reptile to various temperatures in the lab and find that its body temperature and metabolic rate change with the ambient temperature. You conclude that it is an ectotherm.

 D) You note that its environment has a high and stable temperature. Because its body temperature matches the environmental temperature, you conclude that it is an ectotherm.

 E) You measure the metabolic rate of the reptile and because it is higher than that of a related species that lives in temperate forests, you conclude that this reptile is an endotherm and its relative is an ectotherm.

Answer: C

# Chapter 41  Animal Nutrition

1) The body is capable of catabolizing many substances as sources of energy. Which of the following would be used as an energy source only after the depletion of other sources?

A) fat in adipose tissue

B) glucose in the blood

C) protein in muscle cells

D) glycogen in muscle cells

E) calcium phosphate in bone

Answer: C
*Topic: Concept 41.1*
*Skill: Comprehension*

2) An animal that migrates great distances would obtain the greatest benefit from storing its energy as

A) proteins.

B) minerals.

C) carbohydrates.

D) amino acids.

E) fats.

Answer: E
*Topic: Concept 41.1*
*Skill: Application*

3) Which one of the following statements about obesity is *false*?

A) The majority of the people in the United States are either obese or overweight.

B) Obesity contributes to diabetes, cancer of the colon and breasts, and cardiovascular disease.

C) Inheritance is a major factor in obesity.

D) As adipose tissue increases, leptin blood levels rise.

E) If a person's excess calories were stored as carbohydrates instead of fat, that person would weigh less.

Answer: E
*Topic: Concept 41.1*
*Skill: Knowledge*

4) Some nutrients are considered "essential" in the diets of certain animals because

A) only those animals use the nutrients.

B) they are subunits of important polymers.

C) they cannot be manufactured by the organism.

D) they are necessary coenzymes.

E) only some foods contain them.

Answer: C
*Topic: Concept 41.2*
*Skill: Knowledge*

5) Which of the following is *not* one of the four classes of essential nutrients?

A) essential sugars

B) essential amino acids

C) essential fatty acids

D) essential vitamins

E) essential minerals

Answer: A
*Topic: Concept 41.2*
*Skill: Knowledge*

6) Animals require certain basic amino acids in their diet. An amino acid that is referred to as nonessential would be best described as one that

A) can be made by the animal's body from other substances.

B) is not used by the animal in biosynthesis.

C) must be ingested in the diet.

D) is less important than an essential amino acid.

E) is not found in many proteins.

Answer: A
*Topic: Concept 41.2*
*Skill: Comprehension*

7) Which of the following vitamins is *incorrectly* associated with its use?

A) vitamin C—synthesis of connective tissue

B) vitamin A—incorporated into the visual pigment of the eye

C) vitamin D—calcium absorption and bone formation

D) vitamin E—protection of membrane phospholipids from oxidation

E) vitamin K—production of red blood cells

Answer: E
*Topic: Concept 41.2*
*Skill: Knowledge*

8) Which of the following is a fat-soluble vitamin?

A) vitamin A

B) vitamin $B_{12}$

C) vitamin C

D) iodine

E) calcium

Answer: A
*Topic: Concept 41.2*
*Skill: Knowledge*

9) Because they accumulate in the body, excess ingestion of which of the following can have toxic effects?

A) fat-soluble vitamins

B) water-soluble vitamins

C) calcium and phosphorus

D) proteins

E) sugars

Answer: A
*Topic: Concept 41.2*
*Skill: Knowledge*

10) Which of the following minerals is *incorrectly* associated with its use in animals?

A) calcium—construction and maintenance of bone

B) magnesium—cofactor in enzymes that split ATP

C) iron—regulation of metabolic rate

D) phosphorus—ingredient of nucleic acids

E) sodium—important in nerve function

Answer: C
*Topic: Concept 41.2*
*Skill: Knowledge*

11) Which of the following terms could be applied to any organism with a digestive system?

A) heterotroph

B) autotroph

C) herbivore

D) omnivore

E) chemoautotroph

Answer: A
*Topic: Concept 41.3*
*Skill: Comprehension*

12) During the process of digestion, fats are broken down when fatty acids are detached from glycerol. In addition, proteins are digested to yield amino acids. What do these two processes have in common? Both

A) are catalyzed by the same enzyme.

B) occur intracellularly in most organisms.

C) involve the addition of a water molecule to break bonds (hydrolysis).

D) require the presence of hydrochloric acid to lower the pH.

E) require ATP as an energy source.

Answer: C
*Topic: Concept 41.3*
*Skill: Comprehension*

13) Which of the following digestive processes requires enzymes?

A) ingestion

B) peristalsis

C) absorption

D) hydrolysis

E) elimination

Answer: D
*Topic: Concept 41.3*
*Skill: Comprehension*

14) To leave the digestive tract, a substance must cross a cell membrane. During which stage of food processing does this take place?

A) ingestion

B) digestion

C) hydrolysis

D) absorption

E) elimination

Answer: D
*Topic: Concept 41.3*
*Skill: Comprehension*

15) Intracellular digestion is usually immediately preceded by which process?

A) hydrolysis

B) endocytosis

C) absorption

D) elimination

E) secretion

Answer: B
*Topic: Concept 41.3*
*Skill: Comprehension*

16) Which of these animals has a gastrovascular cavity?

A) pigeon

B) hydra

C) elephant

D) beetle

E) leech

Answer: B
*Topic: Concept 41.3*
*Skill: Knowledge*

17) Increasing the surface area facilitates which of the following digestive processes?

A) hydrolysis

B) absorption

C) elimination

D) A and B only

E) A, B, and C

Answer: D
*Topic: Concept 41.3*
*Skill: Comprehension*

18) Which of the following is an advantage of a complete digestive system over a gastrovascular cavity?

    A) Extracellular digestion is not needed.

    B) Specialized regions are possible.

    C) Digestive enzymes can be more specific.

    D) Extensive branching is possible.

    E) Intracellular digestion is easier.

Answer: B
*Topic: Concept 41.3*
*Skill: Comprehension*

19) Which of the following do not need a digestive system?

    A) heterotrophs

    B) autotrophs

    C) herbivores

    D) omnivores

    E) carnivores

Answer: B
*Topic: Concept 41.3*
*Skill: Comprehension*

20) Which one of the following has a shape most like an animal with a gastrovascular cavity?

    A) a drinking straw

    B) a baseball bat

    C) a garden hose

    D) an umbrella

    E) a vase

Answer: E
*Topic: Concept 41.3*
*Skill: Application*

21) What is peristalsis?

    A) a process of fat emulsification in the small intestine

    B) voluntary control of the rectal sphincters regulating defecation

    C) the transport of nutrients to the liver through the hepatic portal vessel

    D) a common cause of loss of appetite, fatigue, and dehydration

    E) smooth muscle contractions that move food through the alimentary canal

Answer: E
*Topic: Concept 41.4*
*Skill: Knowledge*

22) After ingestion, the first type of macromolecule to be worked on by enzymes in the human digestive system is

    A) protein.

    B) carbohydrate.

    C) fat.

    D) nucleic acid.

    E) glucose.

Answer: B
*Topic: Concept 41.4*
*Skill: Comprehension*

23) What is the substrate of salivary amylase?

    A) protein

    B) starch

    C) sucrose

    D) glucose

    E) maltose

Answer: B
*Topic: Concept 41.4*
*Skill: Knowledge*

24) Which of the following statements about the mammalian digestive system is *true*?

    A) All foods begin their enzymatic digestion in the mouth.

    B) After leaving the oral cavity, the bolus enters the larynx.

    C) The epiglottis prevents food from entering the trachea.

    D) Enzyme production continues in the esophagus.

    E) The trachea leads to the esophagus and then to the stomach.

Answer: C
*Topic: Concept 41.4*
*Skill: Knowledge*

25) What part(s) of the digestive system have secretions with a pH of 2?

    A) small intestine

    B) stomach

    C) pancreas

    D) A and B only

    E) A, B, and C

Answer: B
*Topic: Concept 41.4*
*Skill: Comprehension*

26) Which of the following statements about pepsin is *true*? Pepsin

    A) is manufactured by the pancreas.

    B) helps stabilize fat-water emulsions.

    C) splits maltose into monosaccharides.

    D) begins the hydrolysis of proteins in the stomach.

    E) is denatured and rendered inactive in solutions with low pH.

Answer: D
*Topic: Concept 41.4*
*Skill: Knowledge*

27) Without functioning parietal cells, an individual would

    A) not be able to initiate protein digestion in the stomach.

    B) not be able to initiate mechanical digestion in the stomach.

    C) only be able to digest fat in the stomach.

    D) not be able to produce pepsinogen.

    E) not be able to initiate digestion in the small intestine.

Answer: A
*Topic: Concept 41.4*
*Skill: Comprehension*

28) Most enzymatic hydrolysis of the macromolecules in food occurs in the

    A) small intestine.

    B) large intestine.

    C) stomach.

    D) liver.

    E) mouth.

Answer: A
*Topic: Concept 41.4*
*Skill: Knowledge*

29) Most nutrients are absorbed across the epithelium of the

    A) colon.

    B) stomach.

    C) esophagus.

    D) small intestine.

    E) large intestine.

Answer: D
*Topic: Concept 41.4*
*Skill: Knowledge*

30) A structure that does *not* manufacture any digestive substances is the

    A) duodenum.

    B) pancreas.

    C) salivary gland.

    D) gallbladder.

    E) liver.

Answer: D
*Topic: Concept 41.4*
*Skill: Knowledge*

31) Which of the following statement(s) about bile salts is (are) *true*? Bile salts

    A) are enzymes.

    B) are manufactured by the pancreas.

    C) emulsify fats in the duodenum.

    D) increase the efficiency of pepsin action.

    E) are normally an ingredient of gastric juice.

Answer: C
*Topic: Concept 41.4*
*Skill: Knowledge*

32) Most nutrients absorbed into the lymph or bloodstream are in which form?

    A) disaccharides

    B) polymers

    C) monomers

    D) enzymes

    E) peptides

Answer: C
*Topic: Concept 41.4*
*Skill: Comprehension*

33) Which of the following enzymes has the lowest pH optimum?

    A) amylase

    B) pepsin

    C) lipase

    D) trypsin

    E) sucrase

Answer: B
*Topic: Concept 41.4*
*Skill: Comprehension*

*The following questions refer to the digestive system structures in Figure 41.1.*

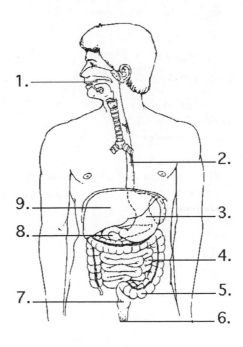

**Figure 41.1**

34) Where are the agents that help emulsify fat produced?

    A) 1

    B) 2

    C) 3

    D) 8

    E) 9

Answer: E
*Topic: Concept 41.4*
*Skill: Knowledge*

35) Where does the complete digestion of carbohydrates occur?

  A) 3 only

  B) 4 only

  C) 1 and 4

  D) 3 and 4

  E) 1, 3, and 4

Answer: B
*Topic: Concept 41.4*
*Skill: Knowledge*

36) Where does the digestion of fats occur?

  A) 3 only

  B) 4 only

  C) 1 and 4

  D) 3 and 4

  E) 1, 3, and 4

Answer: B
*Topic: Concept 41.4*
*Skill: Knowledge*

37) Which structure is home to bacteria that produce vitamins as by-products of their metabolism?

  A) 3

  B) 4

  C) 5

  D) 7

  E) 8

Answer: C
*Topic: Concept 41.4*
*Skill: Knowledge*

38) Which one of the following statements about digestion is *false*?

  A) Digestion is catalyzed by enzymes.

  B) Digestion cleaves nucleic acids into nucleotides.

  C) Digestion cleaves fats into glycerol and fatty acids.

  D) During digestion the essential macromolecules are directly absorbed.

  E) During digestion polysaccharides and disaccharides are split into simple sugars.

Answer: D
*Topic: Concept 41.4*
*Skill: Comprehension*

39) How does the digestion and absorption of fat differ from that of carbohydrates?

  A) Processing of fat does not require any digestive enzymes, whereas the processing of carbohydrates does.

  B) Fat absorption occurs in the stomach, whereas carbohydrates are absorbed from the small intestine.

  C) Carbohydrates need to be emulsified before they can be digested, whereas fats do not.

  D) Most absorbed fat first enters the lymphatic system, whereas carbohydrates directly enter the blood.

  E) Only fat must be worked on by bacteria in the large intestine before it can be absorbed.

Answer: D
*Topic: Concept 41.4*
*Skill: Comprehension*

40) Which of the following is *not* a nutritional monomer that can be transported in the blood?

A) sucrose

B) glucose

C) fatty acid

D) amino acid

E) nucleotide

Answer: A
*Topic: Concept 41.4*
*Skill: Comprehension*

41) In which blood vessel is glucose concentration likely to vary the *most*?

A) abdominal artery

B) coronary arteries

C) pulmonary veins

D) hepatic portal vessel

E) hepatic vein, which drains the liver

Answer: D
*Topic: Concept 41.4*
*Skill: Application*

42) Which of the following glandular secretions involved in digestion would be most likely released initially as inactive precursors?

A) protein-digesting enzymes

B) fat-solubilizing bile salts

C) acid-neutralizing bicarbonate

D) carbohydrate-digesting enzymes

E) hormones such as gastrin

Answer: A
*Topic: Concept 41.4*
*Skill: Comprehension*

43) In humans, about 7 liters of fluid are secreted each day into the intestinal tract. Which of the following does *not* secrete fluid?

A) salivary glands

B) stomach

C) liver

D) pancreas

E) large intestine

Answer: E
*Topic: Concept 41.4*
*Skill: Comprehension*

44) Adult lampreys attach onto large fish and feed regularly on their body fluids. Given this continuous supply of food, which one of the following is *most* likely missing in lampreys?

A) liver

B) pancreas

C) intestine

D) stomach

E) gallbladder

Answer: D
*Topic: Concept 41.4*
*Skill: Application*

45) Which portion of the digestive tract is most like a hallway in a school building, connecting one classroom to another?

A) stomach

B) esophagus

C) small intestine

D) liver

E) pancreas

Answer: B
*Topic: Concept 41.4*
*Skill: Application*

46) Which of the following would probably contribute to constipation? A substance that

A) contains plenty of fiber.

B) promotes water reabsorption in the large intestine.

C) speeds up movement of material in the large intestine.

D) decreases water reabsorption in the large intestine.

E) stimulates peristalsis.

Answer: B
*Topic: Concept 41.4*
*Skill: Application*

47) In general, herbivorous mammals have molars modified for

A) cutting.

B) ripping.

C) grinding.

D) splitting.

E) piercing.

Answer: C
*Topic: Concept 41.5*
*Skill: Knowledge*

48) In which group of animals would you expect to find a relatively long cecum?

A) carnivores

B) herbivores

C) autotrophs

D) heterotrophs

E) omnivores

Answer: B
*Topic: Concept 41.5*
*Skill: Comprehension*

49) All of the following are adaptations to an herbivorous diet *except*

A) broad, flat molars.

B) a rumen.

C) ingestion of feces.

D) bile salts.

E) amylase.

Answer: D
*Topic: Concept 41.5*
*Skill: Comprehension*

50) Why are cattle able to survive on a diet consisting almost entirely of plant material?

A) They are autotrophic.

B) Cattle, like the rabbit, reingests its feces.

C) They manufacture all 15 amino acids out of sugars in the liver.

D) Cattle saliva has enzymes capable of digesting cellulose.

E) They have cellulose-digesting, symbiotic microorganisms in chambers of their stomachs.

Answer: E
*Topic: Concept 41.5*
*Skill: Comprehension*

# Media Activity Questions

1) Your small intestine can absorb _____ without their being further digested.

   A) starches

   B) fats

   C) proteins

   D) fructoses

   E) nucleic acids

Answer: D
*Topic: Web/CD Activity: Digestive System Function*

2) Starch can be broken down into the disaccharide known as

   A) lactose.

   B) glucose.

   C) sucrose.

   D) fructose.

   E) maltose.

Answer: E
*Topic: Web/CD Activity: Digestive System Function*

3) What is the main component of gastric juice?

   A) inactive pepsin

   B) amylase

   C) hydrochloric acid

   D) water

   E) bile

Answer: D
*Topic: Web/CD Activity: Digestive System Function*

4) Secretin stimulates the _____ to secrete _____.

   A) pancreas; bicarbonate

   B) pancreas; pancreatic enzymes

   C) small intestine; disaccharidases

   D) stomach; bicarbonate

   E) liver; liver enzymes

Answer: E
*Topic: Activity: Hormonal Control of Digestion*

5) The acidity of the stomach contents triggers the small intestine to secrete a hormone known as

   A) cholecystokinin, or CCK.

   B) histones.

   C) TSH.

   D) secretin.

   E) pepsin.

Answer: D
*Topic: Activity: Hormonal Control of Digestion*

# Self-Quiz Questions

1) Which of the following animals is *incorrectly* paired with its feeding mechanism?

   A) lion—substrate feeder

   B) baleen whale—suspension feeder

   C) aphid—fluid feeder

   D) earthworm—deposit feeder

   E) snake—bulk feeder

   Answer: A

2) If you were to jog a mile a few hours after lunch, which stored fuel would you probably tap?

   A) muscle proteins

   B) muscle and liver glycogen

   C) fat stored in the liver

   D) fats stored in adipose tissue

   E) blood proteins

   Answer: B

3) Individuals whose diet consists primarily of corn would likely become

   A) obese.

   B) anorexic.

   C) overnourished.

   D) undernourished.

   E) malnourished.

   Answer: E

4) The mammalian trachea and esophagus both open into the

   A) large intestine.

   B) stomach.

   C) pharynx.

   D) rectum.

   E) epiglottis.

   Answer: C

5) Which of the following enzymes has the lowest pH optimum?

   A) salivary amylase

   B) trypsin

   C) pepsin

   D) pancreatic amylase

   E) pancreatic lipase

   Answer: C

6) Which of the following organs is *incorrectly* paired with its function?

   A) stomach—protein digestion

   B) oral cavity—starch digestion

   C) large intestine—bile production

   D) small intestine—nutrient absorption

   E) pancreas—enzyme production

   Answer: C

7) Enteropeptidase, an enzyme bound to the intestinal epithelium, has which of the following actions?

   A) inhibits bile secretion

   B) inhibits duodenal secretion

   C) activates pancreatic enzymes

   D) inhibits peristalsis in the stomach

   E) increases the pH of chyme

   Answer: C

8) After surgical removal of an infected gallbladder, a person must be especially careful to restrict his or her dietary intake of

   A) starch.

   B) protein.

   C) sugar.

   D) fat.

   E) water.

   Answer: D

9) Our oral cavity, with its dentition, is most functionally analogous to an earthworm's

   A) intestine.

   B) pharynx.

   C) gizzard.

   D) stomach.

   E) anus.

   Answer: C

10) The symbiotic microbes that help nourish a ruminant live mainly in specialized regions of the

   A) large intestine.

   B) liver.

   C) small intestine.

   D) pharynx.

   E) stomach.

   Answer: E

# Chapter 42  Circulation and Gas Exchange

1) What would be expected if the amount of interstitial fluid surrounding the capillary beds of the lungs were to increase significantly?

    A) The amount of carbon dioxide entering the lungs from the blood would increase.

    B) The amount of oxygen entering the circulation from the lungs would increase.

    C) The amount of oxygen entering the circulation from the lungs would decrease.

    D) The pressure would cause the capillary beds to burst.

    E) Both C and D would be expected.

Answer: C
*Topic: Concept 42.1*
*Skill: Comprehension*

2) Which is a correct statement concerning the insect circulatory system?

    A) The circulating fluid bathes tissues directly.

    B) Blood is always contained in a system of tubes called tracheae.

    C) Blood transports oxygen and nutrients to all the tissues.

    D) There is no heart, or pump.

    E) There is no blood, or circulating fluid.

Answer: A
*Topic: Concept 42.1*
*Skill: Comprehension*

3) Organisms in which a circulating body fluid is distinct from the fluid that directly surrounds the body's cells are likely to have

    A) an open circulatory system.

    B) a closed circulatory system.

    C) a gastrovascular cavity.

    D) branched tracheae.

    E) hemolymph.

Answer: B
*Topic: Concept 42.1*
*Skill: Comprehension*

4) Which of the following blood components would interfere with the functioning of an open circulatory system but *not* a closed one?

    A) electrolytes

    B) water

    C) red blood cells

    D) amino acids

    E) antibodies

Answer: C
*Topic: Concept 42.1*
*Skill: Comprehension*

5) In which animal does blood flow from the pulmocutaneous circulation to the heart before circulating through the rest of the body?

    A) annelid

    B) mollusc

    C) fish

    D) frog

    E) insect

Answer: D
*Topic: Concept 42.1*
*Skill: Knowledge*

6) Three-chambered hearts generally consist of which of the following numbers of atria and ventricles?

A) one atrium; one ventricle

B) two atria; one ventricle

C) three atria; no ventricles

D) no atria; three ventricles

E) one atrium; two ventricles

Answer: B
*Topic: Concept 42.1*
*Skill: Knowledge*

7) Which of the following are the only vertebrates in which blood flows directly from respiratory organs to body tissues without first returning to the heart?

A) amphibians

B) birds

C) fishes

D) mammals

E) reptiles

Answer: C
*Topic: Concepts 42.1, 42.2*
*Skill: Comprehension*

8) To adjust blood pressure independently in the capillaries of the gas-exchange surface and in the capillaries of the general body circulation, an organism would need a(n)

A) open circulatory system.

B) hemocoel.

C) lymphatic system.

D) two-chambered heart.

E) four-chambered heart.

Answer: E
*Topic: Concept 42.1*
*Skill: Comprehension*

9) A human red blood cell in an artery of the left arm is on its way to deliver oxygen to a cell in the thumb. From this point in the artery, how many capillary beds must this red blood cell pass through before it returns to the left ventricle of the heart?

A) one

B) two

C) three

D) four

E) five

Answer: B
*Topic: Concept 42.2*
*Skill: Application*

10) Through how many capillary beds must a human red blood cell travel if it takes the shortest possible route from the right ventricle to the right atrium?

A) one

B) two

C) three

D) four

E) five

Answer: B
*Topic: Concept 42.2*
*Skill: Comprehension*

*Refer to the diagram of the human heart in Figure 42.1 to answer the following questions.*

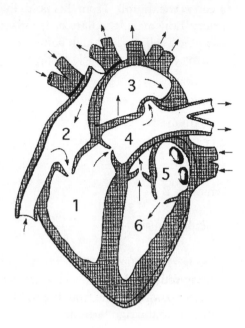

**Figure 42.1**

11) Chambers or vessels that carry oxygenated blood include which of the following?

 A) 1 and 2 only

 B) 3 and 4 only

 C) 5 and 6 only

 D) 1, 2, and 4

 E) 3, 5, and 6

Answer: E
*Topic: Concept 42.2*
*Skill: Knowledge*

12) Blood is carried directly to the lungs from which of the following?

 A) 2

 B) 3

 C) 4

 D) 5

 E) 6

Answer: C
*Topic: Concept 42.2*
*Skill: Knowledge*

13) What is the *correct* sequence of blood flow, beginning at the pulmonary artery?

 A) 2–1–4–systemic circulation–3–5–6

 B) 3–5–6–systemic circulation–2–1–4

 C) 4–5–6–3–systemic circulation–2–1

 D) 4–systemic circulation–2–1–6–3–5

 E) 5–6–3–2–1–4

Answer: C
*Topic: Concepts 42.1, 42.2*
*Skill: Knowledge*

14) Which sequence of blood flow can be observed in either a reptile or a mammal?

 A) left ventricle → aorta → lungs → systemic circulation

 B) right ventricle → pulmonary vein → pulmocutaneous circulation

 C) pulmonary vein → left atrium → ventricle → pulmonary circuit

 D) vena cava → right atrium → ventricle → pulmonary circuit

 E) right atrium → pulmonary artery → left atrium → ventricle

Answer: D
*Topic: Concepts 42.1, 42.2*
*Skill: Comprehension*

15) In order for an insect to grow as large as an elephant, what changes or modifications would need to be made in the circulatory systems of insects?

 A) The circulating body fluid would need to be contained in closed vessels.

 B) The heart would need to have multiple chambers.

 C) The heart would need to have multiple ostia.

 D) Only A and B are correct.

 E) A, B, and C are correct.

Answer: D
*Topic: Concepts 42.1, 42.2*
*Skill: Comprehension*

16) A patient has a blood pressure of 120/75, a
pulse rate of 40 beats/min, a stroke
volume of 70 mL/beat, and a respiratory
rate of 25 breaths/min. This person's
cardiac output per minute will be

   A) 500 mL.

   B) 1,000 mL.

   C) 1,750 mL.

   D) 2,800 mL.

   E) 4,800 mL.

Answer: D
*Topic: Concepts 42.2–42.3*
*Skill: Application*

17) Damage to the sinoatrial node in humans

   A) is a major contributor to heart attacks.

   B) would block conductance between the
   bundle branches and the Purkinje
   fibers.

   C) would have a negative effect on
   peripheral resistance.

   D) would disrupt the rate and timing of
   cardia muscle contractions.

   E) would have an effect on blood
   pressure monitors in the aorta.

Answer: D
*Topic: Concept 42.2*
*Skill: Comprehension*

18) If the atrioventricular node could be
surgically removed from the heart
without disrupting signal transmission
to the Purkinje fibers, what would be
the effect?

   A) No apparent effect on heart activity
   would be observed.

   B) The heart rate would be decreased.

   C) Only the ventricles would contract.

   D) Only the atria would contract.

   E) Atria and ventricles would contract at
   about the same time.

Answer: E
*Topic: Concept 42.2*
*Skill: Comprehension*

19) A nonfunctional sinoatrial node would

   A) have no adverse effects on heart
   contraction.

   B) cause the heart to stop beating in an
   autorhythmic fashion.

   C) result in a block in ventricular
   contractions.

   D) cause no effects because hormones
   will take over regulation of the heart
   beat.

   E) have no significant effect on stroke
   volume.

Answer: E
*Topic: Concept 42.2*
*Skill: Comprehension*

20) Why is the velocity of blood flow the lowest in capillaries?

A) The capillary walls are not thin enough to allow oxygen to exchange with the cells.

B) Capillaries are far from the heart, and blood flow slows as distance from the heart increases.

C) The diastolic blood pressure is too low to deliver blood to the capillaries at a high flow rate.

D) The systemic capillaries are supplied by the left ventricle, which has a lower cardiac output than the right ventricle.

E) The total surface area of the capillaries is larger than the total surface area of the arterioles.

Answer: E
*Topic: Concept 42.3*
*Skill: Comprehension*

21) Average blood pressure is lowest in which structure(s)?

A) the aorta

B) arteries

C) arterioles

D) capillaries

E) venae cavae

Answer: E
*Topic: Concept 42.3*
*Skill: Knowledge*

22) Which of the following is correct for a blood pressure reading of 130/80?
I. The systolic pressure is 130.
II. The diastolic pressure is 80.
III. The blood pressure during heart contraction is 80.

A) I only

B) III only

C) I and II only

D) II and III only

E) I, II, and III

Answer: C
*Topic: Concept 42.3*
*Skill: Comprehension*

23) What can be expected to happen to the blood pressure of a healthy individual during inhalation?

A) The systolic pressure would rise and the diastolic pressure would decrease.

B) The extra pressure exerted by the inflating lungs will increase blood pressure.

C) There will be a transient decrease in blood pressure.

D) Blood pressure will initially increase and then immediately decrease.

E) Nothing will happen in healthy individuals.

Answer: C
*Topic: Concept 42.3*
*Skill: Comprehension*

24) What is the reason that fluid is forced out of systemic capillaries at the arteriole end?

A) The osmotic pressure of the interstitial fluid is greater than that of the blood.

B) The hydrostatic pressure of the blood is less than that of the interstitial fluid.

C) The hydrostatic pressure of the blood is greater than the osmotic pressure of the blood.

D) The osmotic pressure of the interstitial fluid is greater than the hydrostatic pressure of the blood.

E) The osmotic pressure of the blood is greater than the hydrostatic pressure of the interstitial fluid.

Answer: C
*Topic: Concept 42.3*
*Skill: Comprehension*

25) If, during protein starvation, the osmotic pressure on the venous side of capillary beds drops below the hydrostatic pressure, then

A) hemoglobin will not release oxygen.

B) fluids will tend to accumulate in tissues.

C) the pH of the interstitial fluids will increase.

D) most carbon dioxide will be bound to hemoglobin and carried away from tissues.

E) plasma proteins will escape through the endothelium of the capillaries.

Answer: B
*Topic: Concept 42.3*
*Skill: Application*

26) If a person were suffering from edema, which of the following conditions would help to reduce the accumulation of interstitial fluid?

A) decrease of plasma protein production by the liver

B) constriction of the smooth layer of the arteriole

C) removal of an obstruction in the lymphatic system

D) decrease of the systolic blood pressure

E) enlargement of clefts between capillary endothelial cells

Answer: D
*Topic: Concept 42.3*
*Skill: Comprehension*

27) What would be the long-term effect if the lymphatic vessels associated with a capillary bed were to become blocked?

A) More fluid would enter the venous capillaries.

B) Blood pressure in the capillary bed would increase.

C) Fluid would accumulate in interstitial areas.

D) Fewer proteins would leak into the interstitial fluid from the blood.

E) Nothing would happen.

Answer: C
*Topic: Concept 42.3*
*Skill: Comprehension*

28) Human plasma proteins include which of the following?

      I.   fibrinogen

      II.  hemoglobin

      III. immunoglobulin

A) I only

B) II only

C) I and III only

D) II and III only

E) I, II, and III

Answer: C
*Topic: Concept 42.4*
*Skill: Knowledge*

29) Which of the following is *not* a function of plasma proteins in humans?

A) maintenance of blood osmotic pressure

B) transport of water–insoluble lipids

C) blood clotting

D) immune responses

E) oxygen transport

Answer: E
*Topic: Concept 42.4*
*Skill: Knowledge*

30) Cyanide acts as a mitochondrial poison by blocking the final step in the electron transport chain. What will happen to human red blood cells if they are placed in an isotonic solution containing cyanide?

A) The cell shape will be maintained, but the mitochondria will be poisoned.

B) The cells will lyse as the cyanide concentration increases inside the cell.

C) As a protective mechanism, the cells will switch to anaerobic metabolism.

D) The cells will not be able to carry oxygen.

E) The cells will probably be unaffected.

Answer: E
*Topic: Concept 42.4*
*Skill: Comprehension*

*The following phrases refer to the five terms below. Each term can be used as an answer once, more than once, or not at all.*

    A.  low–density lipoproteins

    B.  immunoglobulins

    C.  erythropoietin

    D.  epinephrine

    E.  platelets

31) speeds up heart rate

Answer: D
*Topic: Concept 42.2*
*Skill: Knowledge*

32) part of the cellular elements of the blood

Answer: E
*Topic: Concept 42.4*
*Skill: Knowledge*

33) stimulates the production of red blood cells

Answer: C
*Topic: Concept 42.4*
*Skill: Knowledge*

34) involved in the early stages of blood clotting

Answer: E
*Topic: Concept 42.4*
*Skill: Knowledge*

35) The meshwork that forms the fabric of a blood clot consists mostly of which protein?

   A) fibrinogen

   B) fibrin

   C) thrombin

   D) prothrombin

   E) collagen

Answer: B
*Topic: Concept 42.4*
*Skill: Knowledge*

36) Which of the following is *not* a normal event in the process of blood clotting?

   A) production of erythropoietin

   B) conversion of fibrinogen to fibrin

   C) activation of prothrombin to thrombin

   D) adhesion of platelets

   E) clotting factor release by clumped platelets

Answer: A
*Topic: Concept 42.4*
*Skill: Knowledge*

*Match the following phrases to the conditions. Each condition may be used once, more than once, or not at all.*

   A. atherosclerosis
   B. arteriosclerosis
   C. hypertension
   D. heart murmur
   E. cardiovascular thrombus

37) high blood pressure

Answer: C
*Topic: Concept 42.4*
*Skill: Knowledge*

38) defect in one or more of the valves of the heart

Answer: D
*Topic: Concept 42.2*
*Skill: Knowledge*

39) plaque formation by infiltration of lipids into arterial smooth muscles

Answer: A
*Topic: Concept 42.4*
*Skill: Knowledge*

40) Which of the following features do all gas exchange systems have in common?

   A) The exchange surfaces are moist.

   B) They are enclosed within ribs.

   C) They are maintained at a constant temperature.

   D) They are exposed to air.

   E) They are found only in animals.

Answer: A
*Topic: Concepts 42.1–42.5*
*Skill: Comprehension*

41) Why is gas exchange more difficult for aquatic animals with gills than for terrestrial animals with lungs?

   A) Water is denser than air.

   B) Water contains much less $O_2$ than air per unit volume.

   C) Gills have less surface area than lungs.

   D) Only A and B are correct.

   E) A, B, and C are correct.

Answer: D
*Topic: Concept 42.5*
*Skill: Comprehension*

42) Which of the following is an example of countercurrent exchange?

A) the flow of water across the gills of a fish and that of blood within those gills

B) the flow of blood in the dorsal vessel of an insect and that of air within its tracheae

C) the flow of air within the primary bronchi of a human and that of blood within the pulmonary veins

D) the flow of water across the skin of a frog and that of blood within the ventricle of its heart

E) the flow of fluid out of the arterial end of a capillary and that of fluid back into the venous end of the same capillary

Answer: A
*Topic: Concept 42.5*
*Skill: Comprehension*

43) Countercurrent exchange in the fish gill helps to maximize

A) endocytosis.

B) blood pressure.

C) diffusion.

D) active transport.

E) osmosis.

Answer: C
*Topic: Concept 42.5*
*Skill: Comprehension*

44) Which one of the following statements about gills operating in water is *false*?

A) Water can support the delicate gill features.

B) Most fish actively pump water over their gills.

C) Keeping membranes moist is no problem.

D) Water carries more oxygen than air, and therefore gills need to be more efficient than lungs.

E) Gills have evolved many times in aquatic animals.

Answer: D
*Topic: Concept 42.5*
*Skill: Comprehension*

45) Tracheal systems for gas exchange are found in which organism?

A) crustacean

B) earthworm

C) insect

D) jellyfish

E) vertebrate

Answer: C
*Topic: Concept 42.5*
*Skill: Knowledge*

46) Where do air-breathing insects carry out gas exchange?

A) in specialized external gills

B) in specialized internal gills

C) in the alveoli of their lungs

D) across the membranes of cells

E) across the thin cuticular exoskeleton

Answer: D
*Topic: Concept 42.5*
*Skill: Knowledge*

47) An oil–water mixture is used as a spray against mosquitoes. How might this spray also affect gas exchange in other insects?

    A) The oil might coat their lungs.

    B) The oil might block the openings into the tracheal system.

    C) The oil might interfere with gas exchange across the capillaries.

    D) Only A and B are correct.

    E) A, B, and C are correct.

Answer: B
*Topic: Concept 42.5*
*Skill: Comprehension*

48) All of the following respiratory surfaces are associated with capillary beds *except* the

    A) gills of fishes.

    B) alveoli of lungs.

    C) tracheae of insects.

    D) skin of earthworms.

    E) skin of frogs.

Answer: C
*Topic: Concepts 42.1–42.5*
*Skill: Comprehension*

49) If a molecule of $CO_2$ released into the blood in your left toe travels out of your nose, it must pass through all of the following structures *except* the

    A) right atrium.

    B) pulmonary vein.

    C) alveolus.

    D) trachea.

    E) right ventricle.

Answer: B
*Topic: Concepts 42.2, 42.6*
*Skill: Application*

50) Air rushes into the lungs of humans during inhalation because

    A) the rib muscles and diaphragm contract, increasing the lung volume.

    B) pressure in the alveoli increases.

    C) gas flows from a region of lower pressure to a region of higher pressure.

    D) pulmonary muscles contract and pull on the outer surface of the lungs.

    E) a positive respiratory pressure is created when the diaphragm relaxes.

Answer: A
*Topic: Concept 42.6*
*Skill: Comprehension*

51) Which of the following occurs with the exhalation of air from human lungs?

    A) The volume of the thoracic cavity decreases.

    B) The residual volume of the lungs decreases.

    C) The diaphragm contracts.

    D) The epiglottis closes.

    E) The rib cage expands.

Answer: A
*Topic: Concept 42.6*
*Skill: Comprehension*

52) Which of the following lung volumes would be different in a person at rest compared with when the person exercises?

    A) tidal volume

    B) vital capacity

    C) residual volume

    D) total lung capacity

    E) All of the above would be different.

Answer: A
*Topic: Concept 42.6*
*Skill: Comprehension*

53) Tidal volume in respiration is analogous to what measurement in cardiac physiology?

   A) cardiac output

   B) heart rate

   C) stroke volume

   D) systolic pressure

   E) diastolic pressure

Answer: C
*Topic: Concepts 42.2, 42.6*
*Skill: Comprehension*

54) A person with a tidal volume of 450 mL, a vital capacity of 4,000 mL, and a residual volume of 1,000 mL would have a potential total lung capacity of

   A) 1,450 mL.

   B) 4,000 mL.

   C) 4,450 mL.

   D) 5,000 mL.

   E) 5,450 mL.

Answer: D
*Topic: Concept 42.6*
*Skill: Application*

55) Air flows in only one direction through the lungs of which animals?

   A) frogs

   B) birds

   C) mammals

   D) crocodiles

   E) flying insects

Answer: B
*Topic: Concept 42.6*
*Skill: Comprehension*

56) Why is the respiratory system of a bird more efficient than the human respiratory system?

   A) The bird respiratory system does not mix exhaled air with inhaled air.

   B) A bird lung contains multiple alveoli, which increases the amount of surface area available for gas exchange.

   C) The human respiratory system ends in small parabronchi, which reduce the amount of surface area available for gas exchange.

   D) Only B and C are correct.

   E) A, B, and C are correct.

Answer: A
*Topic: Concept 42.6*
*Skill: Knowledge*

57) The blood level of which gas is *most* important in controlling human respiration rate?

   A) nitric acid

   B) nitrogen

   C) oxygen

   D) carbon dioxide

   E) carbon monoxide

Answer: D
*Topic: Concept 42.6*
*Skill: Knowledge*

58) Breathing is usually regulated by

   A) erythropoietin levels in the blood.

   B) the concentration of red blood cells.

   C) hemoglobin levels in the blood.

   D) $CO_2$ and $O_2$ concentration and pH–level sensors.

   E) the lungs and the larynx.

Answer: D
*Topic: Concept 42.6*
*Skill: Comprehension*

59) At an atmospheric pressure of 870 mm Hg, what is the contribution of oxygen?

    A) 100 mm Hg

    B) 127 mm Hg

    C) 151 mm Hg

    D) 182 mm Hg

    E) 219 mm Hg

Answer: D
*Topic: Concept 42.6*
*Skill: Application*

60) At sea level, atmospheric pressure is 760 mm Hg. Oxygen gas is approximately 21% of the total gases in the atmosphere. What is the approximate partial pressure of oxygen?

    A) 0.2 mm Hg

    B) 20.0 mm Hg

    C) 76.0 mm Hg

    D) 160.0 mm Hg

    E) 508.0 mm Hg

Answer: D
*Topic: Concept 42.6*
*Skill: Comprehension*

61) At the summit of a high mountain, the atmospheric pressure is 380 mm Hg. If the atmosphere is still composed of 21% oxygen, what is the partial pressure of oxygen at this altitude?

    A) 0 mm Hg

    B) 80 mm Hg

    C) 160 mm Hg

    D) 380 mm Hg

    E) 760 mm Hg

Answer: B
*Topic: Concept 42.6*
*Skill: Application*

62) Which one of these statements about lungs is *false*?

    A) Gas exchange takes place across moist membranes.

    B) The gases move across the exchange membranes by diffusion.

    C) The total exchange surface area is relatively large.

    D) The lining of the alveoli is only one cell thick.

    E) The concentration of $CO_2$ is higher in the air than in the alveolar capillaries.

Answer: E
*Topic: Concept 42.6*
*Skill: Comprehension*

*The following questions refer to the data shown below.*

Blood entering a capillary bed of a vertebrate was measured for the pressures exerted by various factors.

|  | Arterial End of Capillary Bed | Venous End of Capillary Bed |
|---|---|---|
| Hydrostatic pressure | 8 mm Hg | 14 mm Hg |
| Osmotic pressure | 26 mm Hg | 26 mm Hg |
| $P_{O_2}$ | 100 mm Hg | 42 mm Hg |
| $P_{CO_2}$ | 40 mm Hg | 46 mm Hg |

63) For this capillary bed, which of the following statements is *correct*?

A) The pH is lower on the arterial side than on the venous side.

B) Oxygen is taken up by the erythrocytes within the capillaries.

C) The osmotic pressure remains constant due to carbon dioxide compensation.

D) The hydrostatic pressure declines from the arterial side to the venous side because oxygen is lost.

E) Fluids will leave the capillaries on the arterial side of the bed and re-enter on the venous side.

Answer: E
*Topic: Concepts 42.3, 42.5, 42.6*
*Skill: Application*

64) The site of this capillary bed could be all of the following *except* the

A) pancreas.

B) muscle tissue.

C) medulla.

D) alveoli.

E) kidneys.

Answer: D
*Topic: Concept 42.6*
*Skill: Comprehension*

65) Which of the following is *false* concerning the hemoglobin molecule?

A) It contains amino acids.

B) It contains iron.

C) It is composed of four polypeptide chains.

D) It can bind four $O_2$ molecules.

E) It is found in humans only.

Answer: E
*Topic: concept 42.7*
*Skill: Knowledge*

66) Which of the following is a characteristic of *both* hemoglobin and hemocyanin?

A) found within blood cells

B) red in color

C) contains the element iron as an oxygen–binding component

D) transports oxygen

E) occurs in mammals

Answer: D
*Topic: concept 42.7*
*Skill: Knowledge*

67) The Bohr shift on the oxygen–hemoglobin dissociation curve is produced by changes in

A) the partial pressure of oxygen.

B) the partial pressure of carbon monoxide.

C) hemoglobin concentration.

D) temperature.

E) pH.

Answer: E
*Topic: concept 42.7*
*Skill: Knowledge*

68) How is most of the carbon dioxide transported by the blood in humans?

    A) bicarbonate ions in the plasma

    B) $CO_2$ attached to hemoglobin

    C) carbonic acid in the erythrocytes

    D) $CO_2$ dissolved in the plasma

    E) bicarbonate attached to hemoglobin

Answer: A
*Topic: concept 42.7*
*Skill: Knowledge*

69) Hydrogen ions produced in human red blood cells are prevented from significantly lowering pH by combining with

    A) hemoglobin.

    B) plasma proteins.

    C) carbon dioxide.

    D) carbonic acid.

    E) plasma buffers.

Answer: A
*Topic: concept 42.7*
*Skill: Knowledge*

# Media Activity Questions

1) From the pulmonary veins, blood flow to the

   A) right atrium.

   B) left atrium.

   C) aorta.

   D) capillaries of the lungs.

   E) posterior vena cava.

Answer: B
*Topic: Activity: Path of Blood Flow in Mammals*

2) From the capillaries of the abdominal organs and hind limbs, blood flows to the

   A) right atrium.

   B) left atrium.

   C) aorta.

   D) capillaries of the lungs.

   E) posterior vena cava.

Answer: E
*Topic: Activity: Path of Blood Flow in Mammals*

3) Blood pressure is highest in the

   A) aorta.

   B) posterior vena cava.

   C) anterior vena cava.

   D) pulmonary artery.

   E) capillaries.

Answer: A
*Topic: Mammalian Cardiovascular System Function*

4) Most carbon dioxide is carried from the body tissues to the lungs

   A) as bicarbonate ions.

   B) combined with hemoglobin.

   C) by the trachea.

   D) as hydrogen ions.

   E) dissolved in blood plasma.

Answer: A
*Topic: Activity: Transport of Respiratory Gases*

5) In the blood, most of the oxygen that will be used in cellular respiration is carried from the lungs to the body tissues

   A) as bicarbonate ions.

   B) combined with hemoglobin.

   C) by the trachea.

   D) by water.

   E) dissolved in blood plasma.

Answer: B
*Topic: Activity: Transport of Respiratory Gases*

# Self-Quiz Questions

1) Which of the following respiratory systems is not closely associated with a blood supply?
   A) vertebrate lungs
   B) fish gills
   C) tracheal systems of insects
   D) the outer skin of an earthworm
   E) the parapodia of a polychaete worm

   Answer: C

2) Blood returning to the mammalian heart in a pulmonary vein will drain first into the
   A) vena cava.
   B) left atrium.
   C) right atrium.
   D) left ventricle.
   E) right ventricle.

   Answer: B

3) Pulse is a direct measure of
   A) blood pressure.
   B) stroke volume.
   C) cardiac output.
   D) heart rate.
   E) breathing rate.

   Answer: D

4) When you hold your breath, which of the following blood gas changes first leads to the urge to breathe?
   A) rising $O_2$
   B) falling $O_2$
   C) rising $CO_2$
   D) falling $CO_2$
   E) rising $CO_2$ and falling $O_2$

   Answer: C

5) In negative pressure breathing, inhalation results from
   A) forcing air from the throat down into the lungs.
   B) contracting the diaphragm.
   C) relaxing the muscles of the rib cage.
   D) using muscles of the lungs to expand the alveoli.
   E) contracting the abdominal muscles.

   Answer: B

6) The conversion of fibrinogen to fibrin
   A) occurs when fibrinogen is released from broken platelets.
   B) occurs within red blood cells.
   C) is linked to hypertension and may damage artery walls.
   D) is likely to occur too often in an individual with hemophilia.
   E) is the final step of a clotting process that involves multiple clotting factors.

   Answer: E

7) A decrease in the pH of human blood caused by exercise would
   A) decrease breathing rate.
   B) increase heart rate.
   C) decrease the amount of $O_2$ unloaded from hemoglobin.
   D) decrease cardiac output.
   E) decrease $CO_2$ binding to hemoglobin.

   Answer: B

8) Compared to the interstitial fluid that bathes active muscle cells, blood reaching these cells in arteries has a

   A) higher $P_{O_2}$.

   B) higher $P_{CO_2}$.

   C) greater bicarbonate concentration.

   D) lower pH.

   E) lower osmotic pressure.

   Answer: A

9) Which of the following reactions prevails in red blood cells traveling through pulmonary capillaries? (Hb = hemoglobin)

   A) $Hb + 4\,O_2 \rightarrow Hb(O_2)_4$

   B) $Hb(O_2)_4 \rightarrow Hb + 4\,O_2$

   C) $CO_2 + H_2O \rightarrow H_2CO_3$

   D) $H_2CO_3 \rightarrow H^+ + HCO_3^-$

   E) $Hb + 4\,CO_2 \rightarrow Hb(CO_2)_4$

   Answer: A

10) The relationship between blood pressure (*bp*), cardiac output (*co*), and peripheral resistance (*pr*) can be expressed as $bp = co \times pr$. All of the following changes would result in an increase in blood pressure *except*

   A) increase in the stroke volume.

   B) increase in the heart rate.

   C) increase in the duration of ventricular diastole.

   D) contraction of the smooth muscle in arteriole walls.

   E) reduction in diameter of arterioles.

   Answer: C

# Chapter 43 The Immune System

1) The innate immunity that protects a person digging in the garden from developing a microbial infection includes all of the following *except*

A) lymphocytes.

B) the skin.

C) mucous membranes.

D) acidic secretions.

E) antimicrobial proteins.

Answer: A
*Topic: Concept 43.1*
*Skill: Comprehension*

2) Physical barriers to invasion by other organisms

A) include the skin and the mucous membranes.

B) are difficult for bacteria and viruses to penetrate.

C) may work in conjunction with secretions like tears, perspiration, and mucus.

D) Only A and C are correct.

E) A, B, and C are correct.

Answer: E
*Topic: Concept 43.1*
*Skill: Knowledge*

3) Both the eye and the respiratory tract are protected against infections by which of the following?

A) the mucous membranes that cover their surface

B) the secretion of complement proteins

C) the release of slightly acidic secretions

D) the secretion of lysozyme onto their surface

E) interferons produced by immune cells

Answer: D
*Topic: Concept 43.1*
*Skill: Comprehension*

4) How do people contract salmonella poisoning?

A) The microbe can survive the acidic environment of the stomach and resist lysosomal degradation in macrophages.

B) The chemotactic messengers released by the salmonella bacterium did not attract sufficient neutrophils to entirely destroy the infection.

C) There was a delay in selection of the population of eosinophils that recognize and are responsible for fighting these bacterial infections.

D) The bacterium released chemical messengers that make it resistant to phagocytosis.

E) The combination of foods eaten at the meal reduced the pH of the stomach sufficiently so that the bacterium was not destroyed.

Answer: A
*Topic: Concept 43.1*
*Skill: Comprehension*

5) The lymphatic system involves which of the following organs?

   A) spleen and lymph nodes

   B) adenoids and tonsils

   C) appendix and special portions of the small intestine

   D) A and B only

   E) A, B, and C

Answer: E
*Topic: Concept 43.1*
*Skill: Knowledge*

6) Which statement about the complement system is true?

   A) These proteins are involved in innate immunity and not acquired immunity.

   B) These proteins are secreted by cytotoxic T cells.

   C) This group of proteins includes interferons.

   D) These proteins are one group of antimicrobial proteins.

   E) none of the above

Answer: D
*Topic: Concept 43.1*
*Skill: Comprehension*

7) In the inflammatory response, the absence of which of the following would prevent all the others from happening?

   A) dilation of arterioles

   B) increased permeability of blood vessels

   C) increased population of phagocytes in the area

   D) release of histamine

   E) leakage of plasma to the affected area

Answer: D
*Topic: Concept 43.1*
*Skill: Comprehension*

8) Which action below is affected by an antihistamine?

   A) blood vessel dilation

   B) phatocytosis of antigens

   C) MHC presentation by macrophages

   D) the secondary immune response

   E) clonal selection by antigens

Answer: A
*Topic: Concept 43.1*
*Skill: Comprehension*

9) Which cell and signaling molecule are responsible for initiating an immune response?

   A) phagocytes: lysozyme

   B) phagocytes: chemokines

   C) dendritic cells: interferon

   D) mast cells: histamine

   E) lymphocytes: interferon

Answer: D
*Topic: Concept 43.1*
*Skill: Comprehension*

10) Inflammatory responses may include all of the following *except*

    A) clotting proteins sealing off a localized area.

    B) increased activity of phagocytes in an inflamed area.

    C) reduced permeability of blood vessels to conserve plasma.

    D) release of substances to increase the blood supply to an inflamed area.

    E) increased release of white blood cells from bone marrow.

Answer: C
*Topic: Concept 43.1*
*Skill: Comprehension*

11) Each indication below is a clinical characteristic of inflammation *except*

A) decreased temperature.

B) edema.

C) redness.

D) pain.

E) increased blood flow.

Answer: A
*Topic: Concept 43.1*
*Skill: Knowledge*

12) A bacterium entering the body through a small cut in the skin will do which of the following?

A) inactivate the hemocytes

B) stimulate apoptosis of body cells

C) stimulate release of interferons

D) stimulate natural killer cell activity

E) activate a group of proteins called complement

Answer: E
*Topic: Concept 43.1*
*Skill: Comprehension*

13) Which of the following is a *false* statement about innate immunity?

A) They include inflammatory responses.

B) They include physical and chemical barriers.

C) They must be primed by the presence of antigen.

D) They may involve the formation of membrane attack complexes.

E) Macrophages and natural killer cells are participants in the process.

Answer: C
*Topic: Concept 43.1*
*Skill: Comprehension*

14) What is the single most important event establishing a primary immune response?

A) the presentation of viral protein complexed to class I MHC

B) the lyses of virally infected cells by cytotoxic T cells

C) the phagocytosis of microbes by antigen-presenting cells

D) the recognition of self versus foreign

E) apoptosis of virally infected cells

Answer: D
*Topic: Concept 43.1*
*Skill: Application*

15) What are antigens?

A) proteins found in the blood that cause foreign blood cells to clump

B) proteins embedded in B cell membranes

C) proteins that consist of two light and two heavy polypeptide chains

D) foreign molecules that trigger the generation of antibodies

E) proteins released during an inflammatory response

Answer: D
*Topic: Concept 43.2*
*Skill: Knowledge*

16) Which of the following is *not* a part of an antibody molecule?

A) the epitope

B) the constant or C regions

C) the variable or V regions

D) the light chains

E) the heavy chains

Answer: A
*Topic: Concept 43.2*
*Skill: Knowledge*

17) If a newborn were accidentally given a drug that destroyed the thymus, what would most likely happen?

    A) His cells would lack class I MHC molecules on their surface.

    B) His immune system would not function.

    C) Genetic rearrangement of antigen receptors would not occur.

    D) His T cells would not undergo the test of self-tolerance.

    E) His B cells would be reduced in number.

Answer: D
*Topic: Concept 43.2*
*Skill: Comprehension*

18) The clonal selection theory implies that

    A) brothers and sisters have similar immune responses.

    B) antigens activate specific lymphocytes.

    C) only certain cells can produce interferon.

    D) a B cell has multiple types of antigen receptors.

    E) the body selects which antigens it will respond to.

Answer: B
*Topic: Concept 43.2*
*Skill: Comprehension*

19) The clonal selection theory is an explanation for how

    A) a single type of stem cell can produce both red blood cells and white blood cells.

    B) V gene and J gene segments are rearranged.

    C) an antigen can provoke development of very few cells to result in production of high levels of specific antibodies.

    D) HIV can disrupt the immune system.

    E) macrophages can recognize specific T cells and B cells.

Answer: C
*Topic: Concept 43.2*
*Skill: Comprehension*

20) A person exposed to a new cold virus would not feel better for one to two weeks because

    A) specific B cells and T cells must be selected prior to a protective response.

    B) it takes up to two weeks to stimulate immunologic memory cells.

    C) phagocytic cells must first be activated by the complement system.

    D) antigen receptors are not the same.

    E) V-J gene rearrangement must occur prior to a response.

Answer: C
*Topic: Concept 43.2*
*Skill: Comprehension*

*Use the graph in Figure 43.1 to answer the following questions.*

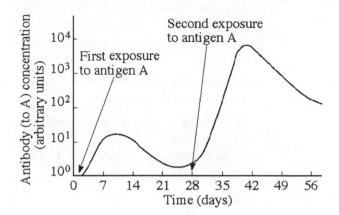

**Figure 43.1**

21) When would B cells produce effector cells?

    A) between 0 and 7 days

    B) between 7 and 14 days

    C) between 28 and 35 days

    D) both A and B

    E) both A and C

Answer: A
*Topic: Concept 43.2*
*Skill: Application*

22) When would memory cells be produced?

    A) between 0 and 7 days

    B) between 7 and 14 days

    C) between 28 and 35 days

    D) between 35 and 42 days

    E) both A and C

Answer: E
*Topic: Concept 43.2*
*Skill: Application*

23) When would you find antibodies being produced?

    A) between 3 and 7 days

    B) between 14 and 21 days

    C) between 28 and 35 days

    D) both B and C

    E) both A and C

Answer: E
*Topic: Concept 43.2*
*Skill: Application*

24) Which of the following cell types are responsible for initiating a secondary immune response?

    A) memory cells

    B) macrophages

    C) stem cells

    D) B cells

    E) T cells

Answer: A
*Topic: Concept 43.2*
*Skill: Knowledge*

25) If a person's bone marrow were destroyed by radiation, which of the following cells could *not* be produced?

    A) B cells

    B) T cells

    C) erythrocytes

    D) neutrophils

    E) all of the above

Answer: E
*Topic: Concept 43.2*
*Skill: Application*

26) Which of the following is true of both T cells and B cells?

   A) They produce effector cells against specific pathogens.

   B) They are produced from stem cells of the bone marrow.

   C) They can attack and destroy invading pathogens.

   D) Only A and B are true.

   E) A, B, and C are true.

Answer: D
*Topic: Concept 43.2*
*Skill: Comprehension*

27) The MHC is important in

   A) distinguishing self from nonself.

   B) recognizing parasitic pathogens.

   C) identifying bacterial pathogens.

   D) identifying cancer cells.

   E) both A and D

Answer: E
*Topic: Concept 43.2*
*Skill: Comprehension*

28) A patient can produce antibodies against some bacterial pathogens, but he does not produce antibodies against viral infections. This is probably due to a disorder in which cells of the immune system?

   A) B cells

   B) plasma cells

   C) natural killer cells

   D) T cells

   E) macrophages

Answer: D
*Topic: Concept 43.2*
*Skill: Application*

29) In which of the following situations will helper T cells be activated?

   A) when an antigen is displayed by a dendritic cell

   B) when a cytotoxic T cell releases cytokines

   C) when natural killer (NK) cells come in contact with a tumor cell

   D) in the bone marrow during the self tolerance test

   E) when B cells respond to T-independent antigens

Answer: A
*Topic: Concept 43.2*
*Skill: Comprehension*

30) Which statement about antibodies is false?

   A) Antibodies are immunoglobulin proteins.

   B) Antibodies bind with foreign cells and lyse them.

   C) The structure of antibodies includes both a constant and a variable region.

   D) Antibodies act as signals to blood complement proteins or phagocytes.

   E) Plasma cells are responsible for the production of antibodies.

Answer: B
*Topic: Concept 43.2*
*Skill: Comprehension*

*For the questions below, match the following answers with the phrase that best describes them.*

    A.   cytotoxic T cells
    B.   natural killer cells
    C.   helper T cells
    D.   macrophages
    E.   B cells

31) These cells are involved in cell–mediated immunity and destroy virally infected cells.

    Answer: A
    *Topic: Concept 43.3*
    *Skill: Knowledge*

32) These cells have a function that is similar to the function of dendritic cells.

    Answer: D
    *Topic: Concept 43.3*
    *Skill: Knowledge*

33) These cells are involved in cell–mediated immunity, and they respond to class I MHC molecule–antigen complexes.

    Answer: A
    *Topic: Concept 43.3*
    *Skill: Knowledge*

34) These cells are involved in innate immunity, and a person lacking these cells may have a higher than normal chance of developing malignant tumors.

    Answer: B
    *Topic: Concept 43.3*
    *Skill: Knowledge*

35) Which of the following is (are) *not* involved in the activation and functioning of cytotoxic T cells?

    A) interleukins

    B) antigen–presenting cells

    C) class I MHC molecules

    D) T cell surface protein CD8

    E) perforin

    Answer: B
    *Topic: Concept 43.3*
    *Skill: Comprehension*

36) Which of the following is a pathway that would lead to the activation of cytotoxic T cells?

    A) B cell contact antigen → helper T cell is activated → clonal selection occurs

    B) body cell becomes infected with a virus → synthesis of new viral proteins → class I MHC molecule–antigen complex displayed on cell surface

    C) self–tolerance of immune cells → B cells contact antigen → cytokines released

    D) complement cells → B cell contacts antigen → helper T cell activated → cytokines released

    E) cytotoxic T cells → class II MHC molecule–antigen complex displayed → cytokines released → cell lysis

    Answer: B
    *Topic: Concept 43.3*
    *Skill: Application*

37) Which of the following is the last line of defense against an extracellular pathogen?

   A) lysozyme production

   B) phagocytosis by neutrophils

   C) antibody production by plasma cells

   D) histamine release by basophils

   E) lysis by natural killer cells

Answer: C
*Topic: Concept 43.3*
*Skill: Knowledge*

38) The following events occur when a mammalian immune system first encounters a pathogen. Place them in correct sequence and then choose the answer that indicates that sequence.
I.   Pathogen is destroyed.
II.  Lymphocytes secrete antibodies.
III. Antigenic determinants from pathogen bind to antigen receptors on lymphocytes.
IV.  Lymphocytes specific to antigenic determinants from pathogen become numerous.
V.   Only memory cells remain.

   A) I, III, II, IV, V

   B) III, II, I, V, IV

   C) II, I, IV, III, V

   D) IV, II, III, I, V

   E) III, IV, II, I, V

Answer: E
*Topic: Concept 43.3*
*Skill: Comprehension*

39) Which cell type interacts with both the humoral and cell-mediated immune pathways?

   A) plasma cells

   B) cytotoxic T cells

   C) natural killer cells

   D) CD8 cells

   E) helper T cells

Answer: E
*Topic: Concept 43.3*
*Skill: Knowledge*

40) Both lysozyme and cytotoxic T cells

   A) kill cells through chemical interactions.

   B) kill cells by inducing apoptosis.

   C) kill cells by generating a membrane attack complex.

   D) are part of innate immunity.

   E) are involved in cell–mediated immune responses.

Answer: A
*Topic: Concepts 43.1, 43.3*
*Skill: Comprehension*

41) A nonfunctional CD4 protein on a helper T cell would result in the helper T cell being unable to

   A) respond to T–independent antigens.

   B) lyse tumor cells.

   C) stimulate a cytotoxic T cell.

   D) interact with a class I MHC–antigen complex.

   E) interact with a class II MHC–antigen complex.

Answer: E
*Topic: Concept 43.3*
*Skill: Comprehension*

42) CD4 and CD8 are proteins

    A) secreted by antigen–presenting cells.

    B) present on the surface of natural killer (NK) cells.

    C) that are T–independent antigens.

    D) that are present on the surface of T cells where they enhance cellular interaction.

    E) that are on the surface of antigen-presenting cells where they enhance B cell activity.

Answer: D
*Topic: Concept 43.3*
*Skill: Comprehension*

43) Which cells will respond whether you have a viral infection or a bacterial infection?

    A) plasma cells

    B) helper T cells

    C) cytotoxic T cells

    D) only A and B

    E) A, B, and C

Answer: D
*Topic: Concept 43.3*
*Skill: Comprehension*

44) Which of the following are all types of T cells that participate in the immune response system?

    A) CD4, CD8, and helper cells

    B) cytotoxic and helper cells

    C) plasma, antigen–presenting, and memory cells

    D) lymphocytes, macrophages, and dendritic cells

    E) class I MHC, class II MHC, and memory cells

Answer: B
*Topic: Concept 43.3*
*Skill: Knowledge*

45) B cells interacting with helper T cells are stimulated to differentiate when

    A) B cells produce IgE antibodies.

    B) B cells release cytokines.

    C) helper T cells present the class II MHC molecule–antigen complex on their surface.

    D) helper T cells differentiate into cytotoxic T cells.

    E) helper T cells release cytokines.

Answer: E
*Topic: Concept 43.3*
*Skill: Comprehension*

46) Why can normal immune responses be described as polyclonal?

    A) Blood contains many different antibodies to many different antigens.

    B) Construction of a hybridoma requires multiple types of cells.

    C) Multiple immunoglobulins are produced from descendants of a single B cell.

    D) Diverse antibodies are produced for different epitopes of a specific antigen.

    E) Macrophages, T cells, and B cells all are involved in normal immune response.

Answer: D
*Topic: Concept 43.3*
*Skill: Comprehension*

47) Antibodies of the different classes IgM, IgG, IgA, IgD, and IgE differ from each other in the

A) way they are produced.

B) way they interact with the antigen.

C) type of cell that produces them.

D) antigenic determinants that they recognize. .

E) number of carbohydrate subunits they have.

Answer: B
*Topic: Concept 43.3*
*Skill: Comprehension*

48) Which of the following types of cells is *not* involved in *both* antibody-mediated immunity and cell-mediated immunity?

A) pathogenic cells

B) plasma cells

C) helper T cells

D) macrophages

E) memory cells

Answer: B
*Topic: Concept 43.3*
*Skill: Comprehension*

49) When antibodies attack antigens, clumping of the affected cells generally occurs. This is best explained by

A) the shape of the antibody with at least two binding regions.

B) disulfide bridges between the antigens.

C) complement that makes the affected cells sticky.

D) bonds between class I and class II MHC molecules.

E) denaturation of the antibodies.

Answer: A
*Topic: Concept 43.3*
*Skill: Comprehension*

50) Phagocytosis of microbes by macrophages is enhanced by

A) the binding of antibodies to the surface of microbes.

B) antibody–mediated agglutination of microbes.

C) the release of cytokines by activated B cells.

D) A and B only

E) A, B, and C

Answer: D
*Topic: Concept 43.3*
*Skill: Comprehension*

51) Which of the following statements about humoral immunity is correct?

A) It primarily defends against fungi and protozoa.

B) It is responsible for transplant tissue rejection.

C) It protects the body against cells that become cancerous.

D) It is mounted by lymphocytes that have matured in the bone marrow.

E) It primarily defends against bacteria and viruses that have already infected cells.

Answer: D
*Topic: Concept 43.3*
*Skill: Comprehension*

52) What happens to people who receive flu vaccinations?

A) They develop active immunity to the flu.

B) They develop passive immunity to the flu.

C) They have immunity to smallpox infection.

D) They have an increased number of natural killer (NK) cells.

E) They develop a hypersensitive humoral immune response.

Answer: B
*Topic: Concept 43.3*
*Skill: Comprehension*

53) Naturally acquired passive immunity would involve the

A) injection of vaccine.

B) ingestion of interferon.

C) placental transfer of antibodies.

D) absorption of pathogens through mucous membranes.

E) injection of antibodies.

Answer: C
*Topic: Concept 43.3*
*Skill: Comprehension*

54) A major difference between active and passive immunity is that active immunity requires

A) acquisition and activation of antibodies.

B) proliferation of lymphocytes in bone marrow.

C) transfer of antibodies from the mother across the placenta.

D) direct exposure to a living or simulated pathogen.

E) secretion of interleukins from macrophages.

Answer: D
*Topic: Concept 43.3*
*Skill: Comprehension*

55) Jenner successfully used cowpox virus as a vaccine against the virus that causes smallpox. Why was he successful even though he used viruses of different kinds?

A) The immune system responds nonspecifically to antigens.

B) The cowpox virus made antibodies in response to the presence of smallpox.

C) Cowpox and smallpox are antibodies with similar immunizing properties.

D) There are some antigenic determinants common to both pox viruses.

E) All of the above are true.

Answer: D
*Topic: Concept 43.3*
*Skill: Application*

56) Which of the following would be *most* beneficial in treating an individual who has been bitten by a poisonous snake that has a fast-acting toxin?

A) vaccination with a weakened form of the toxin

B) injection of antibodies to the toxin

C) injection of interleukin-1

D) injection of interleukin-2

E) injection of interferon

Answer: B
*Topic: Concept 43.3*
*Skill: Application*

57) The successful development of a vaccine to be used against a pathogen

A) is dependent on the surface antigens of the pathogen not changing.

B) requires a rearrangement of the B cell receptor antibodies.

C) is not possible without knowing the structure of the surface antigens on the pathogen.

D) is dependent on the pathogen having only one epitope.

E) is dependent on MHC molecules being heterozygous.

Answer: A
*Topic: Concept 43.3*
*Skill: Comprehension*

58) What would be the major concern for an individual with type A blood who receives a transfusion of type B blood?

A) the antibodies in the serum of the donor

B) the antibodies in the serum of the recipient

C) the anti-A antibodies produced by the donor

D) the production of memory cells that will occur in the recipient

E) antibodies in both the donor's and recipient's serum

Answer: B
*Topic: Concept 43.4*
*Skill: Comprehension*

59) A transfusion of type A blood given to a person who has type O blood would result in which of the following?

A) the recipient's B antigens reacting with the donated anti-B antibodies

B) the recipient's anti-A antibodies clumping the donated red blood cells

C) the recipient's anti-A and anti-O antibodies reacting with the donated red blood cells if the donor was a heterozygote (*Ai*) for blood type

D) no reaction because type O is a universal donor

E) no reaction because the O-type individual does not have antibodies

Answer: B
*Topic: Concept 43.4*
*Skill: Comprehension*

*The next questions refer to the following data.*

|        | Case 1 | Case 2 | Case 3 |
|--------|--------|--------|--------|
| Mother | Rh$^-$ | Rh$^-$ | Rh$^+$ |
| Fetus  | Rh$^+$ | Rh$^-$ | Rh$^-$ |

60) In which of the cases could the mother exhibit an anti-Rh-factor reaction to the developing fetus?

A) case 1 only

B) case 3 only

C) cases 1 and 2 only

D) cases 1, 2, and 3

E) It cannot be determined from the data given.

Answer: A
*Topic: Concept 43.4*
*Skill: Application*

61) In which of the cases would the mother *not* exhibit an anti-Rh-factor reaction to the developing fetus?

A) case 1 only

B) case 3 only

C) cases 2 and 3 only

D) cases 1, 2, and 3

E) It cannot be determined from the data given.

Answer: C
*Topic: Concept 43.4*
*Skill: Application*

62) In which of the cases would the precaution likely be taken to give the mother anti-Rh antibodies before delivering her baby?

A) case 1 only

B) case 3 only

C) cases 1 and 2 only

D) cases 1, 2, and 3

E) It cannot be determined from the data given.

Answer: A
*Topic: Concept 43.4*
*Skill: Application*

63) There is usually no concern if the mother's blood type is different from that of the developing fetus unless the Rh factor is involved. This is because

A) the mother naturally develops a passive immunity to Rh unless she has had an Rh-positive child.

B) fetal blood cells can cross the placenta.

C) maternal blood cells can cross the placenta.

D) maternal Rh antibodies can cross the placenta, whereas those against the ABO blood groups cannot.

E) maternal Rh antibodies cannot cross the placenta, whereas those against the ABO blood groups can.

Answer: D
*Topic: Concept 43.4*
*Skill: Comprehension*

64) In order to investigate the immune system of an invertebrate animal, a scientist grafts a section of epidermis from one earthworm to another. What might be the result of such an experiment?

A) Invertebrates do not have immune responses, so the graft will be accepted.

B) The graft will be recognized as nonself and rejected.

C) This graft will be accepted, but a second graft would be rejected.

D) The graft may recognize the host as foreign and react to it.

E) Both B and D would happen.

Answer: B
*Topic: Concept 43.4*
*Skill: Application*

65) An immune response to a tissue graft will differ from an immune response to a bacterium because

    A) MHC molecules of the host may stimulate rejection of the graft tissue.

    B) the tissue graft, unlike the bacterium, is isolated from the circulation and will not enter into an immune response.

    C) a response to the graft will involve T cells and a response to the bacterium will not.

    D) a bacterium cannot escape the immune system by replicating inside normal body cells.

    E) the graft will stimulate an autoimmune response in the recipient.

Answer: A
*Topic: Concept 43.4*
*Skill: Comprehension*

66) Which of the following could prevent the appearance of the symptoms of an allergy attack?

    A) blocking the attachment of the IgE antibodies to the mast cells

    B) blocking the antigenic determinants of the IgM antibodies

    C) reducing the number of helper T cells in the body

    D) A and B only

    E) B and C only

Answer: A
*Topic: Concept 43.5*
*Skill: Application*

67) A patient reports severe symptoms of watery, itchy eyes and sneezing after being given a flower bouquet as a birthday gift. A reasonable initial treatment would involve the use of

    A) a vaccine.

    B) complement.

    C) sterile pollen.

    D) antihistamines.

    E) monoclonal antibodies.

Answer: D
*Topic: Concept 43.5*
*Skill: Application*

68) What aspect of the immune response would a patient who has a parasitic worm infection and another patient responding to an allergen such as ragweed pollen have in common?

    A) Both patients would have an increase in cytotoxic T cell number.

    B) Both patients would suffer from anaphylactic shock.

    C) Both patients would risk development of an autoimmune disease.

    D) Both patients would be suffering from a decreased level of innate immunity.

    E) Both patients would have increased levels of IgE.

Answer: E
*Topic: Concept 43.5*
*Skill: Application*

69) All of the following are usually considered disorders of the immune system *except*

 A) AIDS.

 B) SCID.

 C) lupus erythematosus.

 D) multiple sclerosis.

 E) MHC–induced transplant rejection.

Answer: E
*Topic: Concepts 43.4, 43.5*
*Skill: Comprehension*

70) A person with AIDS would be *unlikely* to suffer from which of the following diseases?

 A) cancer

 B) rheumatoid arthritis

 C) hepatitis

 D) tuberculosis

 E) influenza

Answer: B
*Topic: Concept 43.5*
*Skill: Application*

71) Which choice could be used as an analogy to describe how HIV affects the body?

 A) bypassing a light switch so that electricity is constantly flowing to a light

 B) rebooting a computer after getting a program error message

 C) snipping the wires coming from a car battery so that no electricity flows to the car components

 D) an elevator stopping at the floor for which the button has been pushed

 E) changing the color of your house to match the color of your car

Answer: C
*Topic: Concept 43.5*
*Skill: Comprehension*

# Media Activity Questions

1) B cells that have been stimulated by interleukin-2 develop into
   A) macrophages.
   B) helper T cells.
   C) cytotoxic T cells.
   D) antigens.
   E) plasma cells.

Answer: E
*Topic: Web/CD Activity: Immune Responses*

2) Clonal selection is the division of _____ that have been stimulated by binding to an antigen, which results in the production of cloned _____.
   A) helper T cells; plasma cells
   B) B cells; plasma cells and memory cells
   C) T cells; B cells
   D) B cells; macrophages
   E) macrophages; B cells and T cells

Answer: B
*Topic: Web/CD Activity: Immune Responses*

3) Which of these cells secretes antibodies?
   A) helper T cells
   B) macrophages
   C) bacterial cells
   D) plasma cells
   E) cytotoxic T cells

Answer: D
*Topic: Web/CD Activity: Immune Responses*

4) The genetic material of HIV consists of
   A) single-stranded DNA.
   B) single-stranded RNA.
   C) double-stranded DNA.
   D) double-stranded RNA.
   E) none of the above

Answer: B
*Topic: Web/CD Activity: HIV Reproductive Cycle*

5) Double-stranded viral DNA is incorporated into a host cell as a
   A) promoter.
   B) provirus.
   C) transposon.
   D) lac.
   E) homeobox.

Answer: B
*Topic: Web/CD Activity: HIV Reproductive Cycle*

# Self–Quiz Questions

1) Which of the following is *not* part of the body's innate, nonspecific defense system?

   A) natural killer (NK) cells

   B) inflammation

   C) phagocytosis by neutrophils

   D) phagocytosis by macrophages

   E) antibodies

   Answer: E

2) Which of the following is a characteristic of the early stages of local inflammation?

   A) arteriole constriction

   B) fever

   C) attack by cytotoxic T cells

   D) release of histamine

   E) antibody- and complement-mediated lysis of microbes

   Answer: D

3) Which of the following is *not* a component of an insect's defense against infection?

   A) phenoloxidase activation, leading to the formation of large deposits around parasites

   B) activation of natural killer cells

   C) phagocytosis by hemocytes

   D) production of antimicrobial peptides

   E) a protective exoskeleton

   Answer: B

4) An epitope associates with which part of an antibody?

   A) the antibody-binding site

   B) the heavy-chain constant regions only

   C) the variable regions of a heavy chain and light chain combined

   D) the light-chain constant regions only

   E) the antibody tail

   Answer: C

5) Which of the following is *not* true about helper T cells?

   A) They function in both cell-mediated and humoral immune responses.

   B) They recognize polysaccharide fragments presented by class II MHC molecules.

   C) They bear surface CD4 molecules.

   D) They are subject to infection by HIV.

   E) When activated, they secrete cytokines.

   Answer: B

6) Which of the following molecules is *incorrectly* paired with a source?

   A) lysozyme—tears

   B) interferons—virus-infected cells

   C) antibodies—B cells

   D) chemokines—cytotoxic T cells

   E) cytokines—helper T cells

   Answer: D

7) Which of the following best describes the difference in the way B cells and cytotoxic T cells respond to invaders?

   A) B cells confer active immunity; cytotoxic T cells confer passive immunity.

   B) B cells kill viruses directly; cytotoxic T cells kill virus-infected cells.

   C) B cells secrete antibodies against a virus; cytotoxic T cells kill virus-infected cells.

   D) B cells accomplish cell-mediated immunity; cytotoxic T cells accomplish humoral immunity.

   E) B cells respond the first time the invader is present; cytotoxic T cells respond subsequent times.

   Answer: C

8) Which of the following results in long-term immunity?
   A) the passage of maternal antibodies to a developing fetus
   B) the inflammatory response to a splinter
   C) the administration of serum obtained from people immune to rabies
   D) the administration of the chicken pox vaccine
   E) the passage of maternal antibodies to a nursing infant

Answer: D

9) After an Rh-positive baby is born to an Rh-negative mother, the mother is treated with antibodies specific for the Rh factor. The purpose of this treatment is to
   A) protect her from the baby's red blood cells.
   B) prevent her from generating memory B cells specific for the Rh factor.
   C) protect her future Rh-positive babies.
   D) induce an immune response to Rh antibodies.
   E) both B and C

Answer: E

10) HIV targets include all of the following *except*
   A) macrophages.
   B) cytotoxic T cells.
   C) helper T cells.
   D) cells bearing CD4 and fusin.
   E) brain cells.

Answer: B

# Chapter 44  Osmoregulation and Excretion

1) A marine sea star was mistakenly placed in freshwater and it died.  What is the most likely explanation for its death?

   A) The sea star was stressed and needed more time to adapt to new conditions.

   B) The sea star is hypertonic to the freshwater, and it could not osmoregulate.

   C) The osmoregulatory system of the sea star could not handle the change in ionic content presented by the freshwater.

   D) The contractile vacuoles used to regulate water content ruptured in the freshwater.

   E) The cells of the sea star dehydrated and lost the ability to metabolize.

Answer: B
*Topic: Concept 44.1*
*Skill: Comprehension*

2) Organisms categorized as osmoconformers are most likely

   A) terrestrial.

   B) marine.

   C) amphibious.

   D) found in freshwater streams.

   E) found in freshwater lakes.

Answer: B
*Topic: Concept 44.1*
*Skill: Knowledge*

3) The body fluids of an osmoconformer would be _____ with its _____ environment.

   A) hypertonic; freshwater

   B) isotonic; freshwater

   C) hyperosmotic; saltwater

   D) isoosmotic; saltwater

   E) hypoosmotic; saltwater

Answer: D
*Topic: Concept 44.1*
*Skill: Comprehension*

4) Compared to the seawater around them, most marine invertebrates are

   A) hyperosmotic.

   B) hypoosmotic.

   C) isoosmotic.

   D) hyperosmotic and isoosmotic.

   E) hypoosmotic and isoosmotic.

Answer: C
*Topic: Concept 44.1*
*Skill: Comprehension*

5) Which feature of osmoregulation is found in both marine and freshwater bony fish?

   A) loss of water through the gills

   B) gain of salt through the gills

   C) loss of water in the urine

   D) no drinking of water

   E) gain of water through food

Answer: E
*Topic: Concept 44.1*
*Skill: Comprehension*

6) In addition to their role in gas exchange, fish gills are also directly involved in

   A) digestion.

   B) osmoregulation.

   C) thermoregulation.

   D) the excretion of uric acid.

   E) the release of atrial natriuretic proteins.

   Answer: B
   *Topic: Concept 44.1*
   *Skill: Comprehension*

7) All of the following represent adaptations by terrestrial animals to drying conditions *except*

   A) anhydrobiosis.

   B) salt glands.

   C) efficient kidneys.

   D) impervious surfaces.

   E) increased thirst.

   Answer: B
   *Topic: Concept 44.1*
   *Skill: Comprehension*

8) The digestion and utilization of which nutrient creates the greatest need for osmoregulation by the kidneys?

   A) protein

   B) starch

   C) fat

   D) oil

   E) cellulose

   Answer: A
   *Topic: Concept 44.2*
   *Skill: Comprehension*

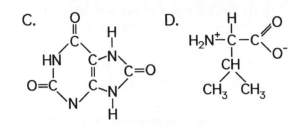

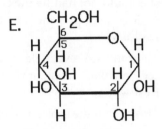

**Figure 44.1**

9) Which of the molecules shown in Figure 44.1 represents urea?

   Answer: B
   *Topic: Concept 44.2*
   *Skill: Knowledge*

10) Where and from what compound(s) is urea produced?

   A) liver from $NH_3$ and $CO_2$

   B) liver from glycogen

   C) kidneys from glucose

   D) kidneys from glycerol and fatty acids

   E) bladder from uric acid and $H_2O$

   Answer: A
   *Topic: Concept 44.2*
   *Skill: Knowledge*

11) Which of the following is true of urea? It is

A) insoluble in water.

B) more toxic to human cells than ammonia.

C) the primary nitrogenous waste product of humans.

D) the primary nitrogenous waste product of most birds.

E) the primary nitrogenous waste product of most aquatic invertebrates.

Answer: C
*Topic: Concept 44.2*
*Skill: Knowledge*

12) Which of the following is true of ammonia?

A) It is soluble in water.

B) It can be stored as a precipitate.

C) It has low toxicity relative to urea.

D) Only A and C are true.

E) A, B, and C are true.

Answer: A
*Topic: Concept 44.2*
*Skill: Comprehension*

13) Which of the following is *not* a function of the liver?

A) storage of glycogen

B) secretion of urea

C) production of plasma proteins

D) removal of glucose from the blood

E) detoxification of chemical poisons in the blood

Answer: B
*Topic: Concept 44.2*
*Skill: Comprehension*

14) The advantage of excreting wastes as urea rather than as ammonia is that

A) urea can be exchanged for $Na^+$.

B) urea is less toxic than ammonia.

C) urea requires more water for excretion than ammonia.

D) urea does not affect the osmolar gradient.

E) less nitrogen is removed from the body.

Answer: B
*Topic: Concept 44.2*
*Skill: Knowledge*

15) What is the main nitrogenous waste excreted by birds?

A) ammonia

B) nitrate

C) nitrite

D) urea

E) uric acid

Answer: E
*Topic: Concept 44.2*
*Skill: Knowledge*

16) Which of the following is a nitrogenous waste that requires hardly any water for its excretion?

A) amino acid

B) urea

C) uric acid

D) ammonia

E) nitrogen gas

Answer: C
*Topic: Concept 44.2*
*Skill: Knowledge*

17) What is the process called by which materials are returned to the blood from the nephron fluid?
    A) filtration
    B) ultrafiltration
    C) selective reabsorption
    D) secretion
    E) active transport

Answer: C
*Topic: Concept 44.3*
*Skill: Knowledge*

18) Which organism(s) has excretory structures known as protonephridia?
    A) flatworms
    B) earthworms
    C) insects
    D) vertebrates
    E) both C and D

Answer: A
*Topic: Concept 44.3*
*Skill: Knowledge*

19) Which organism(s) has excretory organs known as Malpighian tubules?
    A) earthworms
    B) flatworms
    C) insects
    D) jellyfish
    E) both A and B

Answer: C
*Topic: Concept 44.3*
*Skill: Knowledge*

20) Which of the following mechanisms for osmoregulation or nitrogen removal is *incorrectly* paired with its corresponding animal?
    A) metanephridium—earthworm
    B) Malpighian tubule—insect
    C) kidney—frog
    D) flame bulb—snake
    E) direct cellular exchange—marine invertebrate

Answer: D
*Topic: Concept 44.3*
*Skill: Knowledge*

21) Which of the following excretory systems is partly based on the filtration of fluid under high hydrostatic pressure?
    A) flame-bulb system of flatworms
    B) protonephridia of rotifers
    C) metanephridia of earthworms
    D) Malpighian tubules of insects
    E) kidneys of vertebrates

Answer: E
*Topic: Concept 44.3*
*Skill: Knowledge*

22) What is the functional unit of the kidney?
    A) cortex
    B) vasa recta
    C) nephron
    D) bladder
    E) glomerulus

Answer: C
*Topic: Concept 44.4*
*Skill: Knowledge*

23) The transfer of fluid from the glomerulus to Bowman's capsule

    A) results from active transport.

    B) transfers large molecules as easily as small ones.

    C) is very selective as to which small molecules are transferred.

    D) is mainly a consequence of blood pressure force–filtering the fluid.

    E) usually includes the transfer of red blood cells to the nephron tubule.

Answer: D
*Topic: Concept 44.4*
*Skill: Comprehension*

24) Which part of the vertebrate nephron consists of capillaries?

    A) glomerulus

    B) loop of Henle

    C) distal tubule

    D) Bowman's capsule

    E) collecting duct

Answer: A
*Topic: Concept 44.4*
*Skill: Comprehension*

25) Which of the following normally contains blood?

    A) vasa recta

    B) Bowman's capsule

    C) loop of Henle

    D) proximal tubule

    E) collecting duct

Answer: A
*Topic: Concept 44.4*
*Skill: Knowledge*

*Refer to Figure 44.2, a diagram of a renal tubule, to answer the following questions.*

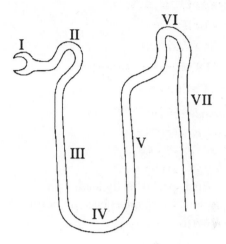

**Figure 44.2**

26) In which region would filtration occur?

    A) I

    B) III

    C) IV

    D) V

    E) VII

Answer: A
*Topic: Concept 44.4*
*Skill: Knowledge*

27) In which region would urine become more concentrated?

    A) I

    B) III

    C) IV

    D) V

    E) VII

Answer: E
*Topic: Concept 44.4*
*Skill: Knowledge*

28) In which region would nutrients be actively transported to the blood?

   A) I

   B) II

   C) IV

   D) V

   E) VI

   Answer: B
   *Topic: Concept 44.4*
   *Skill: Knowledge*

29) Which part directly leads to the area where membranes become permeable to urea?

   A) III

   B) IV

   C) V

   D) VI

   E) VII

   Answer: E
   *Topic: Concept 44.4*
   *Skill: Knowledge*

30) What substance is secreted by the proximal-tubule cells and prevents the pH of urine from becoming too acidic?

   A) bicarbonate

   B) salt

   C) glucose

   D) ammonia

   E) HCl

   Answer: D
   *Topic: Concept 44.4*
   *Skill: Knowledge*

31) Which structure passes urine to the renal pelvis?

   A) loop of Henle

   B) collecting duct

   C) Bowman's capsule

   D) proximal tubule

   E) glomerulus

   Answer: B
   *Topic: Concept 44.4*
   *Skill: Knowledge*

32) Which structure possesses specialized cells called podocytes?

   A) loop of Henle

   B) collecting duct

   C) Bowman's capsule

   D) proximal tubule

   E) glomerulus

   Answer: C
   *Topic: Concept 44.4*
   *Skill: Knowledge*

33) Which structure is the first section of the nephron tubule into which the filtrate enters?

   A) loop of Henle

   B) collecting duct

   C) ureter

   D) proximal tubule

   E) glomerulus

   Answer: D
   *Topic: Concept 44.4*
   *Skill: Knowledge*

34) Which structure descends deep into the renal medulla only in juxtamedullary nephrons?

A) loop of Henle

B) collecting duct

C) Bowman's capsule

D) proximal convoluted tubule

E) glomerulus

Answer: A
*Topic: Concept 44.4*
*Skill: Knowledge*

35) All of the following are functions of the mammalian kidney *except*

A) water reabsorption.

B) filtration of blood.

C) excretion of nitrogenous waste.

D) regulation of salt balance in the blood.

E) production of urea as a waste product of protein catabolism.

Answer: E
*Topic: Concept 44.4*
*Skill: Knowledge*

36) Which one of the following structures is found in birds and mammals but *not* in other vertebrates?

A) juxtamedullary nephrons

B) nephrons

C) urethra

D) ureter

E) Bowman's capsule

Answer: A
*Topic: Concept 44.4*
*Skill: Knowledge*

37) Which of the following is *not* true concerning transport epithelia involved in water balance?

A) One surface of the epithelium faces the outside environment directly or indirectly.

B) The epithelium is a semipermeable barrier.

C) The surface area is small, which prevents excessive water loss.

D) The epithelium regulates the movement of solutes.

E) Cells are joined by tight junctions.

Answer: C
*Topic: Concept 44.4*
*Skill: Comprehension*

38) Which of the following processes of osmoregulation by the kidney is the *least* selective?

A) salt pumping to control osmolarity

B) $H^+$ pumping to control pH

C) reabsorption

D) filtration

E) secretion

Answer: D
*Topic: Concept 44.4*
*Skill: Comprehension*

39) Proper functioning of the human kidney requires considerable active transport of sodium in the kidney tubules. If these active transport mechanisms were to stop completely, how would urine production be affected?

A) No urine would be produced.

B) A less-than-normal volume of hypoosmotic urine would be produced.

C) A greater-than-normal volume of isoosmotic urine would be produced.

D) A greater-than-normal volume of hyperosmotic urine would be produced.

E) A less-than-normal volume of isoosmotic urine would be produced.

Answer: C
*Topic: Concept 44.4*
*Skill: Application*

40) Which one of the following is extremely important for water conservation in mammals?

A) juxtamedullary nephrons

B) Bowman's capsule

C) urethra

D) podocytes

E) ureter

Answer: A
*Topic: Concept 44.4*
*Skill: Comprehension*

41) Which one of the following, if present in a urine sample, would likely be caused by trauma?

A) amino acids

B) glucose

C) salts

D) erythrocytes

E) vitamins

Answer: D
*Topic: Concept 44.5*
*Skill: Application*

42) A toxin that specifically blocks active transport in the loop of Henle might result in which of the following?

A) a decrease in the interstitial concentration of NaCl

B) a decrease in the filtrate concentration ability of the kidney

C) an increase in the amount of interstitial urea to maintain interstitial osmolarity

D) A and C only

E) A, B and C

Answer: E
*Topic: Concept 44.5*
*Skill: Application*

43) Depending on salt intake and water availability, humans can produce urine that is

A) hyperosmotic to body fluids.

B) hypoosmotic to body fluids.

C) isoosmotic to body fluids.

D) A and B are true.

E) A, B, and C are true.

Answer: E
*Topic: Concept 44.5*
*Skill: Comprehension*

44) Which structure increases the reabsorption of $Na^+$ when stimulated by aldosterone?

A) loop of Henle

B) collecting duct

C) Bowman's capsule

D) proximal tubule

E) distal tubules

Answer: E
*Topic: Concept 44.5*
*Skill: Knowledge*

45) What would account for increased urine production as a result of drinking alcoholic beverages?

 A) increased aldosterone production

 B) increased blood pressure

 C) decreased amount of antidiuretic hormone (ADH)

 D) increased reabsorption of water in the proximal tubule

 E) the osmoregulator cells of the brain increasing their activity

Answer: C
*Topic: Concept 44.5*
*Skill: Knowledge*

46) In a laboratory experiment with three groups, one group of people drinks pure water, a second group drinks an equal amount of beer, and a third group drinks an equal amount of concentrated salt solution all during the same time period. Their urine production is monitored for several hours. At the end of the measurement period, which group will have produced the greatest volume of urine and which group the least?

 A) beer the most, salt solution the least

 B) salt solution the most, water the least

 C) water the most, beer the least

 D) beer the most, water the least

 E) There will be no significant difference between these groups.

Answer: A
*Topic: Concept 44.5*
*Skill: Application*

47) Which of the following activities would initiate an osmoregulatory adjustment brought about primarily through the renin–angiotensin–aldosterone system?

 A) sleeping

 B) spending several hours mowing the lawn on a hot day

 C) eating a bag of potato chips

 D) eating a pizza with olives and pepperoni

 E) drinking several glasses of water

Answer: B
*Topic: Concept 44.5*
*Skill: Application*

48) Hormones involved in the production of urine include all of the following *except*

 A) aldosterone.

 B) angiotensin.

 C) ADH.

 D) atrial natriuretic factor.

 E) secretin.

Answer: E
*Topic: Concept 44.5*
*Skill: Knowledge*

49) Which statement is true about marine fishes?

 A) Compared to marine fishes, freshwater fishes have fewer glomeruli.

 B) The kidneys of marine fishes excrete little urine.

 C) Marine fishes lack proximal tubules.

 D) Marine fishes secrete uric acid to conserve water.

 E) Their kidneys produce filtrate at high rates.

Answer: B
*Topic: Concept 44.6*
*Skill: Comprehension*

# Media Activity Questions

1) The _____ are the major blood vessels transporting blood to the kidneys.

   A) pulmonary arteries

   B) glomerulus

   C) renal arteries

   D) renal veins

   E) venae cavae

   Answer: C
   *Topic: Structure of the Human Excretory System*

2) The outer part of the kidney is the

   A) medulla.

   B) nephron.

   C) lacteal.

   D) cortex.

   E) Bowman's capsule.

   Answer: D
   *Topic: Structure of the Human Excretory System*

3) The movement of substances from the blood into the proximal tubule is known as

   A) filtration.

   B) dialysis.

   C) secretion.

   D) reabsorption

   E) none of these

   Answer: C
   *Topic: Web/CD Activity: Nephron Function*

4) The most abundant solute in urine is

   A) glucose.

   B) water.

   C) plasma proteins.

   D) sodium chloride.

   E) urea (and other nitrogenous wastes).

   Answer: E
   *Topic: Web/CD Activity: Nephron Function*

5) Glucose is removed from filtrate by

   A) secretion.

   B) diffusion.

   C) dialysis.

   D) active transport.

   E) osmosis.

   Answer: D
   *Topic: Web/CD Activity: Nephron Function*

# Self-Quiz Questions

1) *Unlike* an earthworm's metanephridia, a mammalian nephron
   - A) is intimately associated with a capillary network.
   - B) forms urine by changing the composition of fluid inside the tubule.
   - C) functions in both osmoregulation and the excretion of nitrogenous wastes.
   - D) processes blood instead of coelomic fluid.
   - E) has a transport epithelium.

   Answer: D

2) Which of the following is *not* a normal response to increased blood osmolarity in humans?
   - A) increased permeability of the collecting duct to water
   - B) increased thirst
   - C) release of ADH by the pituitary gland
   - D) production of more dilute urine
   - E) reduced urine production

   Answer: D

3) The high osmolarity of the renal medulla is maintained by all of the following *except*
   - A) diffusion of salt from the ascending limb of the loop of Henle.
   - B) active transport of salt from the upper region of the ascending limb.
   - C) the spatial arrangement of juxtamedullary nephrons.
   - D) diffusion of urea from the collecting duct.
   - E) diffusion of salt from the descending limb of the loop of Henle.

   Answer: E

4) Select the pair in which the nitrogenous waste is *incorrectly* matched with the benefit of its excretion.
   - A) urea—low toxicity relative to ammonia
   - B) uric acid—can be stored as a precipitate
   - C) ammonia—very soluble in water
   - D) uric acid—minimal loss of water when excreted
   - E) urea—very insoluble in water

   Answer: E

5) The body fluids of freshwater crustaceans generally have a lower osmolarity than the body fluids of their nearest marine crustacean relatives. Which of the following is a benefit of reduced osmolarity of body fluids in freshwater crustaceans?
   - A) an increase in the rate of water flow into the body fluids
   - B) a decrease in the rate of water loss to the surrounding environment
   - C) a reduction in energy expenditures for osmoregulation
   - D) an increase in the rate of salt loss to the surrounding environment
   - E) a decrease in the rate of salt gain from the environment

   Answer: C

6) Which process in the nephron is *least* selective?
   - A) secretion
   - B) reabsorption
   - C) active transport
   - D) filtration
   - E) salt pumping by the loop of Henle

   Answer: D

7) Which of the following animals generally has the lowest volume of urine production?

   A) a marine shark

   B) a salmon in freshwater

   C) a marine bony fish

   D) a freshwater bony fish

   E) a shark inhabiting Lake Nicaragua

Answer: C

8) African lungfish, which are often found in small stagnant pools of fresh water, produce urea as a nitrogenous waste. What is the advantage of this adaptation?

   A) Urea takes less energy to synthesize then ammonia.

   B) Small stagnant pools do not provide enough water to dilute the toxic ammonia.

   C) The highly toxic urea makes the pool uninhabitable to potential competitors.

   D) Urea forms a precipitate and does not accumulate in the surrounding water.

   E) A buildup of urea in the blood makes a lungfish hypoosmotic to its environment.

Answer: B

9) Natural selection should favor the highest proportion of juxtamedullary nephrons in which of the following species?

   A) a river otter

   B) a mouse species living in a tropical rain forest

   C) a mouse species living in a temperate broadleaf forest

   D) a mouse species living in the desert

   E) a beaver

Answer: D

10) A clinical condition known as diabetes insipidus results in the production of large volumes of dilute urine. Which of the following is consistent with this condition?

   A) a high concentration of sodium in the urine

   B) very low production of ADH

   C) overproduction of ADH

   D) high production of aldosterone

   E) high production of angiotensin II

Answer: B

# Chapter 45  Hormones and the Endocrine System

1) Which of the following statements about hormones is *incorrect*?

   A) They are produced by endocrine glands.

   B) They are modified amino acids, peptides, or steroid molecules.

   C) They are carried by the circulatory system.

   D) They are used to communicate between different organisms.

   E) They elicit specific biological responses from target cells.

   Answer: D
   *Topic: Concepts 45.1–45.4*
   *Skill: Comprehension*

2) The secretion of hormone A causes a change in the amount of protein X in an organism. If this mechanism works by positive feedback, which of the following statements represents that fact?

   A) An increase in A produces an increase in X.

   B) An increase in X produces a decrease in A.

   C) A decrease in A produces an increase in X.

   D) A and B are correct.

   E) B and C are correct.

   Answer: A
   *Topic: Concept 45.1*
   *Skill: Comprehension*

3) Which of the following is (are) true?

   A) Hormones regulate cellular functions, and negative feedback regulates hormone levels.

   B) The circulating level of a hormone is held constant through a series of positive feedback loops.

   C) Both lipid–soluble hormones and water–soluble hormones bind to intracellular protein receptors.

   D) Only A and D are true.

   E) A, B, and C are true.

   Answer: A
   *Topic: Concepts 45.1, 45.2*
   *Skill: Knowledge*

4) What do nitric oxide and epinephrine have in common?

   A) They both function as neurotransmitters.

   B) They both function as hormones.

   C) They are both involved in the "fight–or–flight" response.

   D) Only A and B are correct.

   E) A, B, and C are correct.

   Answer: D
   *Topic: Concepts 45.1, 45.2*
   *Skill: Comprehension*

5) Substance X is secreted by one cell, travels a short distance through interstitial fluid, and produces an effect in a cell immediately adjacent to the original secreting cell. All of the following terms could describe this substance *except*

A) nitric oxide.

B) neurotransmitter.

C) prostaglandin.

D) pheromone.

E) growth factor.

Answer: D
*Topic: Concepts 45.1, 45.2*
*Skill: Comprehension*

6) Based on their effects, which pair below could be considered antagonistic?

A) prostaglandin F and nitric oxide

B) growth hormone and ecdysone

C) endocrine and exocrine glands

D) hormones and target cells

E) neurosecretory cells and neurotransmitters

Answer: A
*Topic: Concept 45.2*
*Skill: Comprehension*

7) Which of the following is a local regulator responsible for activating an enzyme that relaxes smooth muscle cells?

A) nitric oxide

B) prostaglandin F

C) epinephrine

D) A and B only

E) A, B, and C

Answer: A
*Topic: Concept 45.2*
*Skill: Comprehension*

8) Prostaglandins are local regulators whose basic structure is derived from

A) oligosaccharides.

B) fatty acids.

C) steroids.

D) amino acids.

E) both A and B

Answer: B
*Topic: Concept 45.2*
*Skill: Knowledge*

9) Which of the following examples is incorrectly paired with its class?

A) histamine—local regulator

B) estrogen—steroid hormone

C) prostaglandin—peptide hormone

D) ecdysone—steroid hormone

E) neurotransmitter—local regulator

Answer: C
*Topic: Concept 45.2*
*Skill: Comprehension*

10) What is the mode of action of aspirin and ibuprofen?

A) They inhibit the synthesis of prostaglandins.

B) They inhibit the release of nitric oxide, a potent vasodilator.

C) They block paracrine signaling pathways.

D) They stimulate the release of oxytocin.

E) They stimulate the release of endorphins.

Answer: A
*Topic: Concept 45.2*
*Skill: Application*

11) A cell that contains proteins enabling a hormone to selectively bind to its plasma membrane is called a(n)

   A) secretory cell.

   B) plasma cell.

   C) endocrine cell.

   D) target cell.

   E) regulatory cell.

Answer: D
*Topic: Concept 45.2*
*Skill: Knowledge*

12) Only certain cells in the body are target cells for the steroid hormone aldosterone. Which of the following is the best explanation for why these are the only cells that respond to this hormone?

   A) Only target cells are exposed to aldosterone.

   B) Only target cells contain receptors for aldosterone.

   C) Aldosterone is unable to enter nontarget cells.

   D) Nontarget cells destroy aldosterone before it can produce its effect.

   E) Nontarget cells convert aldosterone to a hormone to which they do respond.

Answer: B
*Topic: Concept 45.2*
*Skill: Comprehension*

13) Why is it that some body cells respond differently to the same peptide hormones?

   A) Different target cells have different genes.

   B) Each cell knows how it fits into the body's master plan.

   C) A target cell's response is determined by the product of a signal transduction pathway.

   D) The circulatory system regulates responses to hormones by routing the hormones to specific targets.

   E) The hormone is chemically altered in different ways as it travels through the circulatory system.

Answer: C
*Topic: Concept 45.2*
*Skill: Comprehension*

14) How is a cell's response to a water–soluble hormone amplified?

   A) regulation of intracellular hormone levels

   B) regulation of cell volume

   C) changes in the intracellular levels of cytokines

   D) regulatory proteins present inside of the cell

   E) regulation of the number of surface receptors

Answer: D
*Topic: Concept 45.2*
*Skill: Comprehension*

15) Frequently, very few molecules of a hormone are required to affect changes in a target cell. This is because
   A) hormones are lipid–soluble and readily penetrate the membranes of the target cell.
   B) hormones are large molecules that remain in circulation for months and can repeatedly stimulate the same cell.
   C) the mechanism of hormonal action involves an enzyme cascade that amplifies the response to a hormone.
   D) the mechanism of hormonal action involves the rapid replication of the hormone within the target cell.
   E) the mechanism of hormonal action involves memory cells that have had prior contact with the hormone.

Answer: C
*Topic: Concept 45.2*
*Skill: Application*

16) Why would a liver cell and a lung cell respond differently to the same steroid hormone?
   A) They have different receptor proteins within the cell.
   B) They have different acceptor proteins on the chromatin.
   C) Steroid hormones usually transmit signals that are antagonistic.
   D) The acceptor proteins are associated with different genes in the two kinds of cells.
   E) The hormone–receptor complex is transcribed and processed differently in the two kinds of cells.

Answer: D
*Topic: Concept 45.2*
*Skill: Application*

17) Hormone X produces its effect in its target cells via the cAMP second messenger system. Which of the following will produce the greatest effect in the cell?
   A) a molecule of hormone X applied to the extracellular fluid surrounding the cell
   B) a molecule of hormone X injected into the cytoplasm of the cell
   C) a molecule of cAMP applied to the extracellular fluid surrounding the cell
   D) a molecule of cAMP injected into the cytoplasm of the cell
   E) a molecule of activated, cAMP–dependent protein kinase injected into the cytoplasm of the cell

Answer: A
*Topic: Concept 45.2*
*Skill: Application*

18) Which of the following statements about hormones is *correct*?
   A) Steroid and peptide hormones produce different effects but use the same biochemical mechanisms.
   B) Steroid and peptide hormones produce the same effects but differ in the mechanisms that produce the effects.
   C) Steroid hormones affect the synthesis of proteins, whereas peptide hormones affect the activity of proteins already present in the cell.
   D) Steroid hormones affect the activity of certain proteins within the cell, whereas peptide hormones directly affect the processing of mRNA.
   E) Steroid hormones affect the synthesis of proteins to be exported from the cell, whereas peptide hormones affect the synthesis of proteins that remain in the cell.

Answer: C
*Topic: Concept 45.2*
*Skill: Comprehension*

19) Where is it likely that you will find the receptor molecules for chemical signals?

A) in the nucleus of target cells

B) in the interstitial fluid surrounding target cells

C) in the cytoplasm of target cells

D) in the cell membrane of target cells

E) associated with the DNA of target cells

Answer: D
*Topic: Concept 45.2*
*Skill: Comprehension*

20) Hormones from the hypothalamus affect the release of all of the following *except*

A) prolactin.

B) oxytocin.

C) growth hormone.

D) thyroid-stimulating hormone.

E) adrenocorticotropic hormone.

Answer: B
*Topic: Concept 45.3*
*Skill: Comprehension*

21) The endocrine system and the nervous system are structurally related. Which of the following cells best illustrates this relationship?

A) a neuron in the spinal cord

B) a steroid-producing cell in the adrenal cortex

C) a neurosecretory cell in the hypothalamus

D) a brain cell in the cerebral cortex

E) a cell in the pancreas that produces digestive enzymes

Answer: C
*Topic: Concept 45.3*
*Skill: Comprehension*

22) The hypothalamus controls the anterior pituitary by means of

A) releasing hormones.

B) second messengers.

C) third messengers.

D) antibodies.

E) pyrogens.

Answer: A
*Topic: Concept 45.3*
*Skill: Knowledge*

23) Short blood vessels connect two capillary beds lying in which of the following?

A) hypothalamus and thalamus

B) anterior pituitary and posterior pituitary

C) hypothalamus and anterior pituitary

D) posterior pituitary and thyroid gland

E) anterior pituitary and adrenal gland

Answer: C
*Topic: Concept 45.3*
*Skill: Knowledge*

24) Oxytocin and ADH are produced by the _____ and stored in the _____.

A) hypothalamus; neurohypophysis

B) adenohypophysis; kidneys

C) anterior pituitary; thyroid

D) adrenal cortex; adrenal medulla

E) posterior pituitary; anterior pituitary

Answer: A
*Topic: Concepts 45.3, 45.4*
*Skill: Knowledge*

25) If a person drinks a large amount of water in a short period of time, he or she may die from water toxicity. ADH can help prevent water retention through interaction with target cells in the

A) anterior pituitary.

B) posterior pituitary.

C) adrenal gland.

D) bladder.

E) kidney.

Answer: E
*Topic: Concept 45.3*
*Skill: Comprehension*

26) Which of the following statements about the hypothalamus is *incorrect*?

A) It functions as an endocrine gland.

B) It is part of the central nervous system.

C) It is subject to feedback inhibition by certain hormones.

D) It secretes tropic hormones that act directly on the gonads.

E) Its neurosecretory cells terminate in the posterior pituitary.

Answer: D
*Topic: Concept 45.3*
*Skill: Comprehension*

27) Which combination of hormones helps a mother to produce milk and nurse her baby?

A) prolactin and calcitrone

B) oxytocin and prolactin

C) follicle-stimulating hormone and luteinizing hormone

D) luteinizing hormone and oxytocin

E) oxytocin, prolactin, and luteinizing hormone

Answer: B
*Topic: Concept 45.3*
*Skill: Comprehension*

28) Prolactin stimulates mammary gland growth and development in mammals and regulates salt and water balance in freshwater fish. Many scientists think that this wide range of functions indicates which of the following?

A) Prolactin is a nonspecific hormone.

B) Prolactin has a unique mechanism for eliciting its effects.

C) Prolactin is an evolutionary conserved hormone.

D) Prolactin is derived from two separate sources.

E) Prolactin interacts with many different receptor molecules.

Answer: C
*Topic: Concept 45.3*
*Skill: Knowledge*

29) Which of the following have nontropic effects only?

A) FSH

B) LH

C) TSH

D) MSH

E) ACTH

Answer: D
*Topic: Concept 45.3*
*Skill: Knowledge*

30) Iodine is added to commercially-prepared table salt to help prevent deficiencies of this essential mineral. Which gland(s) require(s) iodine to function properly?

A) parathyroids

B) adrenal

C) thyroid

D) pancreas

E) ovaries and testes

Answer: C
*Topic: Concept 45.4*
*Skill: Comprehension*

31) Tropic hormones from the anterior pituitary directly affect the release of which of the following?

A) parathyroid hormone

B) calcitonin

C) epinephrine

D) thyroxine

E) glucagon

Answer: D
*Topic: Concept 45.4*
*Skill: Comprehension*

32) Which of the following endocrine disorders is *not* correctly matched with the malfunctioning gland?

A) diabetes and pancreas

B) giantism and pituitary

C) cretinism and adrenal medulla

D) tetany and parathyroid

E) dwarfism and pituitary

Answer: C
*Topic: Concept 45.4*
*Skill: Knowledge*

33) One reason a person might be severely overweight is due to

A) an undersecretion of thyroxine.

B) a defect in hormone release from the posterior pituitary.

C) a lower than normal level of insulin-like growth factors.

D) hyposecretion of oxytocin.

E) a higher than normal level of endorphins.

Answer: A
*Topic: Concept 45.4*
*Skill: Comprehension*

34) Which of the following statements about endocrine glands is *incorrect*?

A) The parathyroids regulate metabolic rate.

B) The thyroid participates in blood calcium regulation.

C) The pituitary participates in the regulation of the gonads.

D) The adrenal medulla produces "fight-or-flight" responses.

E) The pancreas helps to regulate blood sugar concentration.

Answer: A
*Topic: Concept 45.4*
*Skill: Knowledge*

35) Which of the following is an endocrine gland?

A) parathyroid gland

B) salivary gland

C) sweat gland

D) sebaceous gland

E) gallbladder

Answer: A
*Topic: Concept 45.4*
*Skill: Knowledge*

36) Which hormone exerts antagonistic action to PTH (parathyroid hormone)?

A) thyroxine

B) epinephrine

C) growth hormone

D) calcitonin

E) glucagon

Answer: D
*Topic: Concept 45.4*
*Skill: Comprehension*

37) Which of the following glands shows both endocrine and exocrine activity?

A) pituitary

B) parathyroid

C) salivary

D) pancreas

E) adrenal

Answer: D
*Topic: Concept 45.4*
*Skill: Knowledge*

38) All of the following are steroid hormones *except*

A) androgen.

B) cortisol.

C) estrogen.

D) insulin.

E) testosterone.

Answer: D
*Topic: Concept 45.4*
*Skill: Knowledge*

39) Blood samples taken from an individual who had been fasting for 24 hours would have which of the following?

A) high levels of insulin

B) high levels of glucagon

C) low levels of insulin

D) low levels of glucagon

E) both B and C

Answer: E
*Topic: Concept 45.4*
*Skill: Application*

40) What happens when beta cells of the pancreas release insulin into the blood?

A) Blood glucose levels rise to a set point and stimulate glucagon release.

B) Body cells take up more glucose.

C) The liver breaks down glycogen to glucose.

D) Alpha cells are stimulated to release glucose into the blood.

E) Both B and D are correct.

Answer: B
*Topic: Concept 45.4*
*Skill: Comprehension*

41) Which of the following endocrine structures are derived from nervous tissue?

A) thymus and thyroid glands

B) ovaries and the testes

C) liver and the pancreas

D) anterior pituitary and the adrenal cortex

E) posterior pituitary and the adrenal medulla

Answer: E
*Topic: Concepts 45.3, 45.4*
*Skill: Knowledge*

42) The endocrine system and the nervous system are chemically related. Which of the following substances best illustrates this relationship?

A) estrogen

B) calcitonin

C) norepinephrine

D) calcium

E) ecdysone

Answer: C
*Topic: Concept 45.4*
*Skill: Comprehension*

43) Which of the following are synthesized from the amino acid tyrosine?

   A) epinephrine

   B) catecholamines

   C) norepinephrine

   D) A and B only

   E) A, B, and C

Answer: E
*Topic: Concept 45.4*
*Skill: Comprehension*

44) Which of the following glands is controlled directly by the hypothalamus or central nervous system but *not* the anterior pituitary?

   A) ovary

   B) adrenal medulla

   C) adrenal cortex

   D) testis

   E) thyroid

Answer: B
*Topic: Concept 45.4*
*Skill: Knowledge*

45) If the adrenal cortex were removed, which group of hormones would be most affected?

   A) steroid

   B) peptide

   C) tropic

   D) amino acid–derived

   E) paracrine

Answer: A
*Topic: Concept 45.4*
*Skill: Comprehension*

46) Which of the following statements about the adrenal gland is *correct*?

   A) During stress, TSH stimulates the adrenal cortex and medulla to secrete acetylcholine.

   B) During stress, the alpha cells of islets secrete insulin and simultaneously the beta cells of the islets secrete glucagon.

   C) During stress, ACTH stimulates the adrenal cortex, and neurons of the sympathetic nervous system stimulate the adrenal medulla.

   D) At all times, the anterior portion secretes ACTH, while the posterior portion secretes oxytocin.

   E) At all times, the adrenal gland monitors calcium levels in the blood and regulates calcium by secreting the two antagonistic hormones, epinephrine and norepinephrine.

Answer: C
*Topic: Concept 45.4*
*Skill: Comprehension*

47) Which of the following hormones is (are) secreted by the adrenal gland in response to stress and promote(s) the synthesis of glucose from noncarbohydrate substrates?

   A) glucagon

   B) glucocorticoids

   C) epinephrine

   D) thyroxine

   E) ACTH

Answer: B
*Topic: Concept 45.4*
*Skill: Knowledge*

*The question below refers to the following information.*

In an experiment, rats' ovaries were removed immediately after impregnation and then the rats were divided into two groups. Treatments and results are summarized in the table below.

|  | Group 1 | Group 2 |
| --- | --- | --- |
| Daily injections of progesterone (milligrams) | 0.25 | 2.0 |
| Percentage of rats that carried fetuses to birth | 0 | 100 |

48) The results most likely occurred because progesterone exerts an effect on the

   A) general health of the rat.

   B) size of the fetus.

   C) maintenance of the uterus.

   D) gestation period of rats.

   E) number of eggs fertilized.

Answer: C
*Topic: Concept 45.4*
*Skill: Application*

49) Which of the following hormone sequences is *correct*?

   A) LH → FSH → adrenal glands

   B) GnRH → FSH → ovaries

   C) CRH → ACTH → FSH → thyroid gland

   D) CRH → LH → testes

   E) GnRH → FSH → LH → pineal gland

Answer: B
*Topic: Concept 45.4*
*Skill: Knowledge*

50) Which of the following pairs of hormones do *not* have antagonistic effects?

   A) insulin and glucagon

   B) thyroid–releasing hormone and $T_3$ and $T_4$

   C) parathyroid hormone and calcitonin

   D) follicle-stimulating hormone and luteinizing hormone

   E) aldosterone and atrial natriuretic factor

Answer: D
*Topic: Concept 45.4*
*Skill: Knowledge*

51) Melatonin has been found to participate in all of the following *except*

   A) skin pigmentation.

   B) monitoring day length.

   C) reproduction.

   D) biological rhythms.

   E) calcium deposition in bone.

Answer: E
*Topic: Concept 45.4*
*Skill: Knowledge*

52) Which combination of gland and hormone would be linked to winter hibernation and spring reproduction in bears?

   A) pineal gland, melatonin

   B) hypothalamus gland, melatonin

   C) anterior pituitary gland, gonadotropin-releasing hormone

   D) pineal gland, estrogen

   E) posterior pituitary gland, thyroid–stimulating hormone

Answer: A
*Topic: Concept 45.4*
*Skill: Comprehension*

*The following questions refer to the list of hormones below. Each hormone may be used once, more than once, or not at all.*

A. ecdysone
B. glucagon
C. thyroxine
D. oxytocin
E. growth hormone

53) secreted by the pancreas

Answer: B
*Topic: Concept 45.4*
*Skill: Knowledge*

54) stimulates and maintains metabolic processes

Answer: C
*Topic: Concept 45.4*
*Skill: Knowledge*

55) stimulates the contraction of uterine muscle

Answer: D
*Topic: Concept 45.4*
*Skill: Knowledge*

56) secreted by the anterior pituitary

Answer: E
*Topic: Concept 45.4*
*Skill: Knowledge*

57) steroid hormone that triggers molting in arthropods

Answer: A
*Topic: Concept 45.4*
*Skill: Knowledge*

58) Which of the following endocrine structures is (are) *not* controlled by a tropic hormone from the anterior pituitary?
A) pancreatic islet cells
B) thyroid gland
C) adrenal cortex
D) ovaries
E) testes

Answer: A
*Topic: Concept 45.4*
*Skill: Knowledge*

*The questions below refer to the following list of hormones. Each hormone may be used once, more than once, or not at all.*

A androgens
B. estrogens
C. progestins
D. catecholamines
E. melatonin

59) testosterone

Answer: A
*Topic: Concept 45.4*
*Skill: Knowledge*

60) estradiol

Answer: B
*Topic: Concept 45.4*
*Skill: Knowledge*

61) secreted by the pineal gland

Answer: E
*Topic: Concept 45.4*
*Skill: Knowledge*

62) epinephrine

Answer: D
*Topic: Concept 45.4*
*Skill: Knowledge*

63) Insect brain hormone is most analogous to which of the following in humans?

A) insulin from the pancreas

B) parathyroid hormone from the parathyroid gland

C) ADH from the posterior pituitary

D) releasing hormones from the hypothalamus

E) androgens from the adrenal cortex

Answer: D
*Topic: Concepts 45.3, 45.5*
*Skill: Comprehension*

64) The star of a recent movie was a caterpillar that never matured into an adult. It simply got larger with each molt. What is the probable reason why the caterpillar did not mature into an adult?

A) lack of ecdysone

B) lack of juvenile hormone

C) decreased level of ecdysone

D) increased level of juvenile hormone

E) lack of the melatonin hormone

Answer: D
*Topic: Concept 45.5*
*Skill: Knowledge*

65) Synthetic versions of which of the following hormones are being used as insecticides to prevent insects from maturing into reproducing adults?

A) ecdysone

B) juvenile hormone

C) oxytocin

D) brain hormone

E) prothoracic hormone

Answer: B
*Topic: Concept 45.5*
*Skill: Comprehension*

# Media Activity Questions

1) Which of these is the second of the three stages of cell signaling?

   A) reception

   B) transduction

   C) gene activation

   D) binding of a neurotransmitter to a plasma membrane receptor

   E) cell response

   Answer: B
   *Topic: Web/CD Activity: Overview of Cell Signaling*

2) Receptors for nonsteroid hormones are located in

   A) the nucleus.

   B) the extracellular fluid.

   C) the cytoplasm.

   D) the cytosol.

   E) association with a cell's plasma membrane.

   Answer: E
   *Topic: Web/CD Activity: Peptide Hormone Action*

3) The primary reason steroid hormones usually act slowly is that

   A) target cells tend to ignore steroid hormones in favor of nonsteroid hormones.

   B) they are produced at very low concentrations.

   C) they are too large to enter a cell and therefore must first bind to a plasma membrane receptor before having an effect on a cell.

   D) acting via a signal transduction pathway makes for slower responses than does directly interacting with a cell's DNA.

   E) they turn genes on or off and it takes time for gene products to build up or become depleted.

   Answer: E
   *Topic: Web/CD Activity: Steroid Hormone Action*

4) Steroid hormone–receptor complexes act in

   A) the nucleus.

   B) the plasma membrane.

   C) the cytoplasm.

   D) lysosomes

   E) vesicles

   Answer: A
   *Topic: Web/CD Activity: Steroid Hormone Action*

5) _____ are the main male hormones.

   A) Androgens

   B) Estrogens

   C) Mineralocorticoids

   D) Luteinizing hormones

   E) Progesterones

   Answer: A
   *Topic: Web/CD Activity: Human Endocrine Glands*

# Self–Quiz Questions

1) Which of the following is *not* an accurate statement about hormones?

   A) Hormones are chemical messengers that travel to target cells through the circulatory system.

   B) Hormones often regulate homeostasis through antagonistic functions.

   C) Hormones of the same chemical class usually have the same function.

   D) Hormones are secreted by specialized cells usually located in endocrine glands.

   E) Hormones are often regulated through feedback loops.

   Answer: C

2) A distinctive feature of the mechanism of action of thyroid hormones and steroid hormones is that

   A) these hormones are regulated by feedback loops.

   B) target cells react more rapidly to these hormones than to local regulators.

   C) these hormones bind with specific receptor proteins on the plasma membrane of target cells.

   D) these hormones bind to receptors inside cells.

   E) these hormones affect metabolism.

   Answer: D

3) Growth factors are local regulators that

   A) are produced by the anterior pituitary.

   B) are modified fatty acids that stimulate bone and cartilage growth.

   C) are found on the surface of cancer cells and stimulate abnormal cell division.

   D) are proteins that bind to cell-surface receptors and stimulate growth and development of target cells.

   E) convey messages between nerve cells.

   Answer: D

4) Which of the following hormones is *incorrectly* paired with its action?

   A) oxytocin—stimulates uterine contractions during childbirth

   B) thyroxine—stimulates metabolic processes

   C) insulin—stimulates glycogen breakdown in the liver

   D) ACTH—stimulates the release of glucocorticoids by the adrenal cortex

   E) melatonin—affects biological rhythms, seasonal reproduction

   Answer: C

5) An example of antagonistic hormones controlling homeostasis is

   A) thyroxine and parathyroid hormone in calcium balance.

   B) insulin and glucagon in glucose metabolism.

   C) progestins and estrogens in sexual differentiation.

   D) epinephrine and norepinephrine in fight–or–flight responses.

   E) oxytocin and prolactin in milk production.

   Answer: B

6) Which of the following is *not* an example of the close structural and functional relationship between the nervous and endocrine systems?

A) the secretion of hormones by neurosecretory cells

B) the multiple functions of norepinephrine

C) the stimulation of the adrenal medulla in the short-term response to stress

D) the embryonic development of the posterior pituitary from the hypothalamus

E) the alteration of gene expression by steroid hormones

Answer: E

7) A portal vessel carries blood from the hypothalamus directly to the

A) thyroid.

B) pineal gland.

C) anterior pituitary.

D) posterior pituitary.

E) liver.

Answer: C

8) Which of the following is the most likely explanation for hypothyroidism in a patient whose iodine level is normal?

A) a disproportionate production of $T_3$ to $T_4$

B) hyposecretion of TSH

C) hypersecretion of TSH

D) hypersecretion of MSH

E) a decrease in the thyroid secretion of calcitonin

Answer: B

9) The main target organs for tropic hormones are

A) muscles.

B) blood vessels.

C) endocrine glands.

D) kidneys.

E) nerves.

Answer: C

10) The relationship between the insect hormones ecdysone and brain hormone

A) is an example of the interaction between the endocrine and nervous systems.

B) illustrates homeostasis achieved by positive feedback.

C) demonstrates that peptide-derived hormones have more widespread effects than steroidal hormones.

D) illustrates homeostasis maintained by antagonistic hormones.

E) demonstrates competitive inhibition for the hormone receptor.

Answer: A

# Chapter 46  Animal Reproduction

1) What do budding and fragmentation have in common?
   A) Both are types of asexual reproduction.
   B) Both produce large numbers of offspring.
   C) Both occur in sea stars.
   D) Both involve meiosis.
   E) A and B only

Answer: A
*Topic: Concept 46.1*
*Skill: Comprehension*

2) Asexual reproduction in animals might involve
   A) fission and budding.
   B) fragmentation and mitosis.
   C) regeneration.
   D) A and B only
   E) A, B, and C

Answer: E
*Topic: Concept 46.1*
*Skill: Knowledge*

3) Which of the following are possible advantages of asexual reproduction?
   A) It allows the species to endure periods of fluctuating or unstable environmental conditions.
   B) It enhances genetic variability in the species.
   C) It enables the species to colonize new regions rapidly.
   D) Both A and B are true.
   E) A, B, and C are true.

Answer: C
*Topic: Concept 46.1*
*Skill: Comprehension*

4) Why do genetic mutations in asexually reproducing organisms lead to more evolutionary change than do genetic mutations in sexually reproducing ones?
   A) The haploid mutations of asexually reproducing organisms are passed to all of their offspring.
   B) Asexually reproducing organisms devote more time and energy to the process of reproduction.
   C) Sexually reproducing organisms can produce more offspring in a given time.
   D) More genetic variation is present in organisms that reproduce asexually.
   E) Asexually reproducing organisms have more dominant genes than organisms that reproduce sexually.

Answer: A
*Topic: Concept 46.1*
*Skill: Comprehension*

5) What are the advantages of asexual reproduction?
   A) It promotes genetic stability.
   B) It enhances the survival rates of parents.
   C) The limited number of offspring prevents overpopulation.
   D) It promotes geographic distribution of species.
   E) It allows animals to replace lost appendages.

Answer: A
*Topic: Concept 46.1*
*Skill: Comprehension*

6) Which of the following is a form of sexual reproduction?

 A) fragmentation

 B) budding

 C) hermaphroditism

 D) parthenogenesis

 E) fission

Answer: C
*Topic: Concept 46.1*
*Skill: Knowledge*

7) You observe an organism with the following characteristics: parthenogenetic reproduction, internal development of embryos, presence of an amnion, lack of parental care of young. Of the following, the organism is probably a(n)

 A) earthworm.

 B) lizard.

 C) bird.

 D) frog.

 E) mammal.

Answer: B
*Topic: Concept 46.1*
*Skill: Application*

8) Why is sexual reproduction important?

 A) It allows animals to conserve resources and reproduce only during optimal conditions.

 B) The resulting diverse phenotypes may enhance survival of a population in a changing environment.

 C) It can result in numerous offspring in a short amount of time.

 D) It enables isolated animals to colonize a habitat rapidly.

 E) Both A and D are important.

Answer: B
*Topic: Concept 46.1*
*Skill: Comprehension*

9) Which of the following is *not* required for internal fertilization?

 A) copulatory organ

 B) sperm receptacle

 C) behavioral interaction

 D) internal development of the embryo

 E) All of the above are necessary for internal fertilization.

Answer: D
*Topic: Concept 46.2*
*Skill: Knowledge*

10) What advantage does internal fertilization have compared with external fertilization?

 A) Usually many offspring are produced, ensuring survival of the species.

 B) The time and energy devoted to reproduction is decreased.

 C) The smaller number of offspring often receive a greater amount of parental protection.

 D) The increased survival rate results in rapid population increases.

 E) Usually a smaller number of genes are present, which promotes genetic stability.

Answer: C
*Topic: Concept 46.2*
*Skill: Comprehension*

11) Internal and external fertilization both

 A) produce a zygote.

 B) occur in vertebrates.

 C) occur only in terrestrial animals.

 D) A and B only

 E) A and C only

Answer: D
*Topic: Concept 46.2*
*Skill: Comprehension*

12) Organisms that produce amniote eggs, in general,

    A) have a higher embryo mortality rate than do those with unprotected embryos.

    B) invest most of their reproductive energy in the embryonic and early postnatal development of their offspring.

    C) invest more energy in parenting than do placental animals.

    D) produce more gametes than do those animals with external fertilization and development.

    E) All of the above are correct.

Answer: B
*Topic: Concept 46.2*
*Skill: Comprehension*

13) Which statement about reproduction in invertebrates is *incorrect*?

    A) Many invertebrates have separate sexes.

    B) Many invertebrates utilize external fertilization.

    C) A few species split open to release gametes to the environment.

    D) Some invertebrates have structures that store sperm.

    E) Invertebrates do not engage in internal fertilization.

Answer: E
*Topic: Concept 46.2*
*Skill: Knowledge*

14) A cloaca is an anatomical structure found in many nonmammalian vertebrates, which functions as

    A) a specialized sperm–transfer device produced by males.

    B) a common exit for the digestive, excretory, and reproductive systems.

    C) a region bordered by the labia minora and clitoris in females.

    D) a source of nutrients for developing sperm in the testes.

    E) a gland that secretes mucus to lubricate the vaginal opening.

Answer: B
*Topic: Concept 46.2*
*Skill: Knowledge*

15) Which of the following produce testosterone?

    A) sperm cells

    B) hypothalamus

    C) Leydig cells

    D) anterior pituitary

    E) seminiferous tubules

Answer: C
*Topic: Concept 46.3*
*Skill: Knowledge*

16) After sperm cells are produced, they are mainly stored in the

    A) urethra.

    B) prostate.

    C) epididymis.

    D) seminal vesicles.

    E) bulbourethral gland.

Answer: C
*Topic: Concept 46.3*
*Skill: Knowledge*

17) In men, the excretory and reproductive systems share which structure?

A) vas deferens

B) urinary bladder

C) seminal vesicle

D) urethra

E) ureter

Answer: D
*Topic: Concept 46.3*
*Skill: Knowledge*

18) Which of these does *not* contribute to the fluids that make up human semen?

A) bulbourethral glands

B) vas deferens

C) prostate gland

D) seminal vesicles

E) both A and B

Answer: B
*Topic: Concept 46.3*
*Skill: Knowledge*

19) Where are human sperm cells produced?

A) prostate gland

B) vas deferens

C) the seminiferous tubules of the testes

D) epididymis

E) Sertoli cells

Answer: C
*Topic: Concept 46.3*
*Skill: Knowledge*

20) What effect would surgical removal of the seminal vesicles have on the human male reproductive system?

A) It would cause sterility because sperm would not be produced.

B) It would cause sterility because sperm would not be able to exit the body.

C) The failure rate for the withdrawal method of birth control would go down.

D) There would be a minimal loss in semen volume.

E) Semen would not contain energy-providing nutrients for the sperm.

Answer: E
*Topic: Concept 46.3*
*Skill: Application*

21) What comprises the fluid part of human semen?

A) androgens such as testosterone

B) sperm and secretions from the prostate and bulbourethral glands

C) sperm and secretions from the prostate gland, bulbourethral glands, and seminal vesicles

D) sperm and prostaglandins

E) sperm and anticoagulant enzymes

Answer: C
*Topic: Concept 46.3*
*Skill: Knowledge*

22) In humans, the egg is released from the ovary and enters the oviduct. How is this accomplished?

 A) The force of the follicular ejection propels the egg into the oviduct.

 B) The egg is drawn into the oviduct by the action of beating cilia located in the opening of the oviduct.

 C) The egg moves through a small tube that connects the ovary and the oviduct.

 D) The egg propels itself into the oviduct by the beating action of its flagellum.

 E) Peristalsis of ovarian muscles moves the egg into the oviduct.

Answer: B
*Topic: Concept 46.3*
*Skill: Comprehension*

23) What is the narrow opening of the human uterus called?

 A) vagina

 B) cervix

 C) oviduct

 D) fallopian tube

 E) vas deferens

Answer: B
*Topic: Concept 46.3*
*Skill: Knowledge*

24) Which of the following male and female structures consist largely of erectile tissue richly supplied with nerve endings?

 A) penis and clitoris

 B) vas deferens and oviduct

 C) testes and ovaries

 D) seminiferous tubules and vagina

 E) prostate and ovaries

Answer: A
*Topic: Concept 46.3*
*Skill: Comprehension*

25) During the human sexual response, vasocongestion

 A) occurs in the clitoris, vagina, and penis.

 B) occurs in the testes.

 C) can cause vaginal lubrication.

 D) A and B only

 E) A, B, and C

Answer: E
*Topic: Concept 46.3*
*Skill: Knowledge*

26) During sexual arousal, myotonia is to nipple as

 A) orgasm is to resolution.

 B) excitement is to plateau.

 C) estrogen is to the mammary glands.

 D) vasocongestion is to the penis.

 E) labia minora is to labia majora.

Answer: D
*Topic: Concept 46.3*
*Skill: Comprehension*

27) The diploid chromosome number for humans is 46. How many chromatids will there be in a secondary spermatocyte?

 A) 23

 B) 46

 C) 69

 D) 92

 E) 184

Answer: B
*Topic: Concept 46.4*
*Skill: Comprehension*

28) Which cells are diploid?

   A) spermatids

   B) spermatogonia

   C) mature sperm cells

   D) A and B only

   E) A, B, and C

Answer: B
*Topic: Concept 46.4*
*Skill: Comprehension*

29) Which of these statements is *true* about human sperm cells?

   A) They are rich in nutrient material.

   B) They are liberated from the corpus luteum.

   C) They are less numerous than ova.

   D) They are highly motile.

   E) They have 46 chromosomes.

Answer: D
*Topic: Concept 46.4*
*Skill: Knowledge*

30) In vertebrate animals, spermatogenesis and oogenesis differ, in that

   A) oogenesis begins at the onset of sexual maturity.

   B) oogenesis produces four haploid cells, whereas spermatogenesis produces only one functional spermatozoon.

   C) oogenesis produces one functional ovum, whereas spermatogenesis produces four functional spermatozoa.

   D) spermatogenesis begins before birth.

   E) spermatogenesis is not complete until fertilization occurs.

Answer: C
*Topic: Concept 46.4*
*Skill: Comprehension*

31) In which of the following ways are mature human sperm and ova similar?

   A) They both have the same number of chromosomes.

   B) They are approximately the same size.

   C) They each have a flagellum that provides motility.

   D) They are produced from puberty until death.

   E) They are formed before birth.

Answer: A
*Topic: Concept 46.4*
*Skill: Comprehension*

32) Which of the following statements about gametogenesis is *incorrect*?

   A) Spermatogenesis continues throughout the male's life; oogenesis stops at menopause.

   B) Oogenesis results in one ovum, while spermatogenesis results in millions of sperm.

   C) Spermatogenesis is a continuous, uninterrupted process; oogenesis undergoes long "resting" periods.

   D) The process of oogenesis is completed when the egg cell is penetrated by sperm.

   E) The primary spermatocyte is a haploid cell.

Answer: E
*Topic: Concept 46.4*
*Skill: Comprehension*

33) Which of these is a male primary sex characteristic?

A) deepening of the voice

B) facial and pubic hair

C) increased muscle growth

D) development of external reproductive structures

E) both B and D

Answer: D
*Topic: Concept 46.4*
*Skill: Knowledge*

34) Which of these is a male secondary sex characteristic?

A) development of external reproductive structures

B) development of vasa deferentia and other ducts

C) sperm production

D) increased muscle growth

E) B and C only

Answer: D
*Topic: Concept 46.4*
*Skill: Knowledge*

35) How do the estrous and menstrual cycles compare?

A) Endometrial bleeding occurs during the menstrual cycle; the endometrium is reabsorbed by the uterus during the estrous cycle.

B) There are more pronounced behavioral changes during menstrual cycles than during estrous cycles.

C) There are stronger effects of season and climate on menstrual cycles.

D) Copulation can only occur during the period surrounding ovulation in both the estrous and menstrual cycles.

E) The length of both cycles averages 28 days.

Answer: A
*Topic: Concept 46.4*
*Skill: Comprehension*

36) What is the breakdown and discharge of the soft uterine tissues that occurs if no egg is fertilized?

A) menstruation

B) lactation

C) fertilization

D) menopause

E) ovulation

Answer: A
*Topic: Concept 46.4*
*Skill: Knowledge*

37) Which of these best describes the menstrual cycle?

A) It refers specifically to changes that occur in the endometrium of the uterus.

B) The cycle length is 28 days and varies little from one woman to another.

C) It continues from puberty until death.

D) It begins with the follicular phase.

E) It is primarily regulated by follicle–stimulating hormone (FSH).

Answer: A
*Topic: Concept 46.4*
*Skill: Comprehension*

38) The secretory phase of the menstrual cycle

A) is associated with dropping levels of estrogen and progesterone.

B) starts when the endometrium begins to degenerate.

C) corresponds with the luteal phase of the ovarian cycle.

D) corresponds with the follicular phase of the ovarian cycle.

E) is the beginning of the menstrual flow.

Answer: C
*Topic: Concept 46.4*
*Skill: Comprehension*

39) What are the three phases of the ovarian cycle?

A) menstrual, ovulation, and luteal

B) follicular, luteal, and secretory

C) menstrual, proliferative, and secretory

D) follicular, ovulation, and luteal

E) proliferative, luteal, and ovulation

Answer: D
*Topic: Concept 46.4*
*Skill: Knowledge*

40) There are five hormones regulating the human menstrual and ovarian cycles. Which of these structures secrete(s) these hormones?

A) hypothalamus

B) pancreas

C) ovaries

D) A and C only

E) A, B, and C

Answer: D
*Topic: Concept 46.4*
*Skill: Knowledge*

41) Inhibition of the release of GnRH from the hypothalamus will

A) stimulate production of estrogen and progesterone.

B) initiate ovulation.

C) inhibit secretion of gonadotropins from the pituitary.

D) stimulate secretion of LH and FSH.

E) initiate the flow phase of the menstrual cycle.

Answer: C
*Topic: Concept 46.4*
*Skill: Comprehension*

42) If the release of LH were inhibited in a human female, which of the following events would *not* occur?

A) release of FSH from the pituitary

B) maturation of a primary follicle and oocyte

C) ovulation of a secondary oocyte

D) release of GnRH from the hypothalamus

E) production of estrogen by follicle cells

Answer: C
*Topic: Concept 46.4*
*Skill: Application*

43) Which structure is *not* correctly paired with its function?

A) seminiferous tubules—add fluid containing mucus, fructose, and prostaglandin to semen

B) scrotum—encases testes and holds them below the abdominal cavity

C) epididymis—stores sperm

D) prostate gland—adds alkaline secretions to semen

E) ovary—secretes estrogen and progesterone

Answer: A
*Topic: Concept 46.3*
*Skill: Knowledge*

44) One function of the corpus luteum is to

A) nourish and protect the egg cell.

B) produce prolactin in the alveoli.

C) produce progesterone and estrogen.

D) convert into a hormone–producing follicle after ovulation.

E) stimulate ovulation.

Answer: C
*Topic: Concept 46.4*
*Skill: Knowledge*

45) During the menstrual cycle, what is the main source of progesterone in females?

    A) adrenal cortex

    B) anterior pituitary

    C) corpus luteum

    D) developing follicle

    E) placenta

Answer: C
*Topic: Concept 46.4*
*Skill: Knowledge*

*For the following questions, choose the term from the list below that best fits each description. Each term may be used once, more than once, or not at all.*

    A)  LH
    B)  FSH
    C)  ICSH
    D)  GnRH
    E)  estrogen

46) hormone that triggers ovulation

Answer: A
*Topic: Concept 46.4*
*Skill: Knowledge*

47) hormone secreted by the growing follicle

Answer: E
*Topic: Concept 46.4*
*Skill: Knowledge*

48) stimulates the corpus luteum in females

Answer: A
*Topic: Concept 46.4*
*Skill: Knowledge*

49) hypothalamic hormone that stimulates the secretion of gonadotropins by the anterior pituitary

Answer: D
*Topic: Concept 46.4*
*Skill: Knowledge*

50) the anterior pituitary hormone that stimulates the maturation of the follicle in the ovary during the beginning of the menstrual cycle

Answer: B
*Topic: Concept 46.4*
*Skill: Knowledge*

51) Which of the following hormones is *incorrectly* paired with its action?

    A) GnRH—controls release of FSH and LH

    B) estrogen—responsible for primary and secondary female sex characteristics

    C) human chorionic gonadotropin—maintains secretions from the corpus luteum

    D) luteinizing hormone—stimulates ovulation

    E) progesterone—stimulates follicles to develop

Answer: E
*Topic: Concept 46.4*
*Skill: Knowledge*

52) The hormone progesterone is produced

    A) by the pituitary and acts directly on the ovary.

    B) in the ovary and acts directly on the testes.

    C) in the ovary and acts directly on the uterus.

    D) in the pituitary and acts directly on the uterus.

    E) in the uterus and acts directly on the pituitary.

Answer: C
*Topic: Concept 46.4*
*Skill: Knowledge*

53) What happens if the hormone progesterone is not secreted in a human female?

   A) Secondary sex characteristics do not develop.

   B) The pituitary is stimulated to secrete gonadotropins.

   C) Uterine contractions begin stimulating childbirth.

   D) Enlargement of arteries supplying blood to the endometrium and growth of endometrial glands do not occur properly.

   E) The ovary begins to form the corpus luteum.

Answer: D
*Topic: Concept 46.4*
*Skill: Application*

54) What causes menopause?

   A) The follicle supply is exhausted.

   B) A decline in production of estrogens by the ovaries.

   C) Temperature increases inhibit ova maturation.

   D) There is a lack of adequate blood supply to the ovaries.

   E) Progesterone blocks the ovarian cycle.

Answer: B
*Topic: Concept 46.4*
*Skill: Comprehension*

55) For normal human fertilization to occur,

   A) many ova must be released.

   B) the uterus must be enlarged.

   C) only one sperm must penetrate the egg.

   D) secretion of pituitary FSH and LH must decrease.

   E) the secondary oocyte must implant in the uterus.

Answer: C
*Topic: Concept 46.5*
*Skill: Comprehension*

56) Fertilization of human eggs usually takes place in the

   A) ovary.

   B) uterus.

   C) vagina.

   D) oviduct.

   E) labia minora.

Answer: D
*Topic: Concept 46.5*
*Skill: Knowledge*

57) Which of the following structures is *incorrectly* paired with its function?

   A) epididymis—maturation and storage of sperm

   B) oviduct —site of normal embryonic implantation

   C) seminal vesicles—add sugar and mucus to semen

   D) placenta—maternal and fetal exchange organ

   E) prostate gland—adds alkaline substances to semen

Answer: B
*Topic: Concept 46.5*
*Skill: Knowledge*

58) During human gestation, organogenesis occurs during the first trimester. What is the significance of this fact?

    A) It allows for early detection of genetic disorders.

    B) This may block progesterone production and thus cause a spontaneous abortion.

    C) It may stimulate infant cardiovascular problems.

    D) Radiation and drugs should be avoided, as the embryo is extremely sensitive to birth defects at this time.

    E) It may compress the mother's abdominal organs, causing frequent urination and constipation.

Answer: D
*Topic: Concept 46.5*
*Skill: Application*

*Choose the term from the list below that best fits each of the following descriptions. Each term may be used once, more than once, or not at all.*

    A) luteinizing hormone (LH)
    B) follicle–stimulating hormone (FSH)
    C) progesterone
    D) human chorionic gonadotropin (HCG)
    E) gonadotropin–releasing hormone (GnRH)

59) embryonic hormone that maintains progesterone and estrogen secretion by the corpus luteum through the first trimester of pregnancy

Answer: D
*Topic: Concept 46.5*
*Skill: Knowledge*

60) triggers ovulation of the secondary oocyte

Answer: A
*Topic: Concept 46.4*
*Skill: Knowledge*

61) hormone produced by the corpus luteum when stimulated by LH

Answer: C
*Topic: Concept 46.4*
*Skill: Knowledge*

62) hypothalamic hormone that triggers the secretion of FSH

Answer: E
*Topic: Concept 46.4*
*Skill: Knowledge*

63) Which substance, when found in urine, indicates pregnancy?

    A) progesterone

    B) estrogen

    C) follicle–stimulating hormone

    D) human chorionic gonadotropin

    E) hypothalamus releasing factors

Answer: D
*Topic: Concept 46.5*
*Skill: Knowledge*

*For the following questions, choose the term from the list below that best fits each description or statement.*

    A) human chorionic gonadotropin
    B) testosterone
    C) oxytocin
    D) prolactin
    E) progesterone

64) secreted by the Leydig cells of the testes

Answer: B
*Topic: Concept 46.3*
*Skill: Knowledge*

65) participates in the regulation of labor contractions

Answer: C
*Topic: Concept 46.5*
*Skill: Knowledge*

66) initiates the growth of the placenta and enlargement of the uterus

Answer: E
*Topic: Concept 46.5*
*Skill: Knowledge*

67) high concentration of this hormone inhibits secretion of LH from the pituitary

Answer: E
*Topic: Concept 46.4*
*Skill: Knowledge*

68) required so that the corpus luteum can function through the first and part of the second trimesters of pregnancy

Answer: A
*Topic: Concept 46.5*
*Skill: Knowledge*

69) What would happen if a woman in the later stages of pregnancy were given a combination of estrogen and oxytocin?
    A) Oxytocin receptors would develop on uterine smooth muscle cells.
    B) Prostaglandins would be secreted from the placenta.
    C) Contractions of uterine muscles would begin.
    D) A and C only
    E) A, B, and C

Answer: E
*Topic: Concept 46.5*
*Skill: Application*

70) Which of these is *not* a correct statement about human reproduction?
    A) The ability of a pregnant woman not to reject her "foreign" fetus may be due to the suppression of the immune response in her uterus.
    B) By the eighth week, organogenesis is complete and the embryo is referred to as a fetus.
    C) Lactation is the production and release of milk from the mammary glands.
    D) Parturition begins with conception and ends with gestation.
    E) Puberty is the onset of reproductive ability.

Answer: D
*Topic: Concept 46.5*
*Skill: Comprehension*

71) Which of the following birth control methods is *least* effective?
    A) diaphragm
    B) condom
    C) coitus interruptus
    D) vasectomy
    E) rhythm method

Answer: C
*Topic: Concept 46.5*
*Skill: Knowledge*

For the following questions, choose the description from the list below that best fits each term. Each description may be used once, more than once, or not at all.

A. prevents release of mature eggs from the ovaries
B. prevents fertilization by keeping sperm and egg physically separated by a barrier
C. prevents implantation of an embryo
D. prevents sperm from entering the urethra
E. prevents oocytes from traveling into the uterus

72) birth control pill

Answer: A
Topic: Concept 46.5
Skill: Knowledge

73) intrauterine device

Answer: C
Topic: Concept 46.5
Skill: Knowledge

74) tubal ligation

Answer: E
Topic: Concept 46.5
Skill: Knowledge

75) vasectomy

Answer: D
Topic: Concept 46.5
Skill: Knowledge

76) diaphragm

Answer: B
Topic: Concept 46.5
Skill: Knowledge

77) How do different contraceptive methods work?

A) prevent the release of sperm and eggs
B) keep sperm and eggs separated
C) prevent implantation of an embryo
D) A and B only
E) A, B, and C

Answer: E
Topic: Concept 46.5
Skill: Comprehension

78) Which of these statements explains the primary mechanism by which birth control pills work?

A) They stop the release of GnRH, FSH, and LH.
B) They cause a woman's cervical mucus to change and block sperm from entering the uterus.
C) They cause spontaneous abortions.
D) They block progesterone, thus pregnancy cannot be maintained.
E) They prevent uterine implantation by irritating the endometrium.

Answer: A
Topic: Concept 46.5
Skill: Knowledge

79) The drug RU486 functions by

A) inhibiting release of gonadotropins from the pituitary.
B) blocking progesterone receptors in the uterus.
C) preventing release of the secondary oocyte from the ovary.
D) A and B
E) A, B, and C

Answer: B
Topic: Concept 46.5
Skill: Knowledge

80) Human fertility drugs increase the chance of multiple births, probably because they

    A) enhance implantation.

    B) stimulate follicle development.

    C) mimic progesterone.

    D) stimulate spermatogenesis.

    E) prevent parturition.

Answer: B
*Topic: Concept 46.5*
*Skill: Comprehension*

# Media Activity Questions

1) Which pituitary secretion stimulates sperm production?

A) LH

B) ACTH

C) TSH

D) PRL

E) FSH

Answer: E
*Topic: Reproductive System of the Human Male*

2) Which hormone(s) is (are) directly responsible for triggering the development of the secondary sex characteristics of males, such as beard growth?

A) androgens

B) thymosin

C) epinephrine

D) insulin

E) parathyroid hormone

Answer: A
*Topic: Reproductive System of the Human Male*

3) Ovulation usually occurs on or about day _____ of a 28-day ovarian cycle.

A) 1

B) 7

C) 14

D) 21

E) 28

Answer: C
*Topic: Reproductive System of the Human Female*

4) After ovulation, high levels of _____ inhibit _____ secretion.

A) estrogen and progesterone; FSH and LH

B) FSH and LH; estrogen and progesterone

C) HCG; estrogen and progesterone

D) estrogen; FSH

E) androgens; FSH and LH

Answer: A
*Topic: Reproductive System of the Human Female*

5) If there is no fertilization, degeneration of the corpus luteum results in a drop in _____, which results in the sloughing off of the uterus's endometrium.

A) FSH

B) estrogen and progesterone

C) hypothalamic secretion of releasing hormones

D) HCG

E) LH

Answer: B
*Topic: Reproductive System of the Human Female*

# Self-Quiz Questions

1) Which of the following characterizes parthenogenesis?

   A) An individual may change its sex during its lifetime.

   B) Specialized groups of cells may be released and grow into new individuals.

   C) An organism is first a male and then a female.

   D) An egg develops without being fertilized.

   E) Both mates have male and female reproductive organs.

   Answer: D

2) Which structure is *incorrectly* paired with its function?

   A) gonads—produce gametes

   B) spermatheca—stores sperm in male honeybees

   C) cloaca—serves as the common opening for reproductive, excretory, and digestive systems

   D) baculum—bone that stiffens the penis in some mammals

   E) endometrium—forms the maternal part of the placenta

   Answer: B

3) Which of the following male and female structures are *least* alike in function?

   A) seminiferous tubules—vagina

   B) Leydig cells—follicle cells

   C) spermatogonia—oogonia

   D) testes—ovaries

   E) vas deferens—oviduct

   Answer: A

4) A difference between estrous and menstrual cycles is that

   A) nonmammalian vertebrates have estrous cycles, whereas mammals have menstrual cycles.

   B) the endometrial lining is shed in menstrual cycles but reabsorbed in estrous cycles.

   C) estrous cycles occur more often than menstrual cycles.

   D) estrous cycles are not controlled by hormones.

   E) ovulation occurs before the endometrium thickens in estrous cycles.

   Answer: B

5) Peaks of LH and FSH production occur during

   A) the flow phase of the menstrual (uterine) cycle.

   B) the beginning of the follicular phase of the ovarian cycle.

   C) the period just before ovulation.

   D) the end of the luteal phase of the ovarian cycle.

   E) the secretory phase of the menstrual cycle.

   Answer: C

6) In sequential hermaphroditism,

   A) some individuals may change from male to female.

   B) individuals fertilize themselves.

   C) males rather than females release pheromones.

   D) diploid ova are produced.

   E) the adult gonads are undifferentiated.

   Answer: A

7) During human gestation, rudiments of all organs develop
   A) in the first trimester.
   B) in the second trimester.
   C) in the third trimester.
   D) while the embryo is in the oviduct.
   E) during the blastocyst stage.

   Answer: A

8) Which pharmacological strategy is most likely to result in a successful male contraceptive?
   A) preventing the production of functionally normal sperm
   B) maintaining high circulating concentrations of androgen
   C) blocking testosterone receptors on Leydig cells
   D) blocking androgen receptors within the hypothalamus
   E) maintaining high circulating concentrations of FSH

   Answer: A

9) Fertilization of human eggs most often takes place in the
   A) vagina.
   B) ovary.
   C) uterus.
   D) oviduct.
   E) vas deferens.

   Answer: D

10) In male mammals, excretory and reproductive systems share
   A) the testes.
   B) the urethra.
   C) the ureter.
   D) the vas deferens.
   E) the prostate.

   Answer: B

# Chapter 47 Animal Development

1) Russian nesting dolls, which are a set of smaller dolls packed inside larger dolls, most resemble which one of the following developmental theories?

   A) epigenesis

   B) preformation

   C) cell differentiation

   D) morphogenesis

   E) cell theory

   Answer: B
   *Topic: Overview*
   *Skill: Application*

2) You buy a pie that contains a mixture of cherries and blueberries. When you cut the pie up, you notice that some slices have more blueberries than cherries and other slices have more cherries than blueberries. This uneven distribution of cherries and blueberries is most like the uneven distribution of

   A) nuclei in a zygote.

   B) nuclei in an early embryo.

   C) nuclei in an egg.

   D) cytoplasmic determinants in a zygote.

   E) cytoplasmic determinants in an early embryo.

   Answer: D
   *Topic: Overview*
   *Skill: Application*

3) A puppy is born with a malformed right leg. A veterinarian studies the animal and determines that all of the correct types of cells are present, but that the leg simply took on the wrong shape. This is most likely a problem of

   A) morphogenesis.

   B) cell differentiation.

   C) histogenesis.

   D) preformation.

   E) fertilization.

   Answer: A
   *Topic: Overview*
   *Skill: Application*

4) As an embryo develops, new cells are formed and different types of cells develop by the process of

   A) differentiation and morphogenesis.

   B) preformation and cell differentiation.

   C) cell division and differentiation.

   D) preformation and morphogenesis.

   E) preformation and epigenesis.

   Answer: C
   *Topic: Overview*
   *Skill: Knowledge*

5) Fertilization of an egg without activation is most like

   A) placing the key in the ignition of a car but not starting the engine.

   B) resting during halftime of a basketball game.

   C) preparing a pie from scratch and baking it in the oven.

   D) walking to a store and buying some groceries.

   E) boarding a train in Chicago and riding it to Philadelphia.

   Answer: A
   *Topic: Concept 47.1*
   *Skill: Application*

6) In some rare all–female salamander species, the females require the sperm from males of another species. However, the developing embryos show no signs of a genetic contribution from the sperm. In this case, the sperm appear to be used only for

   A) morphogenesis.

   B) epigenesis.

   C) egg activation.

   D) cell differentiation.

   E) the creation of a diploid cell.

   Answer: C
   *Topic: Concept 47.1*
   *Skill: Application*

7) Which of the following is a function of the acrosome contents during fertilization?

   A) block polyspermy

   B) help propel the sperm toward the egg

   C) digest the exterior coats of the egg

   D) nourish the mitochondria of the sperm

   E) trigger the completion of meiosis by the sperm cell

   Answer: C
   *Topic: Concept 47.1*
   *Skill: Comprehension*

8) Which of the following statements is (are) *true* concerning the vitelline layer of the sea urchin egg?

   A) It is outside the fertilization membrane.

   B) It releases calcium, which initiates the cortical reaction.

   C) It has receptor molecules that are specific for binding acrosomal proteins.

   D) A and B are true.

   E) A, B, and C are true.

   Answer: C
   *Topic: Concept 47.1*
   *Skill: Knowledge*

9) The cortical reaction functions directly in the

   A) formation of a fertilization envelope.

   B) production of a fast block to polyspermy.

   C) release of hydrolytic enzymes from the sperm cell.

   D) generation of a nervelike impulse by the egg cell.

   E) fusion of egg and sperm nuclei.

   Answer: A
   *Topic: Concept 47.1*
   *Skill: Knowledge*

10) What causes the "slow block" to polyspermy?

   A) a transient voltage change across the membrane

   B) the consumption of yolk protein

   C) the jelly coat blocking sperm penetration

   D) formation of the fertilization envelope

   E) inactivation of the sperm acrosome

   Answer: D
   *Topic: Concept 47.1*
   *Skill: Knowledge*

11) Which of the following is *least* related to the others?

   A) slow block to polyspermy

   B) cortical granules

   C) cortical reaction

   D) depolarization

   E) fertilization envelope

   Answer: D
   *Topic: Concept 47.1*
   *Skill: Comprehension*

12) If an egg cell contained EDTA, a chemical that binds calcium and magnesium, what effect would this have on reproduction?

A) The acrosomal reaction would be blocked.

B) The fusion of sperm and egg nuclei would be blocked.

C) The fast block to polyspermy would not occur.

D) The fertilization envelope would not be formed.

E) The zygote would not contain maternal and paternal chromosomes.

Answer: D
*Topic: Concept 47.1*
*Skill: Comprehension*

13) Which statement about egg development is *true*?

A) Eggs without a nucleus cannot initiate division.

B) A second messenger system is activated following fertilization.

C) The sperm and egg micronuclei have fused by the end of the cortical reaction.

D) The contents of the cortical granules contribute to the fast block to polyspermy.

E) The mRNA involved with early activation of the egg arises from the sperm nucleus.

Answer: B
*Topic: Concept 47.1*
*Skill: Comprehension*

14) Arrange the following stages of fertilization and early development into a proper sequence.
I. onset of new DNA synthesis
II. cortical reaction
III. first cell division
IV. acrosomal reaction; plasma membrane depolarization
V. fusion of egg and sperm nuclei complete

A) III, V, I, IV, II

B) V, I, IV, II, III

C) I, III, II, IV, V

D) V, III, I, II, IV

E) IV, II, V, I, III

Answer: E
*Topic: Concept 47.1*
*Skill: Comprehension*

15) Which of the following statements about fertilization is *false*?

A) Fertilization reinstates diploidy.

B) Fertilization invaginates the blastula to form the gastrula.

C) During fertilization, egg cell depolarization initiates the cortical reaction.

D) During fertilization, gamete fusion depolarizes the egg cell membrane and sets up a fast block to polyspermy.

E) During fertilization, a slow block to polyspermy occurs when cortical granules erect a fertilization envelope.

Answer: B
*Topic: Concept 47.1*
*Skill: Knowledge*

16) What part of the sperm first contacts the egg plasma membrane?

   A) the vitelline membrane

   B) the cortical granules

   C) the acrosomal membrane

   D) the actin proteins

   E) the fertilization membrane

Answer: C
*Topic: Concept 47.1*
*Skill: Knowledge*

17) Which one of the following occurs in sea urchin but not mammalian fertilization?

   A) the binding of a sperm cell to the egg

   B) a fast block to polyspermy

   C) hydrolytic enzymes are spilled from the acrosome

   D) a slow block to polyspermy

   E) a fusion of the egg and sperm membranes

Answer: B
*Topic: Concept 47.1*
*Skill: Comprehension*

18) As cleavage continues during frog development, the number of blastomeres

   A) increases as the size of the blastomeres decreases.

   B) increases as the size of the blastomeres increases.

   C) decreases as the size of the blastomeres increases.

   D) decreases as the size of the blastomeres decreases.

   E) increases as the size of the blastomeres stays the same.

Answer: A
*Topic: Concept 47.1*
*Skill: Comprehension*

19) Which of the following does *not* occur during early cleavage of a frog zygote?

   A) The developing cell undergoes mitosis.

   B) The nuclear-to-cytoplasmic ratio of the two resulting cells increases.

   C) The ratio of surface area to volume of the two resulting cells increases.

   D) The embryo grows significantly in mass.

   E) The developing cell undergoes cytokinesis.

Answer: D
*Topic: Concept 47.1*
*Skill: Comprehension*

20) How does the vegetal pole differ from the animal pole of a zygote?

   A) The vegetal pole has a higher concentration of yolk.

   B) The blastomeres originate only in the vegetal pole.

   C) The posterior end of the embryo forms at the vegetal pole.

   D) The vegetal pole cells undergo mitosis but not cytokinesis.

   E) The polar bodies bud from this region.

Answer: A
*Topic: Concept 47.1*
*Skill: Comprehension*

21) Which region of the frog blastula corresponds to the future dorsal side of the embryo?

   A) morula

   B) primitive streak

   C) archenteron

   D) gray crescent

   E) blastocoel

Answer: D
*Topic: Concept 47.1*
*Skill: Knowledge*

22) The yolk of the frog egg
   A) prevents gastrulation.
   B) is concentrated at the animal pole.
   C) is homogeneously arranged in the egg.
   D) impedes the formation of a primitive streak.
   E) leads to unequal rates of cleavage for the animal pole compared to the vegetal pole.

Answer: E
*Topic: Concept 47.1*
*Skill: Comprehension*

23) You observe an embryo with meroblastic cleavage, extraembryonic membranes, and a primitive streak. How would you identify this organism, based on the information given?
   A) insect
   B) fish
   C) amphibian
   D) bird
   E) sea urchin

Answer: D
*Topic: Concept 47.1*
*Skill: Application*

24) Meroblastic cleavage occurs in which of the following?
   I.   sea urchins
   II.  humans
   III. birds
   A) I only
   B) II only
   C) III only
   D) I and III only
   E) II and III only

Answer: C
*Topic: Concept 47.1*
*Skill: Knowledge*

25) Which developmental sequence is *correct*?
   A) cleavage, blastula, gastrula, morula
   B) cleavage, gastrula, morula, blastula
   C) cleavage, morula, blastula, gastrula
   D) gastrula, morula, blastula, cleavage
   E) morula, cleavage, gastrula, blastula

Answer: C
*Topic: Concept 47.1*
*Skill: Knowledge*

26) What is the process called that involves the movement of cells into new relative positions in an embryo and results in the establishment of three germ tissue layers?
   A) determination
   B) cleavage
   C) fertilization
   D) induction
   E) gastrulation

Answer: E
*Topic: Concept 47.1*
*Skill: Knowledge*

27) After gastrulation, the outer-to-inner sequence of tissue layers in a vertebrate is
   A) endoderm, ectoderm, mesoderm.
   B) mesoderm, endoderm, ectoderm.
   C) ectoderm, mesoderm, endoderm.
   D) ectoderm, endoderm, mesoderm.
   E) endoderm, mesoderm, ectoderm.

Answer: C
*Topic: Concept 47.1*
*Skill: Knowledge*

28) What would be the consequence if gastrulation did not occur?

   A) Cleavage would not occur in the zygote.

   B) Embryonic germ layers would not form.

   C) Fertilization would be blocked.

   D) The blastula would not be formed.

   E) The blastopore would form above the gray crescent in the animal pole.

Answer: B
*Topic: Concept 47.1*
*Skill: Comprehension*

29) The archenteron of the developing frog eventually develops into which structure?

   A) reproductive organs

   B) the blastocoel

   C) heart and lungs

   D) digestive tract

   E) brain and spinal cord

Answer: D
*Topic: Concept 47.1*
*Skill: Knowledge*

30) Without the formulation of an ectoderm, vertebrates would not form

   A) a nervous system.

   B) a liver.

   C) a pancreas.

   D) a heart.

   E) kidneys.

Answer: A
*Topic: Concept 47.1*
*Skill: Comprehension*

*The following questions refer to the diagram of the embryo in Figure 47.1.*

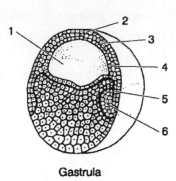

Gastrula

**Figure 47.1**

31) What type of embryo is most likely depicted here?

   A) dog

   B) frog

   C) chick

   D) snake

   E) human

Answer: B
*Topic: Concept 47.1*
*Skill: Knowledge*

32) The next stage of development for the embryo depicted in Figure 47.1 is

   A) gastrulation.

   B) organogenesis.

   C) blastula formation.

   D) morula formation.

   E) morphogenesis.

Answer: B
*Topic: Concept 47.1*
*Skill: Comprehension*

33) In Figure 47.1, ectoderm, mesoderm, and endoderm are, respectively,

A) 1, 2, and 6.

B) 3, 4, and 5.

C) 2, 3, and 4.

D) 5, 6, and 3.

E) 1, 3, and 6.

Answer: C
*Topic: Concept 47.1*
*Skill: Application*

34) Which of the following will form the lumen of the digestive tract?

A) 1

B) 4

C) 5

D) 6

E) 7

Answer: A
*Topic: Concept 47.1*
*Skill: Knowledge*

35) The blastopore in this organism will become the

A) anus.

B) ears.

C) eyes.

D) nose.

E) mouth.

Answer: A
*Topic: Concept 47.1*
*Skill: Knowledge*

36) In a frog embryo, gastrulation

A) produces a blastocoel displaced into the animal hemisphere.

B) occurs along the primitive streak in the animal hemisphere.

C) is impossible because of the large amount of yolk in the ovum.

D) proceeds by involution as cells roll over the lip of the blastopore.

E) occurs within the inner cell mass that is embedded in the large amount of yolk.

Answer: D
*Topic: Concept 47.1*
*Skill: Comprehension*

*The following questions refer to the diagram of an embryo in Figure 47.2. Match the word or statement to the lettered structures.*

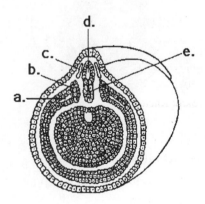

**Figure 47.2**

37) coelom

Answer: a
*Topic: Concept 47.1*
*Skill: Knowledge*

38) somite

Answer: b
*Topic: Concept 47.1*
*Skill: Knowledge*

39) notochord

Answer: e
*Topic: Concept 47.1*
*Skill: Knowledge*

40) gives rise to the muscles

Answer: b
*Topic: Concept 47.1*
*Skill: Knowledge*

41) gives rise to the brain and spinal cord

Answer: d
*Topic: Concept 47.1*
*Skill: Knowledge*

**Figure 47.3**

42) The drawing in Figure 47.3 is from what stage of amphibian development?

A) blastula
B) neural stage
C) early gastrula
D) late gastrula
E) gray crescent stage

Answer: B
*Topic: Concept 47.1*
*Skill: Knowledge*

43) Which of the following is *least* related to the others?

A) germ layers
B) morula
C) blastopore
D) gastrulation
E) invagination

Answer: B
*Topic: Concept 47.1*
*Skill: Comprehension*

44) Which of the following is mismatched?

A) mesoderm—notochord
B) endoderm—lungs
C) ectoderm—liver
D) mesoderm—somites
E) ectoderm—eye

Answer: C
*Topic: Concept 47.1*
*Skill: Knowledge*

45) Which of the following is *least* related to the others?

A) ectoderm
B) mesoderm
C) archenteron
D) endoderm
E) germ layers

Answer: C
*Topic: Concept 47.1*
*Skill: Comprehension*

*Use the following information to answer the questions below.*

In a study of the development of frog embryos, several early gastrulas were stained with vital dyes. The locations of the dyes after gastrulation were noted. The results are shown in the following table.

| Tissue | Stain |
|---|---|
| Brain | red |
| Notochord | yellow |
| Liver | green |
| Lens of the eye | blue |
| Lining of the digestive tract | purple |

46) Ectoderm would give rise to tissues containing which of the following colors?

    A) yellow and purple

    B) purple and green

    C) green and red

    D) red and blue

    E) red and yellow

Answer: D
*Topic: Concept 47.1*
*Skill: Comprehension*

47) The mesoderm was probably stained with which color?

    A) blue

    B) yellow

    C) red

    D) purple

    E) green

Answer: B
*Topic: Concept 47.1*
*Skill: Comprehension*

48) The endoderm was probably stained with which color?

    A) red and yellow

    B) yellow and green

    C) green and purple

    D) blue and yellow

    E) purple and red

Answer: C
*Topic: Concept 47.1*
*Skill: Comprehension*

49) Which of the following helps direct the formation of the primitive streak but contributes no cells to the embryo?

    A) endoderm

    B) mesoderm

    C) ectoderm

    D) neural crest

    E) hypoblast

Answer: E
*Topic: Concept 47.1*
*Skill: Knowledge*

50) The primitive streak in a bird is the functional equivalent of

    A) the lip of the blastopore in the frog.

    B) the archenteron in a frog.

    C) polar bodies in a sea urchin.

    D) the notochord in a mammal.

    E) neural crest cells in a mammal.

Answer: A
*Topic: Concept 47.1*
*Skill: Knowledge*

51) What does the development of all vertebrates require?

A) a large supply of yolk

B) an aqueous environment

C) extraembryonic membranes

D) an amnion

E) a primitive streak

Answer: B
*Topic: Concept 47.1*
*Skill: Knowledge*

52) Which of the following is *not* an extraembryonic membrane that develops from the embryos of reptiles, birds, and mammals?

A) chorion

B) yolk sac

C) egg shell

D) amnion

E) allantois

Answer: C
*Topic: Concept 47.1*
*Skill: Knowledge*

53) Which of the following is *least* related to the others?

A) zona pellucida

B) amnion

C) chorion

D) allantois

E) yolk sac

Answer: A
*Topic: Concept 47.1*
*Skill: Comprehension*

54) The least amount of yolk would be found in the egg of a

A) bird.

B) fish.

C) frog.

D) eutherian (placental) mammal.

E) reptile.

Answer: D
*Topic: Concept 47.1*
*Skill: Knowledge*

55) A primitive streak forms during the early embryonic development of which of the following?

   I.  birds

   II.  frogs

   III.  humans

A) I only

B) II only

C) III only

D) I and III only

E) II and III only

Answer: D
*Topic: Concept 47.1*
*Skill: Knowledge*

56) Which structure in bird and mammalian embryos functions like the blastopore of frog embryos?

A) primitive streak

B) neural plate

C) archenteron

D) notochord

E) somites

Answer: A
*Topic: Concept 47.1*
*Skill: Comprehension*

57) Extraembryonic membranes develop in which of the following?

    I. mammals
    II. birds
    III. lizards

A) I only

B) II only

C) III only

D) I and II only

E) I, II, and III

Answer: E
*Topic: Concept 47.1*
*Skill: Knowledge*

58) At the time of implantation, what is the human embryo called?

A) blastocyst

B) gastrula

C) fetus

D) somite

E) zygote

Answer: A
*Topic: Concept 47.1*
*Skill: Knowledge*

59) Which one of the following initiates implantation by secreting enzymes that break down the endometrium?

A) inner cell mass

B) endoderm

C) chorion

D) mesoderm

E) trophoblast

Answer: E
*Topic: Concept 47.1*
*Skill: Knowledge*

60) In placental mammals, what is the major function of the yolk sac during development?

A) It transfers nutrients from the yolk to the embryo.

B) It differentiates into the placenta.

C) It becomes a fluid–filled sac that surrounds and protects the embryo.

D) It produces blood cells that then migrate into the embryo.

E) It stores waste products from the embryo until the placenta develops.

Answer: D
*Topic: Concept 47.1*
*Skill: Knowledge*

61) Which one of the following plays a major role in gas exchange in a mammalian embryo?

A) amnion

B) hypoblast

C) chorion

D) trophoblast

E) yolk sac

Answer: C
*Topic: Concept 47.1*
*Skill: Knowledge*

62) Thalidomide is a chemical that was prescribed as a sedative in the early 1960s. Many women who took the drug during their first trimester gave birth to children with arm and leg deformities. What developmental process did this drug affect?

A) early cleavage divisions

B) determination of the polarity of the zygote

C) differentiation of bone tissue

D) morphogenesis

E) organogenesis

Answer: D
*Topic: Concept 47.1*
*Skill: Application*

63) Changes in both cell shape and cell position are involved with which process(es)?

A) gastrulation

B) organogenesis

C) cleavage

D) A and B only

E) A, B, and C

Answer: E
*Topic: Concept 47.2*
*Skill: Knowledge*

64) Changes in the shape of a cell usually involve a reorganization of the

A) nucleus.

B) cytoskeleton.

C) extracellular matrix.

D) transport proteins.

E) none of the above

Answer: B
*Topic: Concept 47.2*
*Skill: Knowledge*

65) The term applied to a morphogenetic process whereby cells extend themselves, making the mass of cells narrower and longer, is

A) convergent extension.

B) induction.

C) elongational streaming.

D) bi-axial elongation.

E) blastomere formation.

Answer: A
*Topic: Concept 47.2*
*Skill: Knowledge*

66) Which of the following would probably have the *greatest* effect on convergent extension?

A) stopping DNA synthesis

B) stopping mRNA synthesis

C) releasing an enzyme that digests glycoproteins

D) A and B only

E) A, B, and C

Answer: C
*Topic: Concept 47.2*
*Skill: Comprehension*

67) Which statement about cell adhesion molecules (CAMs) is *false*?

A) They are glycoproteins.

B) They bind to CAMs on other cells.

C) They are all produced by the same gene.

D) They contribute to cell migration.

E) They contribute to stable tissue structure.

Answer: C
*Topic: Concept 47.2*
*Skill: Knowledge*

68) If an amphibian zygote is manipulated so that the first cleavage plane does *not* divide the gray crescent, what is the expected fate of the two daughter cells?

A) The daughter cell with the entire gray crescent will die.

B) Both daughter cells will develop normally because amphibians are totipotent at this stage.

C) Only the daughter cell with the gray crescent will develop normally.

D) Both daughter cells will develop abnormally.

E) Both daughter cells will die immediately.

Answer: C
*Topic: Concept 47.3*
*Skill: Comprehension*

69) In humans, identical twins are possible because
    A) of the heterogeneous distribution of cytoplasmic determinants in unfertilized eggs.
    B) of interactions between extraembryonic cells and the zygote nucleus.
    C) of convergent extension.
    D) early blastomeres can form a complete embryo if isolated.
    E) the gray crescent divides the dorsal-ventral axis into new cells.

Answer: D
*Topic: Concept 47.3*
*Skill: Comprehension*

70) Hans Spemann has referred to which of the following structures as the primary organizer in the early development of amphibian embryos?
    A) optic cup
    B) notochord
    C) neural tube
    D) dorsal ectoderm
    E) dorsal lip of the blastopore

Answer: E
*Topic: Concept 47.3*
*Skill: Knowledge*

71) In frogs, formation of the eye lens is induced by chemical signals from
    A) cells that will become the neural plate.
    B) cells that are forming the inner ear.
    C) an outgrowth of the developing brain.
    D) both A and B
    E) both A and C

Answer: E
*Topic: Concept 47.3*
*Skill: Comprehension*

72) The arrangement of organs and tissues in their characteristic places in three-dimensional space defines
    A) pattern formation.
    B) induction.
    C) differentiation.
    D) determination.
    E) organogenesis.

Answer: A
*Topic: Concept 47.3*
*Skill: Knowledge*

73) Which mathematical situation has a parallel in embryonic limb development?
    A) using X, Y, and Z coordinates to plot a graph
    B) plotting a graph of an exponential growth curve
    C) plotting a graph of a linear growth curve
    D) using parallel lines to construct a parallelogram
    E) $E = mc^2$

Answer: A
*Topic: Concept 47.3*
*Skill: Comprehension*

74) Which of the following is not involved in positional information for pattern formation?
    A) apical ectodermal ridge
    B) zone of polarizing activity
    C) cadherins
    D) fibroblast growth factors
    E) Sonic hedgehog

Answer: C
*Topic: Concept 47.3*
*Skill: Knowledge*

# Media Activity Questions

1) As cleavage continues, a zygote forms into a solid multicellular ball called a(n)

    A) endometrium.

    B) morula.

    C) trophoblast.

    D) gastrula.

    E) blastula.

Answer: B
*Topic: Web/CD Activity: Sea Urchin Development*

2) During gastrulation, invagination occurs at the

    A) archenteron.

    B) blastocoel.

    C) endometrium.

    D) blastopore.

    E) trophoblast.

Answer: D
*Topic: Web/CD Activity: Sea Urchin Development*

3) During gastrulation in frogs, a rod of mesoderm under the dorsal surface forms the

    A) notochord.

    B) ectoderm.

    C) endoderm.

    D) archenteron.

    E) blastopore.

Answer: A
*Topic: Web/CD Activity: Frog Development*

4) During gastrulation in frogs, cells from the animal pole spread over the embryo and form the

    A) endoderm.

    B) ectoderm.

    C) archenteron.

    D) blastopore.

    E) blastula

Answer: B
*Topic: Web/CD Activity: Frog Development*

5) The posterior portion of the neural tube will develop into the frog's

    A) spinal cord.

    B) brain.

    C) blastocoel.

    D) digestive tract.

    E) anus.

Answer: A
*Topic: Web/CD Activity: Frog Development*

# Self–Quiz Questions

1) The cortical reaction of sea urchin eggs functions directly in the
   - A) formation of a fertilization envelope.
   - B) production of a fast block to polyspermy.
   - C) release of hydrolytic enzymes from the sperm cell.
   - D) generation of an electrical impulse by the egg cell.
   - E) fusion of egg and sperm nuclei.

   Answer: A

2) Which of the following is common to both avian and mammalian development?
   - A) holoblastic cleavage
   - B) epiblast and hypoblast
   - C) trophoblast
   - D) yolk plug
   - E) gray crescent

   Answer: B

3) The archenteron develops into
   - A) the mesoderm.
   - B) the blastocoel.
   - C) the endoderm.
   - D) the placenta.
   - E) the lumen of the digestive tract.

   Answer: E

4) In a frog embryo, the blastocoel is
   - A) completely obliterated by yolk platelets.
   - B) lined with endoderm during gastrulation.
   - C) located primarily in the animal hemisphere.
   - D) the cavity that becomes the coelom.
   - E) the cavity that later forms the archenteron.

   Answer: C

5) What structural adaptation in chickens allows them to lay their eggs in arid environments, rather than in water?
   - A) extraembryonic membranes
   - B) yolk
   - C) cleavage
   - D) gastrulation
   - E) development of the brain from ectoderm

   Answer: A

6) In an amphibian embryo, a band of cells called the neural crest
   - A) rolls up to form the neural tube.
   - B) develops into the main sections of the brain.
   - C) produces cells that migrate to form teeth, skull bones, and other structures in the embryo.
   - D) has been shown by experiments to be the organizer region of the developing embryo.
   - E) induces the formation of the notochord.

   Answer: C

7) Differences in the development of different cells in the early frog embryo (zygote to blastula) are due to
   - A) the differences between meroblastic and holoblastic cleavage.
   - B) the heterogeneous distribution of cytoplasmic determinants, such as proteins and mRNA.
   - C) inductive interactions occurring between the developing cells.
   - D) concentration gradients for regulatory molecules such as BMP–4.
   - E) the position of the cells relative to the zone of polarizing activity (ZPA).

   Answer: B

8) During convergent extension,

   A) cells on the opposite side of the embryo follow converging developmental pathways leading to bilateral symmetry.

   B) the cells of the neural folds adhere to one another to complete the neural tube.

   C) the cells of a tissue layer reorganize, forming a narrowed, elongated sheet.

   D) the dorsal-ventral axis is established.

   E) cell adhesion molecules are expressed, causing the eight blastomeres to adhere tightly to one another.

   Answer: C

9) In the early development of an amphibian embryo, an important "organizer" is located in the

   A) neural tube.

   B) notochord.

   C) archenteron roof.

   D) dorsal ectoderm.

   E) dorsal lip of the blastopore.

   Answer: E

10) Any blastomere removed from an eight-cell mammalian embryo can develop into a normal late-stage embryo. This finding supports the idea that

   A) only the zygote is totipotent.

   B) the progressive restriction of potency hypothesis applies.

   C) the first cleavage event must be transverse to the animal-vegetal axis of the zygote.

   D) cell divisions producing the earliest blastomeres do not result in an asymmetrical distribution of cytoplasmic determinants.

   E) there is no organizer in mammals.

   Answer: D

# Chapter 48  Nervous Systems

1) Which of the following is (are) characteristic of a simple nervous system?

 A) a nerve net such as is found in cnidarians

 B) nerve cell ganglia

 C) having electrical impulses traveling in both directions

 D) both A and C

 E) A, B, and C

Answer: D
*Topic: Concept 48.1*
*Skill: Knowledge*

2) Which of the following is associated with the evolution of a central nervous system?

 A) a complete gut

 B) bilateral symmetry

 C) radial symmetry

 D) a closed circulatory system

 E) excitable membranes

Answer: B
*Topic: Concept 48.1*
*Skill: Knowledge*

3) An organism that lacks integration centers

 A) cannot receive stimuli.

 B) will not have a nervous system.

 C) will not be able to interpret stimuli.

 D) can be expected to lack myelinated neurons.

 E) both A and D

Answer: C
*Topic: Concept 48.1*
*Skill: Comprehension*

4) Where is the most likely location of a group of nerve cell bodies known as a ganglion?

 A) in the central nervous system

 B) in the peripheral nervous system

 C) anywhere in the nervous system

 D) within the brain

 E) within the spinal cord

Answer: B
*Topic: Concept 48.1*
*Skill: Knowledge*

5) The general functions of the nervous system include which of the following?

 I.   integration
 II.  motor output
 III. sensory input

 A) I only

 B) II only

 C) III only

 D) I and II only

 E) I, II, and III

Answer: E
*Topic: Concept 48.1*
*Skill: Comprehension*

6) What do muscles, nerves, and glands have in common?

 A) They synapse with neurons.

 B) They are referred to as postsynaptic cells.

 C) They are target cells.

 D) A and B only

 E) A, B, and C

Answer: E
*Topic: Concept 48.1*
*Skill: Comprehension*

7) Integration of simple responses to certain stimuli, such as the patellar reflex, is accomplished by which of the following?

    A) spinal cord

    B) hypothalamus

    C) corpus callosum

    D) cerebellum

    E) medulla

Answer: A
*Topic: Concept 48.1*
*Skill: Knowledge*

8) The blood–brain barrier

    A) is formed by tight junctions.

    B) is formed by oligodendrocytes.

    C) tightly regulates the intracellular environment of the CNS.

    D) uses chemical signals to communicate with the spinal cord.

    E) provides support to the brain tissue.

Answer: A
*Topic: Concept 48.1*
*Skill: Comprehension*

9) Which of the following statements is *false*?

    A) All cells have a membrane potential.

    B) Gray matter is the site of neuronal integration.

    C) Astrocytes can communicate with nerve cells.

    D) The outside of a cell is negative with respect to the inside of a cell.

    E) Squid axons are a model system for nerve conductance.

Answer: D
*Topic: Concept 48.2*
*Skill: Comprehension*

10) If the concentration of potassium in the cytoplasm of a nerve cell with a resting membrane potential of –70 mV were elevated above normal, the new resting potential would

    A) still be –70 mV.

    B) be –69 mV or higher.

    C) be –71 mV or lower.

    D) be 0 mV.

    E) reverse polarity.

Answer: B
*Topic: Concept 48.2*
*Skill: Application*

11) Neurons at rest are not at the equilibrium potential for $K^+$ because the cell membrane is

    A) only permeable to $K^+$.

    B) slightly permeable to $Na^+$.

    C) not permeable to $Na^+$.

    D) not permeable to $K^+$.

    E) only permeable to $Na^+$.

Answer: B
*Topic: Concept 48.2*
*Skill: Knowledge*

12) If an otherwise normal nerve cell were made permeable to large negative ions, what would happen?

    A) The membrane potential would not form.

    B) Potassium would not leave the resting cell.

    C) Sodium would not enter the resting cell.

    D) The membrane potential would become positive.

    E) The sodium–potassium pump would not function.

Answer: A
*Topic: Concept 48.2*
*Skill: Comprehension*

13) The sodium–potassium pump of neurons pumps

    A) $Na^+$ and $K^+$ into the cell.

    B) $Na^+$ and $K^+$ out of the cell.

    C) $Na^+$ into the cell and $K^+$ out of the cell.

    D) $Na^+$ out of the cell and $K^+$ into the cell.

    E) $Na^+$ and $K^+$ into the cell and $H^+$ out of the cell through an antiport.

Answer: D
*Topic: Concept 48.2*
*Skill: Knowledge*

*The questions below refer to the following information:*

A previously unknown organism has been discovered. It contains long cells with excitable membranes that scientists suspect are used for rapid information transfer. The membrane of the cell is permeable only to ion X, which carries a negative charge. Active transport pumps in the membrane move X into the cell while simultaneously moving ion Y, also carrying a negative charge, out of the cell.

14) Which of the following is *true* about the establishment of the resting membrane potential in this cell?

    A) The resting potential of this cell will be zero.

    B) The resting potential of this cell will be negative.

    C) A negative resting potential is directly produced by the pump moving a negative charge into the cell.

    D) A negative resting potential is directly produced by the diffusion of $Y^-$ into the cell.

    E) A positive resting potential is directly produced by the diffusion of $X^-$ out of the cell.

Answer: E
*Topic: Concept 48.2*
*Skill: Application*

15) When neurotransmitter Z is released into the extracellular fluid in contact with a portion of the cell membrane, channels open that allow both $X^-$ and $Y^-$ through the membrane. Which of the following is *incorrect*?

    A) The magnitude of the potential will immediately increase.

    B) $Y-$ will diffuse into the cell.

    C) $X-$ will diffuse out of the cell.

    D) The membrane will depolarize.

    E) The channels are chemically gated.

Answer: A
*Topic: Concept 48.2*
*Skill: Application*

16) Which of the following is a *correct* statement about a resting neuron?

    A) It releases lots of acetylcholine.

    B) The membrane is very leaky to sodium.

    C) The membrane is equally permeable to sodium and potassium.

    D) The membrane potential is more negative than the threshold potential.

    E) The concentration of sodium is greater inside the cell than outside.

Answer: D
*Topic: Concept 48.2*
*Skill: Knowledge*

17) Which of following is a true statement about the threshold potential of a membrane?

   A) It is equal to about 35 mV.

   B) It is equal to about 70 mV.

   C) It opens voltage–sensitive gates that result in the rapid outflow of sodium ions.

   D) It is the depolarization that is needed to generate an action potential.

   E) It is a graded potential that is proportional to the strength of a stimulus.

Answer: D
*Topic: Concept 48.3*
*Skill: Knowledge*

18) Which statement about transmission along neurons is *false*?

   A) The rate of transmission of a nerve impulse is directly related to the diameter of the axon.

   B) The intensity of a stimulus is related to the magnitude of the action potential.

   C) The resting potential is maintained by differential ion permeabilities and the sodium–potassium pump.

   D) Once initiated, local depolarizations stimulate a propagation of serial action potentials down the axon.

   E) A stimulus that affects the membrane's permeability to ions can either depolarize or hyperpolarize the membrane.

Answer: B
*Topic: Concept 48.3*
*Skill: Comprehension*

19) What is the mode of action of a toxin that binds specifically to the voltage–gated sodium channels of axons?

   A) block all sodium movement

   B) block repolarization

   C) prevent the axon from reaching the threshold potential

   D) A and B only

   E) A, B, and C

Answer: C
*Topic: Concept 48.3*
*Skill: Application*

20) After an action potential, the resting potential is restored by

   A) the opening of sodium activation gates.

   B) the opening of voltage–sensitive potassium channels and the closing of sodium activation gates.

   C) an increase in the membrane's permeability to potassium and chloride ions.

   D) the delay in the action of the sodium–potassium pump.

   E) the refractory period in which the membrane is hyperpolarized.

Answer: B
*Topic: Concept 48.3*
*Skill: Knowledge*

21) Repolarization of the membrane of a neuron after an action potential is a consequence of which of the following?

    I.   calcium channels opening

    II.  Na$^+$ channels inactivating

    III. K$^+$ channels opening

A) I only

B) II only

C) III only

D) I and II only

E) II and III only

Answer: E
*Topic: Concept 48.3*
*Skill: Comprehension*

22) In the sequence of permeability changes that depolarizes and then repolarizes the membrane of a neuron during an action potential, which of the following changes occurs first?

A) Sodium gates open.

B) The sodium–potassium pump shuts down.

C) The sodium–potassium pump is activated.

D) Potassium gates close.

E) Potassium gates open.

Answer: A
*Topic: Concept 48.3*
*Skill: Knowledge*

*For the following questions, refer to the graph of an action potential in Figure 48.1 and use the letters to indicate your answer.*

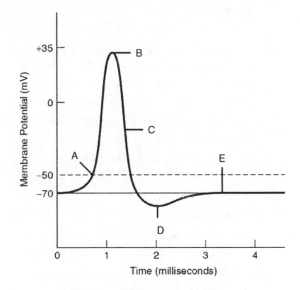

**Figure 48.1**

23) The membrane is unable to respond to any further stimulation, regardless of intensity.

Answer: D
*Topic: Concept 48.3*
*Skill: Comprehension*

24) The sodium gates open.

Answer: A
*Topic: Concept 48.3*
*Skill: Comprehension*

25) The threshold potential is reached.

Answer: A
*Topic: Concept 48.3*
*Skill: Comprehension*

26) Repolarization occurs, sodium gates close, and some potassium gates reopen.

Answer: C
*Topic: Concept 48.3*
*Skill: Comprehension*

27) The membrane is at resting potential.

Answer: E
*Topic: Concept 48.3*
*Skill: Comprehension*

28) Action potentials are normally carried in one direction from the axon hillock to the axon terminals. By using an electronic probe, you experimentally depolarize the middle of the axon to threshold. What do you expect?

A) No action potential will be initiated.

B) An action potential will be initiated and proceed in the normal direction toward the axon terminal.

C) An action potential will be initiated and proceed back toward the axon hillock.

D) Two action potentials will be initiated, one going toward the axon terminal and one going back toward the hillock.

E) An action potential will be initiated, but it will die out before it reaches the axon terminal.

Answer: D
*Topic: Concept 48.3*
*Skill: Application*

29) Saltatory conduction is a term applied to conduction of impulses

A) across electrical synapses.

B) along the postsynaptic membrane from dendrite to axon hillock.

C) in two directions at the same time.

D) from one neuron to another.

E) along myelinated nerve fibers.

Answer: E
*Topic: Concept 48.3*
*Skill: Knowledge*

30) Which animal movement could be used to represent impulse conductance along a myelinated axon?

A) a person out on a power walk

B) an earthworm moving along the surface of the ground

C) an amoeba extending pseudopodia

D) a moth moving toward a light

E) a frog leaping between lily pads

Answer: E
*Topic: Concept 48.3*
*Skill: Application*

31) Where do synaptic vesicles discharge their contents by exocytosis?

A) dendrite

B) axon hillock

C) nodes of Ranvier

D) postsynaptic membrane

E) presynaptic membrane

Answer: E
*Topic: Concept 48.4*
*Skill: Knowledge*

32) Neurotransmitters are released from presynaptic axon terminals into the synaptic cleft by which mechanism?

A) osmosis

B) active transport

C) diffusion

D) endocytosis

E) exocytosis

Answer: E
*Topic: Concept 48.4*
*Skill: Knowledge*

33) Which of the following offers the best description of neural transmission across a mammalian synaptic gap?

  A) Neural impulses involve the flow of $K^+$ and $Na^+$ across the gap.

  B) Neural impulses travel across the gap as electrical currents.

  C) Neural impulses cause the release of chemicals that diffuse across the gap.

  D) Neural impulses travel across the gap in both directions.

  E) The calcium within the axons and dendrites of nerves adjacent to a synapse acts as the neurotransmitter.

Answer: C
*Topic: Concept 48.4*
*Skill: Knowledge*

34) One disadvantage to a nerve net is that it can conduct impulses in two directions from the point of the stimulus. The vertebrate system conducts in only one direction. This one-way conduction occurs

  A) as a result of the nodes of Ranvier.

  B) as a result of voltage-gated sodium channels found in the vertebrate system.

  C) because vertebrate nerve cells have dendrites.

  D) because only the postsynaptic cells can bind neurotransmitters.

  E) because the sodium-potassium pump moves ions in one direction.

Answer: D
*Topic: Concept 48.4*
*Skill: Comprehension*

35) During an IPSP, the membrane of the postsynaptic cell becomes more permeable to

  A) $K^+$.

  B) $Na^+$.

  C) $Ca^{2+}$.

  D) GABA.

  E) serotonin.

Answer: A
*Topic: Concept 48.4*
*Skill: Knowledge*

36) Given the steps shown below, which of the following is the correct sequence for transmission at a chemical synapse?
1.   Neurotransmitter binds with receptors associated with the postsynaptic membrane.
2.   $Ca_2^+$ ions rush into neuron's cytoplasm.
3.   Action potential depolarizes the synaptic terminal membrane.
4.   Ligand-gated ion channels open.
5.   Synaptic vesicles release neurotransmitter into the synaptic cleft.

  A) 1, 2, 3, 4, 5

  B) 2, 3, 5, 4, 1

  C) 3, 2, 5, 1, 4

  D) 4, 3, 1, 2, 5

  E) 5, 1, 2, 4, 3

Answer: C
*Topic: Concept 48.4*
*Skill: Comprehension*

37) A drug might act as a stimulant of the somatic nervous system if it

A) makes the membrane permanently impermeable to sodium.

B) stimulates the activity of acetylcholinesterase in the synaptic cleft.

C) increases the release of substances that cause the hyperpolarization of the neurons.

D) increases the sensitivity of the postsynaptic membrane to acetylcholine.

E) increases the sensitivity of the presynaptic membrane to acetylcholine.

Answer: D
*Topic: Concept 48.4*
*Skill: Comprehension*

38) How does an EPSP facilitate depolarization of the postsynaptic membrane?

A) by increasing the permeability of the membrane to Na$^+$

B) by increasing the permeability of the membrane to K$^+$

C) by insulating the hillock region of the axon

D) by allowing Cl$^-$ to enter the cell

E) by stimulating the sodium–potassium pump

Answer: A
*Topic: Concept 48.4*
*Skill: Knowledge*

39) The postsynaptic membrane of a nerve may be stimulated by certain neurotransmitters to permit the influx of negative chloride ions into the cell. This process will result in

A) membrane depolarization.

B) an action potential.

C) the production of an IPSP.

D) the production of an EPSP.

E) the membrane becoming more positive.

Answer: C
*Topic: Concept 48.5*
*Skill: Comprehension*

40) Neurotransmitters categorized as inhibitory would *not* be expected to

A) bind to receptors.

B) open K$^+$ channels.

C) open Na$^+$ channels.

D) open Cl$^-$ channels.

E) hyperpolarize the membrane.

Answer: C
*Topic: Concept 48.4*
*Skill: Comprehension*

41) Which of the following statements is *true* regarding temporal summation?

    A) The sum of simultaneously arriving neurotransmitters from different presynaptic nerve cells determines whether the postsynaptic cell fires.

    B) Several action potentials arrive in fast succession without allowing the postsynaptic cell to return to its resting potential.

    C) Several IPSPs arrive concurrently, bringing the presynaptic cell closer to its threshold.

    D) Several postsynaptic cells fire at the same time when neurotransmitters are released from several synaptic terminals simultaneously.

    E) The voltage spike of the action potential that is initiated is higher than normal.

Answer: B
*Topic: Concept 48.4*
*Skill: Knowledge*

42) A single inhibitory postsynaptic potential has a magnitude of 0.5 mV at the axon hillock, and a single excitatory postsynaptic potential has a magnitude of 0.5 mV. What will be the membrane potential at the hillock after the spatial summation of 6 IPSPs and 2 EPSPs, if the initial membrane potential is –70 mV?

    A) –72 mV

    B) –71 mV

    C) –70 mV

    D) –69 mV

    E) –68 mV

Answer: A
*Topic: Concept 48.4*
*Skill: Application*

43) A neurotransmitter can trigger different responses in postsynaptic cells due to which of the following?

    A) receptor mode of action

    B) receptors present

    C) concentration of neurotransmitter

    D) A and B only

    E) A, B, and C

Answer: D
*Topic: Concept 48.4*
*Skill: Comprehension*

*The next questions refer to the following terms. Each term may be used once, more than once, or not at all.*

    A. meninges
    B. ganglion
    C. axon hillocks
    D. myelin sheaths
    E. postsynaptic membranes

44) possess neurotransmitter receptors

Answer: E
*Topic: Concept 48.4*
*Skill: Knowledge*

45) usually the sites of the initial action potential in neurons

Answer: C
*Topic: Concept 48.4*
*Skill: Knowledge*

46) produced by oligodendrocytes and Schwann cells

Answer: D
*Topic: Concept 48.4*
*Skill: Knowledge*

47) Which statement could be applied to *both* the nervous system and the endocrine system?

    A) They both use chemical signaling.

    B) The final response depends on the receptor mode of action.

    C) Specific parts of both systems use chemical messengers produced by axons.

    D) Only A and B are correct.

    E) A, B, and C are correct.

Answer: E
*Topic: Concept 48.4*
*Skill: Comprehension*

48) Neurotransmitters affect postsynaptic cells by

    A) initiating signal transduction pathways in the cells.

    B) causing molecular changes in the cells.

    C) affecting ion–channel proteins.

    D) altering the permeability of the cells.

    E) all of the above

Answer: E
*Topic: Concept 48.4*
*Skill: Knowledge*

49) What is the main neurotransmitter of the parasympathetic system?

    A) acetylcholine

    B) cholinesterase

    C) norepinephrine

    D) adrenaline

    E) dopamine

Answer: A
*Topic: Concept 48.4*
*Skill: Knowledge*

50) What is the major inhibitory neurotransmitter of the brain?

    A) acetylcholine

    B) cholinesterase

    C) norepinephrine

    D) dopamine

    E) GABA

Answer: E
*Topic: Concept 48.4*
*Skill: Knowledge*

*The questions below refer to the following choices of neurotransmitters. Each choice may be used once, more than once, or not at all.*

    A.  acetylcholine
    B.  epinephrine
    C.  endorphin
    D.  serotonin
    E.  GABA

51) a neuropeptide that functions as a natural analgesic

Answer: C
*Topic: Concept 48.4*
*Skill: Knowledge*

52) an amino acid that operates at inhibitory synapses in the brain

Answer: E
*Topic: Concept 48.4*
*Skill: Knowledge*

53) Which statement is *true*?

A) Nitric oxide is an example of a neurotransmitter stored in presynaptic vesicles.

B) Learning does not appear to require a specific number of neurons.

C) Organisms with bilateral symmetry were first to have nerve nets.

D) Biogenic amines are derived from proteins.

E) Serotonin is a neurotransmitter synthesized from tyrosine.

Answer: B
*Topic: Concept 48.4*
*Skill: Comprehension*

54) Cerebrospinal fluid can be described as all of the following *except*

A) functioning in transport of nutrients and hormones through the brain.

B) a product of the filtration of blood by the brain.

C) formed from layers of connective tissue.

D) functioning to cushion the brain.

E) filling cavities in the brain called ventricles.

Answer: C
*Topic: Concept 48.4*
*Skill: Knowledge*

55) The divisions of the nervous system that have antagonistic actions, or opposing actions are

A) motor and sensory.

B) sympathetic and parasympathetic.

C) presynaptic and postsynaptic.

D) forebrain and hindbrain.

E) central nervous system and peripheral nervous system.

Answer: B
*Topic: Concept 48.5*
*Skill: Comprehension*

56) Which part of the vertebrate nervous system is most involved in preparation for the fight-or-flight response?

A) sympathetic

B) somatic

C) central

D) visceral

E) parasympathetic

Answer: A
*Topic: Concept 48.5*
*Skill: Knowledge*

57) Which of the following activities would be associated with the parasympathetic division of the nervous system?

A) rest and digestion

B) release of both acetylcholine and epinephrine

C) increased metabolic rate

D) fight-or-flight response

E) release of epinephrine only

Answer: A
*Topic: Concept 48.5*
*Skill: Knowledge*

58) Which of the following is correct about the telencephalon region of the brain?

A) It develops as the neural tube differentiates.

B) It develops from the midbrain.

C) It is the brain region most like that of ancestral vertebrates.

D) It gives rise to the cerebrum.

E) It divides further into the metencephalon and myelencephalon.

Answer: D
*Topic: Concept 48.5*
*Skill: Comprehension*

59) What controls the heart rate?

   A) neocortex

   B) medulla

   C) thalamus

   D) pituitary

   E) cerebellum

Answer: B
*Topic: Concept 48.5*
*Skill: Knowledge*

60) Which area of the brain is most intimately associated with the unconscious control of respiration and circulation?

   A) thalamus

   B) cerebellum

   C) medulla

   D) corpus callosum

   E) cerebrum

Answer: C
*Topic: Concept 48.5*
*Skill: Knowledge*

61) Which selection is incorrectly paired?

   A) forebrain—diencephalon

   B) forebrain—cerebrum

   C) midbrain—brainstem

   D) midbrain—cerebellum

   E) brainstem—pons

Answer: D
*Topic: Concept 48.5*
*Skill: Knowledge*

62) What would be most affected if an accident caused trauma to the hypothalamus?

   A) sorting of sensory information

   B) processing of motor information in the cerebellum

   C) the production of CSF

   D) regulation of body temperature

   E) cognitive response ability

Answer: D
*Topic: Concept 48.5*
*Skill: Comprehension*

*For the next questions, choose the best answer from the following list. Each answer may be used once, more than once, or not at all.*

   A.  cerebrum
   B.  cerebellum
   C.  thalamus
   D.  hypothalamus
   E.  medulla oblongata

63) produces hormones that are secreted by the pituitary gland

Answer: D
*Topic: Concept 48.5*
*Skill: Knowledge*

64) coordinates muscle actions

Answer: B
*Topic: Concept 48.6*
*Skill: Knowledge*

65) regulates body temperature

Answer: D
*Topic: Concept 48.5*
*Skill: Knowledge*

66) contains regulatory centers for the respiratory and circulatory systems

Answer: E
*Topic: Concept 48.5*
*Skill: Knowledge*

67) contains regions that help regulate hunger and thirst

Answer: D
*Topic: Concept 48.5*
*Skill: Knowledge*

68) Which processes in animals are regulated by circadian rhythms?

A) sleep cycles

B) hormone release

C) sex drive

D) A and B only

E) A, B, and C

Answer: E
*Topic: Concept 48.5*
*Skill: Knowledge*

69) By comparing the size and degree of convolution of various vertebrate cerebral cortices, biologists would gain insight into the relative

A) size of the brain centers of taxonomic groups.

B) emotions and learning capabilities of vertebrate classes.

C) motor impulse complexities.

D) sophistication of behaviors.

E) sensory stimuli that regulate motor impulses.

Answer: D
*Topic: Concept 48.5*
*Skill: Comprehension*

70) Which of the following statements about the nervous system is *incorrect*?

A) The three evolutionary changes in the vertebrate brain include increases in relative size, increases in compartmentalization of function, and decreases in cephalization.

B) The size of the primary motor and sensory areas of the cortex devoted to controlling each part of the body is proportional to the importance of that part of the body.

C) Human emotions are believed to originate from interactions between the cerebral cortex and the limbic system.

D) The localization of pain involves the somatosensory cortex.

E) The autonomic nervous system is subdivided into the parasympathetic and sympathetic nervous systems.

Answer: A
*Topic: Concept 48.6*
*Skill: Comprehension*

71) The motor cortex is part of which part of the nervous system?

A) cerebrum

B) cerebellum

C) spinal cord

D) midbrain

E) medulla

Answer: A
*Topic: Concept 48.6*
*Skill: Knowledge*

72) What do Wernicke's and Broca's regions of the brain affect?

   A) olfaction

   B) vision

   C) speech

   D) memory

   E) hearing

Answer: C
*Topic: Concept 48.6*
*Skill: Comprehension*

73) If you were writing an essay, which part of the brain would be most active?

   A) temporal and frontal lobes

   B) parietal lobe

   C) Broca's area

   D) Wernicke's area

   E) occipital lobe

Answer: A
*Topic: Concept 48.6*
*Skill: Comprehension*

74) The establishment and expression of emotions involves the

   A) frontal lobes and limbic system.

   B) frontal lobes and parietal lobes.

   C) parietal lobes and limbic system.

   D) frontal and occipital lobes.

   E) occipital lobes and limbic system.

Answer: A
*Topic: Concept 48.6*
*Skill: Comprehension*

75) Our understanding of mental illness has been most advanced by discoveries involving

   A) degree of convolutions in the brain's surface.

   B) evolution of the telencephalon.

   C) sequence of developmental specialization.

   D) chemicals involved in brain communications.

   E) nature of the blood–brain barrier.

Answer: D
*Topic: Concept 48.7*
*Skill: Comprehension*

*The following questions refer to Figure 48.2.*

*(See page 775 for Figure 48.2.)*

76) Axons are pushed away from the spinal cord by being repelled by Netrin-1 and Slit from the floor plate.

Answer: D
*Topic: Concept 48.7*
*Skill: Comprehension*

77) Axons are pulled toward the midline by binding to molecules on the floor plate.

Answer: B
*Topic: Concept 48.7*
*Skill: Comprehension*

78) Axons are pulled toward the floor plate by the presence of Netrin-1 molecules.

Answer: A
*Topic: Concept 48.7*
*Skill: Comprehension*

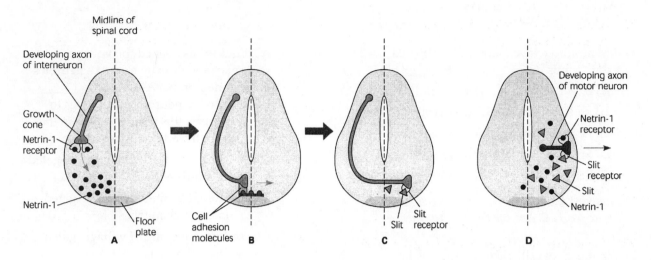

**Figure 48.2**

# Media Activity Questions

1) An impulse relayed along a myelinated axon "jumps" from _____ to _____.

   A) oligodendrocyte; Schwann cell

   B) node of Ranvier; Schwann cell

   C) node of Ranvier; node of Ranvier

   D) Schwann cell; Schwann cell

   E) Schwann cell; node of Ranvier

   Answer: C
   *Topic: Web/CD Activity: Neuron Structure*

2) What type of cell makes up the myelin sheath of a motor neuron?

   A) astrocytes

   B) microglial cells

   C) Ranvier cells

   D) ependymal cells

   E) Schwann cells

   Answer: E
   *Topic: Web/CD Activity: Neuron Structure*

3) What part of a neuron relays signals from one neuron to another neuron or to an effector?

   A) dendrite

   B) axon hillock

   C) synaptic terminal

   D) axon

   E) node of Ranvier

   Answer: C
   *Topic: Web/CD Activity: Neuron Structure*

4) A stimulus has opened the voltage-gated sodium channels in an area of a neuron's plasma membrane. As a result, _____ rushes into the neuron and diffuses to adjacent areas; this in turn results in the _____ in the adjacent areas.

   A) potassium; opening of voltage-gated potassium channels

   B) sodium; opening of voltage-gated potassium channels

   C) sodium; opening of voltage-gated sodium channels

   D) sodium; closing of voltage-gated sodium channels

   E) potassium; opening of voltage-gated sodium channels

   Answer: C
   *Topic: Web/CD Activity: Action Potentials*

5) Which of these causes the release of neurotransmitter molecules?

   A) the receipt of a signal from the postsynaptic neuron

   B) the opening of voltage-gate calcium channels and the diffusion of calcium ions out of the neuron

   C) an action potential reaching the end of the cell body

   D) an action potential reaching the end of the axon

   E) an action potential reaching the end of the dendrite

   Answer: D
   *Topic: Activity: Signal Transmission at a Synapse*

# Self–Quiz Questions

1) What happens when a neuron's membrane depolarizes?

A) There is a net diffusion of $Na^+$ out of the cell.

B) The $K^+$ equilibrium potential becomes more positive.

C) The magnitude of the membrane voltage is reduced.

D) The neuron becomes less likely to generate an action potential.

E) The inside of the cell becomes more negative relative to the outside.

Answer: C

2) Why are action potentials usually conducted in only one direction along an axon?

A) The nodes of Ranvier conduct only in one direction.

B) The brief refractory period prevents reopening of voltage–gated $Na^+$ channels.

C) The axon hillock has a higher membrane potential than the terminals of the axon.

D) Ions can flow along the axon in only one direction.

E) Voltage–gated channels for both $Na^+$ and $K^+$ open in only one direction.

Answer: B

3) Which of the following is a direct result of depolarizing the presynaptic membrane of an axon terminal?

A) Voltage–gated $Ca^{2+}$ channels in the membrane open.

B) Synaptic vesicles fuse with the membrane.

C) The postsynaptic cell produces an action potential.

D) Ligand–gated channels open allowing neurotransmitters to enter the synaptic cleft.

E) An EPSP or IPSP is generated in the postsynaptic cell.

Answer: A

4) What is the neocortex?

A) a primitive brain region common to reptiles and mammals

B) a region deep in the cortex that is associated with the formation of emotional memories

C) a central part of the cortex that receives olfactory information

D) an additional outer layer of neurons in the cerebral cortex that is unique to mammals

E) an association area of the frontal lobe that is involved in higher cognitive functions

Answer: D

5) Which of the following provides evidence that brain circuits involved in emotion form early during human development?

   A) Humans are more likely to be able to recall emotional memories from childhood than factual memories.

   B) Infants can understand language before they can speak.

   C) Such circuits involve parts of the brain that evolved before the neocortex evolved.

   D) Young infants can bond to a caregiver and express fear, distress, and anger.

   E) Individuals with damage to the amygdala no longer have autonomic responses to stressful stimuli.

   Answer: D

6) Which of the following structures or regions is *incorrectly* paired with its function?

   A) limbic system—motor control of speech

   B) medulla oblongata—homeostatic control

   C) cerebellum—coordination of movement and balance

   D) corpus callosum—communication between the left and right cerebral cortices

   E) hypothalamus—regulation of temperature, hunger, and thirst

   Answer: A

7) Where are neurotransmitter receptors located?

   A) on the nuclear membrane

   B) at nodes of Ranvier

   C) on the postsynaptic membrane

   D) on the membranes of synaptic vesicles

   E) in the myelin sheath

   Answer: C

8) A common feature of action potentials is that they

   A) cause the membrane to hyperpolarize and then depolarize.

   B) can undergo temporal and spatial summation.

   C) are triggered by a depolarization that reaches the threshold.

   D) move at the same speed along all axons.

   E) result from the diffusion of $Na^+$ and $K^+$ through ligand-gated channels.

   Answer: C

9) Which disease or disorder is caused by the death of brain neurons that release dopamine?

   A) schizophrenia

   B) bipolar disorder

   C) major depression

   D) Alzheimer's disease

   E) Parkinson's disease

   Answer: D

10) Which of the following best describes how an axon grows toward its target cell?

    A) The axon grows in a direct path, attracted by signal molecules released by target cells.

    B) Cells along the growth path release signal molecules that either attract or repel the axon, and the interaction of CAMs on the growth cone and neighboring cells may provide tracks that guide axon growth.

    C) Nerve growth factor released by astrocytes stimulates a neural progenitor cell to differentiate into a neuron, whose axon then grows toward an increasing concentration of signal molecules.

    D) The axon produces growth-promoting proteins only in its growth cone, causing the axon to grow in an outward direction toward its target cells.

    E) Glia first migrate to the target cells, leaving a trail of CAMs along the path that the growth cone of the axon follows.

Answer: B

# Chapter 49 Sensory and Motor Mechanisms

1) Which of the following is a sensation and not a perception?
   A) seeing the colors in a rainbow
   B) a nerve impulse induced by sugar stimulating sweet receptors on the tongue
   C) the smell of natural gas escaping from an open burner on a gas stove
   D) the unique taste of french fries with cheese
   E) the sound of a fire-truck siren as it passes by your car

   Answer: B
   *Topic: Concept 49.1*
   *Skill: Comprehension*

2) An interoreceptor would detect which of the following stimuli?
   A) a person rolling over in their bed
   B) a drop of water falling from one's face onto one's arm
   C) feeling the pain associated with a bee sting
   D) a drop in blood pressure from standing too quickly
   E) A and D only

   Answer: E
   *Topic: Concept 49.1*
   *Skill: Comprehension*

3) Why are we able to differentiate tastes and smells?
   A) The action potentials initiated by taste receptors are transmitted to a separate region of the brain than those initiated by receptors for smell.
   B) The sensory region of the cerebral cortex distinguishes something we taste from something we smell by the difference in the action potential.
   C) The brain distinguishes between taste, arising from interoreceptors, from smell arising from exteroreceptors.
   D) Because we are able to see what we are tasting, the brain uses this information to distinguish taste from smell.
   E) Taste receptors are able to detect fewer molecules of the stimulus, which means these receptors will initiate a receptor potential before smell receptors do.

   Answer: A
   *Topic: Concept 49.1*
   *Skill: Comprehension*

4) Sensory receptors have all of the following functions in common *except*
   A) increased permeability to sodium and potassium ions.
   B) conversion of stimulus energy to membrane potential.
   C) strengthening of stimulus energy sent to the nervous system.
   D) processing information through graded potentials.
   E) conduction of impulses to the central nervous system.

   Answer: A
   *Topic: Concept 49.1*
   *Skill: Comprehension*

5) If a stimulus is to be perceived by the nervous system, which part of the sensory pathway must occur *first*?

A) integration

B) transmission

C) transduction

D) reception

E) amplification

Answer: D
*Topic: Concept 49.1*
*Skill: Comprehension*

6) What is the correct sequence of events that would lead to a person hearing a sound?

1. transmission
2. transduction
3. integration
4. amplification

A) 1, 2, 3, 4

B) 1, 4, 2, 3

C) 2, 4, 1, 3

D) 3, 1, 2, 4

E) 3, 1, 4, 2

Answer: C
*Topic: Concept 49.1*
*Skill: Application*

7) Immediately after putting on a shirt, your skin feels itchy. However, the itching stops after a few minutes and you are unaware that you are wearing a shirt. Why?

A) Sensory adaptation has occurred.

B) Accommodation has increased.

C) Transduction has increased.

D) Motor unit recruitment has decreased.

E) Receptor amplification has decreased.

Answer: A
*Topic: Concept 49.1*
*Skill: Comprehension*

8) Which of the following is a good example of sensory adaptation?

A) olfactory receptors ceasing to produce receptor potentials when triggered by the smell of the second batch of cookies you are baking

B) hair cells in the organ of Corti not responding to high–pitched sounds after you have worked on the same construction job for 30 years

C) cones in the human eye failing to respond to light in the infrared range

D) hair cells in the utricle and saccule responding to a change in orientation when you bend your neck forward after you have been reading a book

E) rods in the human eye responding to mechanical stimulation from a blow to the back of the head so that a flash of light is perceived

Answer: A
*Topic: Concept 49.1*
*Skill: Comprehension*

9) Why does your arm feel cold when you reach inside the refrigerator to get a container of milk?

A) Circulating levels of prostaglandins increase.

B) The temperature of the blood circulating to the arm decreases.

C) Thermoreceptors send signals to the cerebral cortex where the change from room temperature to refrigerator temperature is transduced.

D) Thermoreceptors in the skin undergo accommodation, which increases their sensitivity.

E) Thermoreceptors send signals to the posterior hypothalamus.

Answer: E
*Topic: Concept 49.1*
*Skill: Comprehension*

10) Which of the following receptors is incorrectly paired with the type of energy it transduces?

  A) mechanoreceptors—sound

  B) electromagnetic receptors—magnetism

  C) chemoreceptors—solute concentrations

  D) thermoreceptors—heat

  E) pain receptors—electricity

Answer: E
*Topic: Concept 49.1*
*Skill: Knowledge*

11) What do hearing, touch, and a full stomach have in common?

  A) The transducers are all proprioceptors.

  B) The sensory information from all three is sent to the thalamus.

  C) The sensory receptors are all hair cells.

  D) Electrical energy is transduced to form an action potential.

  E) Only A and B are correct.

Answer: D
*Topic: Concept 49.1*
*Skill: Comprehension*

12) Which of the following is *incorrectly* paired?

  A) hair cell—mechanoreceptor

  B) muscle spindle—mechanoreceptor

  C) gustatory receptor—chemoreceptor

  D) electromagnetic energy—photoreceptors

  E) motor neuron—thermoreceptor

Answer: E
*Topic: Concept 49.1*
*Skill: Knowledge*

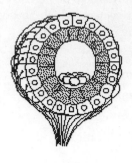

**Figure 49.1**

13) What is the structure diagrammed in Figure 49.1?

  A) a neuromast

  B) a statocyst

  C) a taste bud

  D) an ommatidium

  E) an olfactory bulb

Answer: B
*Topic: Concept 49.2*
*Skill: Knowledge*

14) What impact would a non-functioning statocyst have on an earthworm? The earthworm would not be able to

  A) move.

  B) sense light.

  C) hear.

  D) orient with respect to gravity.

  E) respond to touch.

Answer: D
*Topic: Concept 49.2*
*Skill: Comprehension*

15) The pathway leading to the perception of sound begins with the

    A) hair cells of the organ of Corti, which rests on the basilar membrane, coming in contact with the tectorial membrane.

    B) hair cells of the organ of Corti, which rests on the tympanic membrane, coming in contact with the tectorial membrane.

    C) hair cells of the organ of Corti, which rests on the tectorial membrane, coming in contact with the basilar membrane.

    D) hair cells of the organ of Corti coming in contact with the tectorial membrane as a result of fluid waves in the cochlea causing vibrations in the round window.

    E) hair cells on the tympanic membrane that stimulate the tectorial membrane neurons leading to the auditory section of the brain.

Answer: A
*Topic: Concept 49.2*
*Skill: Comprehension*

16) The perceived pitch of a sound depends on

    A) vibrations of the tympanic membrane being transmitted through the incus.

    B) vibrations of the oval window creating wave formation in the fluid of the vestibular canal.

    C) the region of the basilar membrane where the signal originated.

    D) A and C only

    E) A, B, and C

Answer: C
*Topic: Concept 49.2*
*Skill: Comprehension*

*The following questions refer to the diagram of the ear in Figure 49.2.*

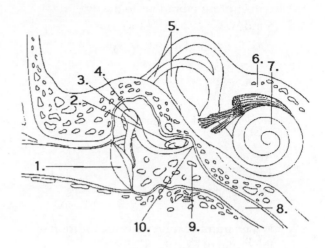

**Figure 49.2**

17) Which structure(s) is (are) involved in equalizing the pressure between the ear and the atmosphere?

    A) 1 and 8

    B) 5 and 7

    C) 8

    D) 9

    E) 10

Answer: C
*Topic: Concept 49.2*
*Skill: Knowledge*

18) Which structure(s) is (are) involved in equilibrium?

    A) 2, 3, and 4

    B) 2, 5, and 7

    C) 4

    D) 5

    E) 7 and 8

Answer: D
*Topic: Concept 49.2*
*Skill: Knowledge*

19) Which number(s) represent(s) the structure or structures involved in transmitting vibrations to the oval window?

A) 1, 2, 3, and 4

B) 2, 3, and 4

C) 3 and 4

D) 4

E) 5

Answer: C
*Topic: Concept 49.2*
*Skill: Comprehension*

20) Which number represents the location of the organ of Corti?

A) 3

B) 4

C) 5

D) 6

E) 7

Answer: E
*Topic: Concept 49.2*
*Skill: Knowledge*

21) Hair cells are found in structures represented by numbers

A) 1 and 2.

B) 3 and 4.

C) 5 and 7.

D) 6 and 8.

E) 9 and 10.

Answer: C
*Topic: Concept 49.2*
*Skill: Knowledge*

22) Which of the following statements about either hearing or balance is *incorrect*?

A) The semicircular canals respond to rotation of the head.

B) Fish have inner ears that sense vibrations in the water.

C) The volume of sound is a function of the action potential that reaches the brain.

D) In mammals, the tympanic membrane transmits sound to the three middle ear bones.

E) In mammals, the middle ear bones transmit sound through the oval window to the coiled cochlea of the inner ear.

Answer: C
*Topic: Concept 49.2*
*Skill: Knowledge*

23) What are sensillae?

A) smell receptors in animals with hydrostatic skeletons

B) mechanoreceptors that help birds remain oriented during flight

C) a specific type of hair cell in the human ear

D) insect taste receptors found on feet and mouthparts

E) olfactory hairs located on insect antennae

Answer: D
*Topic: Concept 49.3*
*Skill: Knowledge*

24) Which statement below about taste receptors in humans is *incorrect*?

   A) Each type of taste receptor can only be stimulated by a particular type of substance.

   B) Taste receptors are modified epithelial cells organized into taste buds.

   C) Depolarization in taste receptors causes the cells to release neurotransmitter onto a sensory neuron.

   D) There are five categories of taste perceptions associated with taste receptors.

   E) Transduction in taste receptors occurs by several different mechanisms.

Answer: A
*Topic: Concept 49.3*
*Skill: Knowledge*

25) What portion of the brain has neurons that receive action potentials from chemoreceptor cells in the nose?

   A) gustatory complex

   B) anterior hypothalamus

   C) olfactory bulb

   D) occipital lobe

   E) posterior pituitary

Answer: C
*Topic: Concept 49.3*
*Skill: Knowledge*

26) What do planarians, insects, and humans have in common?

   A) photopigments, photoreceptors, and associated nerves

   B) the ability to detect light

   C) the ability to detect light and form an image

   D) A and B only

   E) A, B, and C

Answer: D
*Topic: Concept 49.4*
*Skill: Comprehension*

27) Focusing the eye by changing the shape of the lens is called

   A) zooming.

   B) refraction.

   C) conditioning.

   D) habituation.

   E) accommodation.

Answer: E
*Topic: Concept 49.4*
*Skill: Knowledge*

28) Which of the following would be affected by damage to the ciliary muscles?

   A) hearing

   B) dilation of the pupil

   C) extension of the arm

   D) accommodation

   E) formation of vitreous humor

Answer: D
*Topic: Concept 49.4*
*Skill: Comprehension*

29) It is very difficult to sneak up to a grasshopper and catch it. Why?

A) They have excellent hearing for detecting predators.

B) They have compound eyes with multiple ommatidia.

C) They have eyes with multiple fovea.

D) They have a camera–like eye with multiple fovea.

E) They have binocular vision.

Answer: B
*Topic: Concept 49.4*
*Skill: Comprehension*

30) Individuals in which profession would be most affected by a vitamin A deficiency?

A) a baker

B) a piano tuner

C) a painter

D) a singer

E) a dancer

Answer: C
*Topic: Concept 49.4*
*Skill: Comprehension*

31) Which of the following is a *correct* statement about the cells of the human retina?

A) Cone cells can detect color, but rod cells cannot.

B) Cone cells are more sensitive to light than rod cells are.

C) Cone cells, but not rod cells, have a visual pigment.

D) Rod cells are most highly concentrated in the center of the retina.

E) Rod cells require higher illumination for stimulation than do cone cells.

Answer: A
*Topic: Concept 49.4*
*Skill: Knowledge*

32) The axons of rods and cones synapse with

A) ganglion cells.

B) horizontal cells.

C) amacrine cells.

D) bipolar cells.

E) lateral cells.

Answer: D
*Topic: Concept 49.4*
*Skill: Knowledge*

33) Which of the following statements about vision is *incorrect*?

A) Perception of visual information takes place in the brain.

B) Rods contain the light–absorbing molecule called rhodopsin.

C) Rods are more light–sensitive than cones and are responsible for night vision.

D) The conjunctiva covers the cornea and keeps it moist.

E) Visual acuity is sharpest in the fovea because the ganglion cells have a small receptor field.

Answer: D
*Topic: Concept 49.4*
*Skill: Comprehension*

34) Which of the following structures is the *last* one that sensory information would encounter during visual processing?

A) ganglion cells

B) bipolar cells

C) primary visual cortex

D) optic chiasma

E) lateral geniculate nuclei

Answer: C
*Topic: Concept 49.4*
*Skill: Knowledge*

35) If a baseball player is hit in the back of the head, which part of his brain would be the most likely injured?
   A) the primary visual cortex
   B) the thalamus
   C) the optic chiasma
   D) the lateral geniculate nuclei
   E) the tectorial membrane

Answer: A
*Topic: Concept 49.4*
*Skill: Comprehension*

36) What structural feature(s) contribute(s) most to the diverse adaptations for animal movement?
   A) sensory system
   B) skeletal system
   C) muscular system
   D) nervous system
   E) B and C only

Answer: E
*Topic: Concept 49.5*
*Skill: Comprehension*

37) What are animals with hydrostatic skeletons able to do that animals with exoskeletons or internal skeletons cannot do?
   A) elongate
   B) crawl
   C) live in aquatic environments
   D) grow without replacing their skeleton
   E) A, B, and D

Answer: A
*Topic: Concept 49.5*
*Skill: Comprehension*

*Use Figure 49.3 to answer the following questions.*

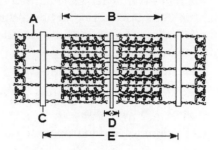

**Figure 49.3**

38) The structure pictured in Figure 49.3 can be found in which types of muscles?
   A) skeletal
   B) cardiac
   C) smooth
   D) A and B only
   E) A, B, and C

Answer: D
*Topic: Concept 49.6*
*Skill: Knowledge*

39) Which section consists only of myosin filaments?

Answer: D
*Topic: Concept 49.6*
*Skill: Knowledge*

40) Which section consists of both actin and myosin filaments?

Answer: B
*Topic: Concept 49.6*
*Skill: Knowledge*

41) When an organism dies, its muscles remain in a contracted state termed "rigor mortis" for a brief period of time. Which of the following most directly contributes to this phenomenon? There is no

A) ATP to move cross-bridges.

B) ATP to break bonds between the thick and thin filaments.

C) calcium to bind to troponin.

D) oxygen supplied to muscle.

E) glycogen remaining in the muscles.

Answer: B
*Topic: Concept 49.6*
*Skill: Application*

42) Which of the following does not form part of the thin filaments of a muscle cell?

A) actin

B) troponin

C) tropomyosin

D) myosin

E) calcium–binding site

Answer: D
*Topic: Concept 49.6*
*Skill: Knowledge*

43) What is the role of calcium in muscle contractions?

A) break the cross–bridges as a cofactor in the hydrolysis of ATP

B) bind to the troponin complex, which leads to the exposure of the myosin–binding sites

C) transmit the action potential across the neuromuscular junction

D) spread the action potential through the T tubules

E) reestablish the polarization of the plasma membrane following an action potential

Answer: B
*Topic: Concept 49.6*
*Skill: Knowledge*

44) Muscle cells are stimulated by neurotransmitters released from the synaptic terminal of

A) T tubules.

B) motor neuron axons.

C) sensory neuron axons.

D) motor neuron dendrites.

E) sensory neuron dendrites.

Answer: B
*Topic: Concept 49.6*
*Skill: Comprehension*

45) Which function associated with muscle would be most directly affected by low levels of calcium?

A) ATP hydrolysis

B) the initiation of an action potential

C) the muscle fiber resting membrane potential

D) muscle contraction

E) muscle fatigue

Answer: D
*Topic: Concept 49.6*
*Skill: Comprehension*

46) Which of the following is the *correct* sequence that occurs during the excitation and contraction of a muscle cell?

1. Tropomyosin shifts and unblocks the cross–bridge binding sites.
2. Calcium is released and binds to the troponin complex.
3. Transverse tubules depolarize the sarcoplasmic reticulum.
4. The thin filaments are ratcheted across the thick filaments by the heads of the myosin molecules using energy from ATP.
5. An action potential in a motor neuron causes the axon to release acetylcholine, which depolarizes the muscle cell membrane.

A) 1, 2, 3, 4, 5
B) 2, 1, 3, 5, 4
C) 2, 3, 4, 1, 5
D) 5, 3, 1, 2, 4
E) 5, 3, 2, 1, 4

Answer: E
*Topic: Concept 49.6*
*Skill: Application*

47) Which of the following could you find in the lumen of a transverse tubule?

A) extracellular fluid
B) cytoplasm
C) actin
D) myosin
E) sarcomeres

Answer: A
*Topic: Concept 49.6*
*Skill: Comprehension*

48) A sustained muscle contraction due to a lack of relaxation between successive stimuli is called

A) tonus.
B) tetanus.
C) an all–or–none response.
D) fatigue.
E) a spasm.

Answer: B
*Topic: Concept 49.6*
*Skill: Knowledge*

49) Which of the following are shared by skeletal, cardiac, and smooth muscle?

A) A bands and I bands
B) transverse tubules
C) gap junctions
D) motor units
E) thick and thin filaments

Answer: E
*Topic: Concept 49.6*
*Skill: Comprehension*

50) Which of the following could be associated with peristalsis?

A) hydrostatic skeletons and smooth muscle
B) hydrostatic skeletons and movement in earthworms
C) smooth muscle and contractions along the human digestive tract causing movement of the contents within
D) A and C only
E) A, B, and C

Answer: E
*Topic: Concept 49.7*
*Skill: Comprehension*

# Media Activity Questions

1) What name is given to the tough layer that forms the "white" of the eye?

   A) blind spot

   B) choroid

   C) fovea

   D) sclera

   E) aqueous humor

   Answer: D
   *Topic: Activity: Structure and Function of the Eye*

2) The _____ changes shape to focus light on the retina.

   A) vitreous humor

   B) blind spot

   C) cornea

   D) lens

   E) optic nerve

   Answer: D
   *Topic: Activity: Structure and Function of the Eye*

3) A single muscle cell is referred to as a

   A) myofibril.

   B) muscle fiber.

   C) muscle neuron.

   D) sarcolemma.

   E) sarcomere.

   Answer: B
   *Topic: Web/CD Activity: Skeletal Muscle Structure*

4) During the course of muscle contraction the potential energy stored in ATP is transferred to potential energy stored in

   A) the myosin head.

   B) the myosin tail.

   C) the thin filament.

   D) actin.

   E) the Z line.

   Answer: A
   *Topic: Web/CD Activity: Muscle Contraction*

5) Of these events, the first to occur when a motor neuron stops sending an impulse to a muscle is

   A) the pumping of calcium ions out of the cytoplasm and back in the sarcoplasmic reticulum.

   B) the release of myosin heads from the thin filament.

   C) thin filaments slide back to their relaxed positions.

   D) proteins on the thin filaments block actin's myosin-binding sites.

   E) All of these events occur simultaneously.

   Answer: A
   *Topic: Web/CD Activity: Muscle Contraction*

# Self–Quiz Questions

1) Which of the following sensory receptors is *incorrectly* paired with its category?

   A) hair cell—mechanoreceptor

   B) muscle spindle—mechanoreceptor

   C) taste receptor—chemoreceptor

   D) rod—electromagnetic receptor

   E) olfactory receptor—electromagnetic receptor

   Answer: E

2) Some sharks close their eyes just before they bite. Although they cannot see their prey, their bites are on target. Researchers have noted that sharks often misdirect their bites at metal objects, and the sharks can find batteries buried under the sand of an aquarium. This evidence suggests that sharks keep track of their prey during the split second before they bite in the same way that a

   A) rattlesnake finds a mouse in its burrow.

   B) male silkworm moth locates a mate.

   C) bat finds moths in the dark.

   D) platypus locates its prey in a muddy river.

   E) flatworm avoids light places.

   Answer: D

3) The transduction of sound waves to action potentials takes place

   A) within the tectorial membrane as it is stimulated by the hair cells.

   B) when hair cells are bent against the tectorial membrane, causing them to depolarize and release neurotransmitter that stimulates sensory neurons.

   C) as the basilar membrane becomes more permeable to sodium ions and depolarizes, initiating an action potential in a sensory neuron.

   D) as the basilar membrane vibrates at different frequencies in response to the varying volume of sounds.

   E) within the middle ear as the vibrations are amplified by the malleus, incus, and stapes.

   Answer: B

4) Which of the following is an *incorrect* statement about the vertebrate eye?

   A) The vitreous humor regulates the amount of light entering the pupil.

   B) The transparent cornea is an extension of the sclera.

   C) The fovea is the center of the visual field and contains only cones.

   D) The ciliary muscle functions in accommodation.

   E) The retina lies just inside the choroid and contains the photoreceptor cells.

   Answer: A

5) When light strikes the rhodopsin in a rod, retinal dissociates from opsin, initiating a signal transduction pathway that

A) depolarizes the neighboring bipolar cells and initiates an action potential in a ganglion cell.

B) depolarizes the rod, causing it to release the neurotransmitter glutamate, which excites bipolar cells.

C) hyperpolarizes the rod, reducing its release of glutamate, which excites some bipolar cells and inhibits others.

D) hyperpolarizes the rod, increasing its release of glutamate, which excites amacrine cells but inhibits horizontal cells.

E) converts cGMP to GMP, opening sodium channels and hyperpolarizing the membrane, causing the rhodopsin to become bleached.

Answer: C

6) Clams and lobsters both have an exoskeleton, but lobsters have much greater mobility. Why?

A) Clams have only adductor muscles that hold the shell closed, whereas lobsters have both abductor and adductor muscles.

B) The paramyosin of clam muscles hold the muscles in a low–energy state of contraction, whereas lobster muscles are very similar to vertebrate striated muscles.

C) Clams can grow only by adding to the outer edge of the shell, whereas lobsters molt and repeatedly replace their exoskeleton with a larger, more flexible one.

D) The lobster skeleton can actively contract, while the clam skeleton lacks its own contractile mechanism.

E) Lobsters have a jointed exoskeleton, allowing for the flexible movement of appendages and body parts at the joints.

Answer: E

7) During the contraction of a vertebrate skeletal muscle fiber, calcium ions

A) break cross–bridges by acting as a cofactor in the hydrolysis of ATP.

B) bind with troponin, changing its shape so that the myosin–binding sites on actin are exposed.

C) transmit action potentials from the motor neuron to the muscle fiber.

D) spread action potential through the T tubules.

E) reestablish the polarization of the plasma membrane following an action potential.

Answer: B

8) Tetanus refers to

   A) the partial sustained contraction of major supporting muscles.

   B) the all-or-none contraction of a single muscle fiber.

   C) a stronger contraction resulting from the activation of multiple motor units.

   D) a smooth and sustained contraction, resulting from wave summation.

   E) a state of muscle fatigue caused by the depletion of ATP and the accumulation of lactate.

   Answer: D

9) Which of the following is a *true* statement about cardiac muscle cells?

   A) They lack an orderly arrangement of actin and myosin filaments.

   B) They have less extensive sarcoplasmic reticulum and thus contract more slowly than smooth muscle cells.

   C) They are connected by intercalated discs, through which action potentials spread to all cells in the heart.

   D) They have a resting potential more positive than an action potential threshold.

   E) They contract only when stimulated by neurons.

   Answer: C

10) Which of the following changes occurs when a skeletal muscle fiber contracts?

   A) The A bands shorten.

   B) The I bands shrink.

   C) The Z lines slide farther apart.

   D) The thin filaments contract.

   E) The thick filaments contract.

   Answer: B

# Chapter 50  An Introduction to Ecology and the Biosphere

1) Important abiotic factors in ecosystems include which of the following?

   A) temperature

   B) water

   C) wind

   D) A and C only

   E) A, B, and C

   Answer: E
   *Topic: Concept 50.1*
   *Skill: Comprehension*

2) "How does the foraging of animals on tree seeds affect the distribution and abundance of the trees?" This question

   A) is a valid ecological question.

   B) is difficult to answer because a large experimental area would be required.

   C) is difficult to answer because a long-term experiment would be required.

   D) A and B only

   E) A, B, and C are correct.

   Answer: E
   *Topic: Concept 50.1*
   *Skill: Comprehension*

3) Which of the following statements about ecology is *incorrect*?

   A) Ecologists may study populations and communities of organisms.

   B) Ecological studies may involve the use of models and computers.

   C) Ecology is a discipline that is independent from natural selection and evolutionary history.

   D) Ecology spans increasingly comprehensive levels of organization, from individuals to ecosystems.

   E) Ecology is the study of the interactions between biotic and abiotic aspects of the environment.

   Answer: C
   *Topic: Concept 50.1*
   *Skill: Comprehension*

4) Which of the following levels of organization is arranged in the *correct* sequence from most to least inclusive?

   A) community, ecosystem, individual, population

   B) ecosystem, community, population, individual

   C) population, ecosystem, individual, community

   D) individual, population, community, ecosystem

   E) individual, community, population, ecosystem

   Answer: B
   *Topic: Concept 50.1*
   *Skill: Knowledge*

5) Ecology as a discipline directly deals with all of the following levels of biological organization *except*

  A) population.

  B) cellular.

  C) organismal.

  D) ecosystem.

  E) community.

Answer: B
*Topic: Concept 50.1*
*Skill: Comprehension*

6) Landscape ecology is best described as the study of

  A) the array of interacting species within a community.

  B) abiotic factors and the community of species that exist in a particular area.

  C) related arrays of ecosystems.

  D) physiological and behavioral ways in which organisms meet the challenges of their environment.

  E) the factors affecting the abundance of single species.

Answer: C
*Topic: Concept 50.1*
*Skill: Comprehension*

7) You are working for the Environmental Protection Agency and researching the effect of a potentially toxic chemical in drinking water. There is no documented scientific evidence showing that the chemical is toxic, but many suspect it to be a health hazard. Using the precautionary principle, what would be a reasonable environmental policy?

  A) Establish no regulations until there are conclusive scientific studies.

  B) Set the acceptable levels of the chemical conservatively low, and keep them there unless future studies show that they can be safely raised.

  C) Set the acceptable levels at the highest levels encountered, and keep them there unless future studies demonstrate negative health effects.

  D) Caution individuals to use their own judgment in deciding whether to drink water from a potentially contaminated area.

  E) Establish a contingency fund to handle insurance claims in the event that the chemical turns out to produce negative health effects.

Answer: B
*Topic: Concept 50.1*
*Skill: Application*

8) The biogeographic realms described by Darwin, Wallace, and others are associated with patterns of

  A) continental drift.

  B) precipitation and temperature.

  C) rocks and soil.

  D) climate.

  E) light intensity.

Answer: A
*Topic: Concept 50.2*
*Skill: Knowledge*

9) Species transplants are one direct way of

A) determining the abundance of a species in a specified area.

B) determining the distribution of a species in a specified area.

C) developing mathematical models for distribution and abundance of organisms.

D) determining if dispersal is a key factor in limiting distribution of organisms.

E) consolidating a landscape into a single ecosystem.

Answer: D
*Topic: Concept 50.2*
*Skill: Comprehension*

10) Introduced species

A) often fail to colonize the new area.

B) may become common enough to become pests.

C) can disrupt the balance of the natural species with which they become associated.

D) B and C only

E) A, B, and C are all correct.

Answer: E
*Topic: Concept 50.2*
*Skill: Comprehension*

11) Which of the following are important biotic factors that can affect the structure and organization of biological communities?

A) precipitation, wind

B) nutrient availability, soil pH

C) predation, competition

D) temperature, water

E) light intensity, seasonality

Answer: C
*Topic: Concept 50.2*
*Skill: Comprehension*

12) Which of the following abiotic factors has the greatest influence on the metabolic rates of plants and animals?

A) water

B) wind

C) temperature

D) rocks and soil

E) disturbances

Answer: C
*Topic: Concept 50.2*
*Skill: Comprehension*

13) Which of the following statements about light in aquatic environments is (are) *correct*?

A) Water selectively reflects and absorbs certain wavelengths of light.

B) Photosynthetic organisms that live in deep water probably use red light.

C) Light intensity is an important abiotic factor in limiting the distribution of photosynthetic organisms.

D) A and C only

E) A, B, and C are correct.

Answer: D
*Topic: Concept 50.2*
*Skill: Comprehension*

14) Which of the following statements about aquatic biomes is *false*?

A) The distribution of photosynthetic organisms is not limited by the quality and intensity of light in marine biomes.

B) Many lakes in temperate regions are characterized by seasonal thermal stratification.

C) Marine algae and photosynthetic bacteria produce a substantial portion of the biosphere's atmospheric oxygen.

D) Many aquatic biomes exhibit pronounced vertical stratification of chemical variables.

E) Marine biomes generally have a salt concentration that averages 3%.

Answer: A
*Topic: Concept 50.2*
*Skill: Knowledge*

15) All of the following would have a direct effect on the amount of precipitation in an area *except*

A) air circulation cells.

B) continental drift.

C) ocean currents.

D) mountain ranges.

E) evaporation from vegetation.

Answer: B
*Topic: Concept 50.2*
*Skill: Comprehension*

16) Westerly winds in temperate zones are the result of

A) descending air masses flowing toward the poles.

B) the rotation of Earth.

C) the unequal speed of land moving through space at the equator and the poles.

D) A and B only

E) A, B, and C

Answer: E
*Topic: Concept 50.2*
*Skill: Comprehension*

17) In mountainous areas of western North America, north-facing slopes (compared with south-facing slopes) would be expected to

A) receive more sunlight.

B) be warmer and drier.

C) support biological communities similar to those found at lower elevations and higher latitudes.

D) support biological communities similar to those found at higher elevations and higher latitudes.

E) B and C only

Answer: D
*Topic: Concept 50.2*
*Skill: Comprehension*

18) Coral reefs can be found on the southern east coast of the United States but not at similar latitudes on the southern west coast. Differences in which of the following most likely account for this?

A) sunlight

B) precipitation

C) day length

D) ocean currents

E) salinity

Answer: D
*Topic: Concept 50.2*
*Skill: Comprehension*

19) Deserts typically occur in a band at 30 degrees north and south latitude or at different latitudes in the interior of continents. This supports the idea that

A) descending air masses tend to be dry.

B) trade winds have a little moisture.

C) water is heavier than air and is not carried far over land.

D) ascending air tends to be moist.

E) these locations get more than their share of sunlight.

Answer: A
*Topic: Concept 50.2*
*Skill: Comprehension*

20) In an altitudinal gradient, all of the following would change in the same way as in a latitudinal gradient *except*

A) temperature.

B) humidity.

C) vegetation.

D) day length.

E) communities.

Answer: D
*Topic: Concept 50.2*
*Skill: Comprehension*

21) Thorough mixing of water in temperate lakes during the spring and fall turnovers is made possible by which of the following?

A) warm water layered at the top

B) cold water layered at the bottom

C) a pronounced thermocline under the surface

D) changing water temperature profiles

E) currents generated by nektonic animals

Answer: D
*Topic: Concept 50.2*
*Skill: Knowledge*

22) In temperate lakes, the surface water is replenished with nutrients during turnovers that occur in the

A) autumn and spring.

B) autumn and winter.

C) spring and summer.

D) summer and winter.

E) summer and autumn.

Answer: A
*Topic: Concept 50.2*
*Skill: Comprehension*

23) Which of the following is responsible for the summer and winter stratification of lakes?

A) Water is densest at 4°C.

B) Oxygen is most abundant in deeper waters.

C) Winter ice sinks in the summer.

D) Stratification is caused by a thermocline.

E) Stratification always follows the fall and spring turnovers.

Answer: A
*Topic: Concept 50.2*
*Skill: Comprehension*

24) Generally speaking, deserts are located in places where air masses are usually

A) cold.

B) humid.

C) rising.

D) falling.

E) expanding.

Answer: D
*Topic: Concept 50.2*
*Skill: Comprehension*

25) Which of the following causes Earth's seasons?

 A) global air circulation

 B) global wind patterns

 C) ocean currents

 D) changes in Earth's distance from the sun

 E) the tilt of Earth's axis

Answer: E
*Topic: Concept 50.2*
*Skill: Comprehension*

26) Which of the following events might you predict to occur if the tilt of Earth's axis relative to its plane of orbit was increased beyond 23.5 degrees?

 A) Summers in the United States might become warmer.

 B) Winters in Australia might become more severe.

 C) Seasonal variation at the equator might decrease.

 D) Only A and B are correct.

 E) A, B, and C are correct.

Answer: D
*Topic: Concept 50.2*
*Skill: Comprehension*

27) Imagine some cosmic catastrophe jolts Earth so that its axis is perpendicular to the orbital plane between Earth and the sun. The most obvious effect of this change would be

 A) the elimination of tides.

 B) an increase in the length of night.

 C) an increase in the length of a year.

 D) the elimination of the greenhouse effect and a cooling of the equator.

 E) the elimination of seasonal variation.

Answer: E
*Topic: Concept 50.2*
*Skill: Comprehension*

28) Polar regions are cooler than the equator because

 A) there is more ice at the poles.

 B) sunlight strikes the poles at an oblique angle.

 C) the poles are farther from the sun.

 D) the poles have a thicker atmosphere.

 E) the poles are permanently tilted away from the sun.

Answer: B
*Topic: Concept 50.2*
*Skill: Comprehension*

29) Which of the following environmental features might influence microclimates?

 A) a discarded soft-drink can

 B) a tree

 C) a fallen log

 D) a stone

 E) all of the above

Answer: E
*Topic: Concept 50.2*
*Skill: Comprehension*

30) The success with which plants extend their range northward following glacial retreat is best determined by

 A) whether there is simultaneous migration of herbivores.

 B) their tolerance to shade.

 C) their seed dispersal rate.

 D) their size.

 E) their growth rate.

Answer: C
*Topic: Concept 50.2*
*Skill: Comprehension*

31) As climate changes because of global warming, species' ranges in the northern hemisphere may move northward. The trees that are most likely to avoid extinction in such an environment are those that

A) have wind-dispersed seeds.

B) have animal-dispersed seeds.

C) produce well-provisioned seeds.

D) A and B only

E) A, B, and C

Answer: D
*Topic: Concept 50.2*
*Skill: Application*

32) Which marine zone would have the lowest rates of primary productivity (photosynthesis)?

A) pelagic

B) abyssal

C) neritic

D) continental shelf

E) intertidal

Answer: B
*Topic: Concept 50.3*
*Skill: Comprehension*

33) The benthic zone in an aquatic biome

A) often supports communities of organisms that feed largely on detritus.

B) is the site of most photosynthesis within the biome.

C) is where one would most expect to find a thermocline.

D) B and C only

E) A, B, and C

Answer: A
*Topic: Concept 50.3*
*Skill: Knowledge*

34) Where would an ecologist find the most phytoplankton in a lake?

A) profundal zone

B) benthic zone

C) photic zone

D) oligotrophic zone

E) aphotic zone

Answer: C
*Topic: Concept 50.3*
*Skill: Comprehension*

35) Phytoplankton is most frequently found in which of the following zones?

A) oligotrophic

B) photic

C) benthic

D) abyssal

E) aphotic

Answer: B
*Topic: Concept 50.3*
*Skill: Knowledge*

36) You are planning a dive in a lake, and are eager to watch underwater organisms both close up and far away. You would do well to choose

A) a nutrient-poor lake.

B) a nutrient-rich lake.

C) a relatively deep lake.

D) A and C only

E) B and C only

Answer: D
*Topic: Concept 50.3*
*Skill: Application*

37) You are interested in studying how organisms react to a gradient of abiotic conditions and how they coexist in this gradient. The best biome in which to conduct such a study is

A) mountains.

B) an intertidal zone.

C) a river.

D) tropical forest.

E) an eutrophic lake.

Answer: B
*Topic: Concept 50.3*
*Skill: Application*

38) Which of the following statements about the ocean pelagic biome is true?

A) The ocean is a vast, deep storehouse that always provides sustenance; it is the next "frontier" for feeding humanity.

B) Because it is so immense, the ocean is a uniform environment.

C) More photosynthesis occurs in the ocean than in any other biome.

D) Pelagic ocean photosynthetic activity is disproportionately low in relation to the size of the biome.

E) The most abundant animals are unicellular zooplankton.

Answer: D
*Topic: Concept 50.3*
*Skill: Knowledge*

39) Coral animals

A) are a diverse group of cnidarians.

B) are predominantly photosynthetic, multicellular algae.

C) excrete external, carbonaceous skeletons.

D) A and C only

E) B and C only

Answer: D
*Topic: Concept 50.3*
*Skill: Knowledge*

40) If a meteor impact or volcanic eruption injected a lot of dust into the atmosphere and reduced the sunlight reaching Earth's surface by 70% for one year, all of the following marine communities most likely would be greatly affected *except*

A) deep-sea vent communities.

B) coral reef communities.

C) benthic communities.

D) pelagic communities.

E) estuary communities.

Answer: A
*Topic: Concept 50.3*
*Skill: Comprehension*

41) Which of the following is *not* true about estuaries?

A) Estuaries are often bordered by mudflats and salt marshes.

B) Estuaries contain waters of varying salinity.

C) Estuaries support a variety of animal life that humans consume.

D) Estuaries usually contain no or few producers.

E) Estuaries support many semiaquatic species.

Answer: D
*Topic: Concept 50.3*
*Skill: Knowledge*

42) Which of the following statements best describes the effect of climate on biome distribution?

A) Knowledge of annual temperature and precipitation is sufficient to predict which biome will be found in an area.

B) Fluctuation of environmental variables is not important if areas have the same annual temperature and precipitation means.

C) It is not only the average climate that is important in determining biome distribution, but also the pattern of climatic variation.

D) Temperate forests, coniferous forests, and grasslands all have the same mean annual temperatures and precipitation.

E) Correlation of climate with biome distribution is sufficient to determine the cause of biome patterns.

Answer: C
*Topic: Concept 50.4*
*Skill: Comprehension*

43) Probably the most important factor(s) affecting the distribution of biomes is (are)

A) wind and water current patterns.

B) species diversity.

C) community succession.

D) climate.

E) day length and rainfall.

Answer: D
*Topic: Concepts 50.3, 50.4*
*Skill: Knowledge*

44) In the development of terrestrial biomes, which factor is most dependent on all the others?

A) the species of colonizing animals

B) prevailing temperature

C) prevailing rainfall

D) mineral nutrient availability

E) soil structure

Answer: A
*Topic: Concept 50.4*
*Skill: Comprehension*

45) Within any given type of terrestrial biome

A) species composition is typically uniform.

B) there is little or no vertical stratification.

C) periodic disturbance is rare.

D) A and B only

E) None of the above is true.

Answer: E
*Topic: Concept 50.4*
*Skill: Knowledge*

46) An area in which different terrestrial biomes grade into each other is known as a(n)

A) littoral zone.

B) vertically stratified canopy.

C) ecotone.

D) abyssal zone.

E) cline.

Answer: C
*Topic: Concept 50.4*
*Skill: Knowledge*

47) Which of the following statements about biomes is *incorrect*?

A) Biomes are major terrestrial communities.

B) Within biomes there may be extensive patchiness.

C) Climographs are often used to demonstrate climatic differences among biomes.

D) Temperature and precipitation account for most of the variation between biomes.

E) Biomes can be recognized as separate entities because they have sharp, well-defined boundaries.

Answer: E
*Topic: Concept 50.4*
*Skill: Knowledge*

48) Two plant species live in the same biome but on different continents. Although the two species are not at all closely related, they may appear quite similar as a result of

A) parallel evolution.

B) convergent evolution.

C) allopatric speciation.

D) introgression.

E) gene flow.

Answer: B
*Topic: Concept 50.4*
*Skill: Knowledge*

49) Which of the following terrestrial biomes is (are) adapted to frequent fires?

A) savanna

B) chaparral

C) temperate grasslands

D) only A and B

E) A, B, and C

Answer: E
*Topic: Concept 50.4*
*Skill: Knowledge*

50) Fire suppression by humans

A) will always result in an increase in the number of species in a given biome.

B) can change the species composition within biological communities.

C) will result ultimately in sustainable production of increased amounts of wood for human use.

D) is necessary for the protection of threatened and endangered forest species.

E) both C and D

Answer: B
*Topic: Concept 50.4*
*Skill: Comprehension*

51) Which of the following statements best describes the interaction between fire and ecosystems?

A) The chance of fire in a given ecosystem is highly predictable over the short term.

B) Many kinds of plants and plant communities have adapted to frequent fires.

C) The prevention of forest fires has allowed more productive and stable plant communities to develop.

D) Chaparral communities have evolved to the extent that they rarely burn.

E) Fire is unnatural in ecosystems and should be prevented.

Answer: B
*Topic: Concept 50.4*
*Skill: Comprehension*

52) Tropical dry forests may be characterized by

A) extreme variation in temperature.

B) extreme variation in precipitation.

C) thorny shrubs.

D) low competition for available sunlight.

E) both B and C

Answer: E
*Topic: Concept 50.4*
*Skill: Knowledge*

53) Which biome is able to support many large animals despite receiving moderate amounts of rainfall?

A) tropical rain forest

B) temperate forest

C) chaparral

D) taiga

E) savanna

Answer: E
*Topic: Concept 50.4*
*Skill: Knowledge*

54) Tropical grasslands with scattered trees are also known as

A) taigas.

B) tundras.

C) savannas.

D) chaparrals.

E) temperate plains.

Answer: C
*Topic: Concept 50.4*
*Skill: Knowledge*

55) Which type of biome would most likely occur in a climate with mild, rainy winters and hot, dry summers?

A) desert

B) taiga

C) temperate grassland

D) chaparral

E) savanna

Answer: D
*Topic: Concept 50.4*
*Skill: Comprehension*

56) In which community would organisms most likely have adaptations enabling them to respond to different photoperiods?

A) tropical forest

B) coral reef

C) savanna

D) temperate forest

E) abyssal

Answer: D
*Topic: Concept 50.4*
*Skill: Knowledge*

57) The growing season would generally be shortest in which of the following biomes?

A) savanna

B) temperate broadleaf forest

C) temperate grassland

D) tropical rain forest

E) taiga

Answer: E
*Topic: Concept 50.4*
*Skill: Knowledge*

# Media Activity Questions

1) In Africa, a public health official would
_____ the use of DDT by saying that
DDT _____.

   A) condemn; leads to long–term negative
   health effects in humans

   B) defend; is the cheapest method to
   control pests

   C) defend; reduces cases of malaria and
   sleeping sickness in humans

   D) condemn; leads to birth defects in
   birds and small mammals

   E) none of the above

Answer: C
*Topic: Activity: DDT*

2) Desert owls are inactive during the day
and active at night. They also have small
bodies. This describes _____ adaptation
to the hot and dry desert.

   A) anatomical

   B) behavioral

   C) physiological

   D) anatomical and behavioral

   E) anatomical, behavioral, and
   physiological

Answer: D
*Topic: Adaptations to Biotic and Abiotic Factors*

3) Which of these abiotic factors is a major
determinant of composition of the biotic
communities that inhabit aquatic biomes?

   A) light

   B) water depth

   C) temperature

   D) oxygen content

   E) All of the above are major factors that
   affect the makeup of the biotic
   communities that inhabit aquatic
   biomes.

Answer: E
*Topic: Activity: Aquatic Biomes*

4) Which of these life zones is a component of
a marine biome but *not* a component of a
freshwater biome?

   A) aphotic zone

   B) intertidal zone

   C) photic zone

   D) benthic zone

   E) both the aphotic and benthic zones

Answer: B
*Topic: Activity: Aquatic Biomes*

5) Biomes are

   A) all of the populations of a particular
   species.

   B) recognized on the basis of the
   dominant animal life.

   C) a major type of ecosystem.

   D) unaffected by climatic factors.

   E) limited to aquatic regions.

Answer: C
*Topic: Activity: Terrestrial Biomes*

# Self–Quiz Questions

1) Which of the following areas of study focuses on the exchange of energy, organisms, and materials between ecosystems?

    A) population ecology

    B) organismal ecology

    C) landscape ecology

    D) ecosystem ecology

    E) community ecology

    Answer: C

2) Which statement about dispersal is *false*?

    A) Dispersal is a common component of the life cycles of plants and animals.

    B) Colonization of devastated areas after floods or volcanic eruptions depends on dispersal.

    C) Dispersal occurs only on an evolutionary time scale.

    D) Seeds are important dispersal stages in the life cycles of most flowering plants.

    E) The ability to disperse can limit the geographic distribution of a species.

    Answer: C

3) Imagine some cosmic catastrophe that jolts Earth so that it is no longer tilted. Instead, its axis is perpendicular to the line between the sun and Earth. The most predictable effect of this change would be

    A) no more night and day.

    B) a big change in the length of the year.

    C) a cooling of the equator.

    D) a loss of seasonal variations at northern and southern latitudes.

    E) the elimination of ocean currents.

    Answer: D

4) While climbing mountains, we can observe transitions in biological communities that are analogous to the changes

    A) in biomes at different latitudes.

    B) at different depths in the ocean.

    C) in a community through different seasons.

    D) in an ecosystem as it evolves over time.

    E) traveling across the United States from east to west.

    Answer: A

5) The oceans affect the biosphere in all of the following ways *except*

    A) producing a substantial amount of the biosphere's oxygen.

    B) removing carbon dioxide from the atmosphere.

    C) moderating the climate of terrestrial biomes.

    D) regulating the pH of freshwater biomes and terrestrial groundwater.

    E) being the source of most of Earth's rainfall.

    Answer: D

6) Which lake zone would be absent in a very shallow lake?

    A) benthic zone

    B) aphotic zone

    C) pelagic zone

    D) littoral zone

    E) limnetic zone

    Answer: B

7) Which of the following is *true* with respect to oligotrophic lakes and eutrophic lakes?

A) Oligotrophic lakes are more subject to oxygen depletion.

B) Rates of photosynthesis are lower in eutrophic lakes.

C) Eutrophic lake water contains lower concentrations of nutrients.

D) Eutrophic lakes are richer in nutrients.

E) Sediments in oligotrophic lakes contain larger amounts of decomposable organic matter.

Answer: D

8) Which of the following is characteristic of most terrestrial biomes?

A) annual average rainfall in excess of 25 cm

B) a distribution predicted almost entirely by rock and soil patterns

C) clear boundaries between adjacent biomes

D) vegetation demonstrating vertical stratification

E) cold winter months

Answer: D

9) Which of the following biomes is *correctly* paired with the description of its climate?

A) savanna—cool temperature, precipitation uniform during the year

B) tundra—long summers, mild winters

C) temperate broadleaf forest—relatively short growing season, mild winters

D) temperate grasslands—relatively warm winters, most rainfall in summer

E) tropical forests—nearly constant day length and temperature

Answer: E

10) Suppose the number of bird species is determined mainly by the number of vertical strata found in the environment. If so, in which of the following biomes would you find the greatest number of bird species?

A) tropical rain forest

B) savanna

C) taiga

D) temperate broadleaf forest

E) temperate grassland

Answer: A

# Chapter 51  Behavioral Ecology

1) During a field trip, an instructor touched the body of a moth resting on a tree trunk. The moth raised its forewings to reveal large eye–spots on its hind wings. The instructor asked the class why the moth lifted its wings. One student answered that certain sensory receptors had fired and triggered a neuronal reflex culminating in the contraction of certain muscles. A second student responded that the behavior might frighten predators. Which statement best describes the students' explanations?

   A) The first response is correct, but the second is incorrect.

   B) The first response answers a proximate question, whereas the second answers an ultimate question.

   C) The first response is biological, whereas the second is philosophical.

   D) The first explanation is testable as a scientific hypothesis, whereas the second is not.

   E) Both explanations are reasonable and simply represent a difference of opinion.

Answer: B
*Topic: Concept 51.1*
*Skill: Comprehension*

*Use the following information to answer the questions below.*

When a female cat comes into heat, she urinates more frequently and in a large number of places. Male cats from the neighborhood congregate near urine deposits and fight with each other.

2) Which of the following is a proximate cause of this behavior of increased urination?

   A) It announces to the males that she is in heat.

   B) Female cats that did this in the past attracted more males.

   C) It is a result of hormonal changes associated with her reproductive cycle.

   D) The female cat learned the behavior from observing other cats.

   E) All of the above are ultimate causes of behavior.

Answer: C
*Topic: Concept 51.1*
*Skill: Comprehension*

3) Which of the following would be an ultimate cause of the male cats' response to the female's urinating behavior?

A) The males have learned to recognize the specific odor of the urine of a female in heat.

B) By smelling the odor, various neurons in the males' brains were stimulated.

C) Male cats respond to the odor because it is a means of locating females in heat.

D) Male cats' hormones are triggered by the odor released by the female.

E) The odor serves as a releaser for the instinctive behavior of the males.

Answer: C
*Topic: Concept 51.1*
*Skill: Comprehension*

4) Which of the following is a behavioral pattern that results from a proximate cause?

A) A cat kills a mouse to obtain food.

B) A male sheep fights with another male because it helps it to improve its social position and find a mate.

C) A female bird lays its eggs because the amount of daylight is decreasing slightly each day.

D) A goose squats and freezes motionless because that helps it to escape a predator.

E) A cockroach runs into a crack in the wall and avoids being stepped on.

Answer: C
*Topic: Concept 51.1*
*Skill: Comprehension*

5) Which of the following is a behavioral pattern resulting from an ultimate cause?

A) A male robin attacks a red tennis ball because it resembles the breast of another male.

B) A male robin attacks a red tennis ball because it is spring and hormonal changes increase its aggression.

C) A male robin attacks a red tennis ball because a part of its brain is stimulated by objects that are red.

D) A male robin attacks a red tennis ball because several times in the past red tennis balls have been thrown at it, and it has learned that they are dangerous.

E) A male robin attacks a red tennis ball because it confuses it with an encroaching male who will steal his territory.

Answer: E
*Topic: Concept 51.1*
*Skill: Comprehension*

6) The proximate causes of behavior are interactions with the environment, but behavior is ultimately shaped by

A) hormones.

B) evolution.

C) sexuality.

D) pheromones.

E) the nervous system.

Answer: B
*Topic: Concept 51.1*
*Skill: Comprehension*

7) Which of the following groups of scientists is closely associated with ethology?

A) Watson, Crick, and Franklin

B) McClintock, Goodall, and Lyon

C) Fossey, Hershey, and Chase

D) von Frisch, Lorenz, and Tinbergen

E) Hardy, Weinberg, and Castle

Answer: D
*Topic: Concept 51.1*
*Skill: Knowledge*

8) In the territorial behavior of the stickleback fish, the red belly of one male elicits attack from another male by functioning as

A) a pheromone.

B) a sign stimulus.

C) a fixed action pattern.

D) a search image.

E) an imprint stimulus.

Answer: B
*Topic: Concept 51.1*
*Skill: Knowledge*

9) Which of the following statements is (are) *true* of fixed action patterns?

A) They are highly stereotyped, instinctive behaviors.

B) They are triggered by sign stimuli in the environment and, once begun, are continued to completion.

C) An inappropriate stimulus can sometimes trigger them.

D) A and B only

E) A, B, and C

Answer: E
*Topic: Concept 51.1*
*Skill: Knowledge*

10) A cage containing male mosquitoes has a small earphone placed on top, through which the sound of a female mosquito is played. All the males immediately fly to the earphone and thrust their abdomens through the fabric of the cage. Which of the following best describes the reason for this behavior?

A) The males learn to associate the sound with females.

B) Copulation is a fixed action pattern, and the female flight sound is a sign stimulus that initiates it.

C) The sound from the earphone irritates the male mosquitoes, causing them to attempt to sting it.

D) The reproductive drive is so strong that when males are deprived of females, they will attempt to mate with anything that has even the slightest female characteristic.

E) Through classical conditioning, the male mosquitoes have associated the inappropriate stimulus from the earphone with the normal response of copulation.

Answer: B
*Topic: Concept 51.1*
*Skill: Application*

11) What types of questions did Tinbergen study?

A) genetics, biochemistry, development, behavior

B) mechanism, development, evolution, fitness

C) communication, genetics, behavior

D) sexual selection, genetics, development, neurobiology

E) evolution, behavior, sexual selection, development

Answer: B
*Topic: Concept 51.1*
*Skill: Knowledge*

12) If mayflies lay eggs on roads instead of in water, this could involve which of the following?

    A) a defective behavioral gene

    B) trial–and–error learning

    C) misdirected response to a sign stimulus

    D) natural behavioral variation in the mayfly population

    E) insecticide poisoning

Answer: C
*Topic: Concept 51.1*
*Skill: Knowledge*

13) The time during imprinting when specific behaviors can be learned is called the

    A) window of imprinting.

    B) major period.

    C) sensitive period.

    D) timing imprint.

    E) significant window.

Answer: C
*Topic: Concept 51.1*
*Skill: Comprehension*

14) Which of the following is *true* about imprinting?

    A) It may be triggered by visual or chemical stimuli.

    B) It happens to many adult animals, but not to their young.

    C) It is a type of learning that does not involve innate behavior.

    D) It occurs only in birds.

    E) It causes behaviors that last for only a short time (the critical period).

Answer: A
*Topic: Concept 51.1*
*Skill: Comprehension*

15) A type of learning that can occur only during a brief period of early life and results in a behavior that is difficult to modify through later experiences is called

    A) insight.

    B) imprinting.

    C) habituation.

    D) operant conditioning.

    E) trial–and–error learning.

Answer: B
*Topic: Concept 51.1*
*Skill: Knowledge*

16) Which of the following is least related to the others?

    A) fixed action pattern

    B) pheromones

    C) sign stimulus

    D) hormones

    E) optimal foraging

Answer: E
*Topic: Concept 51.1*
*Skill: Comprehension*

17) Sow bugs become more active in dry areas and less active in humid areas. This is an example of

    A) taxis.

    B) tropism.

    C) kinesis.

    D) cognition.

    E) net reflex.

Answer: C
*Topic: Concept 51.1*
*Skill: Comprehension*

18) You turn on a light and observe cockroaches scurrying to dark hiding places. What have you observed?

A) taxis

B) learned behavior

C) migration

D) visual communication

E) operant conditioning

Answer: A
*Topic: Concept 51.1*
*Skill: Application*

19) Imagine that you are designing an experiment aimed at determining whether the initiation of migratory behavior is largely under genetic control. Of the following options, the best way to proceed is to

A) observe different genetically distinct populations in the field and see if they have different migratory habits.

B) perform within–population matings with birds from different populations that have different migratory habits. Do this in the laboratory and see if offspring display parental migratory behavior.

C) bring animals into the laboratory and determine the conditions under which they become restless and attempt to migrate.

D) perform within–population matings with birds from different populations that have different migratory habits. Rear the offspring in the absence of their parents and observe offspring migratory behavior.

E) All of the above are equally productive ways to approach the question.

Answer: D
*Topic: Concept 51.2*
*Skill: Application*

20) Animal communication involves what type of sensory information?

A) visual

B) auditory

C) chemical

D) A and C only

E) A, B, and C

Answer: E
*Topic: Concept 51.2*
*Skill: Comprehension*

*The following is a list of signal types that animals use for communication. Choose the one that best fits the criteria in the following questions.*

A) olfactory

B) visual

C) auditory

D) tactile

E) electrical

21) A long-lasting signal that works at night.

Answer: A
*Topic: Concept 51.2*
*Skill: Comprehension*

22) A brief signal that can work at night or among obstructions.

Answer: C
*Topic: Concept 51.2*
*Skill: Comprehension*

23) A fast signal that requires daylight and no obstructions.

Answer: B
*Topic: Concept 51.2*
*Skill: Comprehension*

24) A chemical produced by an animal that serves as a communication to another animal of the same species is called

    A) a marker.

    B) an inducer.

    C) a pheromone.

    D) an imprinter.

    E) an agonistic chemical.

Answer: C
*Topic: Concept 51.2*
*Skill: Knowledge*

25) Which statement below about mating behavior is *incorrect*?

    A) Some aspects of courtship behavior may have evolved from agonistic interactions.

    B) Courtship interactions ensure that the participating individuals are nonthreatening and of the proper species, sex, and physiological condition for mating.

    C) The degree to which evolution affects mating relationships depends on the degree of prenatal and postnatal input the parents are required to make.

    D) The mating relationship in most mammals is monogamous, to ensure the reproductive success of the pair.

    E) Polygamous relationships most often involve a single male and many females, but in some species this is reversed.

Answer: D
*Topic: Concept 51.2*
*Skill: Comprehension*

26) One way to understand how early environment influences differing behaviors in similar species is through an experimental technique known as "cross fostering." Suppose that the curly-whiskered mud rat differs from the bald mud rat in several ways, for example curly-whiskered rats are much more aggressive. How would you set up a cross-fostering experiment to determine if environment plays a role in this mud rat's aggression?

    A) You would cross curly-whiskered mud rats and bald mud rats and hand-rear the offspring.

    B) You would place newborn curly-whiskered mud rats with bald mud rat parents, newborn bald mud rats with curly-whiskered mud rat parents, and let some mud rats of both species be raised by their own species. Then compare the outcomes.

    C) You would remove the offspring of curly-whiskered mud rats and bald mud rats from their parents and raise them in the same environment.

    D) You would see if curly-whiskered mud rats bred true for aggression.

    E) None of these schemes describes cross fostering.

Answer: B
*Topic: Concept 51.3*
*Skill: Comprehension*

27) Loss of responsiveness to stimuli that convey little or not information is called

    A) adapting.

    B) spacing.

    C) conditioning.

    D) imprinting.

    E) habituation.

Answer: E
*Topic: Concept 51.3*
*Skill: Knowledge*

28) Which of the following would you classify as habituation?

   A) You enter a room and hear a fan motor. After a period of time, you are no longer aware of the sound of the fan motor.

   B) You are driving your car and you hear a horn. You step on the brakes, but notice the sound came from a car on a side street. You resume your previous speed.

   C) One morning you are awoken to a beep-beep-beep from a garbage truck working on a new early morning schedule. The next week the garbage truck arrives at the same time and makes the same noise, but does not wake you up.

   D) A and C only

   E) A, B, and C

Answer: D
*Topic: Concept 51.3*
*Skill: Comprehension*

29) Which of the following is least related to the others?

   A) agonistic behavior

   B) cognitive maps

   C) dominance hierarchy

   D) ritual

   E) territory

Answer: B
*Topic: Concept 51.3*
*Skill: Comprehension*

30) Learning in which an associated stimulus may be used to elicit the same behavioral response as the original sign stimulus is called

   A) concept formation.

   B) trial-and-error.

   C) classical conditioning.

   D) operant conditioning.

   E) habituation.

Answer: C
*Topic: Concept 51.3*
*Skill: Comprehension*

31) Every morning at the same time, John went into the den to feed his new tropical fish. After a few weeks John noticed that the fish would swim to the top of the tank as soon as he would enter the room. This is a good example of

   A) habituation.

   B) imprinting.

   C) classical conditioning.

   D) operant conditioning.

   E) maturation.

Answer: C
*Topic: Concept 51.3*
*Skill: Comprehension*

32) The type of learning that causes specially trained dogs to salivate when they hear bells is called

   A) insight.

   B) imprinting.

   C) habituation.

   D) classical conditioning.

   E) trial-and-error learning.

Answer: D
*Topic: Concept 51.3*
*Skill: Knowledge*

33) Which of the following statements about learning and behavior is *incorrect*?

    A) Operant conditioning involves associating a behavior with a reward or punishment.

    B) Associative learning involves linking one stimulus with another.

    C) Classical conditioning involves trial–and–error learning.

    D) Behavior can be modified by learning, but some apparent learning is due to maturation.

    E) Imprinting is a learned behavior with an innate component acquired during a sensitive period.

Answer: C
*Topic: Concept 51.3*
*Skill: Comprehension*

*Use the following terms to answer the questions below. Match the term that best fits each of the following descriptions of behavior. Each term may be used once, more than once, or not at all.*

    A. sign stimulus
    B. habituation
    C. imprinting
    D. classical conditioning
    E. operant conditioning

34) A type of bird similar to a chickadee learn to peck through the cardboard tops of milk bottles left on doorsteps and drink the cream from the top.

Answer: E
*Topic: Concept 51.3*
*Skill: Comprehension*

35) Male insects attempt to mate with orchids but eventually stop responding to them.

Answer: B
*Topic: Concept 51.3*
*Skill: Comprehension*

36) A salmon goes back to its home stream to spawn.

Answer: C
*Topic: Concept 51.1*
*Skill: Comprehension*

37) A stickleback fish will attack a fish model as long as the model has red coloring.

Answer: A
*Topic: Concept 51.1*
*Skill: Comprehension*

38) Parental protective behavior in turkeys is triggered by the cheeping sound of young chicks.

Answer: A
*Topic: Concept 51.1*
*Skill: Comprehension*

39) A guinea pig loves the lettuce kept in the refrigerator and squeals each time the refrigerator door opens.

Answer: D
*Topic: Concept 51.1*
*Skill: Comprehension*

40) Sparrows are receptive to learning songs only during a sensitive period.

Answer: C
*Topic: Concept 51.1*
*Skill: Comprehension*

41) Classical conditioning and operant conditioning are two forms of associative learning. They differ in that

 A) classical conditioning takes longer.

 B) operant conditioning usually involves more intelligence.

 C) operant conditioning involves consequences for the animal's behavior.

 D) classical conditioning is restricted to mammals and birds.

 E) classical conditioning is much more useful for training domestic animals.

Answer: C
*Topic: Concept 51.3*
*Skill: Comprehension*

42) Some dogs love attention, and Frodo the beagle learns that if he barks, he gets attention. Which of the following might you use to describe this behavior?

 A) The dog is displaying an instinctive fixed action pattern.

 B) The dog is performing a social behavior.

 C) The dog is trying to protect its territory.

 D) The dog has been classically conditioned.

 E) The dog's behavior is a result of operant conditioning.

Answer: E
*Topic: Concept 51.3*
*Skill: Application*

43) Among song birds, a "crystallized" song is one that

 A) is high pitched.

 B) is aimed at attracting mates.

 C) extremely young chicks sing.

 D) is the final song that some species produce.

 E) warns of predators.

Answer: D
*Topic: Concept 51.3*
*Skill: Knowledge*

44) Which of the following is least related to the others?

 A) fixed action pattern

 B) imprinting

 C) operant conditioning

 D) classical conditioning

 E) habituation

Answer: A
*Topic: Concept 51.3*
*Skill: Comprehension*

45) Which of the following statements concerning the evolution of behavior is *correct*?

 A) Natural selection will favor behavior that enhances survival and reproduction.

 B) An animal may show behavior that maximizes reproductive fitness.

 C) If a behavior is less than optimal, it is not yet completely evolved but will eventually become optimal.

 D) A and B only

 E) A, B, and C

Answer: D
*Topic: Concept 51.4*
*Skill: Comprehension*

46) Stevan Arnold discovered that coastal and inland garter snakes reacted differently to banana slug prey. What probably accounts for such a difference?

A) Ancestors of coastal snakes that were able to eat the abundant slugs had increased fitness. No such selection occurred inland, where slugs were absent.

B) Slugs are difficult to see, and inland snakes, which have poor vision compared with coastal snakes, are less able to see them.

C) Garter snakes learn about prey from other garter snakes. Inland snakes are less social, and this lowers prey diversity.

D) Inland snakes overlap with distasteful slugs, and thus learn to avoid them. Coastal slugs are not distasteful.

E) Garter snakes are conditioned to eat what their mother eats. The mothers of Arnold's coastal snakes happened to prefer slugs.

Answer: A
*Topic: Concept 51.4*
*Skill: Knowledge*

47) Animals tend to maximize their energy intake-to-expenditure ratio. What is this behavior called?

A) agonistic behavior

B) optimal foraging

C) dominance hierarchies

D) animal cognition

E) territoriality

Answer: B
*Topic: Concept 51.5*
*Skill: Comprehension*

48) Feeding behavior that has a high energy intake-to-expenditure ratio is called

A) herbivory.

B) autotrophy.

C) heterotrophy.

D) search scavenging.

E) optimal foraging.

Answer: E
*Topic: Concept 51.5*
*Skill: Knowledge*

49) Modern behavioral concepts relate the cost of a behavior to its benefit. Under which relationship might a behavior be performed?

A) cost is greater than the benefit

B) cost is less than the benefit

C) cost is equal to the benefit

D) A and C only

E) B and C only

Answer: E
*Topic: Concept 51.5*
*Skill: Comprehension*

50) Which of the following is *not* a concept associated with sociobiology?

A) parental investment

B) inclusive fitness

C) associative learning

D) reciprocal altruism

E) kin selection

Answer: C
*Topic: Concept 51.5*
*Skill: Comprehension*

51) Optimal foraging involves all of the following *except*

A) maximizing energy gained by the forager.

B) minimizing energy expended by the forager.

C) securing essential nutrients for the forager.

D) minimizing the risk of predation on the forager.

E) maximizing the population size of the forager.

Answer: E
*Topic: Concept 51.5*
*Skill: Comprehension*

52) In the evolution of whelk–eating behavior in the crows studied by Reto Zach, which of the following was being minimized by natural selection?

A) the average number of drops required to break the shell

B) the average height a bird flew to drop a shell

C) the average total energy used to break shells

D) the average size of the shells dropped by the birds

E) the average thickness of the shells dropped by the birds

Answer: C
*Topic: Concept 51.5*
*Skill: Comprehension*

53) Which of the following might affect the foraging behavior of an animal in the context of optimal foraging?

A) risk of predation

B) prey size

C) prey defenses

D) A and B only

E) A, B, and C

Answer: E
*Topic: Concept 51.5*
*Skill: Comprehension*

54) You discover a new bird species. It is quite rare, and you are not able to observe its mating behavior. You see that the male is large and ornamental compared with the female. On this basis, you would be fairly safe in concluding that the bird is

A) polygamous.

B) monogamous.

C) polyandrous.

D) promiscuous.

E) agonistic.

Answer: A
*Topic: Concept 51.5*
*Skill: Application*

55) The evolution of mating systems is most likely affected by

A) population size.

B) care required by young.

C) certainty of paternity.

D) B and C only

E) A, B , and C

Answer: D
*Topic: Concept 51.5*
*Skill: Comprehension*

56) Fred and Joe, two unrelated, mature male gorillas, encounter one another. Fred is courting a female. Fred grunts as Joe comes near. As Joe continues to advance, Fred begins drumming (pounding his chest) and bares his teeth. At this, Joe rolls on the ground on his back, then gets up and quickly leaves. This behavioral pattern is repeated several times during the mating season. Choose the most specific behavior described by this example.

   A) agonistic behavior

   B) territorial behavior

   C) learned behavior

   D) social behavior

   E) fixed action pattern

Answer: A
Topic: Concept 51.5
Skill: Application

57) Which of the following is *least* related to the others?

   A) altruism

   B) polygamy

   C) monogamy

   D) polygyny

   E) polyandry

Answer: A
Topic: Concept 51.6
Skill: Comprehension

58) Which of the following does *not* have a coefficient of relatedness of 0.5?

   A) a father to his daughter

   B) a mother to her son

   C) an uncle to his nephew

   D) a brother to his brother

   E) a sister to her brother

Answer: C
Topic: Concept 51.6
Skill: Comprehension

*Match each phrase to a scientist from the following list.*

   A) Karl von Frisch
   B) Niko Tinbergen
   C) Konrad Lorenz
   D) William Hamilton
   E) Ivan Pavlov

59) determined that digger wasps used landmarks to locate nest entrances

Answer: B
Topic: Concept 51.3
Skill: Knowledge

60) devised a rule that predicts when natural selection should favor altruism

Answer: D
Topic: Concept 51.6
Skill: Knowledge

61) studied imprinting of graylag geese

Answer: C
Topic: Concept 51.1
Skill: Knowledge

62) Animals that help other animals of the same species are expected to

   A) have excess energy reserves.

   B) be bigger and stronger than the other animals.

   C) be genetically related to the other animals.

   D) be male.

   E) have defective genes controlling their behavior.

Answer: C
Topic: Concept 51.6
Skill: Comprehension

63) The presence of altruistic behavior in animals is most likely due to kin selection, a theory maintaining that

A) aggression between sexes promotes the survival of the fittest individuals.

B) genes enhance survival of copies of themselves by directing organisms to assist others who share those genes.

C) companionship is advantageous to animals because in the future they can help each other.

D) critical thinking abilities are normal traits for animals and they have arisen, like other traits, through natural selection.

E) natural selection has generally favored the evolution of exaggerated aggressive and submissive behaviors to resolve conflict without grave harm to participants.

Answer: B
*Topic: Concept 51.6*
*Skill: Comprehension*

64) In Belding's ground squirrels, it is mostly the females that behave altruistically by sounding alarm calls. What is the likely reason for this distinction?

A) Males have smaller vocal cords and are less likely to make sounds.

B) Females invest more in foraging and food stores, so they are more defensive.

C) Females settle in the area in which they were born, so the calling females are warning kin.

D) The sex ratio is biased.

E) Males forage alone; therefore, alarm calls are useless.

Answer: C
*Topic: Concept 51.6*
*Skill: Knowledge*

65) Reconciliation behavior is likely to follow

A) conflict behavior between members of a permanent social group.

B) agonistic behavior between territorial males.

C) mating behavior between a male and a female.

D) ritualized behavior.

E) imprinting by young animals on a member of the wrong species.

Answer: A
*Topic: Concept 51.6*
*Skill: Comprehension*

66) The central concept of sociobiology is that

A) human behavior is rigidly predetermined.

B) the behavior of an individual cannot be modified.

C) our behavior consists mainly of fixed action patterns.

D) most aspects of our social behavior have an evolutionary basis.

E) the social behavior of humans is homologous to the social behavior of honeybees.

Answer: D
*Topic: Concept 51.6*
*Skill: Comprehension*

*Match each of the phrases to a scientist from the following list.*

A) E. O. Wilson
B) Jane Goodall
C) B. S. Haldane
D) Niko Tinbergen
E) William Hamilton

67) formulated four questions that motivate modern behavioral biology

Answer: D
*Topic: Concept 51.1*
*Skill: Knowledge*

68) suggested that human social behavior may
have a genetic basis

Answer: A
*Topic: Concept 51.6*
*Skill: Knowledge*

69) developed the concept of inclusive fitness

Answer: E
*Topic: Concept 51.6*
*Skill: Knowledge*

# Media Activity Question

1) The function of the waggle dance in bees is to

    A) indicate the distance to a food source.

    B) indicate the direction to a food source.

    C) indicate both the direction and the distance to a food source.

    D) attract mates.

    E) depending on the season, attract mates or indicate the direction and distance of a food source.

Answer: C

*Topic: Web/CD Activity: Honeybee Waggle Dance*

# Self–Quiz Questions

1) Which of the following is true of innate behaviors?

   A) Genes have very little influence on the expression of innate behaviors.

   B) Innate behaviors tend to vary considerably among members of a population.

   C) Innate behaviors are limited to invertebrate animals.

   D) Innate behaviors are expressed in most individuals in a population across a wide range of environmental conditions.

   E) Innate behaviors occur in invertebrates and some vertebrates but not in mammals.

   Answer: D

2) Which of the following is an example of taxis?

   A) a navigation of a sparrow during seasonal migration

   B) pulling your hand away from a hot stove

   C) a wasp locating its nest with landmarks

   D) a fish orienting itself into the river

   E) a crow dropping a whelk from a specific height

   Answer: D

3) Which of the following statements provides an ultimate explanation for the observation that adult salmon return from the ocean to spawn in the stream in which they hatched?

   A) Young salmon imprint on the chemical scent of their home stream.

   B) Adult salmon use stellar navigation to relocate their home stream.

   C) Salmon navigate to their home stream using their ability to detect Earth's magnetic field.

   D) Spawning in the home stream results in higher survival of young salmon.

   E) Oceanic currents aid salmon in their search for their home stream.

   Answer: D

4) Researchers have found that a region of the canary forebrain shrinks during the nonbreeding season and then regenerates when breeding season begins. This annual regrowth of brain tissue is probably associated with

   A) the annual addition of new syllables to a canary's song repertoire.

   B) the annual crystallization of subsong into adult songs.

   C) the annual sensitive period in which canary parents imprint on new offspring.

   D) the annual renewal of mating and nest–building behaviors.

   E) the annual elimination of the memorized template for songs sung the previous year.

   Answer: A

5) Although many chimpanzee populations live in environments containing oil–palm nuts, members of only a few populations use stones to crack open the nuts. The most likely explanation for this behavioral difference between populations is that

A) the behavioral difference is caused by genetic differences between populations.

B) members of different populations have different nutritional requirements.

C) the cultural tradition of using stones to crack nuts has arisen in only some populations.

D) members of different populations differ in learning ability.

E) members of different populations differ in manual dexterity.

Answer: C

6) Which of the following is not required for a behavioral trait to evolve by natural selection?

A) In each individual, the form of the behavior is determined entirely by genes.

B) The behavior varies among individuals.

C) An individual's reproductive success depends in part on how the behavior is performed.

D) Some component of the behavior is genetically inherited.

E) An individual's genotype influences its behavioral phenotype.

Answer: A

7) Which of the following is *not* true of agonistic behavior?

A) It is most common among members of the same species.

B) It may be used to establish and defend territories.

C) It may be a basis for competition between individuals for mates.

D) It usually results in death or serious injury to one or both of the competitors.

E) It may be used to establish dominance over other individuals.

Answer: D

8) Female spotted sandpipers aggressively court males and then, after mating, leave the clutch of young for the male to incubate. This sequence may be repeated several times with different males until no available males remain, forcing the female to incubate her last clutch. Which of the following terms best describes this behavior?

A) monogamy

B) polygyny

C) polyandry

D) promiscuity

E) certainty of paternity

Answer: C

9) According to the inequality known as Hamilton's rule ($rB > C$),

    A) natural selection does not favor altruistic behavior that causes the death of the altruist.

    B) natural selection favors altruistic acts when the resulting benefit to the beneficiary, multiplied by the coefficient of relatedness, exceeds the cost to the altruist.

    C) natural selection is more likely to favor altruistic behavior that benefits an offspring than altruistic behavior that benefits a sibling.

    D) the effects of kin selection are larger than the effects of direct natural selection on individuals.

    E) altruism is always reciprocal.

    Answer: B

10) The core idea of sociobiolgy is that

    A) human behavior is rigidly determined by inheritance.

    B) humans cannot choose to change their social behavior.

    C) much human behavior has evolved by natural selection.

    D) the social behavior of humans has many similarities to that of social insects such as honeybees.

    E) the environment plays a larger role than genes in shaping human behavior.

    Answer: C

# Chapter 52  Population Ecology

1) A population is *correctly* defined as having which of the following characteristics?
   I.   inhabiting the same general area
   II.  individuals belonging to the same species
   III. possessing a constant and uniform density and dispersion

   A) I only

   B) III only

   C) I and II only

   D) II and III only

   E) I, II, and III

   Answer: C
   *Topic: Concept 52.1*
   *Skill: Knowledge*

2) A biologist reported that a sample of ocean water had 5 million diatoms of the species *Coscinodiscus centralis* per cubic meter. What was the biologist measuring?

   A) density

   B) dispersion

   C) carrying capacity

   D) quadrats

   E) range

   Answer: A
   *Topic: Concept 52.1*
   *Skill: Knowledge*

3) All of the following phrases could characterize a population *except*

   A) interacting individuals.

   B) dispersion.

   C) density.

   D) several species.

   E) boundaries.

   Answer: D
   *Topic: Concept 52.1*
   *Skill: Comprehension*

4) To measure the population density of monarch butterflies occupying a particular park, 100 butterflies are captured, marked with a small dot on a wing, and then released. The next day, another 100 butterflies are captured, including the recapture of 20 marked butterflies. One would estimate the population to be

   A) 200.

   B) 500.

   C) 1,000.

   D) 10,000.

   E) 900,000.

   Answer: B
   *Topic: Concept 52.1*
   *Skill: Application*

5) You are studying the mice that live in a pasture near your home.  There are lots of mice in this pasture, but you realize that you rarely observe any reproductive females.  This most likely indicates

   A) that there is selective predation on female mice.

   B) that female mice die before reproducing.

   C) that this habitat is not a good place for mice to reproduce.

   D) that you are observing immigrant mice.

   E) both C and D

   Answer: E
   *Topic: Concept 52.1*
   *Skill: Comprehension*

6) You are observing a population of lizards when you notice that the number of adults has increased and is higher than previously observed. One explanation for such an observation would include

A) reduction in death rate.

B) increased immigration.

C) increased emigration.

D) decreased emigration.

E) both B and D

Answer: B
*Topic: Concept 52.1*
*Skill: Knowledge*

7) The most common kind of dispersion in nature is

A) clumped.

B) random.

C) uniform.

D) indeterminate.

E) dispersive.

Answer: A
*Topic: Concept 52.1*
*Skill: Knowledge*

8) How would the dispersion of humans in the United States best be described?

A) dense

B) clumped

C) random

D) intrinsic

E) uniform

Answer: B
*Topic: Concept 52.1*
*Skill: Comprehension*

9) The pattern of dispersion for a certain species of kelp is clumped. The pattern of dispersion for a certain species of snail that lives only on this kelp would likely be

A) absolute.

B) clumped.

C) demographic.

D) random.

E) uniform.

Answer: B
*Topic: Concept 52.1*
*Skill: Comprehension*

10) Uniform spacing patterns in plants such as the creosote bush are most often associated with

A) chance.

B) patterns of high humidity.

C) the random distribution of seeds.

D) antagonistic interactions among individuals in the population.

E) the concentration of resources within the population's range.

Answer: D
*Topic: Concept 52.1*
*Skill: Comprehension*

11) Which of the following would be most likely to exhibit uniform dispersion?

A) red squirrels, which hide food and actively defend territories

B) cattails, which grow primarily at edges of lakes and streams

C) dwarf mistletoes, which parasitize particular species of forest trees

D) tassel-eared squirrels, which are nonterritorial

E) lake trout, which seek out deep water

Answer: A
*Topic: Concept 52.1*
*Skill: Comprehension*

12) If you were to keep records on a cohort of wild animals for the purpose of developing a life table, you would be most successful if you chose to keep records on

 A) migratory birds.

 B) elephants in a national park.

 C) mosquitoes.

 D) earthworms in a backyard.

 E) pelagic squid.

Answer: B
*Topic: Concept 52.1*
*Skill: Application*

13) A table listing such items as age, observed number of organisms alive each year, and life expectancy is known as a (an)

 A) life table.

 B) mortality table.

 C) survivorship table.

 D) rate table.

 E) insurance table.

Answer: A
*Topic: Concept 52.1*
*Skill: Knowledge*

14) Life tables are useful in determining which of the following?
 I. carrying capacity
 II. mortality rates
 III. the fate of a cohort of newborn organisms throughout their lives

 A) I only

 B) II only

 C) III only

 D) I and III only

 E) II and III only

Answer: E
*Topic: Concept 52.1*
*Skill: Comprehension*

*Use the survivorship curves in Figure 52.1 to answer the following questions.*

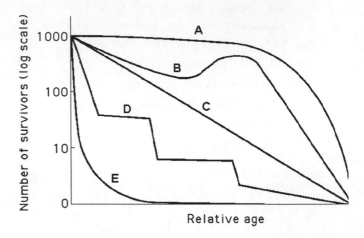

**Figure 52.1**

15) Which curve best describes survivorship in oysters?

Answer: E
*Topic: Concept 52.1*
*Skill: Comprehension*

16) Which curve best describes survivorship in elephants?

Answer: A
*Topic: Concept 52.1*
*Skill: Comprehension*

17) Which curve best describes survivorship in a marine crustacean that molts?

Answer: D
*Topic: Concept 52.1*
*Skill: Comprehension*

18) Which curve best describes survivorship in humans who live in developed nations?

Answer: A
*Topic: Concept 52.1*
*Skill: Comprehension*

19) Which curve best describes survivorship in squirrels?

Answer: C
*Topic: Concept 52.1*
*Skill: Comprehension*

20) Which curve best describes survivorship that is independent of age?

Answer: C
*Topic: Concept 52.1*
*Skill: Comprehension*

21) In order to construct a reproductive table for a sexual species, you need to
   A) assess sperm viability.
   B) keep track of all of the offspring of a cohort.
   C) keep track of the females in a cohort.
   D) keep track of all of the offspring of the females in a cohort.
   E) keep track of the ratio of deaths to births in a cohort.

Answer: C
*Topic: Concept 52.1*
*Skill: Comprehension*

22) A demographer studying a population of a particular organism would be *least* likely to be engaged in which of the following?
   A) constructing a life table for the organism
   B) sampling the population and determining the sex ratio
   C) studying courtship behavior between males and females
   D) measuring birth and death rates
   E) estimating how long an individual of a given age will live

Answer: C
*Topic: Concept 52.1*
*Skill: Comprehension*

23) Life history strategies usually result from
   A) environmental pressures.
   B) natural selection.
   C) conscious choice.
   D) A and B only
   E) A, B, and C

Answer: D
*Topic: Concept 52.2*
*Skill: Comprehension*

24) Natural selection has led to the evolution of diverse natural history strategies, which have in common
   A) many offspring per reproductive episode.
   B) limitation by density–dependent limiting factors.
   C) adaptation to stable environments.
   D) maximum lifetime reproductive success.
   E) relatively large offspring.

Answer: D
*Topic: Concept 52.2*
*Skill: Comprehension*

25) Natural selection involves energetic trade–offs between or among life history traits such as
   A) number of offspring per reproductive episode.
   B) number of reproductive episodes per lifetime.
   C) age at first reproduction.
   D) A and C only
   E) A, B, and C

Answer: E
*Topic: Concept 52.2*
*Skill: Comprehension*

26) Which of the following aspects of an organism's life is *least* relevant to its life history?

A) number of offspring per reproductive bout

B) age at which it first reproduces

C) frequency of reproduction

D) frequency of dispersal

E) all of the above

Answer: D
*Topic: Concept 52.2*
*Skill: Comprehension*

27) A population of ground squirrels has an annual per capita birth rate of 0.06 and an annual per capita death rate of 0.02. Estimate the number of individuals added to (or lost from) a population of 1,000 individuals in one year.

A) 120 individuals added

B) 40 individuals added

C) 20 individuals added

D) 400 individuals added

E) 20 individuals lost

Answer: B
*Topic: Concept 52.3*
*Skill: Application*

28) A small population of white-footed mice has the same intrinsic rate of increase ($r$) as a large population. If everything else is equal,

A) the large population will add more individuals per unit time.

B) the small population will add more individuals per unit time.

C) the two populations will add equal numbers of individuals per unit time.

D) the J-shaped growth curves will look identical.

E) the growth trajectories of the two populations will proceed in opposite directions.

Answer: A
*Topic: Concept 52.3*
*Skill: Comprehension*

29) Imagine that you are managing a large ranch. You know from historical accounts that wild sheep used to live there, but they have been exterminated. You decide to reintroduce them. After doing some research to determine what might be an appropriate founding population, you do so. You then watch the population increase, and graph the number of individuals (vertical axis) against the number of generations (horizontal axis). The graph will

A) be a diagonal line, getting higher with each generation.

B) look like an "S," increasing with each generation.

C) look like an upside-down "U."

D) look like a "J," increasing with each generation.

E) look like none of the above.

Answer: D
*Topic: Concept 52.3*
*Skill: Application*

30) In the logistic equation $dN/dt = rN \dfrac{(K - N)}{K}$, $r$ is a measure of the population's intrinsic rate of increase. It is determined by which of the following?

A) birth rate

B) death rate

C) density

D) A and B only

E) A, B, and C

Answer: D
*Topic: Concept 52.3*
*Skill: Comprehension*

31) Carrying capacity ($K$)

A) is calculated as the product of annual per capita birth rate ($r$).

B) remains constant in the presence of density–dependent population regulation.

C) differs among species, but does not vary within a given species.

D) is often determined by energy limitation.

E) is always eventually reached in any population.

Answer: D
*Topic: Concept 52.4*
*Skill: Knowledge*

*Use the following choices to answer the questions below. Each choice may be used once, more than once, or not at all.*

A. $\dfrac{rN}{K}$

B. $rN$

C. $rN (K + N)$

D. $rN \dfrac{(K - N)}{K}$

E. $rN \dfrac{(N - K)}{K}$

32) Logistic growth of a population is represented by $dN/dt =$

Answer: D
*Topic: Concept 52.4*
*Skill: Knowledge*

33) Exponential growth of a population is represented by $dN/dt =$

Answer: B
*Topic: Concept 52.3*
*Skill: Comprehension*

34) As $N$ approaches $K$ for a certain population, which of the following is predicted by the logistic equation?

A) The growth rate will not change.

B) The growth rate will approach zero.

C) The population will show an Allee effect.

D) The population will increase exponentially.

E) The carrying capacity of the environment will increase.

Answer: B
*Topic: Concept 52.4*
*Skill: Comprehension*

35) Often the growth cycle of one population has an effect on the cycle of another—as moose populations increase, wolf populations also increase. Thus, if we are considering the logistic equation for the wolf population,

$$dN/dt = rN, \frac{(K - N)}{K},$$

which of the factors accounts for the effect on the moose population?

A) $r$

B) $N$

C) $rN$

D) $K$

E) $dt$

Answer: D
*Topic: Concept 52.4*
*Skill: Comprehension*

36) Which of the following might be expected in the logistic model of population growth?

A) As $N$ approaches $K$, $b$ increases.

B) As $N$ approaches $K$, $r$ increases.

C) As $N$ approaches $K$, $d$ increases.

D) Both A and B are true.

E) Both B and C are true.

Answer: C
*Topic: Concept 52.4*
*Skill: Comprehension*

37) In models of sigmoidal (logistic) population growth,

A) population growth rate slows dramatically as $N$ approaches $K$.

B) new individuals are added to the population most rapidly at intermediate population sizes.

C) density-dependent factors affect the rate of population growth.

D) All of the above are true.

E) Only A and C are true.

Answer: D
*Topic: Concept 52.4*
*Skill: Knowledge*

38) The Allee effect is a phenomenon that occurs when population size

A) becomes too small.

B) becomes too large.

C) approaches carrying capacity.

D) exceeds carrying capacity.

E) more than one of the above

Answer: A
*Topic: Concept 52.4*
*Skill: Knowledge*

*The following questions refer to the terms below. Each term may be used once, more than once, or not at all.*

A    cohort
B.   dispersion
C.   Allee effect
D.   iteroparous
E.   semelparous

39) a density-dependent factor

Answer: C
*Topic: Concept 52.4*
*Skill: Comprehension*

40) Pacific salmon or annual plants

Answer: E
*Topic: Concept 52.2*
*Skill: Knowledge*

41) reproduce more than once in a lifetime

Answer: D
*Topic: Concept 52.2*
*Skill: Knowledge*

42) pattern of spacing for individuals within the boundaries of the population

Answer: B
*Topic: Concept 52.1*
*Skill: Knowledge*

43) A predator might be more likely to be spotted if a large number of prey are all together than it would be by a single prey animal.

Answer: C
*Topic: Concept 52.4*
*Skill: Comprehension*

44) Which of the following statements about the logistic model of population growth is *incorrect*?
   A) It fits an S-shaped curve.
   B) It incorporates the concept of carrying capacity.
   C) It describes population density shifts over time.
   D) It accurately predicts the growth of most populations.
   E) It predicts an eventual state in which birth rate equals death rate.

Answer: D
*Topic: Concept 52.4*
*Skill: Comprehension*

45) Which of the following is *true*?
   A) *K*-selection can be density-independent.
   B) *r*-selection occurs in crowded environments.
   C) Different populations of the same species will be consistently *r*- or *K*-selected.
   D) *r*- and *K*-selection are two extremes of a range of life history strategies.
   E) *r*-selection tends to maximize population size, not the rate of increase in population size.

Answer: D
*Topic: Concept 52.4*
*Skill: Knowledge*

46) The life history traits favored by selection are *most* likely to vary with
   A) fluctuations in *K*.
   B) the shape of the J curve.
   C) the maximum size of a population.
   D) population density.
   E) the terms used in the logistic equation.

Answer: D
*Topic: Concept 52.4*
*Skill: Comprehension*

47) A species that is relatively *r*-selected might have all of the following characteristics *except*
   A) a disturbed habitat.
   B) small offspring.
   C) parental care of offspring.
   D) numerous offspring.
   E) little homeostatic capability.

Answer: C
*Topic: Concept 52.4*
*Skill: Comprehension*

48) In which of the following habitats would you expect to find the largest number of K-selected individuals?

A) an abandoned field in Ohio

B) the sand dunes south of Lake Michigan

C) the rain forests of Brazil

D) south Florida after a hurricane

E) a newly emergent volcanic island

Answer: C
*Topic: Concept 52.4*
*Skill: Application*

49) All of the following characteristics are typical of an *r*-selected population *except*

A) occurrence in variable environments.

B) high intrinsic rate of growth.

C) onset of reproduction at an early age.

D) extensive parental care of offspring.

E) occurrence in open habitats.

Answer: D
*Topic: Concept 52.4*
*Skill: Comprehension*

50) Which of the following characterizes relatively K-selected populations?

A) offspring with good chances of survival

B) many offspring per reproductive episode

C) small offspring

D) a high intrinsic rate of increase

E) early parental reproduction

Answer: A
*Topic: Concept 52.4*
*Skill: Comprehension*

51) Which of the following statements about the evolution of life histories is *correct*?

A) Stable environments with limited resources favor *r*-selected populations.

B) K-selected populations are most often found in environments where density-independent factors are important regulators of population size.

C) Most populations have both *r*- and K-selected characteristics that vary under different environmental conditions.

D) The reproductive efforts of *r*-selected populations are directed at producing just a few offspring with good competitive abilities.

E) K-selected populations rarely approach carrying capacity.

Answer: C
*Topic: Concept 52.4*
*Skill: Comprehension*

52) Your friend comes to you with a problem. It seems his shrimp boats aren't catching nearly as much shrimp as they used to. He can't understand it because originally he caught all the shrimp he could handle. Each year he added a new boat, and for a long time each boat caught tons of shrimp. As he added more boats, there came a time when each boat caught a little less shrimp, and now, each boat is catching a lot less shrimp. Which of the following topics might help your friend understand the source of his problem?

A) density-dependent population regulation

B) logistic growth and intrinsic characteristics of population growth

C) density-independent population regulation

D) A and B only

E) A, B, and C

Answer: D
*Topic: Concept 52.4*
*Skill: Comprehension*

53) Unlimited population growth is often prevented when death rates increase as population density increases. This is an example of

A) *K*-selection.

B) *r*-selection.

C) positive feedback.

D) negative feedback.

E) the Allee effect.

Answer: D
*Topic: Concept 52.5*
*Skill: Knowledge*

54) Which of the following can contribute to density-dependent regulation of populations?

A) the accumulation of toxic waste

B) intraspecific competition for nutrients

C) predation

D) all of the above

E) none of the above

Answer: D
*Topic: Concept 52.5*
*Skill: Knowledge*

55) Field observation suggests that populations of a particular species of herbivorous mammal undergo cyclic fluctuations in density at three to five year intervals. Which of the following represent (a) plausible explanation(s) of these cycles?

A) Periodic crowding affects the endocrine system, resulting in increased aggressiveness.

B) Increases in population density lead to increased rates of predation.

C) Increases in rates of herbivory lead to changes in the nutritive value of plants used as food.

D) All of the above are plausible explanations of population cycling.

E) Only B and C are plausible explanations of cycling in this population.

Answer: D
*Topic: Concept 52.5*
*Skill: Comprehension*

56) Which of the following is an *incorrect* statement about the regulation of populations?

A) The logistic equation reflects the effect of density-dependent factors, which can ultimately stabilize populations around the carrying capacity.

B) Density-independent factors have an increasingly greater effect as a population's density increases.

C) High densities in a population may cause physiological changes that inhibit reproduction.

D) Because of the overlapping nature of population-regulating factors, it is often difficult to precisely determine their cause-and-effect relationships.

E) The occurrence of population cycles in some populations may be the result of crowding or lag times in the response to density-dependent factors.

Answer: B
*Topic: Concept 52.5*
*Skill: Comprehension*

57) Which of the following would *not* be considered part of a metapopulation?

A) a prairie-dog town

B) a swarm of locusts

C) birds on a neighboring island

D) mosquitos in tree holes

E) people in a village

Answer: B
*Topic: Concept 52.5*
*Skill: Comprehension*

58) In a mature forest of oak, maple, and hickory trees, a disease causes a reduction in the number of acorns produced by oak trees. Which of the following would *least* likely be a direct result of this?

A) There might be fewer squirrels because they feed on acorns.

B) There might be fewer mice and seed-eating birds because squirrels would eat more seeds and compete with the mice and birds.

C) There might be an increase in the number of hickory trees because the competition between hickory nuts and acorns for germination sites would be reduced or eliminated.

D) There might be fewer owls because they feed on baby squirrels, mice, and young seed-eating birds, whose populations would be reduced.

E) There might be a decrease in the number of maple seeds as the disease spreads to other trees in the forest.

Answer: E
*Topic: Concept 52.5*
*Skill: Comprehension*

59) You are studying a population of finches on one island in an archipelago. You find that your population is much larger than you would predict from your careful recording of hatching, fledgling, and death rates. The likely explanation for this observation is

A) you are dealing with a metapopulation.

B) your island is the source of emigration.

C) your island is the target of immigration.

D) A and C only

E) A, B, and C

Answer: D
*Topic: Concept 52.5*
*Skill: Comprehension*

60) Which of the following is a density–independent factor limiting human population growth?

　A) social pressure for birth control

　B) earthquakes

　C) plagues

　D) famines

　E) pollution

Answer: B
*Topic: Concepts 52.5, 52.6*
*Skill: Comprehension*

61) Consider several human populations of equal size and net reproductive rate, but different in age structure. The population that is likely to grow the most during the next 30 years is the one with the greatest fraction of people in which age range?

　A) 50 to 60 years

　B) 40 to 50 years

　C) 30 to 40 years

　D) 20 to 30 years

　E) 10 to 20 years

Answer: E
*Topic: Concept 52.6*
*Skill: Application*

*The following questions refer to Figure 52.2, which depicts the age structure of three populations.*

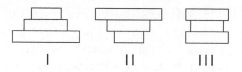

**Figure 52.2**

62) Which population is in the process of decreasing?

　A) I

　B) II

　C) III

　D) I and II

　E) II and III

Answer: B
*Topic: Concept 52.6*
*Skill: Application*

63) Which population appears to be stable?

　A) I

　B) II

　C) III

　D) I and II

　E) II and III

Answer: C
*Topic: Concept 52.6*
*Skill: Application*

64) Assuming these age-structure diagrams describe human populations, in which population is unemployment likely to be most severe in the future?

A) I

B) II

C) III

D) No differences in the magnitude of future unemployment would be expected among these populations.

E) It is not possible to infer anything about future social conditions from age-structure diagrams.

Answer: A
*Topic: Concept 52.6*
*Skill: Application*

65) Assuming these age-structure diagrams describe human populations, which population is likely to experience zero population growth (ZPG)?

A) I

B) II

C) III

D) I and II

E) II and III

Answer: C
*Topic: Concept 52.6*
*Skill: Application*

66) Which of the following is *not* used in calculating an ecological footprint?

A) arable land

B) pasture and forest lands

C) fossil energy land

D) demographically transitional land

E) built-up land

Answer: D
*Topic: Concept 52.6*
*Skill: Knowledge*

67) The unit(s) of measurement for an ecological footprint is (are)

A) weight of biomass per year.

B) number of species per ecosystem.

C) number of individuals per population.

D) number of people per continent.

E) area of land per person.

Answer: E
*Topic: Concept 52.6*
*Skill: Comprehension*

68) All of the following have contributed to the growth of the human population *except*

A) environmental degradation.

B) improved nutrition.

C) vaccines.

D) pesticides.

E) improved sanitation.

Answer: A
*Topic: Concept 52.6*
*Skill: Knowledge*

69) Which of the following variables is (are) important in contributing to the rapid growth of human populations?

A) the high percentage of young people relative to the whole population

B) the average age to first give birth

C) the carrying capacity of the environment

D) A and B only

E) A, B, and C

Answer: D
*Topic: Concept 52.6*
*Skill: Comprehension*

70) Choose the *true* statement from those listed below.

   A) Because humans are the only organisms that can consciously regulate reproduction, we will not exceed carrying capacity.

   B) Because of their relatively high educational levels, developed countries keep their ecological footprints within their ecological capabilities.

   C) Famines are indicators that there is not enough food in the world.

   D) Assumptions about dietary preferences can affect predictions about carrying capacity.

   E) None of the preceding statements is true.

Answer: D
*Topic: Concept 52.6*
*Skill: Comprehension*

# Media Activity Questions

1) You are doing a mark–recapture experiment to determine the population size of MendAliens living on an island. Initially you capture, mark, and release 130 MendAliens. A few days later, you capture 90 MendAliens, 20 of which are marked. What is your estimate of the population size of the MendAliens?

   A) 14

   B) 29

   C) 130

   D) 585

   E) 234,000

   Answer: D
   *Topic: Estimating Population Density and Size*

2) Which of these organisms has a survivorship curve similar to that of oysters?

   A) humans

   B) robins

   C) grasses

   D) elephants

   E) cats

   Answer: C
   *Topic: Activity: Investigating Survivorship Curves*

3) Which of these was the first of the major events that stimulated an increase in the size of the human population?

   A) the Industrial Revolution

   B) the discovery of antibiotics

   C) the advent of agriculture

   D) the discovery of vaccines

   E) the bubonic plague

   Answer: C
   *Topic: Web/CD Activity: Human Population Growth*

4) In the 14th century, _____ was responsible for the death of more than one-third of the entire European population of humans.

   A) tuberculosis

   B) AIDS

   C) influenza

   D) bubonic plague

   E) pneumonia

   Answer: D
   *Topic: Web/CD Activity: Human Population Growth*

5) If most of the individuals of a human population are in their prereproductive years, you would expect the population size to _____ after 20 years.

   A) stay the same

   B) increase

   C) decrease

   D) decrease and then stabilize

   E) decrease and then decrease more sharply

   Answer: B
   *Topic: Activity: Analyzing Age-Structure Pyramids*

# Self–Quiz Questions

1) The observation that members of a population are uniformly distributed suggests that
   A) the size of the area occupied by the population is increasing.
   B) resources are distributed unevenly.
   C) the members of the population are competing for access to a resource.
   D) the members of the population are neither attracted to nor repelled by one another.
   E) the density of the population is low.

   Answer: C

2) Population ecologists follow the fate of same-age cohorts in order to
   A) determine a population's carrying capacity.
   B) determine if a population is regulated by density-dependent processes.
   C) determine the birth rate and death rate of each age group in a population.
   D) determine the factors that regulate the size of a population.
   E) determine if a population's growth is cyclical.

   Answer: C

3) In a population that is growing as described by the logistic growth model,
   A) the number of individuals added per unit time is greatest when $N$ is close to zero. [The key equation is $dn/dt = r_{max} N(K-N/K)$.]
   B) the per capita growth rate ($r$) increases as $N$ approaches $K$.
   C) population growth is zero when $N$ equals $K$.
   D) the population grows exponentially when $K$ is small.
   E) the birth rate ($b$) approaches zero as $N$ approaches $K$.

   Answer: C

4) A population's carrying capacity is
   A) can be accurately calculated using the logistic growth model.
   B) generally remains constant over time.
   C) increases as the per capita growth rate ($r$) decreases.
   D) may change as environmental conditions change.
   E) can never be exceeded.

   Answer: D

5) Which pair of terms most accurately describes life–history traits for a stable population of wolves?
   A) semelparous; $r$-selected
   B) semelparous; $K$-selected
   C) iteroparous; $r$-selected
   D) iteroparous; $K$-selected
   E) iteroparous; $N$-selected

   Answer: B

6) The infant mortality rate is _____ in developing countries than in developed countries (see Figure 52.26 in your textbook).

   A) no different

   B) about two times higher

   C) slightly lower

   D) about three times higher

   E) more than six times higher

Answer: E

7) Scientific study of the population cycles of the snowshoe hare and its predator, the lynx, has revealed that

   A) the prey population is controlled by the predators alone.

   B) hares and lynx are so mutually dependent that each species cannot survive without the other.

   C) the most obvious, plausible hypothesis about the cause of population cycles is not necessarily the correct one.

   D) both hare and lynx populations are regulated mainly by abiotic factors.

   E) the hare population is $r$-selected; the lynx population is $K$-selected.

Answer: C

8) The current size of the human population is closest to

   A) 2 million.

   B) 3 billion.

   C) 4 billion.

   D) 6 billion.

   E) 10 billion.

Answer: D

9) Which of the following statements about human populations in developed countries is *incorrect*?

   A) Average family size is relatively small.

   B) The population has undergone the demographic transition.

   C) Life history is $r$-selected.

   D) The survivorship curve is Type I.

   E) Age distribution is relatively uniform.

Answer: C

10) A recent study of ecological footprints (described in the text) concluded that

   A) Earth's carrying capacity for humans is about 10 billion.

   B) Earth's carrying capacity would increase if per capita meat consumption increased.

   C) current demand by industrialized countries is much smaller than the ecological footprint of those countries.

   D) the ecological footprint of the United States is larger than the ecological capacity of its land.

   E) it is not possible for technological improvements to increase Earth's carrying capacity for humans.

Answer: D

# Chapter 53  Community Ecology

1) Communities can be linked by which of the following?
    I.   predation
    II.  systematics
    III. competition

   A) I only

   B) III only

   C) I and II only

   D) I and III only

   E) I, II, and III

   Answer: D
   *Topic: Concept 53.1*
   *Skill: Knowledge*

2) Which of the following statements is consistent with the competitive exclusion principle?

   A) Bird species generally do not compete for nesting sites.

   B) The density of one competing species will have a positive impact on the population growth of the other competing species.

   C) Two species with the same fundamental niche will exclude other competing species.

   D) Even a slight reproductive advantage will eventually lead to the elimination of inferior species.

   E) Evolution tends to increase competition between related species.

   Answer: D
   *Topic: Concept 53.1*
   *Skill: Comprehension*

3) The presence of all of the following tend to increase species diversity *except*

   A) competitive exclusion.

   B) keystone predators.

   C) patchy environments.

   D) moderate disturbances.

   E) migration of populations.

   Answer: A
   *Topic: Concept 53.1*
   *Skill: Comprehension*

4) According to the competitive exclusion principle, two species cannot continue to occupy the same

   A) habitat.

   B) niche.

   C) territory.

   D) range.

   E) biome.

   Answer: B
   *Topic: Concept 53.1*
   *Skill: Knowledge*

**Figure 53.1**

5) The entire box shown in Figure 53.1 represents the niche of species A. Species A is biologically constrained from the striped area of its niche by species B. This is an example of
   A) dynamic stability.
   B) facilitation.
   C) commensalism.
   D) competitive exclusion.
   E) secondary succession.

   Answer: D
   *Topic: Concept 53.1*
   *Skill: Application*

6) The sum total of an organism's interaction with the biotic and abiotic resources of its environment is called its
   A) habitat.
   B) logistic growth.
   C) biotic potential.
   D) microclimax.
   E) ecological niche.

   Answer: E
   *Topic: Concept 53.1*
   *Skill: Knowledge*

7) Two barnacles, *Balanus* and *Chthamalus*, can both survive on the lower rocks just above the low–tide line on the Scottish coast, but only *Balanus* actually does so, with *Chthamalus* adopting a higher zone. Which of the following best accounts for this niche separation?
   A) competitive exclusion
   B) predation of *Chthamalus* by *Balanus*
   C) cooperative displacement
   D) primary succession
   E) mutualism

   Answer: A
   *Topic: Concept 53.1*
   *Skill: Comprehension*

8) A species of fish is found to require a certain water temperature, a particular oxygen content of the water, a particular depth, and a rocky substrate on the bottom to thrive. These requirements are part of its
   A) dimensional profile.
   B) ecological niche.
   C) prime habitat.
   D) resource partition.
   E) home base.

   Answer: B
   *Topic: Concept 53.1*
   *Skill: Comprehension*

9) All of the following describe possible results of competition between two species *except*
   A) competitive exclusion.
   B) aposematic coloration.
   C) resource partitioning.
   D) reduction in the population of one species.
   E) reduction in the populations of both species.

   Answer: B
   *Topic: Concept 53.1*
   *Skill: Comprehension*

10) Resource partitioning is best described by which of the following statements?

   A) Competitive exclusion results in the success of the superior species.

   B) Slight variations in niche allow similar species to coexist.

   C) Two species can coevolve and share the same niche.

   D) Species diversity is maintained by switching between prey species.

   E) A climax community is reached when no new niches are available.

Answer: B
*Topic: Concept 53.1*
*Skill: Knowledge*

11) As you study two closely related predatory insect species, the two-spot and the three-spot avenger beetles, you notice that each species seeks prey at dawn in areas without the other species. Where their ranges overlap, however, the two-spot avenger beetle hunts at night and the three-spot hunts in the morning. When you bring them into the laboratory, their offspring behave in the same manner. You have discovered an example of

   A) mutualism.

   B) character displacement.

   C) Batesian mimicry.

   D) facultative commensalism.

   E) none of the above

Answer: B
*Topic: Concept 53.1*
*Skill: Application*

12) Resource partitioning would be most likely to occur between

   A) sympatric populations of a predator and its prey.

   B) sympatric populations of species with similar ecological niches.

   C) sympatric populations of a flowering plant and its specialized insect pollinator.

   D) allopatric populations of the same animal species.

   E) allopatric populations of species with similar ecological niches.

Answer: B
*Topic: Concept 53.1*
*Skill: Comprehension*

13) An insect that has evolved to resemble a plant twig will probably be able to avoid

   A) parasitism.

   B) symbiosis.

   C) predation.

   D) competition.

   E) commensalism.

Answer: C
*Topic: Concept 53.1*
*Skill: Comprehension*

14) Which of the following is an example of cryptic coloration?

   A) bands on a coral snake

   B) brown color of tree bark

   C) markings of a viceroy butterfly

   D) colors of an insect-pollinated flower

   E) a "walking stick" insect that resembles a twig

Answer: E
*Topic: Concept 53.1*
*Skill: Comprehension*

15) Batesian mimicry systems involve all of the following *except*

A) the models being noxious or disagreeable.

B) the mimics having no defense mechanism.

C) the ability of predators to "learn" characteristics of their prey.

D) the models being cryptically colored.

E) the models being easily recognized.

Answer: D
*Topic: Concept 53.1*
*Skill: Comprehension*

16) Which of the following is an example of Müllerian mimicry?

A) two species of unpalatable butterfly that have the same color pattern

B) a day-flying hawkmoth that looks like a wasp

C) a katydid whose wings look like a dead leaf

D) two species of rattlesnake that both rattle their tails

E) two species of moths that with wing spots that look like owl's eyes

Answer: A
*Topic: Concept 53.1*
*Skill: Comprehension*

17) Which of the following is an example of Batesian mimicry?

A) an insect that resembles a twig

B) a butterfly that resembles a leaf

C) a nonvenomous snake that looks like a venomous snake

D) a fawn with fur coloring that camouflages it in the forest environment

E) a snapping turtle that uses its tongue to mimic a worm, thus attracting fish

Answer: C
*Topic: Concept 53.1*
*Skill: Comprehension*

18) Which of the following is an example of aposematic coloration?

A) stripes of a skunk

B) eye color in humans

C) green color of a plant

D) colors of an insect–pollinated flower

E) a katydid whose wings look like a dead leaf

Answer: A
*Topic: Concept 53.1*
*Skill: Knowledge*

19) Two species of insects from different geographic areas display characteristic black and red stripes. Which of the following is *unlikely* to be related to this phenomenon?

A) aposematic coloration

B) convergent evolution

C) common ancestry

D) mimicry

E) defense against a predator

Answer: D
*Topic: Concept 53.1*
*Skill: Comprehension*

20) Which of the following is least likely to kill the organism it feeds on?

A) herbivore

B) predator

C) seed eater

D) carnivore

E) parasite

Answer: E
*Topic: Concept 53.1*
*Skill: Application*

21) Dwarf mistletoes are flowering plants that grow on certain forest trees. They obtain nutrients and water from the vascular tissues of the trees. The trees derive no known benefits from the dwarf mistletoes. Which of the following best describes the interactions between dwarf mistletoes and trees?

A) mutualism

B) parasitism

C) commensalism

D) facilitation

E) competition

Answer: B
*Topic: Concept 53.1*
*Skill: Comprehension*

22) Which of the following is *not* an example of a plant defense against herbivory?

A) nicotine

B) cryptic coloration

C) spines

D) thorns

E) strychnine

Answer: B
*Topic: Concept 53.1*
*Skill: Comprehension*

23) The oak tree pathogen *Phytophthora ramorum* migrated 650 km in ten years. West Nile virus spread from New York to 46 others states in five years. The difference in the rate of spread is probably related to

A) how lethal each pathogen is.

B) the mobility of their hosts.

C) the fact that viruses are very small.

D) innate resistance.

E) none of the above

Answer: B
*Topic: Concept 53.1*
*Skill: Application*

24) All of the following represent ways that animals defend themselves against predators *except*

A) incorporating plant toxins into their tissues.

B) cryptic coloration.

C) mobbing.

D) interspecific competition.

E) hiding or fleeing.

Answer: D
*Topic: Concept 53.1*
*Skill: Comprehension*

25) Evidence shows that some grasses benefit from being grazed. Which of the following terms would best describe this plant–herbivore interaction?

A) mutualism

B) commensalism

C) parasitism

D) competition

E) predation

Answer: A
*Topic: Concept 53.1*
*Skill: Comprehension*

26) Which of the following terms best describes the interaction between termites and the protozoans that feed in their gut?

A) commensalism

B) mutualism

C) competitive exclusion

D) ectoparasitism

E) endoparasitism

Answer: B
*Topic: Concept 53.1*
*Skill: Knowledge*

27) Which of the following interactions can correctly be labeled coevolution?

   A) the tendency of coyotes to respond to human habitat encroachment by including pet dogs and cats in their diets

   B) a genetic change in a virus that allows it to exploit a new host, which responds to virus-imposed selection by changing its genetically controlled habitat preferences

   C) a genetic change in foxes that allows them to tolerate human presence (and food)

   D) the adaptation of cockroaches to human habitation

   E) the ability of rats to survive in a variety of novel environments

Answer: B
*Topic: Concept 53.1*
*Skill: Comprehension*

28) Which of the following types of species interaction is *incorrectly* paired to its effects on the density of the two interacting populations?

   A) predation—one increases, one decreases

   B) parasitism—one increases, one decreases

   C) commensalism—both increase

   D) mutualism—both increase

   E) competition—both decrease

Answer: C
*Topic: Concept 53.1*
*Skill: Comprehension*

29) All of the following are terms that ecologists use to describe communities *except* for

   A) species richness.

   B) species diversity.

   C) Batesian diversity.

   D) trophic structure.

   E) stability.

Answer: C
*Topic: Concept 53.2*
*Skill: Comprehension*

30) The species richness of a community refers to the

   A) number of food chains.

   B) number of different species.

   C) energy content of all species.

   D) relative numbers of individuals in each species.

   E) total number of all organisms.

Answer: B
*Topic: Concept 53.2*
*Skill: Knowledge*

31) To measure species diversity in a community, you need to know

   A) the number of species.

   B) the relative abundance of each species.

   C) the physical size of each species.

   D) both A and B

   E) A, B, and C

Answer: D
*Topic: Concept 53.2*
*Skill: Knowledge*

32) Which of the following statements about communities is *not* correct?

A) Many plant species in communities seem to be independently distributed.

B) Some animal species distributions within a community are linked to other species.

C) The distribution of almost all organisms is probably affected, to some extent, by both abiotic gradients and interactions with other species.

D) Ecologists refer to species richness as the number of species within a community.

E) The trophic structure of a community describes abiotic factors such as rainfall and temperature affecting members of the community.

Answer: E
*Topic: Concept 53.2*
*Skill: Comprehension*

33) With a few exceptions, most of the food chains studied by ecologists have a maximum of how many links?

A) 2

B) 3

C) 5

D) 10

E) 15

Answer: C
*Topic: Concept 53.2*
*Skill: Knowledge*

34) Prairie dogs once covered the expanses of the Great Plains. Their grazing made the grass more nutritious for the huge herds of bison, and a variety of snakes, raptors, and mammals preyed on the rodents. In fact, the black–footed ferret (now endangered) specialized in prairie dog predation. Today, growing neighborhoods have covered many prairie dog towns. Which of the following statements about prairie dogs is *not* true?

A) Their realized niche has diminished.

B) They are commensals with bison.

C) They are reasonably considered a keystone species.

D) Their fundamental niche remains unaltered.

E) Their fundamental niche has diminished.

Answer: E
*Topic: Concepts 53.1, 53.2*
*Skill: Comprehension*

35) Which of the following members of a marine food chain is most analogous to a grasshopper in a terrestrial food chain?

A) phytoplankton

B) zooplankton

C) detritivore

D) fish

E) shark

Answer: B
*Topic: Concept 53.2*
*Skill: Comprehension*

36) Consider a field plot containing 200 kg of plant material. Approximately how many kg of carnivore production can be supported?

A) 200

B) 100

C) 20

D) 10

E) 2

Answer: E
*Topic: Concept 53.2*
*Skill: Application*

37) The energetic hypothesis and dynamic stability hypothesis are explanations to account for

A) plant defenses against herbivores.

B) the length of food chains.

C) the evolution of mutualism.

D) resource partitioning.

E) the competitive exclusion principle.

Answer: B
*Topic: Concept 53.2*
*Skill: Knowledge*

38) The dominant species in a community is

A) characterized by very large individuals with long lives.

B) the best competitor in the community.

C) the best predator in the community.

D) the population with the most biomass.

E) the most energetically efficient species in the community.

Answer: D
*Topic: Concept 53.2*
*Skill: Knowledge*

39) In a tide pool, 15 species of invertebrates were reduced to eight after one species was removed. The species removed was likely a(n)

A) community facilitator.

B) keystone species.

C) herbivore.

D) resource partitioner.

E) mutualistic organism.

Answer: B
*Topic: Concept 53.2*
*Skill: Application*

40) Which of the following statements about community interactions is *not* correct?

A) Closely related species may be able to coexist if there is at least one significant difference in their niches.

B) Plants can defend themselves against herbivores by the production of compounds that are irritating or toxic.

C) Keystone predators reduce diversity in a community by holding down or wiping out prey populations.

D) Mutualism is an important biotic interaction that occurs in communities.

E) Some predators use mimicry to attract prey.

Answer: C
*Topic: Concept 53.2*
*Skill: Comprehension*

41) Elephants are not the most common species in African grasslands. The grasslands contain scattered woody plants, but they are kept in check by the uprooting activities of the elephants. Take away the elephants, and the grasslands convert to forests or to shrublands. The newly growing forests support fewer species than the previous grasslands. Elephants can be defined as what type of species in this community?

   A) redundant

   B) dominant

   C) keystone

   D) dominant and keystone

   E) none of the above

Answer: C
*Topic: Concept 53.2*
*Skill: Comprehension*

42) When lichens grow on bare rock, they may eventually accumulate enough organic material around them to supply the foothold for later rooted vegetation. These early pioneering lichens can be said to do what to the later arrivals?

   A) tolerate

   B) inhibit

   C) facilitate

   D) exclude

   E) concentrate

Answer: C
*Topic: Concept 53.2*
*Skill: Comprehension*

43) Which of the following statements concerning the control of community structure is *false*?

   A) A bottom–up community is controlled by nutrients.

   B) A top–down community is controlled by predators.

   C) Increasing the biomass of vegetation in a bottom–up community will increase herbivores.

   D) Increasing the biomass of vegetation in a bottom–up community will increase predators.

   E) Increasing the number of predators in a top–down community will decrease the biomass of vegetation.

Answer: E
*Topic: Concept 53.2*
*Skill: Comprehension*

44) If you wanted to alter the structure of a bottom–up community, your best bet would be to

   A) remove the top predators.

   B) remove the trees and shrubs.

   C) add plenty of fertilizer.

   D) add more predators.

   E) reduce the number of primary producers.

Answer: C
*Topic: Concept 53.2*
*Skill: Comprehension*

45) Which of the following is considered by ecologists a measure of the ability of a community either to resist change or to recover to its original state after change?

A) stability

B) succession

C) partitioning

D) productivity

E) competitive exclusion

Answer: A
*Topic: Concept 53.3*
*Skill: Knowledge*

46) According to the nonequilibrium model,

A) communities will remain in a state of equilibrium in the absence of human activities.

B) community structure remains constant in the absence of interspecific competition.

C) communities are assemblages of closely linked species that function as tightly integrated units.

D) interspecific interactions induce changes in community composition over time.

E) communities are constantly changing because of disturbances.

Answer: E
*Topic: Concept 53.3*
*Skill: Knowledge*

47) Disturbances to ecological communities

A) are frequently related to human activities.

B) can remove organisms and alter resource availability.

C) can create vacated ecological niches that other species can colonize.

D) All of the above are true.

E) Only A and B are true.

Answer: D
*Topic: Concept 53.3*
*Skill: Knowledge*

48) Which of the following statements about the Yellowstone National Park fires of 1988 is *false*?

A) Secondary succession followed the fires.

B) The dominant lodgepole pines required fire to complete their normal life history.

C) Human environmental policy increased the severity of the fires.

D) It took years before new vegetation returned to the area.

E) Severe drought helped to trigger the fires.

Answer: D
*Topic: Concept 53.3*
*Skill: Knowledge*

49) In a particular case of secondary succession, three species of wild grass all invaded a field. By the second season, a single species dominated the field. A possible factor in this secondary succession was

A) equilibrium.

B) facilitation.

C) immigration.

D) inhibition.

E) mutualism.

Answer: D
*Topic: Concept 53.3*
*Skill: Comprehension*

50) You are most likely to observe primary succession when you visit a(n)

A) tropical rain forest.

B) abandoned field.

C) old riverbed.

D) fairly recent volcanic island.

E) deep sea vent.

Answer: D
*Topic: Concept 53.3*
*Skill: Knowledge*

*The next questions refer to the following list of terms. Each term may be used once, more than once, or not at all.*

A.  parasitism
B.  mutualism
C.  inhibition
D.  facilitation
E.  commensalism

51) the relationship between ants and acacia trees

Answer: B
*Topic: Concept 53.1*
*Skill: Knowledge*

52) the relationship between legumes and nitrogen–fixing bacteria

Answer: B
*Topic: Concept 53.1*
*Skill: Knowledge*

53) successional event in which one organism makes the environment more suitable for another organism

Answer: D
*Topic: Concept 53.3*
*Skill: Knowledge*

54) the relationship between the larvae of small wasps and caterpillars

Answer: A
*Topic: Concept 53.1*
*Skill: Knowledge*

55) Following clear–cutting of a broadleaf forest several hundred years ago, the land was colonized by herbaceous species that were replaced largely over time by shrubs, then by forest trees. Assuming the growth of the shrubs and trees was enhanced by the soil-holding properties of the herbaceous plants, which of the following processes best describe the progression from herbaceous plants to forest trees?

A) primary succession; facilitation
B) primary succession; inhibition
C) primary succession; toleration
D) secondary succession; facilitation
E) secondary succession; inhibition

Answer: D
*Topic: Concept 53.3*
*Skill: Comprehension*

56) Which of the following statements about succession is *correct*?

A) Secondary succession occurs where no soil exists.
B) Primary succession occurs in areas where soil remains after a disturbance.
C) Secondary succession can occur where a disturbance has left soil intact.
D) Some cases of succession involve facilitation, a phenomenon in which local species inhibit the growth of newcomers.
E) Through successional dynamics, most communities will eventually become more stable through time.

Answer: C
*Topic: Concept 53.3*
*Skill: Comprehension*

57) Species richness increases

   A) as one travels north from the equator.

   B) as one travels north from the South
      Pole.

   C) on islands as distance from the
      mainland increases.

   D) as rates of evapotranspiration
      decrease.

   E) as community size decreases.

   Answer: B
   *Topic: Concept 53.4*
   *Skill: Comprehension*

58) There are more species in tropical areas
    than in places farther from the equator.
    This is probably a result of

   A) fewer predators.

   B) a longer growing season.

   C) fewer major disturbances.

   D) B and C only

   E) all of the above

   Answer: D
   *Topic: Concept 53.4*
   *Skill: Knowledge*

59) A community's actual evapotranspiration
    is a reflection of

   A) solar radiation, temperature, and
      water availability.

   B) the number of plants and how much
      moisture they lose.

   C) the depth of the water table.

   D) energy availability.

   E) plant biomass and plant water
      content.

   Answer: A
   *Topic: Concept 53.4*
   *Skill: Knowledge*

60) In conservation biology, species–area
    curves for key taxa make it possible to
    predict

   A) the size of an area that needs to be
      sampled.

   B) the area that a keystone species will
      occupy.

   C) whether or not a redundancy model
      will apply to a given area.

   D) how the loss of a certain habitat area
      is likely to affect biodiversity.

   E) whether or not an area will reach
      equilibrium.

   Answer: D
   *Topic: Concept 53.4*
   *Skill: Knowledge*

*The following questions refer to the diagram in Figure 53.2 of
five islands formed at about the same time near a particular
mainland.*

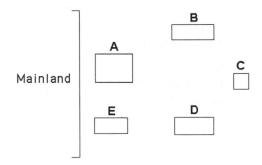

**Figure 53.2**

61) island with the greatest number of species

   Answer: A
   *Topic: Concept 53.4*
   *Skill: Application*

62) island with the least number of species

   Answer: C
   *Topic: Concept 53.4*
   *Skill: Application*

63) island with the lowest extinction rate

Answer: A
*Topic: Concept 53.4*
*Skill: Application*

64) island with the lowest immigration rate

Answer: C
*Topic: Concept 53.4*
*Skill: Application*

65) According to the equilibrium model of island biogeography, all of the following contribute to greater species diversity on an island *except*

A) a relatively recent formation of the island.

B) a shorter distance of the island from the mainland.

C) a bigger island.

D) a lower extinction rate on the island.

E) higher rates of migration to and from the island.

Answer: A
*Topic: Concept 53.4*
*Skill: Comprehension*

66) Which of the following statements about the biogeographical aspects of diversity is *not* correct?

A) The patterns of continental drift are important considerations in the study of the past and present distributions of species.

B) The magnitude of photosynthesis is the factor that accounts for the major variations in species diversity over large areas of Earth.

C) Species richness on an island reaches an equilibrium point when immigration equals extinction.

D) A species may be limited to a particular range because it never dispersed beyond that range, or it dispersed but failed to survive in other locations.

E) Island equilibrium theory applies to the relatively short period of time when colonization is the important process determining species composition; over a longer time, actual speciation affects the composition.

Answer: B
*Topic: Concept 53.4*
*Skill: Comprehension*

67) Which of the following traits does *not* characterize an individualistic community?

A) discrete geographic boundaries

B) strong abiotic influences on species distributions

C) community composition changes along a gradient

D) strong biotic influences on species distribution

E) bottom–up organization

Answer: D
*Topic: Concept 53.5*
*Skill: Comprehension*

68) The rivet model of community structure suggests that

A) damaged communities can be repaired if species are added.

B) communities are tightly integrated units that may be seriously affected by changes in the abundance of only one species.

C) most communities are robust in the face of disturbance.

D) top–down regulation of communities is most important.

E) if one species disappears, another will probably take its place.

Answer: B
*Topic: Concept 53.5*
*Skill: Comprehension*

69) A biologist measures predation rates by crab spiders on flower–visiting insects in a particular field community. Then the biologist experimentally removes as many of the spiders as she can. She discovers that predation rates remain the same but that the major predators shift from spiders to ambush bugs. Which of the following community structure models is most consistent with her findings?

A) individualistic

B) integrated

C) rivet

D) redundancy

E) manipulative

Answer: D
*Topic: Concept 53.5*
*Skill: Comprehension*

70) Which of the following statements is most consistent with F.E. Clements' integrated hypothesis?

A) Species are distributed independently of other species.

B) Communities lack discrete geographic boundaries.

C) The community functions as an interactive unit.

D) The composition of plant species seems to change on a continuum.

E) The community is a chance assemblage of species.

Answer: C
*Topic: Concept 53.5*
*Skill: Comprehension*

# Media Activity Questions

1) Which of these terms applies to the relationship between a dog and a blood-sucking tick?

   A) predation

   B) competition

   C) parasitism

   D) commensalism

   E) mutualism

   Answer: C
   *Topic: Web/CD Activity: Interspecific Interactions*

2) An earthworm that feeds on the remains of plants and animals is acting as a

   A) producer.

   B) primary consumer.

   C) secondary consumer.

   D) tertiary consumer.

   E) detritivore.

   Answer: E
   *Topic: Web/CD Activity: Food Webs*

3) Which of these is a starting point for primary succession?

   A) a surface exposed by a retreating glacier

   B) abandoned farmland

   C) an abandoned city

   D) a neglected yard

   E) none of the above

   Answer: A
   *Topic: Web/CD Activity: Primary Succession*

4) What is the relationship between colonizing success and the number of species already established on an island?

   A) As the number of established species on an island decreases, colonizing success also decreases.

   B) There is no relationship between the number of established species on an island and colonizing success.

   C) As the number of established species on an island increases, colonizing success also decreases.

   D) As the number of established species on an island increases, colonizing success also increases.

   E) As the number of established species on an island decreases, colonizing success also decreases; and as the number of established species on an island increases, colonizing success also increases.

   Answer: C
   *Topic: Activity: Exploring Island Biogeography*

5) The number of species on an island remains relatively constant when

   A) the rate of successful colonization is less than the extinction rate.

   B) the rate of successful colonization equals the extinction rate.

   C) the rate of successful colonization is greater than the extinction rate.

   D) species richness increases.

   E) none of these occur.

   Answer: B
   *Topic: Activity: Exploring Island Biogeography*

# Self–Quiz Questions

1) The feeding relationships among the species in a community determine the community's
   A) secondary succession.
   B) ecological niche.
   C) trophic structure.
   D) species–area curve.
   E) species richness.

   Answer: C

2) The competitive exclusion principle states that
   A) two species cannot coexist in the same habitat.
   B) competition between two species always causes extinction or emigration of one species.
   C) competition in a population promotes survival of the best–adapted individuals.
   D) two species in a community cannot coexist in the same niche.
   E) species that compete usually coevolve.

   Answer: D

3) Keystone predators maintain a community's species diversity by
   A) competitively excluding other predators.
   B) preying on the community's dominant species.
   C) allowing immigration of other predators.
   D) reducing the number of disruptions in the community.
   E) coevolving with their prey.

   Answer: B

4) Food chains are usually short mainly because
   A) only a single herbivore species feeds on each plant species.
   B) local extinction of a species causes the extinction of other species in its food chain.
   C) most of the energy in a trophic level is lost has it passes to the next higher level.
   D) predators are less diverse and less abundant than prey.
   E) most producers are inedible.

   Answer: C

5) According to the rivet model of community structure,
   A) species share a community because of similar abiotic requirements.
   B) communities generally lack sharp geographic boundaries.
   C) If a species disappears from the community, its role will be assumed by another species.
   D) all species in a natural community contribute to the community's integrity.
   E) dependence on a particular type of soil rivets plant species into a tightly networked community.

   Answer: D

6) A community's species diversity is

    A) increased by frequent massive disturbance.

    B) increased by stable conditions with no disturbance.

    C) increased by moderate levels of disturbance.

    D) increased when humans intervene to eliminate disturbance.

    E) increased by intensive disturbance by humans.

Answer: C

7) Which of the following is an example of Müllerian mimicry?

    A) a butterfly that resembles a leaf

    B) two poisonous frogs with similar color patterns

    C) a minnow with spots that look like large eyes

    D) a beetle that resembles a scorpion

    E) a carnivorous fish with a wormlike tongue that lures prey

Answer: B

8) Which of the following could qualify as a top-down control on a grassland community?

    A) limitation of plant biomass by rainfall amount

    B) influence of temperature on competition among plants

    C) influence of soil nutrients on the abundance of grasses versus wildflowers

    D) effect of grazing intensity by bison on plant species diversity

    E) effect of humidity on plant growth rates

Answer: D

9) The most plausible hypothesis to explain why species richness is higher in tropical than in temperate regions is that

    A) tropical communities are younger.

    B) tropical regions have more available water and higher levels of solar radiation.

    C) warmer temperatures cause more rapid speciation.

    D) biodiversity increases as evapotranspiration decreases.

    E) tropical regions have very high rates of immigration and very low rates of extinction.

Answer: B

10) According to the equilibrium model of island biogeography, species richness would be greatest on an island that is

    A) small and remote.

    B) large and remote.

    C) large and close to a mainland.

    D) small and close to a mainland.

    E) environmentally homogeneous.

Answer: C

# Chapter 54  Ecosystems

1) What is the fundamental difference between matter and energy?
   A) Matter is cycled through ecosystems; energy is not.
   B) Energy is cycled through ecosystems; matter is not.
   C) Energy can be converted into matter; matter cannot be converted into energy.
   D) Matter can be converted into energy; energy cannot be converted into matter.
   E) Matter is used in ecosystems; energy is not

Answer: A
*Topic: Concept 54.1*
*Skill: Comprehension*

2) Which of the following best explains why energy cannot cycle through an ecosystem?
   A) the law of conservation of energy
   B) the second law of thermodynamics
   C) the competitive exclusion principle
   D) the green world hypothesis
   E) the principle of biomagnification

Answer: B
*Topic: Concept 54.1*
*Skill: Comprehension*

3) A cow's herbivorous diet indicates that it is a(n)
   A) primary consumer.
   B) secondary consumer.
   C) decomposer.
   D) autotroph.
   E) producer.

Answer: A
*Topic: Concept 54.1*
*Skill: Knowledge*

4) To recycle nutrients, the minimum an ecosystem must have is
   A) producers.
   B) producers and decomposers.
   C) producers, primary consumers, and decomposers.
   D) producers, primary consumers, secondary consumers, and decomposers.
   E) producers, primary consumers, secondary consumers, top carnivores, and decomposers.

Answer: B
*Topic: Concept 54.1*
*Skill: Comprehension*

5) Which of the following terms encompasses all of the others?
   A) heterotrophs
   B) herbivores
   C) carnivores
   D) primary consumers
   E) secondary consumers

Answer: A
*Topic: Concept 54.1*
*Skill: Comprehension*

6) Production, consumption, and decomposition are important ecosystem processes. Which of the following could be decomposers?
   A) bacteria
   B) vertebrates
   C) invertebrates
   D) A and C only
   E) A, B, and C

Answer: E
*Topic: Concept 54.1*
*Skill: Knowledge*

7) Which of the following are responsible for most of the conversion of organic materials into $CO_2$, which can be utilized in primary production?

 A) autotrophs

 B) bacteria

 C) fungi

 D) B and C only

 E) A, B, and C

Answer: D
*Topic: Concept 54.1*
*Skill: Knowledge*

8) The main decomposers in an ecosystem are

 A) fungi.

 B) plants.

 C) insects.

 D) prokaryotes.

 E) both A and D

Answer: E
*Topic: Concept 54.1*
*Skill: Knowledge*

9) Many homeowners mow their lawns during the summer and collect the clippings, which are then hauled to the local landfill. Which of the following alternatives would cause the least disturbance to local ecosystems?

 A) Don't mow the lawn—have sheep graze it and put the sheep's feces into the landfill.

 B) Collect the clippings and burn them.

 C) Either collect the clippings and add them to a compost pile, or don't collect the clippings and let them decompose on the lawn.

 D) Collect the clippings and wash them into the nearest storm sewer that feeds into the local lake.

 E) Dig up the lawn and cover the yard with asphalt.

Answer: C
*Topic: Concept 54.1*
*Skill: Comprehension*

10) The producers in ecosystems include organisms in which of the following groups?

 A) prokaryotes

 B) algae

 C) plants

 D) B and C only

 E) A, B, and C

Answer: E
*Topic: Concept 54.2*
*Skill: Knowledge*

11) Subtraction of which of the following will convert gross primary productivity into net primary productivity?

A) the energy contained in the standing crop

B) the energy used by heterotrophs in respiration

C) the energy used by autotrophs in respiration

D) the energy fixed by photosynthesis

E) all solar energy

Answer: C
*Topic: Concept 54.2*
*Skill: Comprehension*

12) The difference between net and gross primary productivity would likely be greatest for

A) phytoplankton in the ocean.

B) corn plants in a farmer's field.

C) prairie grasses.

D) an oak tree in a forest.

E) sphagnum moss in a bog.

Answer: D
*Topic: Concept 54.2*
*Skill: Comprehension*

13) Which of these ecosystems accounts for the largest amount of Earth's net primary productivity?

A) tundra

B) savanna

C) salt marsh

D) open ocean

E) tropical rain forest

Answer: D
*Topic: Concept 54.2*
*Skill: Knowledge*

14) Which of these ecosystems has the highest net primary productivity per square meter?

A) savanna

B) open ocean

C) boreal forest

D) tropical rain forest

E) temperate forest

Answer: D
*Topic: Concept 54.2*
*Skill: Comprehension*

15) The total biomass of photosynthetic autotrophs present in an ecosystem is known as

A) gross primary productivity.

B) standing crop.

C) net primary productivity.

D) secondary productivity.

E) trophic efficiency.

Answer: B
*Topic: Concept 54.2*
*Skill: Knowledge*

16) How is it that the open ocean produces the highest net primary productivity of Earth's ecosystems, yet net primary productivity per square meter is relatively low?

A) It contains greater concentrations of nutrients.

B) It receives a greater amount of solar energy per unit area.

C) It has the greatest total area.

D) It contains more species of organisms.

E) Its producers are generally much smaller than its consumers.

Answer: C
*Topic: Concept 54.2*
*Skill: Knowledge*

17) Aquatic primary productivity is often limited by which of the following?

A) light

B) nutrients

C) pressure

D) A and B only

E) A, B, and C

Answer: D
*Topic: Concept 54.2*
*Skill: Comprehension*

18) Aquatic ecosystems are unlikely to be limited by insufficient

A) nitrogen.

B) carbon.

C) phosphorus.

D) iron.

E) sodium.

Answer: B
*Topic: Concept 54.2*
*Skill: Comprehension*

19) Which of the following organisms fix nitrogen in aquatic ecosystems?

A) cyanobacteria

B) chemoautotrophs

C) phytoplankton

D) legumes

E) fungi

Answer: A
*Topic: Concept 54.2*
*Skill: Knowledge*

20) As big as it is, the ocean is nutrient-limited. If you wanted to investigate this, one reasonable avenue would be to

A) follow whale migrations in order to determine where most nutrients are.

B) observe Antarctic Ocean productivity and compare that to other areas.

C) experimentally enrich some areas of the ocean and compare them to unmanipulated areas.

D) B and C only

E) A, B, and C

Answer: D
*Topic: Concept 54.2*
*Skill: Comprehension*

21) The amount of chemical energy in consumers' food that is converted to their own new biomass during a given time period is called

A) biomass.

B) standing crop.

C) biomagnification.

D) primary production.

E) secondary production.

Answer: E
*Topic: Concept 54.3*
*Skill: Knowledge*

22) How does inefficient transfer of energy among trophic levels influence the typically high risk of extinction shared by most top predators?

A) Predators are sparsely distributed.

B) Predators have relatively small population sizes.

C) Predators are more disease-prone than animals at lower trophic levels.

D) A and B only

E) A, B, and C

Answer: D
*Topic: Concept 54.3*
*Skill: Comprehension*

23) Trophic efficiency is
   A) the ratio of net secondary production to assimilation of primary production.
   B) the percentage of production transferred from one trophic level to the next.
   C) the ratio of net production at one trophic level to the net production at the level below, expressed as a percentage.
   D) usually greater than production efficiencies.
   E) both B and C

Answer: E
*Topic: Concept 54.3*
*Skill: Comprehension*

24) Which of the following pyramids cannot be inverted?
   A) production
   B) biomass
   C) numbers
   D) A and B only
   E) A, B, and C

Answer: A
*Topic: Concept 54.3*
*Skill: Comprehension*

25) If you wanted to convert excess grain into the greatest amount of animal biomass, to which animal would you feed the grain?
   A) chickens
   B) mice
   C) cattle
   D) carp (a type of fish)
   E) mealworms (larval insects)

Answer: E
*Topic: Concept 54.3*
*Skill: Comprehension*

26) Organisms in which of the following groups can be primary producers?
   A) cyanobacteria
   B) zooplankton
   C) flowering plants
   D) A and C only
   E) A, B, and C

Answer: D
*Topic: Concept 54.3*
*Skill: Knowledge*

27) In general, the total biomass in a terrestrial ecosystem will be greatest for which trophic level?
   A) producers
   B) herbivores
   C) primary consumers
   D) tertiary consumers
   E) secondary consumers

Answer: A
*Topic: Concept 54.3*
*Skill: Knowledge*

28) Some aquatic ecosystems can have inverted biomass pyramids because
   A) phytoplankton are much larger than zooplankton.
   B) phytoplankton have a relatively short life cycle.
   C) consumption of phytoplankton by zooplankton is so rapid that the standing crop of phytoplankton remains relatively low.
   D) B and C only
   E) A, B, and C

Answer: D
*Topic: Concept 54.3*
*Skill: Knowledge*

*Refer to Figure 54.1, a diagram of a food web, for the following questions. (Arrows represent energy flow and letters represent species.)*

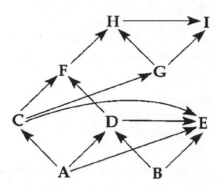

**Figure 54.1**

29) If this were a terrestrial food web, the combined biomass of C + D would probably be

A) greater than the biomass of A.

B) less than the biomass of H.

C) greater than the biomass of B.

D) less than the biomass of A + B.

E) less than the biomass of E.

Answer: D
*Topic: Concept 54.3*
*Skill: Comprehension*

30) If this were a marine food web, the smallest organism might be

A) A.

B) F.

C) C.

D) I.

E) E.

Answer: A
*Topic: Concept 54.3*
*Skill: Application*

31) For most terrestrial ecosystems, pyramids of numbers, biomass, and energy are essentially the same—they have a broad base and a narrow top. The primary reason for this pattern is that

A) secondary consumers and top carnivores require less energy than producers.

B) at each step, energy is lost from the system as a result of keeping the organisms alive.

C) as matter passes through ecosystems, some of it is lost to the environment.

D) biomagnification of toxic materials limits the secondary consumers and top carnivores.

E) top carnivores and secondary consumers have a more general diet than primary producers.

Answer: B
*Topic: Concept 54.3*
*Skill: Comprehension*

32) Which of the following is primarily responsible for limiting the number of trophic levels in most ecosystems?

A) Many primary and higher-order consumers are opportunistic feeders.

B) Most predators require large home ranges.

C) Nutrient cycles involve both abiotic and biotic components of ecosystems.

D) Nutrient cycling rates tend to be limited by decomposition.

E) Each energy transfer is less than 100% efficient.

Answer: E
*Topic: Concept 54.3*
*Skill: Comprehension*

33) Which of the following situations is consistent with the green world hypothesis?

    A) Milkweed plants are eaten by monarch caterpillars.

    B) Some gypsy moths cannot feed and thus die because others moths have defoliated the trees in the area.

    C) Webworms cooperate with each other to build a protective silken structure around themselves.

    D) A mild winter improves the survival rate of overwintering cutworms.

    E) Grasshoppers in a corn field are killed by a viral infection.

Answer: E
*Topic: Concept 54.3*
*Skill: Comprehension*

34) Which of the following statements about energy flow is *incorrect*?

    A) Secondary productivity declines with each trophic level.

    B) Only net primary productivity is available to consumers.

    C) About 90% of the energy at one trophic level does not appear at the next.

    D) Eating meat is probably the most economical way of acquiring the energy of photosynthetic productivity.

    E) Only about one-thousandth of the chemical energy fixed by photosynthesis reaches a tertiary-level consumer.

Answer: D
*Topic: Concept 54.3*
*Skill: Comprehension*

35) Nitrogen is available to plants only in the form of

    A) ammonium.

    B) nitrite.

    C) nitrate.

    D) A and C only

    E) A, B, and C

Answer: D
*Topic: Concept 54.4*
*Skill: Knowledge*

36) In the nitrogen cycle, the bacteria that replenish the atmosphere with $N_2$ are

    A) *Rhizobium* bacteria.

    B) nitrifying bacteria.

    C) denitrifying bacteria.

    D) methanogenic protozoans.

    E) nitrogen-fixing bacteria.

Answer: C
*Topic: Concept 54.4*
*Skill: Knowledge*

37) How does phosphorus normally enter the atmosphere?

    A) respiration

    B) photosynthesis

    C) rock weathering

    D) geological uplifting (subduction and vulcanism)

    E) It does not enter the atmosphere in biologically significant amounts.

Answer: E
*Topic: Concept 54.4*
*Skill: Knowledge*

38) Which of the following statements is correct about biogeochemical cycling?

A) The phosphorus cycle involves the rapid recycling of atmospheric phosphorus.

B) The phosphorus cycle is a sedimentary cycle that involves the weathering of rocks.

C) The carbon cycle is a localized cycle that primarily reflects the burning of fossil fuels.

D) The carbon cycle has maintained a constant atmospheric concentration of $CO_2$ for the past million years.

E) The nitrogen cycle involves movement of nitrogen very little of which is chemically altered by either the biotic or abiotic components of the ecosystem.

Answer: B
*Topic: Concept 54.4*
*Skill: Knowledge*

39) Long-term ecological research at the Hubbard Brook Experimental Forest indicates that

A) intensive logging can dramatically increase levels of nitrate and calcium ions retained in the soil.

B) the amount of nutrients leaving an intact forest ecosystem is controlled by the plants themselves.

C) selective logging can actually increase species richness in temperate forests.

D) A and C only

E) A, B, and C

Answer: B
*Topic: Concept 54.4*
*Skill: Knowledge*

40) If you were tracking a nutrient molecule through an ecosystem, which of the following statements would you expect to verify?

A) Molecules move through all ecosystems at the same constant rate, as the laws of physics would predict.

B) Because of the liquid nature of the aquatic ecosystem, nutrient molecules move through it rapidly compared with forest ecosystems.

C) Vertical mixing is essential for high productivity in aquatic ecosystems.

D) A and B only

E) A, B, and C

Answer: C
*Topic: Concept 54.4*
*Skill: Comprehension*

41) Which of the following statements is (are) true?

A) An ecosystem's trophic structure determines the rate at which energy cycles within the system.

B) At any point in time, it is impossible for consumers to outnumber producers in an ecosystem.

C) Chemoautotrophic prokaryotes near deep-sea vents are primary producers.

D) There has been a well-documented increase in atmospheric carbon dioxide over the past several decades.

E) both C and D

Answer: E
*Topic: Concept 54.5*
*Skill: Knowledge*

42) Human-induced modifications of the nitrogen cycle can result in

   A) eutrophication of freshwater ecosystems.

   B) increased availability of fixed nitrogen to primary producers.

   C) accumulation of toxic levels of nitrates in groundwater.

   D) A and C only

   E) A, B, and C

Answer: E
*Topic: Concept 54.5*
*Skill: Knowledge*

43) The high levels of pesticides found in birds of prey is an example of

   A) eutrophication.

   B) predation.

   C) biological magnification.

   D) the green world hypothesis.

   E) chemical cycling through an ecosystem.

Answer: C
*Topic: Concept 54.5*
*Skill: Knowledge*

44) If the flow of energy in an arctic ecosystem goes through a simple food chain from seaweeds to fish to seals to polar bears, then which of the following is true?

   A) Polar bears can provide more food for people than seals can.

   B) The total energy content of the seaweeds is lower than that of the seals.

   C) Polar bear meat probably contains the highest concentrations of fat-soluble toxins.

   D) Seals are more numerous than fish.

   E) The carnivores can provide more food for people than the herbivores can.

Answer: C
*Topic: Concept 54.5*
*Skill: Application*

*Use Figure 54.2 to answer the following questions. Examine this food web for a particular terrestrial ecosystem. Each letter is a species. The arrows represent energy flow.*

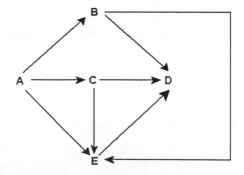

**Figure 54.2**

45) Which species is autotrophic?

Answer: A
*Topic: Concept 54.1*
*Skill: Comprehension*

46) Which species is most likely the decomposer?

Answer: E
*Topic: Concept 54.1*
*Skill: Comprehension*

47) A toxic pollutant would probably reach its highest concentration in which species?

Answer: D
*Topic: Concept 54.5*
*Skill: Comprehension*

48) Species C is toxic to predators. Which species is most likely to benefit from being a mimic of C?

Answer: B
*Topic: Concept 54.1*
*Skill: Application*

49) Excluding the decomposer, biomass would probably be smallest for which species?

Answer: D
*Topic: Concept 54.3*
*Skill: Comprehension*

*The following questions refer to the organisms in a grassland ecosystem listed below. Each term may be used once, more than once, or not at all.*

A. hawks
B. snakes
C. shrews
D. grasshoppers
E. grass

50) an autotroph

Answer: E
*Topic: Concept 54.1*
*Skill: Comprehension*

51) an herbivore

Answer: D
*Topic: Concept 54.1*
*Skill: Comprehension*

52) smallest biomass

Answer: A
*Topic: Concept 54.3*
*Skill: Comprehension*

53) tertiary consumer

Answer: B
*Topic: Concept 54.3*
*Skill: Comprehension*

54) probably contains the highest concentration of toxic pollutants (biological magnification)

Answer: A
*Topic: Concept 54.5*
*Skill: Comprehension*

55) When levels of $CO_2$ are experimentally increased, $C_3$ plants generally respond with a greater increase in productivity than $C_4$ plants. This is because

A) $C_3$ plants are more efficient in their use of $CO_2$.

B) $C_3$ plants are able to obtain the same amount of $CO_2$ by keeping their stomata open for shorter periods of time.

C) $C_4$ plants don't use $CO_2$ as their source of carbon.

D) $C_3$ plants are more limited than $C_4$ plants by $CO_2$ availability.

E) B and D only.

Answer: D
*Topic: Concept 54.5*
*Skill: Comprehension*

*The following questions refer to the terms below. Each term may be used once, more than once, or not at all.*

   A.   green world hypothesis
   B.   turnover
   C.   biological magnification
   D.   greenhouse effect
   E.   cultural eutrophication

56) $CO_2$ and water vapor re-reflect infrared radiation back toward Earth

   Answer: D
   *Topic: Concept 54.5*
   *Skill: Comprehension*

57) caused by excessive nutrient input into lakes

   Answer: E
   *Topic: Concept 54.5*
   *Skill: Comprehension*

58) caused excessively high levels of DDT in fish-eating birds

   Answer: C
   *Topic: Concept 54.5*
   *Skill: Comprehension*

59) occurs at a high rate for nutrients in tropical rain forests

   Answer: B
   *Topic: Concept 54.4*
   *Skill: Comprehension*

60) All of the following are likely results of land–clearing operations such as deforestation and agricultural activity *except*

   A) destruction of plant and animal habitats.

   B) erosion of soil due to increased water runoff.

   C) leaching of minerals from the soil.

   D) rapid eutrophication of streams and lakes.

   E) decreased carbon dioxide in the atmosphere.

   Answer: E
   *Topic: Concept 54.5*
   *Skill: Comprehension*

61) Agricultural lands frequently require nutritional supplementation because

   A) genetically engineered crops require more nutrients.

   B) the nutrients that enter the plants grown on those lands do not return to that soil.

   C) the prairies that comprise good agricultural land tend to be nutrient-poor.

   D) grains raised for feed must be fortified, and thus require additional nutrients.

   E) both A and B

   Answer: B
   *Topic: Concept 54.5*
   *Skill: Comprehension*

62) Burning fossil fuels releases oxides of sulfur and nitrogen. Ultimately, these are probably responsible for

A) the death of fish in Norwegian lakes.

B) rain with a pH of 3.0.

C) calcium deficiency in soils.

D) B and C only

E) A, B, and C

Answer: E
*Topic: Concept 54.5*
*Skill: Knowledge*

63) You have a friend who is wary of environmentalists' claims that global warming could lead to major biological change on Earth. Which of the following statements can you truthfully make in response to your friend's suspicions?

A) We know that atmospheric carbon dioxide has increased in the last 150 years.

B) Through measurements and observations, we know that carbon dioxide and temperature were correlated even in prehistoric times.

C) Global warming could have significant effects on United States agriculture.

D) A and C only

E) A, B, and C

Answer: E
*Topic: Concept 54.5*
*Skill: Comprehension*

# Media Activity Questions

1) 10,000 kcal of producer would support approximately _____ kcal of tertiary consumer.

   A) 1

   B) 0

   C) 1,000

   D) 10

   E) 100

   Answer: D
   *Topic: Web/CD Activity: Pyramids of Production*

2) Which of these removes carbon from the atmosphere?

   A) burning fossil fuels, such as oil

   B) algae

   C) rabbits

   D) bobcats

   E) logging trees

   Answer: B
   *Topic: Web/CD Activity: The Carbon Cycle*

3) Denitrifying bacteria convert _____ to _____.

   A) ammonium; nitrogen gas

   B) nitrates; nitrogen gas

   C) nitrogen gas; nitrates

   D) nitrogen gas; ammonium

   E) nitrogen gas; nitrites

   Answer: B
   *Topic: Web/CD Activity: The Nitrogen Cycle*

4) Which of these are two major sources of nitrate pollution in rivers?

   A) animal waste and fertilizers

   B) the burning of fossil fuels by factories and cars

   C) animal waste and the burning of fossil fuels by cars

   D) fertilizer runoff and the burning of fossil fuels by cars

   E) animal wastes and the burning of fossil fuels by factories

   Answer: A
   *Topic: Activity: Water Pollution from Nitrates*

5) Switching from fossil fuels to _____ energy would significantly decrease the release of carbon dioxide into the atmosphere.

   A) geothermal

   B) solar and geothermal

   C) solar, nuclear, and geothermal

   D) nuclear

   E) solar

   Answer: C
   *Topic: Web/CD Activity: The Greenhouse Effect*

# Self-Quiz Questions

1) Which of the following organisms is *incorrectly* paired with its trophic level?

   A) cyanobacteria—primary producer

   B) grasshopper—primary consumer

   C) zooplankton—secondary consumer

   D) eagle—tertiary consumer

   E) fungi—detritivore

   Answer: C

2) A production pyramid such as the one shown in Figure 54.11 (in the text) implies that

   A) only half the energy in a trophic level is transferred on to the next-higher level.

   B) most of the energy in a trophic level is incorporated into the next-higher level.

   C) as energy is transferred from one trophic level to another, about 10% of the energy is lost.

   D) the most efficient transfer of energy is from producers to primary consumers.

   E) eating grain-fed beef is an inefficient way to obtain the energy captured by photosynthesis.

   Answer: E

3) Nitrifying bacteria participate in the nitrogen cycle mainly by

   A) converting nitrogen gas to ammonia.

   B) releasing ammonia from organic compounds, thus returning it to the soil.

   C) converting ammonia to nitrogen gas, which returns to the atmosphere.

   D) converting ammonia to nitrate, which is absorbed by plants.

   E) incorporating nitrogen into amino acids and organic compounds.

   Answer: D

4) The Hubbard Brook watershed deforestation experiment supported all of the following conclusions *except* that

   A) most minerals were recycled within a forest ecosystem.

   B) the flow of minerals out of a natural watershed was offset by minerals flowing in.

   C) deforestation increased water runoff.

   D) the nitrate concentration in waters draining the deforested area became dangerously high.

   E) calcium levels remained high in the soil of deforested areas.

   Answer: E

5) The main cause of the recent increase in $CO_2$ concentration in Earth's atmosphere is

   A) increased worldwide primary production.

   B) increased worldwide standing crop biomass.

   C) an increase in the amount of infrared radiation absorbed by the atmosphere.

   D) the burning of larger amounts of wood and fossil fuels.

   E) additional respiration by the rapidly growing human population.

   Answer: D

6) Which of the following is a consequence of biological magnification?

   A) Toxic chemicals in the environment pose greater risk to top-level predators than to primary consumers.

   B) Populations of top-level predators are generally smaller than populations of primary consumers.

   C) The biomass of producers in an ecosystem is generally higher than the biomass of primary consumers.

   D) Only a small portion of the energy captured by producers is transferred to consumers.

   E) The amount of biomass in the producer level of an ecosystem decreases if the producer turnover time increases.

   Answer: A

7) Which of these ecosystems has the lowest net primary production per square meter?

   A) a salt marsh

   B) an open ocean

   C) a coral reef

   D) a grassland

   E) a tropical rain forest

   Answer: B

8) Tropical forest soils contain comparatively low levels of mineral nutrients because

   A) the standing crop biomass of tropical forests is comparatively small.

   B) tropical soil microorganisms do not break down organic matter as efficiently as temperate zone soil microorganisms do.

   C) organic matter decomposes more rapidly and plants assimilate soil nutrients more rapidly in the tropics.

   D) nutrients cycle more slowly in the tropics.

   E) many nutrients are destroyed by high temperatures in the tropics.

   Answer: C

9) Imagine that you test samples of coastal water polluted with run-off from farms and find detectable levels of phosphates, but not of nitrogen. In a follow-up experiment, you find that if you enrich some of your samples with nitrogen, algal growth is much greater than in unenriched, control samples. Enriching samples with phosphate, however, does not increase algal growth. From your results, you can conclude that

   A) algae populations in these waters could be reduced by decreasing phosphate runoff.

   B) eutrophication of these waters could be reduced by adding nitrogen.

   C) algae populations in these waters are kept low by high levels of phosphorus.

   D) nitrogen is the limiting nutrient in these waters.

   E) phosphate is the limiting nutrient in these waters.

   Answer: D

10) Which of the following greatest effect on the rate of chemical cycling in an ecosystem?

   A) the ecosystem's rate of primary production

   B) the production efficiency of the ecosystem's consumers

   C) the rate of decomposition in the ecosystem

   D) the trophic efficiency of the ecosystem

   E) the location of the nutrient reservoirs in the ecosystem

Answer: C

# Chapter 55 Conservation Biology and Restoration Ecology

1) What is the estimated number of extant species on Earth?
   A) 1,000 to 50,000
   B) 50,000 to 150,000
   C) 500,000 to 1,000,000
   D) 10,000,000 to 200,000,000
   E) 5 billion–10 billion

   Answer: D
   *Topic: Overview*
   *Skill: Knowledge*

2) Estimates of current rates of extinction
   A) indicate that we have reached a state of unstable equilibrium in which speciation and extinction rates are approximately equal.
   B) suggest that one–half of all animal and plant species may be gone by the year 2100.
   C) indicate that rates may be 1,000 times higher than at any other time in the last 100,000 years.
   D) B and C only
   E) A, B, and C

   Answer: C
   *Topic: Overview*
   *Skill: Knowledge*

3) Extinction is a natural phenomenon. It is estimated that 99% of all species that ever lived are now extinct. Why then do we say that we are now in a biodiversity crisis?
   A) Humans are ethically responsible for protecting endangered species.
   B) Scientists have finally identified most of the species on Earth and are thus able to quantify the number of species becoming extinct.
   C) The current rate of extinction is as much as 1,000 times higher than at any other time in the last 100,000 years.
   D) Humans have greater medical needs than at any other time in history, and many potential medicinal compounds are being lost as plant species become extinct.
   E) Most biodiversity hot spots have been destroyed by recent ecological disasters.

   Answer: C
   *Topic: Overview*
   *Skill: Comprehension*

4) Although extinction is a natural process, current extinctions are of concern to environmentalists because
   A) more animals than ever before are going extinct.
   B) most current extinctions are caused by introduced species.
   C) the rate of extinction is unusually high.
   D) current extinction is primarily affecting plant diversity.
   E) none of the above

   Answer: C
   *Topic: Concept 55.1*
   *Skill: Knowledge*

5) Which of the following terms includes all of the others?

A) species diversity

B) biodiversity

C) genetic diversity

D) ecosystem diversity

E) species richness

Answer: B
*Topic: Concept 55.1*
*Skill: Knowledge*

6) The Nile perch (*Lates niloticus*) is a good example of a(n)

A) introduced predator.

B) endangered endemic.

C) population sink.

D) threatened migratory species.

E) primary consumer.

Answer: A
*Topic: Concept 55.1*
*Skill: Knowledge*

7) According to the U.S. Endangered Species Act (ESA), the difference between an endangered species and a threatened one is that

A) an endangered species is closer to extinction.

B) a threatened species is closer to extinction.

C) threatened species are endangered species outside the U.S. borders.

D) endangered species are mainly tropical.

E) There is no real difference.

Answer: A
*Topic: Concept 55.1*
*Skill: Knowledge*

8) In order to better understand the extent of current extinctions, it will be necessary to

A) monitor atmospheric carbon dioxide levels.

B) differentiate between plant extinction and animal extinction.

C) focus on identifying more species of mammals and birds.

D) identify more of the yet unknown species of organisms on Earth.

E) use the average extinction rates of vertebrates as a baseline.

Answer: D
*Topic: Concept 55.1*
*Skill: Comprehension*

9) Carbon dioxide and other gases prevent some heat from escaping Earth's atmosphere. This is known as the _____ effect.

A) warming

B) summer

C) carbon

D) carbon dioxide

E) greenhouse

Answer: E
*Topic: Concept 55.1*
*Skill: Knowledge*

10) What is the term for a top predator that contributes to the maintenance of species diversity among its animal prey?

A) keystone species

B) keystone mutualist

C) landscape species

D) primary consumer

E) tertiary consumer

Answer: A
*Topic: Concepts 55.1, 55.2*
*Skill: Comprehension*

11) E.O. Wilson coined the term _____ for our innate appreciation of wild environments and living organisms.

A) bioremediation

B) bioethics

C) biophilia

D) biophobia

E) landscape ecology

Answer: C
*Topic: Concept 55.1*
*Skill: Knowledge*

12) In which ocean would you find the island of Madagascar?

A) North Atlantic

B) South Atlantic

C) Indian

D) North Pacific

E) South Pacific

Answer: C
*Topic: Concept 55.1*
*Skill: Knowledge*

13) Which of the following would not qualify as an ecosystem service?

A) rain falling to the ground

B) blowfly larvae infesting a deer carcass

C) bees pollinating an apple tree

D) squirrels burying acorns

E) leaves falling on a forest floor

Answer: A
*Topic: Concept 55.1*
*Skill: Comprehension*

14) Suppose you attend a town meeting at which some experts tell the audience that they have performed a cost–benefit analysis of a proposed transit system that would probably reduce overall air pollution and fossil fuel consumption. The analysis, however, reveals that ticket prices will not cover the cost of operating the system when fuel, wages, and equipment are taken into account. As a biologist, you know that if ecosystem services had been included in the analysis the experts might have arrived at a different answer. Why are ecosystem services rarely included in economic analyses?

A) Their cost is difficult to quantify.

B) They are not worth much.

C) People take them for granted.

D) A and C only

E) A, B and C

Answer: D
*Topic: Concept 55.1*
*Skill: Comprehension*

15) One level of the biodiversity crisis is the potential loss of ecosystems. The most serious consequence of a likely loss in ecosystem diversity would be the

A) increase in global warming and thinning of the ozone layer.

B) loss of ecosystem services on which people depend.

C) increase in the dominance of edge-adapted species.

D) loss of source of genetic diversity to preserve endangered species.

E) loss of species for "bioprospecting."

Answer: B
*Topic: Concept 55.1*
*Skill: Comprehension*

16) Which of the following most directly relates to the current biodiversity crisis?

A) increased atmospheric carbon dioxide

B) ozone depletion

C) overexploitation of species

D) habitat destruction

E) zoned reserves

Answer: D
*Topic: Concept 55.1*
*Skill: Knowledge*

17) According to most conservation biologists, the single greatest threat to global biodiversity is

A) chemical pollution of water and air.

B) stratospheric ozone depletion.

C) insufficient recycling programs for nonrenewable resources.

D) alteration or destruction of the physical habitat.

E) global climate change resulting from a variety of human activities.

Answer: D
*Topic: Concept 55.1*
*Skill: Knowledge*

18) Which of the following statements is false?

A) Within the contiguous United States, more than 50% of wetlands have been drained since the arrival of the first European settlers.

B) In Central America and Mexico, approximately 98% of tropical dry forests have been cleared.

C) Given current trends, we can expect at least 20% of the biosphere eventually to be protected in nature reserves.

D) Of the southern Wisconsin prairie that greeted early settlers, less than 0.1% remains.

E) The United States contains over 50,000 introduced species.

Answer: C
*Topic: Concept 55.1*
*Skill: Knowledge*

19) How is habitat fragmentation related to extinction?

A) Less carbon dioxide is absorbed by plants.

B) More soil is subject to erosion.

C) Populations of organisms in fragments are smaller and, thus, more susceptible to extinction.

D) Animals are forced out of habitat fragments.

E) Fragments generate silt that negatively affects drainages.

Answer: C
*Topic: Concept 55.1*
*Skill: Comprehension*

20) Which of the following is *not* an example of an introduced species?

A) brown tree snakes in Guam

B) timber wolves in Minnesota

C) zebra mussels in the Great Lakes

D) kudzu plants in the southern United States

E) starlings in New York

Answer: B
*Topic: Concept 55.1*
*Skill: Knowledge*

21) Introduced species can have deleterious effects on biological communities by

A) preying on native species.

B) competing with native species for resources.

C) displacing native species.

D) A and B only

E) A, B, and C

Answer: E
*Topic: Concept 55.1*
*Skill: Knowledge*

22) Introduced species

A) are a problem because they can prey on or outcompete native species.

B) are sometimes present as a result of attempts at biological control.

C) are sometimes accidentally transported to new environments.

D) A and B only

E) A, B, and C

Answer: E
*Topic: Concept 55.1*
*Skill: Comprehension*

23) Overexploitation encourages extinction and is most likely to affect

A) animals with restricted habitats.

B) large animals with low intrinsic reproductive ratios.

C) most organisms that live in the oceans.

D) A and B only

E) A, B, and C

Answer: D
*Topic: Concept 55.1*
*Skill: Comprehension*

24) How might the extinction of some Pacific island bats called "flying foxes" threaten survival of over 75% of the tree species in those islands?

A) The bats eat the insects that harm competitor plants.

B) The bats eat fruit that is part of the trees' reproductive cycles.

C) The bats roost in the trees and fertilize soil around the trees.

D) The bats pollinate the trees and disperse seeds.

E) The bats pierce the fruit, which allows the seeds to germinate.

Answer: D
*Topic: Concept 55.1*
*Skill: Knowledge*

25) Which of the following does *not* represent a potential threat to biodiversity?

   A) importing a European insect into the United States to control an undesirable weed

   B) building a new mall on a previously unoccupied piece of midwestern prairie

   C) letting previously used farmland go fallow and begin to fill with weeds and shrubs

   D) harvesting all of the oysters from an oyster bed off the Atlantic coast

   E) shooting wolves because they pose a threat to ranch cattle

Answer: C
*Topic: Concept 55.1*
*Skill: Comprehension*

26) Which of the following does *not* apply to the concept of the extinction vortex?

   A) Populations of the species entering it are small.

   B) The key factor driving the extinction vortex is intraspecific competition.

   C) The genetic variation of the species' population decreases.

   D) It is a concept developed by conservation biologists who adopt the "small population approach."

   E) Interbreeding leads to smaller populations, which leads to more interbreeding, and so on.

Answer: B
*Topic: Concept 55.2*
*Skill: Comprehension*

27) Which of the following conditions is the *most* likely indicator of a population in an extinction vortex?

   A) The population is divided into smaller populations.

   B) The species is rare.

   C) The effective population size of the species falls below 500.

   D) Genetic measurements indicate a continuing loss of genetic variation.

   E) The population is no longer connected by corridors.

Answer: D
*Topic: Concept 55.2*
*Skill: Comprehension*

28) According to the small–population approach, what would be the best strategy for saving a population that is in an extinction vortex?

   A) determining the minimum viable population size by taking into account the effective population size

   B) establishing a nature reserve to protect its habitat

   C) introducing individuals from other populations to increase genetic variation

   D) determining and remedying the cause of its decline

   E) reducing the population size of its predators and competitors

Answer: C
*Topic: Concept 55.2*
*Skill: Comprehension*

29) One chief area of concern among biologists who use the small-population approach is

A) intraspecific competition.

B) sexual selection.

C) genetic diversity.

D) runaway selection.

E) both A and D

Answer: C
*Topic: Concept 55.2*
*Skill: Comprehension*

30) Which of the following is a method of predicting the likelihood that a species will persist in a particular environment?

A) source–sink analysis

B) population viability analysis

C) minimum viable population size

D) A and C only

E) A, B, and C

Answer: B
*Topic: Concept 55.2*
*Skill: Knowledge*

31) Review the formula for effective population size. Imagine a population of 1,000 small rodents. Of these, 300 are breeding females, 300 are breeding males, and 400 are nonbreeding juveniles. What is the effective population size?

A) 1,000

B) 1,200

C) 600

D) 400

E) 300

Answer: C
*Topic: Concept 55.2*
*Skill: Application*

32) If the sex ratio in a population is significantly different from 50:50, then which of the following will always be *true*?

A) The population will enter the extinction vortex.

B) The genetic variation in the population will increase over time.

C) The genetic variation in the population will decrease over time.

D) The effective population size is greater than the actual population size.

E) The effective population size is less than the actual population size.

Answer: E
*Topic: Concept 55.2*
*Skill: Comprehension*

33) Which of the following statements related to genetic variation is *true*?

A) Genetic variation does not contribute to biodiversity.

B) Population size is always positively correlated with genetic variation.

C) Populations with low $N_e$ are relatively susceptible to effects of bottlenecking and genetic drift.

D) Recent increases in population size of the northern sea elephant are probably related to high levels of genetic variation.

E) Cord grass populations that live in salt marshes require great genetic variation to thrive.

Answer: C
*Topic: Concept 55.2*
*Skill: Comprehension*

34) Which of the following life history traits can potentially influence effective population size ($N_e$)?

A) maturation age

B) genetic relatedness among individuals in a population

C) family size

D) A and B only

E) A, B, and C

Answer: E
*Topic: Concept 55.2*
*Skill: Knowledge*

35) A population of strictly monogamous swans consists of 40 males and 10 females. What is the effective population size ($N_e$) for this population?

A) 50

B) 40

C) 32

D) 20

E) 10

Answer: C
*Topic: Concept 55.2*
*Skill: Application*

36) The declining-population approach to conservation strategies

A) emphasizes the development of theories to understand the extinction process.

B) emphasizes smallness of a population as the ultimate cause of extinction.

C) emphasizes the environmental factors that cause a population decline.

D) is proactive.

E) both C and D

Answer: E
*Topic: Concept 55.2*
*Skill: Comprehension*

37) Which of the following statements about the declining-population approach to conservation is *not* correct?

A) We need information on whether the population in question is in decline or not.

B) We need to do something quickly, even if we have no information, because conservation biology is a crisis-intervention discipline.

C) Several hypotheses about why the population is declining should be evaluated.

D) A proposed reason for the decline should be tested experimentally.

E) Humans may not be the cause of every population decline.

Answer: B
*Topic: Concept 55.2*
*Skill: Comprehension*

38) If we say a species is *endemic* to a certain area, we mean that

A) it is found only in one particular area of the world

B) it has been introduced to that area.

C) it is endangered in that area.

D) A and C only

E) A, B, and C

Answer: A
*Topic: Concept 55.2*
*Skill: Knowledge*

39) Conservation biology often highlights the relationships concerning which of the following?

A) science

B) technology

C) society

D) A and C only

E) A, B, and C

Answer: E
*Topic: Concept 55.2*
*Skill: Knowledge*

40) Modern conservation science increasingly aims at
   A) protecting federally listed endangered species.
   B) lobbying for strict enforcement of the U.S. Endangered Species Act.
   C) sustaining biodiversity of entire ecosystems and communities.
   D) maintaining all genetic diversity within all species.
   E) both A and B

Answer: C
*Topic: Concept 55.2*
*Skill: Knowledge*

41) Which of the following would a landscape ecologist consider in designing a nature reserve?
   A) patterns of landscape use by humans
   B) human economic concerns
   C) possible edge effects related to human activities
   D) A and B only
   E) A , B, and C

Answer: E
*Topic: Concept 55.3*
*Skill: Comprehension*

42) Which of the following statements is correct about landscape ecology?
   A) It is the application of ecological principles to the design and construction of sustainable lawns and gardens.
   B) It is the application of ecological principles to land–use planning.
   C) It focuses primarily on human–altered ecological systems.
   D) It deals primarily with ecosystems in urban settings.
   E) It deals with the study of the home ranges of various animals.

Answer: B
*Topic: Concept 55.3*
*Skill: Knowledge*

43) Which of the following statements is *false*?
   A) Edges become more extensive with increased forest fragmentation.
   B) Edges are features of human–altered habitats only.
   C) Edges frequently have their own biological communities.
   D) The proliferation of edge species can have a positive or negative effect on biodiversity.
   E) The interface between a forest and an adjoining field would be considered an edge.

Answer: B
*Topic: Concept 55.3*
*Skill: Comprehension*

44) A movement corridor

    A) is a path used by migratory animals when they move to their wintering locales.

    B) is the path most commonly used by an animal within its home range.

    C) unites otherwise isolated patches of quality habitat.

    D) is always beneficial to a species.

    E) is always some natural component of the environment.

Answer: C
*Topic: Concept 55.3*
*Skill: Comprehension*

45) Which of the following statements about movement corridors is true?

    A) Corridors can be either strips or a series of clumps of quality habitat.

    B) Corridors can be natural or constructed by humans.

    C) Riparian habitats frequently serve as effective corridors.

    D) A and C only

    E) A, B, and C

Answer: E
*Topic: Concept 55.3*
*Skill: Knowledge*

46) Forest fragmentation is likely to result in

    A) a loss of species that live in open habitat.

    B) an increase in species that live in open habitat.

    C) a loss of species that live in the interior of forests.

    D) B and C only

    E) A, B, and C

Answer: D
*Topic: Concept 55.3*
*Skill: Knowledge*

47) Wildlife movement corridors can

    A) promote gene flow.

    B) promote disease transmission.

    C) assist migratory species.

    D) A and C only

    E) A, B, and C

Answer: E
*Topic: Concept 55.3*
*Skill: Comprehension*

48) Relatively small geographic areas with high concentrations of endemic species are known as

    A) endemic sinks.

    B) critical communities.

    C) biodiversity hot spots.

    D) endemic metapopulations.

    E) bottlenecks.

Answer: C
*Topic: Concept 55.3*
*Skill: Knowledge*

49) Which of the following is (are) *true*? Biodiversity hot spots for plants

    A) have high concentrations of endemic species.

    B) have large numbers of endangered and threatened species.

    C) can be underwater.

    D) make up a total of only 1.5% of the global land surface.

    E) All of the above are true.

Answer: E
*Topic: Concept 55.3*
*Skill: Knowledge*

50) Biodiversity hot spots are recognized on the basis of

A) their proximity to national parks and reserves.

B) the number of endemic species they contain

C) the degree to which the included species are threatened with extinction.

D) B and C only

E) A, B, and C

Answer: D
*Topic: Concept 55.3*
*Skill: Knowledge*

51) Problem(s) with biodiversity hot spot designation include

A) a bias toward vertebrates and plants.

B) the fact that not all species of interest occupy the same hot spots.

C) the fact that such designations only apply to terrestrial systems.

D) A and B only

E) A, B, and C

Answer: D
*Topic: Concept 55.3*
*Skill: Comprehension*

52) The term "biotic boundary" refers to the

A) area that an animal defends as its territory.

B) area needed to sustain a population.

C) home range of an animal.

D) distribution of an organism.

E) area where a species evolved.

Answer: B
*Topic: Concept 55.3*
*Skill: Knowledge*

53) Which of the following statements about protected areas is *not* correct?

A) Despite repeated efforts, zoned reserves are usually a failure.

B) National parks are only one type of protected area.

C) Most protected areas are small in size.

D) Protected area management must be coordinated with management of lands outside the protected zone.

E) Biodiversity hot spots are important areas to protect.

Answer: A
*Topic: Concept 55.3*
*Skill: Comprehension*

54) Which of the following nations has become a world leader in the establishment of zoned reserves?

A) Costa Rica

B) Canada

C) China

D) United States

E) Mexico

Answer: A
*Topic: Concept 55.3*
*Skill: Knowledge*

55) After a disturbance, natural recovery of a biological community is most strongly influenced by

A) whether the disturbance has been caused by humans or a natural agent.

B) the spatial scale of the disturbance.

C) whether the site is in temperate or tropical areas.

D) the availability of water nearby.

E) the season in which the disturbance occurred.

Answer: B
*Topic: Concept 55.4*
*Skill: Knowledge*

56) Human use of prokaryotic organisms to help detoxify a polluted wetland would be an example of

    A) ecosystem augmentation.

    B) keystone species introduction.

    C) biological control.

    D) bioremediation.

    E) population viability analysis.

Answer: D
*Topic: Concept 55.4*
*Skill: Knowledge*

57) Which of the following is (are) related to the agenda of the Sustainable Biosphere Initiative?

    A) defining what ecological studies are needed for conserving Earth's resources

    B) maintaining productivity of human-made as well as natural ecosystems

    C) understanding interactions between climate and ecological dynamics

    D) resource management and development

    E) all of the above

Answer: E
*Topic: Concept 55.5*
*Skill: Comprehension*

# Media Activity Questions

1) The human population of Madagascar doubles every _____ years.

   A) 10

   B) 25

   C) 40

   D) 60

   E) 80

   Answer: B
   *Topic: Madagascar and the Biodiversity Crisis*

2) What is the cause of the red color of the waters about Madagascar?

   A) dinoflagellates

   B) a persistent red tide

   C) the high concentration of iron found in these waters

   D) soil that has washed into the ocean

   E) red algae

   Answer: D
   *Topic: Madagascar and the Biodiversity Crisis*

3) In 1958 federal law restricted the movement of soil and plants from areas where fire ants were established. Why was this law unsuccessful in stopping the spread of fire ant colonies?

   A) People were unaware of the federal law, and when they moved, transported plants bearing fire ant colonies.

   B) A single mated queen can be transported without being noticed.

   C) Many states originally thought to be free of fire ant colonies already had them.

   D) A and B only

   E) A, B, and C

   Answer: E
   *Topic: Web/CD Activity: Introduced Species*

4) A sink habitat is where a subpopulation's death rate is

   A) equal to its reproductive rate.

   B) greater than its reproductive rate

   C) less than its reproductive rate

   D) at its lowest

   E) either equal to its reproductive rate or less than its reproductive rate

   Answer: B
   *Topic: Activity: Conservation Biology Review*

5) Most biodiversity hot spots are in the

   A) arctic.

   B) coniferous forests.

   C) deserts.

   D) grasslands.

   E) tropics.

   Answer: E
   *Topic: Activity: Conservation Biology Review*

# Self-Quiz Questions

1) Ecologists conclude that there is a biodiversity crisis because

   A) biophilia causes humans to feel ethically responsible for protecting other species.

   B) scientists have at last discovered and counted most of Earth's species and can now accurately calculate the current extinction rate.

   C) the current extinction rate is far higher than the rate at any time in the past 100,000 years.

   D) many potential life-saving medicines are being lost as species become extinct.

   E) there are too few biodiversity hot spots.

   Answer: C

2) Which of the following directly addresses the growing concern over the loss of ecosystem diversity?

   A) the small-population approach

   B) restoration ecology

   C) the declining-population approach

   D) increasing effective population sizes of endangered species

   E) managing populations to increase genetic diversity

   Answer: B

3) What is the effective population size ($N_e$) of a population of 50 strictly monogamous swans that includes 40 males and 10 females?

   A) 50

   B) 40

   C) 32

   D) 20

   E) 10

   Answer: C

4) One characteristic that distinguishes a population in an extinction vortex from most other populations is that

   A) its habitat is fragmented.

   B) it is a rare, top-level predator.

   C) its effective population size is much lower than its total population size.

   D) its genetic diversity is very low.

   E) it is not well adapted to edge conditions.

   Answer: D

5) The discipline that applies ecological principles to return degraded ecosystems to their natural states is known as

   A) population viability analysis.

   B) landscape ecology.

   C) conservation ecology.

   D) restoration ecology.

   E) resource conservation.

   Answer: D

6) What is the greatest threat to biodiversity?

   A) overexploitation of commercially important species

   B) introduced species that compete with or prey on native species

   C) pollution of Earth's air, water, and soil

   D) disruption of trophic relationships as more and more prey species become extinct

   E) habitat alteration, fragmentation, and destruction

   Answer: E

7) Which of the following is *not* a step in the declining–population approach to conservation biology?

A) Gather data to determine whether a population is in decline.

B) Implement a conservation plan at the outset of a study, as it is too risky to wait until data are gathered and analyzed.

C) Develop multiple alternative hypotheses for the cause of population decline.

D) Include both human activities and natural events in the list of possible causes of a population decline.

E) Test the hypotheses for the cause of the decline, beginning with the hypotheses most likely to be correct.

Answer: B

8) Which of the following strategies would most rapidly increase the genetic diversity of a population in an extinction vortex?

A) Capture all remaining individuals in the population for captive breeding followed by reintroduction to the wild.

B) Establish a reserve that protects the population's remaining habitat.

C) Introduce new individuals transported from other populations of the same species.

D) Sterilize the least fit individuals in the population.

E) Control and reduce populations of the endangered population's predators and competitors.

Answer: C

9) Of the following statements about the protected areas that have been established to preserve biodiversity, which one is *not* correct?

A) About 25% of Earth's land area is now protected.

B) National parks are one of many types of protected areas.

C) Most protected areas are too small to protect.

D) Management of a protected area should be coordinated with management of the land surrounding the area.

E) It is especially important to protect biodiversity hot spots.

Answer: A

10) What is the Sustainable Biosphere Initiative?

A) a plan to convert all natural ecosystems in the biosphere to carefully engineered ones

B) a research agenda to study biodiversity and support sustainable development

C) a conservation practice that sets up zoned reserves surrounded by buffer zones

D) the declining–population approach to conservation that seeks to identify and remedy causes of species' declines

E) a conservation program that uses adaptive management to experiment and learn while working with disturbed ecosystems

Answer: B